S0-BAF-061

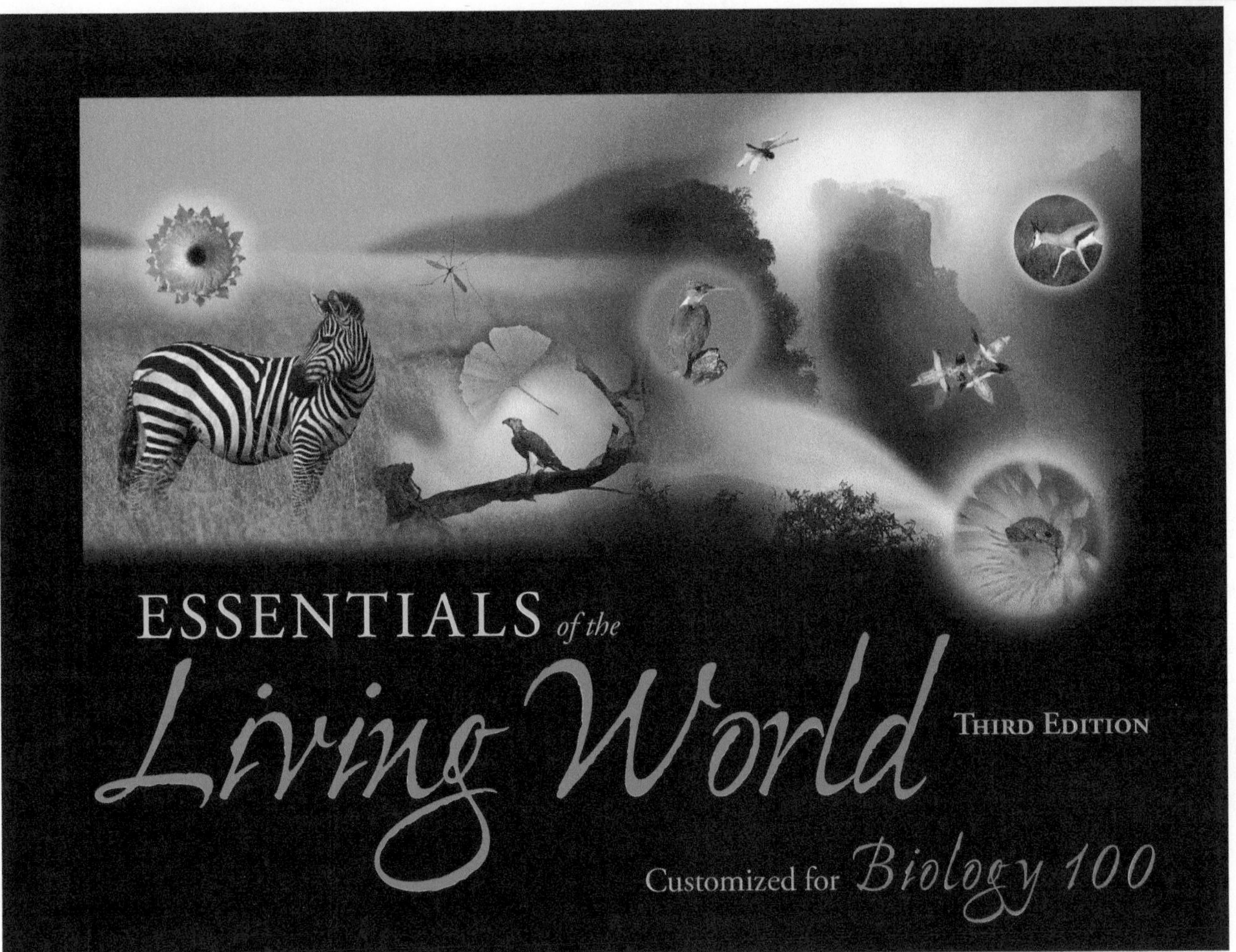
ESSENTIALS of the
Living World
Third Edition
Customized for Biology 100

Giving Biology a Personal Perspective

Connections: Where Biology Impacts Society

Biology and Staying Healthy

Bird and Swine Flu

The influenza virus has been one of the most lethal viruses in human history. Flu viruses are animal RNA viruses containing 11 genes. An individual flu virus resembles a sphere studded

Recombination within humans A person infected with a flu virus can become infected with another type of flu virus by direct contact with birds. The two viruses can undergo genetic recombination to produce a third type of virus, which can spread from human to human.

Recombination within pigs Pigs can contract flu viruses from both birds and humans. The flu viruses can undergo genetic recombination in the pig, to produce a new kind of flu virus, which can spread from pigs to humans.

How New Flu Strains Arise

Worldwide epidemics of the flu in the last century have been caused by shifts in flu virus H-N combinations as mutation creates new versions of H and N. The "killer flu" of 1918, H1N1, thought to have passed directly from birds to humans, killed between 40 and 100 million people worldwide. The Asian flu of 1957, H2N2, killed over 100,000 Americans, and the Hong Kong flu of 1968, H3N2, killed 70,000 Americans.

It is no accident that new strains of flu usually originate in the Far East. The most common hosts of influenza virus are ducks, chickens, and pigs, which in Asia often live in close proximity to each other and to humans. Pigs are subject to infection by both bird and human strains of the virus, and individual animals are often simultaneously infected with multiple strains. This creates conditions favoring genetic recombination between strains, as illustrated above, sometimes putting together novel combinations of H and N spikes unrecognizable by human immune defenses specific for the old configuration. The Hong Kong flu, for example, arose from recombination between H3N8 from ducks and H2N2 from humans. The new strain of influenza, in this case H3N2, then passed back to humans, creating an epidemic because the human population had never experienced that H-N combination before.

Why did so many die? Because so much of the world's population was infected.

Bird Flu

A potentially deadly new strain of flu virus emerged in Hong Kong in 1997, H5N1. Like the 1918 pandemic strain, H5N1 passes to humans directly from infected birds, usually chickens or ducks, and for this reason has been dubbed "bird flu." Bird flu has gotten an unusual amount of public attention, because it satisfies the first two conditions of a pandemic. Bird flu is a novel combination of H and N spikes for which humans have little immunity, and the resulting strain is particularly deadly. Of 256 individuals infected by handling birds by the end of 2006, 151 died of the infection, a mortality of 59% (recall, the mortality of the 1918 strain was only 2%). Fortunately, the third condition for a pandemic is not yet met: The H5N1 strain of flu virus

Applications (Apps): Biology in Your World

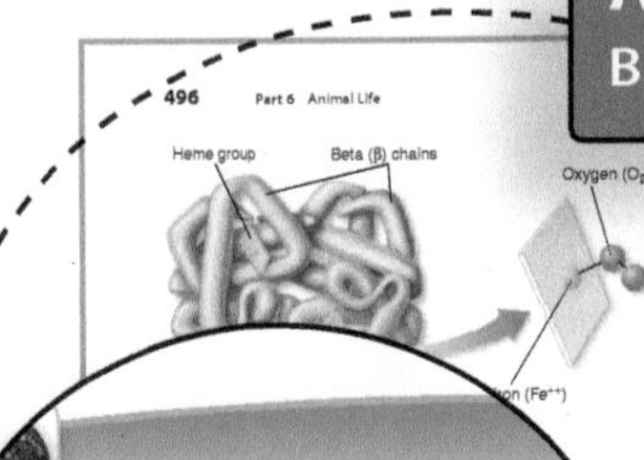

25.4 How Respiration Works: Gas Exchange

CONCEPT PREVIEW: Oxygen molecules move through the circulatory system carried by the protein hemoglobin within red blood cells. Most CO_2 is transported in the blood plasma as bicarbonate.

When oxygen has diffused from the air into the moist cells lining the inner surface of the lung, its journey has just begun. Passing from these cells into the bloodstream, the oxygen travels throughout the body in the circulatory system, described in chapter 24. It has been estimated that it would take a molecule of oxygen three years to diffuse from your lung to your toe if it moved only by diffusion, unassisted by a circulatory system.

O_2 Transport

Oxygen (O_2) moves within the circulatory system carried piggyback on the protein **hemoglobin.** Hemoglobin molecules contain iron, which binds oxygen, as shown in figure 25.5. Hemoglobin molecules act like little oxygen sponges, soaking up oxygen within red blood cells and removing it from the blood plasma. The oxygen binds in a reversible way, which is necessary so that the oxygen can unload when it reaches the tissues of the body. Hemoglobin is manufactured within red blood cells and never leaves these cells, which circulate in the bloodstream like ships bearing cargo.

At the high O_2 levels that occur in the lung (panel 1 in *Essential Biological Process 25B*), most hemoglobin molecules carry a full load of oxygen atoms. In tissue, the presence of carbon dioxide (CO_2) causes the hemoglobin molecule to assume a different shape, one that gives up its oxygen more easily (as in panel 3). The effect of CO_2 on oxygen unloading is important, because CO_2 is produced by the tissues through cell metabolism. For this reason, the blood unloads oxygen more readily within tissues undergoing metabolism.

CO_2 Transport

At the same time the red blood cells are unloading oxygen in panel 3, they are also absorbing CO_2 from the tissue. About 8% of the CO_2 in blood is simply dissolved in plasma. Another 20% is bound to hemoglobin; however, this CO_2 does not bind to the heme group but rather to another site on the hemoglobin molecule, and so it does not compete with oxygen binding. The remaining 72% of the CO_2 diffuses into the red blood cells. To keep CO_2 from diffusing out of the red blood cells back to the plasma where CO_2 levels are low, the enzyme *carbonic anhydrase* combines CO_2 molecules with water molecules (panel 4) to form **carbonic acid** (H_2CO_3) in the cell. This acid dissociates into **bicarbonate** (HCO_3^-) and hydrogen (H^+) ions. The H^+ binds to hemoglobin. A transporter protein in the membrane of the red blood cell moves the bicarbonate out of the red blood cell into the plasma. This transporter protein exchanges one chloride ion (Cl^-) for a bicarbonate, a process called the *chloride shift*. This reaction keeps the levels of CO_2 in the blood plasma low, facilitating the diffusion of more CO_2 into it from the surrounding tissue. The facilitation is critical to CO_2 removal, because the difference in CO_2 concentration between blood and tissue is not large (only 5%). The formation of carbonic acid and bicarbonate is also important in maintaining the acid-base balance of the blood because the molecules act as a buffering system.

The blood plasma carries bicarbonate ions back to the lungs. The lower CO_2 concentration in the air inside the lungs causes the carbonic anhydrase reaction to proceed in

As discussed on page 40 a buffer is an acid-base pair of molecules that adjusts the levels of H^+ in a solution, thereby controlling pH levels. The reversible reaction between carbonic acid and bicarbonate regulates the amount of H^+ in the blood, thereby adjusting pH levels in the body.

BIOLOGY & YOU

Hiccups. A hiccup (pronounced "HICK-up") is a spasmodic contraction of the diaphragm that repeats several times a minute. The abrupt rush of air into your lungs causes your epiglottis to close, making the "hic" noise. Hiccups are caused by irritation of the phrenic and vagus nerves, which activates reflexive motor pathways to the diaphragm muscles. Hiccups often occur after drinking carbonated soda or alcohol, but can be initiated by any of a host of other reasons, like eating too fast or taking a cold drink while eating a hot meal. What do you do when you get the hiccups? In most cases they can be stopped simply by forgetting about them—the basis of the common home remedy of "scaring them away" with a surprise or fright. Increasing respired CO_2 by breathing into a paper bag also often works, for the interesting reason that hiccups may be an evolutionary remnant of earlier amphibian respiration. Air gulping in frogs is inhibited by CO_2, just as your hiccuping is. Frogs and other amphibians don't have a diaphragm, and instead gulp air via a simple motor reflex much like your hiccuping reflex. In humans the hiccuping motor pathway forms early in fetal development, well before the motor pathways that drive normal breathing. Premature infants born before their lung motor pathways are fully functional spend 2.5% of their time hiccuping, gulping air just like amphibians.

Implications: Questioning Yourself

Figure 14.8 Darwin greets his monkey ancestor.

In his time, Darwin was often portrayed unsympathetically, as in this drawing from an 1874 publication.

IMPLICATION In 2008 the Spanish parliament approved resolutions granting to gorillas, chimpanzees, and orangutans statutory rights currently only applicable to humans. This was the first time a country has taken such action. The resolutions were based on the Great Ape Project, a framework designed by scientists and philosophers to provide humans' closest relatives with the right to life, liberty, and protection from torture. Zoos could still legally hold apes, but living conditions must be "optimal." Using apes in performances will be illegal. The law will also ban using apes in potentially useful research, if it might hurt the ape in any way. Do you think this last condition of the law is appropriate? Explain.

in different places. As we will discuss later in this chapter, section 14.9, there are five evolutionary forces that can affect biological diversity, although natural selection is the only evolutionary force that produces *adaptive* changes.

Darwin Drafts His Argument

Darwin drafted the overall argument for evolution by natural selection in a preliminary manuscript in 1842. After showing the manuscript to a few of his closest scientific friends, however, Darwin put it in a drawer, and for years turned to other research.

Wallace Has the Same Idea

Publication of Darwin's Theory

Concept Check

1. How long after his original voyage on HMS *Beagle* did Darwin ... his work and publish *On the Origin of Species?*
2. What did Darwin see on the Galápagos Islands that hinted ...
3. How did Malthus influence both Darwin and Wallace?

Experiments: Thinking Like a Scientist

Inquiry & Analysis

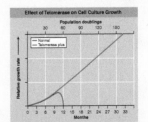

Why Do Human Cells Age?

Human cells appear to have built-in life spans. In 1961 cell biologist Leonard Hayflick reported the startling result that skin cells growing in tissue culture, such as those growing in culture flasks in the photo below, will divide only a certain number of times. After about 50 population doublings cell division stops ...

This led to the hypothesis that a run of some 16 TTAGGGs was where the DNA replicating enzyme, called polymerase, first sat down on the DNA (16 TTAGGGs being the size of the enzyme's "footprint"), and because of being its docking spot, the polymerase was unable to copy that bit. Thus a 100-base portion of the telomere was lost by a chromosome during each doubling as DNA replicated. Eventually, after some 50 doubling cycles, each with a round of DNA replication, the telomere would be used up and there would be no place for the DNA replication enzyme to sit. The cell line would then enter senescence, no longer able to proliferate.

This hypothesis was tested in 1998. Using genetic engineering, researchers transferred into newly established human cell cultures a gene that leads to expression of an enzyme called *telomerase* that all cells possess but no body cell uses. This enzyme adds TTAGGG sequences back to the end of telomeres, in effect rebuilding the lost portions of the telomere. Laboratory cultures of cell lines with (telomerase plus) and without (normal) this gene were then monitored for many generations. The graph above displays the results.

Effect of Telomerase on Cell Culture Growth

Population doublings: 30, 60, 90, 120, 150; Relative growth rate; Months: 0, 3, 6, 9, 12, 15, 18, 21, 24, 27, 30, 33; Normal; Telomerase plus

TTAGGGTTAGGGTTAGGGTTAGGGTTAGGG-------

Analysis

1. **Applying Concepts** Comparing continuous processes, how do normal skin cells (blue line) differ in their growth history from telomerase plus cells with the telomerase gene (red line)?
2. **Interpreting Data** After how many doublings do the normal cells cease to divide? the telomerase plus cells?
3. **Making Inferences** After 9 population doublings, would the rate of cell division be different between the two cultures? after 15? Why?
4. **Drawing Conclusions** How does the addition of the telomerase gene affect the senescence (death by old age) of skin cells growing in culture? Does this result confirm the telomerase hypothesis this experiment had set out to test?

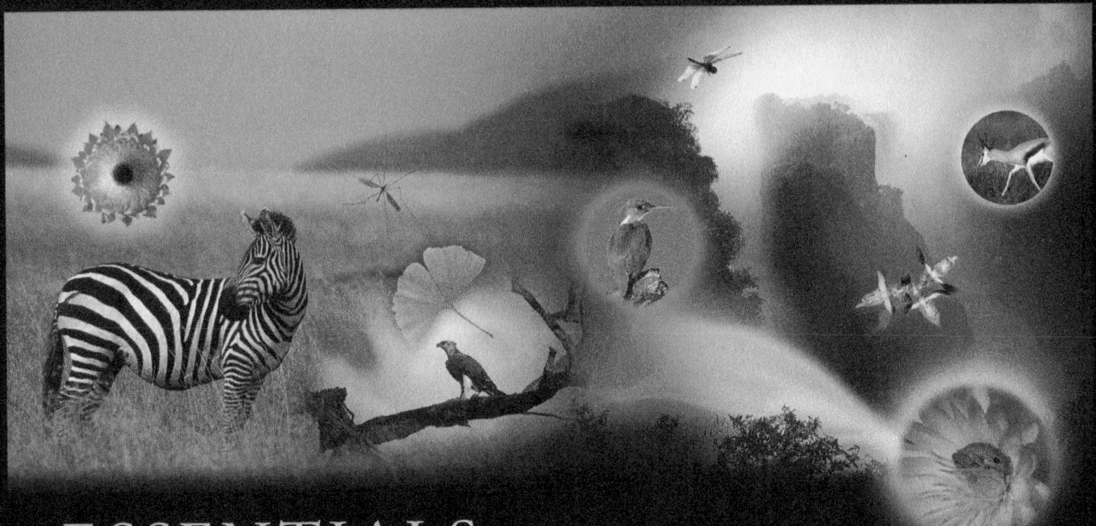

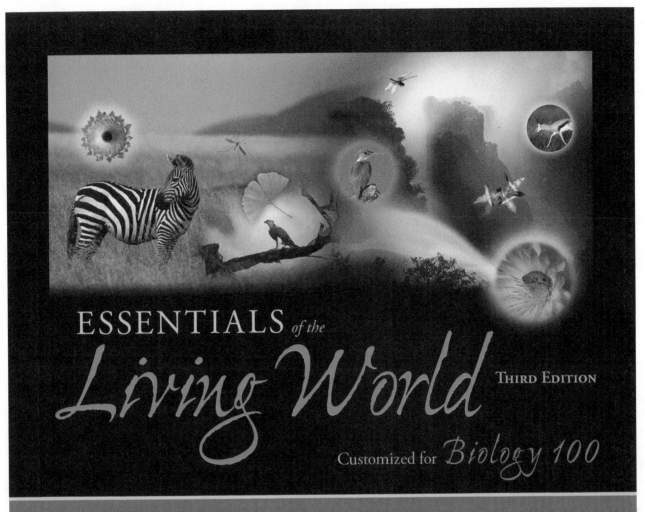

ESSENTIALS of the Living World

THIRD EDITION

Customized for Biology 100

GEORGE B. JOHNSON

WASHINGTON UNIVERSITY

Boston Burr Ridge, IL Dubuque, IA New York San Francisco St. Louis
Bangkok Bogotá Caracas Lisbon London Madrid
Mexico City Milan New Delhi Seoul Singapore Sydney Taipei Toronto

Essentials of the Living World, Third Edition
Customized for Biology 100

9 0 KNG KNG 14 13 12

ISBN-13: 978-0-07-746374-8
ISBN-10: 0-07-746374-9

Learning Solutions Specialist: Jennifer Harrington
Production Editor: Lynn Nagel
Front Cover Photos: Reed Frog on pink lily, Okavango Delta, Botswana © Digital Vision/Getty Images; South African orchid mimicing appearance of female wasp to facilitate pollination by male wasps attempting to copulate with flower © Stephen P. Lynch; Malachite Kingfisher on tree branch, Kwazulu-Natal, South Africa © Digital Vision/PunchStock; Springbok © Image Source/PunchStock; Dragonfly © Burke/Triolo Productions/Brand X Pictures/Getty Images; Victoria Falls, Devil's Cataract on Zambezi River, Zimbabwe, Africa © Digital Vision/Getty Images;
Back Cover Photos: Martial Eagle © Brand X Pictures/PunchStock; Ginkgo leaf © Getty Images/Photographer's Choice RF; Mosquito © Creatas/PunchStock; Zebra in Masai Mara National Reserve, Kenya © DLILLC/Corbis; Queen Protea of South Africa © Burke/Triolo Productions/Getty Images; Masai Ostrich © Anup Shah/Photodisc/Getty Images; Colony of Southern Carmine Bee-eaters © Digital Vision/PunchStock
Cover Design: Fairfax Hutter
Printer/Binder: King Printing

Contents

Part 4
The Evolution and Diversity of Life

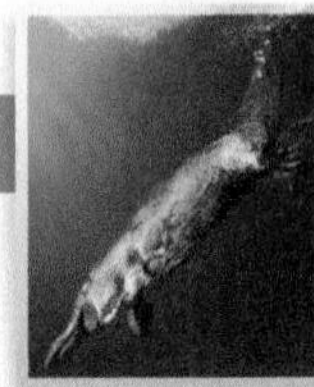

Part 5
The Living Environment

Preface

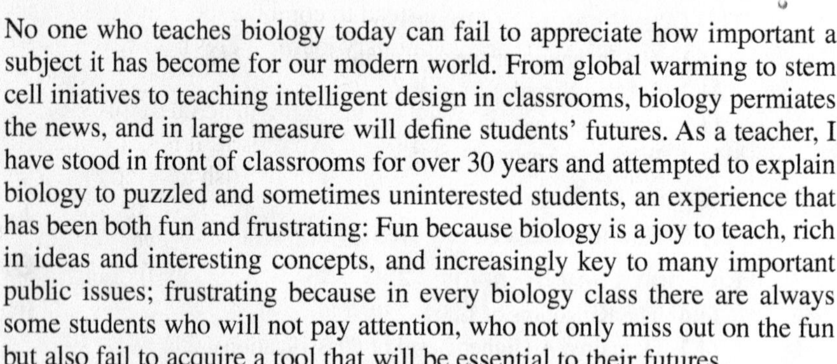

No one who teaches biology today can fail to appreciate how important a subject it has become for our modern world. From global warming to stem cell iniatives to teaching intelligent design in classrooms, biology permiates the news, and in large measure will define students' futures. As a teacher, I have stood in front of classrooms for over 30 years and attempted to explain biology to puzzled and sometimes uninterested students, an experience that has been both fun and frustrating: Fun because biology is a joy to teach, rich in ideas and interesting concepts, and increasingly key to many important public issues; frustrating because in every biology class there are always some students who will not pay attention, who not only miss out on the fun but also fail to acquire a tool that will be essential to their futures.

This text, *Essentials of The Living World*, is my attempt to address this problem. It is short enough to use in one semester, without a lot of technical details to intimidate wary students. I have tried to write it in an informal, friendly way, to engage as well as to teach. The focus of the book is on the biology each student ought to know to live as an informed citizen in the 21st century. I have at every stage addressed ideas and concepts, rather than detailed information, trying to teach *how* things work and *why* things happen the way they do rather than merely naming parts or giving definitions.

Essential Biological Process 4C

Facilitated Diffusion

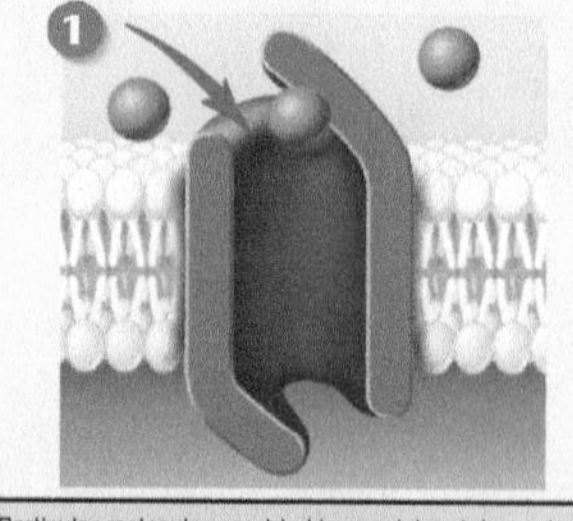

Particular molecules can bind to special protein carriers in the plasma membrane.

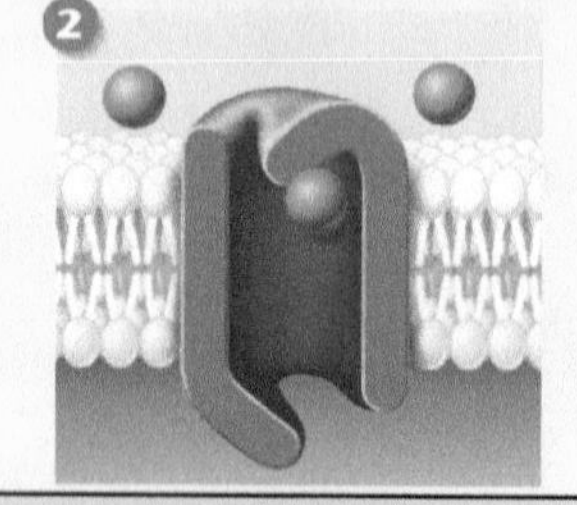

The protein carrier helps (facilitates) the diffusion process and does not require energy.

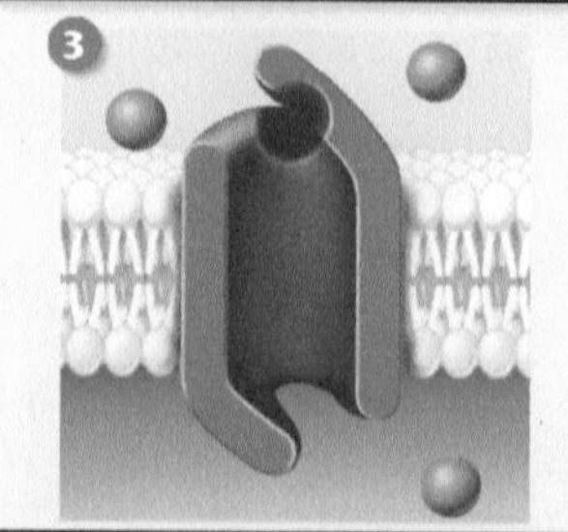

The molecule is released on the far side of the membrane. Protein carriers transport only certain molecules across the membrane but will take them in either direction down their concentration gradients.

An example of an *Essential Biological Process* illustration

Focusing on the Essential Concepts

More than most subjects, biology is at its core a set of ideas, and if students can master these basic ideas, the rest comes easy. Unfortunately, while most of today's students are very interested in biology, they are put off by the terminology. When you don't know what the words mean, it's easy to slip into thinking that the content is difficult, when actually the ideas are simple, easy to grasp, and fun to consider. It's the terms that get in the way, that stand as a wall between students and science. With this text I have tried to turn those walls into windows, so that readers can peer in and join the fun.

Analogies have been my tool. In writing *Essentials of The Living World* I have searched for simple analogies that relate the matter at hand to things we all know. As science, analogies are not exact, but I do not count myself compromised. Analogies trade precision for clarity. If I do my job right, the key idea is not compromised by the analogy I use to explain it, but rather revealed.

There is no way to avoid the fact that some of the important ideas of biology are complex. No student encountering photosynthesis for the first time gets it all on the first pass. To aid in learning the more difficult material, I have given special attention to key concepts and processes like photosynthesis and osmosis that form the core of biology. The essential processes of biology are not optional learning. A student must come to understand every one of them if he or she is to master biology as a science. A student's learning goal should not be simply to memorize a list of terms, but rather to be able to visualize and understand what's going on. With this goal in mind, I have prepared nearly two dozen "this is how it works" *Essential Biological Process* illustrations explaining the important concepts and processes that students encounter in introductory biology. Each of these *Essential Biological Process* illustrations walks the student through a complex process, one step at a time, so that the central idea is not lost in the details.

Teaching Biology as an Evolutionary Journey

This text, and its companion concepts text *The Living World*, were the first texts to combine evolution and diversity into one continuous narrative. Traditionally, students had been exposed to weeks of evolution before being dragged through a detailed tour of the animal phyla, the two areas presented as if unrelated to each other. I chose instead to combine these two areas, presenting biological diversity as an evolutionary journey. This has proven a very powerful way to teach evolution's role in biology, and today you would be hard pressed to find a text that does not organize the material in this way.

Evolution not only organizes biology, it explains it. It is not enough to say that a frog is an amphibian, transitional between fish and reptiles. This correctly organizes frogs on the evolutionary spectrum, but fails to explain *why* frogs are the way they are, with a tadpole life stage and wet skin. Only when the student is taught that amphibians evolved as highly successful land animals, often as big as ponys and armour plated, can students get the point: Of 37 families of amphibians, all but the three that lived in water (frogs, salamanders, and caecilians) were driven extinct with the advent of reptiles. A frog has evolved to invade water, not escape it. It is in this way that evolution explains biology, and that is how I have tried to use evolution in this text, to explain.

A red-eyed tree frog

Linking Essentials Concepts to Everyday Life

One of the principal roles of nonmajor biology courses is to create educated citizens. In writing *Essentials of The Living World* I have endeavored to relate what the student is learning to the biology each student ought to know to live as an informed citizen in the 21st century. Students also engage much more actively in the course when they can see how what they are studying relates to their own everyday lives.

Throughout the text, *Essentials of The Living World* presents full-page **connections,** readings written by the author that make connections between a chapter's contents and the everyday world: *Biology and Staying Healthy* discusses health issues that impact each student; *Today's Biology* examines advances in biology that importantly affect society; *A Closer Look* examines interesting points in more detail; and *Author's Corner* takes a more personal view (the author's) of how science relates to our everyday lives.

It is impossible to thumb through the pages of this new edition without seeing the second way *Essentials of The Living World* links what a student is learning to the world that the student knows. In the margins of many pages are short **apps**—application dialogues: *In the News* relates a page's content to today's news; *Evolution* points to evolutionary connections; and *Biology & You* explains how the page's content is linked to something in a student's everyday life. These short essays do not attempt to teach the content of the page, but rather to relate it to something the student knows or cares about. There are several apps in every chapter, some of them surprising, all of them interesting.

A third way this new edition links what the student is learning to everyday life is the **Implication questions** found below key illustrations in each chapter. These questions are not directed at assessing the student's understanding of the illustration, but rather push the student to think about the implications of the illustration to their own lives. Many are open-ended, probing a student's own opinions on a subject. All of them link the illustration to the student's everyday life.

BIOLOGY & YOU

Vegans. We humans are omnivores, meaning we can eat a broad range of plant and animal tissues—but not all of us choose to do so. Some people don't like spinach and love steak, while others called vegetarians choose not to eat meat. Some become vegetarians because they judge it a more healthy diet—plants are low in saturated fats linked to heart disease. Others make the choice for ethical reasons, sensitive to the animal rights issues associated with livestock agriculture. Still others simply don't like meat. The most extreme form of vegetarian diet is the "vegan" diet. Vegans avoid all animal proteins. They don't eat red meat, poultry, fish, eggs, or milk. Instead, they obtain all protein and nutrients from grains, vegetables, fruits, legumes, nuts, and seeds. The vegan diet, mirroring that of our early human ancestors, is very challenging, because no single fruit, vegetable, or grain contains all the essential amino acids which humans require in their diet. Vegetal foods must be eaten in particular combinations to provide this necessary balance. Beans and rice together provide a balanced diet, but neither food does so when eaten alone. For calcium, which is usually obtained from milk, vegans must eat green leafy vegetables like broccoli or spinach. In practice it is not difficult to achieve this balance if a vegan eats a variety of plants.

An example of an "apps," an application dialogue feature

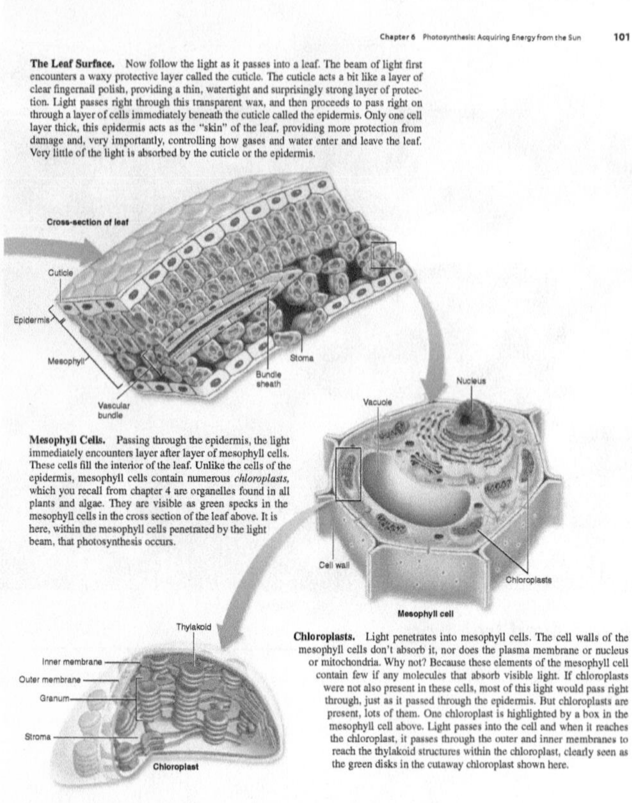

Chapter 6 Photosynthesis: Acquiring Energy from the Sun 101

The Leaf Surface. Now follow the light as it passes into a leaf. The beam of light first encounters a waxy protective layer called the cuticle. The cuticle acts a bit like a layer of clear fingernail polish, providing a thin, watertight and surprisingly strong layer of protection. Light passes right through this transparent wax, and then proceeds to pass right on through a layer of cells immediately beneath the cuticle called the epidermis. Only one cell layer thick, this epidermis acts as the "skin" of the leaf, providing more protection from damage and, very importantly, controlling how gases and water enter and leave the leaf. Very little of the light is absorbed by the cuticle or the epidermis.

Mesophyll Cells. Passing through the epidermis, the light immediately encounters layer after layer of mesophyll cells. These cells fill the interior of the leaf. Unlike the cells of the epidermis, mesophyll cells contain numerous *chloroplasts*, which you recall from chapter 4 are organelles found in all plants and algae. They are visible as green specks in the mesophyll cells in the cross section of the leaf above. It is here, within the mesophyll cells penetrated by the light beam, that photosynthesis occurs.

Chloroplasts. Light penetrates into mesophyll cells. The cell walls of the mesophyll cells don't absorb it, nor does the plasma membrane or nucleus or mitochondria. Why not? Because these elements of the mesophyll cell contain few if any molecules that absorb visible light. If chloroplasts were not also present in these cells, most of this light would pass right through, just as it passed through the epidermis. But chloroplasts are present, lots of them. One chloroplast is highlighted by a box in the mesophyll cell above. Light passes into the cell and when it reaches the chloroplast, it passes through the outer and inner membranes to reach the thylakoid structures within the chloroplast, clearly seen as the green disks in the cutaway chloroplast shown here.

Integration of art into the text

Using Visuals to Teach Concepts

Art has always been a core component of this text, as today's students are visual learners. To help students learn, *Essentials of The Living World* has a clean and simple art style that focuses on concepts and minimizes detail. In this edition I have sought to amplify the power of illustrations to teach concepts by linking the interior content of illustrations directly to the text that describes that part of the illustration. I have set about doing this in three ways: **1. Bubble numbers.** In complex diagrams where there is a lot going on, I have placed numbers (set off in colored balls) at key positions, and the same "bubble numbers" at those locations in the text where that element of the illustration is being described. This makes it much easier for a student to use the illustration as it was intended, to walk through the process and see how the parts are related. **2. Integration of art into text.** In some places like the introduction to photosynthesis (treated on pages 100 to 103) many different processes are covered, each with its own illustration. In these instances, bouncing back and forth between illustration and text makes it difficult for a student to gain or retain perspective, and so I have chosen in these instances to integrate the illustrations directly into the text, providing a single narrative. In setting out to improve this edition of *Essentials of The Living World*, my focus has been on improving it as a learning tool. I have made many changes, some obvious, others more subtle, all of them aimed at making it easier for students using this text to understand and appreciate what they learn in lecture, and so do better in the course.

New to This Edition

Making the Text More Accessible. The most obvious change in this edition is that it no longer presents two columns of text crowded side-by-side onto each page. A single wider column of text, with illustrations in the margin, allows a cleaner, clearer organization of material, making it easier for a student to follow an argument or extended discussion.

Linking to Related Topics. On many pages I have placed "link" arrows that point a student to an earlier place in the text where an important related concept or finding has been discussed, or to a place later in the text where a topic will play an important role. In a course like introductory biology a student is barraged with terms and ideas, and linking them together is an important aspect of mastering them. Link arrows provide the student help in this key task.

Learning How to Learn. In over 30 years of teaching I have seen students do well and others do poorly, and one of the best predictors of who would do well has been how well a student is prepared to learn. Entering a large freshman course, does a student know how to take notes? Does a student know how to use these notes effectively with the textbook? Can a student read a graph? In this edition I decided to tackle this problem head-on, and have added a "chapter 0" at the beginning of the text to help students with these very basic but essential learning tools.

Inquiry & Analysis. One of the most useful things a student can take away from his or her biology class is the ability to judge scientific claims that they encounter as citizens, long after college is over. As a way of teaching that important skill, I have greatly expanded the

Inquiry & Analysis features I introduced in the previous edition. Most chapters now end with a full-page presentation of an actual scientific investigation that requires the student to analyze the data and reach conclusions. Few pages in this text provide more bang for the buck in learning that lasts.

Updating the Content. Biology as a science has advanced rapidly in the years since the last revision of *Essentials of The Living World.* Four examples serve to make the point clearly:

RNA Interference (page 210) This discovery, so important that it won a Nobel Prize in the shortest length of time ever, has totally altered our view of how genes are regulated, and is revolutionizing medicine.

Curing Cancer (pages 138 to 139) The families of many students are affected by cancer, and one quarter of all students will someday experience it.

Transforming Adult Tissue Cells into Embryonic-like Stem Cells (page 233) Using embryonic stem cells to cure disease is a very controversial topic, indeed a political hot potato. This advance of using adult tissue cells may provide a less controversial alternative.

A Closer Look at Content Changes. Many chapters of this revision of *Essentials of The Living World* have been updated to reflect these advances, and to improve the text as a learning tool:

Part 1

- Moved "How Scientists Analyze and Present Experimental Results" to chapter 0, where it is integrated into the discussion of how to study biology.

Part 2

- Moved the content of chapter 2 "Evolution and Ecology" into the appropriate evolution and ecology chapters. The placement of this chapter in the second edition was an attempt to give students an early introduction to the topics of evolution and ecology, providing students with a "macro" view to begin their study, but was seen as confusing when placed out of context.
- Added a new "Biology and Staying Healthy" feature in chapter 3, "Anabolic Steroids in Sports."
- The *Essential Biological Process* art features provide a clear and uncluttered illustration of a process that is essential to the study of biology. These art pieces are called out so they are easily recognized.
- A new visual overview of photosynthesis at the beginning of chapter 6 walks the student through the general process of photosynthesis.
- The discussions of photosynthesis and cellular respiration have been streamlined, focusing on the general concepts and processes.

Part 3

- Added a new "Biology and Staying Healthy" feature in chapter 11, "Protecting Your Genes," which talks about the cancer risks of smoking and sun tanning.
- Separated the discussion of "regulating gene expression" in chapter 12 into regulating mechanisms of prokaryotes and regulating mechanisms of eukaryotes. This new organization is clearer, helping students understand the differences between the processes in prokaryotes and in eukaryotes.

Anabolic Steroids in Sports

Among the most notorious of lipids in recent years has been the class of synthetic hormones known as anabolic steroids. Since the 1950s some athletes have been taking these chemicals to build muscle and so boost athletic performance. Both because of the intrinsic unfairness of this and because of health risks, the use of anabolic steroids has been banned in sports for decades. Controversy over their use in professional baseball has recently returned anabolic steroids to the nation's front pages.

Anabolic steroids were developed in the 1930s to treat hypogonadism, a condition in which the male testes do not produce sufficient amounts of the hormone testosterone for normal growth and sexual development. Scientists soon discovered that by slightly altering the chemical structure of testosterone, they could produce synthetic versions that facilitated the growth of skeletal muscle in laboratory animals. The word "anabolic" means growing or building. Further tweaking reduced the added impact of these new chemicals on sexual development. More than 100 different anabolic steroids have been developed, most of which have to be injected to be effective. All require a prescription to be used legally in the United States, and all are banned in professional, college, and high school sports.

Another way to increase the body's level of testosterone is to use a chemical which is not itself anabolic but one that the body converts to testosterone. One such chemical is 4-androstenedione, more commonly called "andro." It was first developed in the 1970s by East German scientists to try to enhance their athletes' Olympic performances. Because andro does not have the same side effects as anabolic steroids, it was legally available until 2004. It was used by Mark McGwire, but it is now banned in all sports, and possession of andro is a federal crime.

Anabolic steroids work by signalling muscle cells to make more protein. They bind to special "androgenic receptor" proteins within the cells of muscle tissue. Like jabbing these proteins with a poker, the binding prods the receptors into action, causing them to activate genes on the cell's chromosomes that produce muscle tissue proteins, triggering an increase in protein synthesis. At the same time, the anabolic steroid molecules bind to so-called "cortisol receptor" proteins in the cell, preventing these receptors from doing their job of causing protein breakdown, the muscle cell's way of suppressing inflammation and promoting the use of proteins for fuel during exercise. By increasing protein production and inhibiting the breakdown of proteins in muscle cells after workouts, anabolic steroids significantly increase the mass of an athlete's muscle tissue.

If the only effect of anabolic steroids on your body was to enhance your athletic performance by increasing your muscle mass, using them would still be wrong, for one very simple and important reason: fairness. To gain advantage in competition by concealed use of anabolic steroids—"doping"—is simply cheating. That is why these drugs are banned in sports.

The use of anabolic steroids by athletes and others is not only wrong, but also illegal, because increased muscle mass is not the only effect of using these chemicals. Among adolescents, anabolic steroids can also lead to premature termination of the adolescent growth spurt, so that for the rest of their lives, users remain shorter than they would have been without the drugs. Adolescents and adults are also affected by steroids in the following ways. Anabolic steroids can lead to potentially fatal liver cysts and liver cancer (the liver is the organ of the body that attempts to detoxify the blood), cholesterol changes and hypertension (both of which can promote heart attack and stroke), and acne. Other signs of steroid use in men include reduced size of testicles, balding, and development of breasts. In women, signs include the growth of facial hair, lowering of the voice, and cessation of menstruation.

In the fall of 2003, athletic organizations learned that some athletes were using a new performance-enhancing anabolic steroid undetectable by standard antidoping tests, tetrahydrogestrinone (THG). The use of THG was only discovered because an anonymous coach sent a spent syringe to U.S. antidoping officials. THG's chemical structure is similar to gestrinone, a drug used to treat a form of pelvic inflammation, and can be made from it by simply adding four hydrogen atoms, an easy chemical task. THG tends to break down when prepared for analysis by standard means, which explains why antidoping tests had failed to detect it. New urine tests for THG that were developed in 2004 have been used to catch several well-known sports figures, including British athlete Dwain Chambers and baseball slugger Rafael Palmeiro.

Homerun slugger Barry Bonds was involved in a steroid controversy in 2006.

57

Putting Your Genome to Work

Microarrays

A **gene microarray** is a glass square smaller than a postage stamp, covered with hundreds of thousands of different single strands of DNA rising from the surface like blades of grass. At each position on the glass plate, a particular DNA sequence of a hundred or more nucleotides is assembled, forming the microarray. The gene microarray chip you see to the right, called a *GeneChip* by its manufacturer, contains all known human gene sequences and can be purchased for as little as $200.

How could you use such a microarray chip to delve into a person's genes? All you would have to do is to obtain a little of the person's DNA, say from a blood sample, and denature it to form single-stranded DNA. You would then flush fluid containing the person's denatured DNA over the chip surface with known DNA sequences. Wherever the DNA has a gene matching one of the microarray strands, it will stick to it in a way a computer can detect.

Gene microarrays can also be used to determine patterns of gene expression. To do this, mRNA isolated from the cells being studied is reverse transcribed, using fluorescently labeled nucleotides, to make complementary DNA (cDNA, see page 221). Because the cDNA contains fluorescently labeled nucleotides, it is easily recognized by a computer. When this labeled cDNA is mixed with a gene microarray representing many thousands of genes, spots light up on the computer screen corresponding to those genes being transcribed in the cells.

Similarly, two different sources of DNA can be compared, such as DNA from two different individuals, to determine their levels of genetic similarities. In this case, the DNA from the two sources are labeled with different-colored fluorescent labels, typically one labeled with a green fluorescent dye and the other with a red fluorescent dye. Spots that fluoresce are places where the samples of DNA bind to DNA on the microarray; the spots are reddish where one source binds and greenish where the other source binds. Where the two sources have similar DNA sequences, they bind to the same spot on the microarray, and it shows up as yellow spots. The more yellow spots there are, the more similar the source DNAs are.

Researchers are busily comparing the "reference sequence" of the human genome with the DNA of individual people, and noting any differences they detect. In this way, they are finding SNPs (single nucleotide polymorphisms), or spot differences in the identity of particular nucleotides, which record every way in which a particular individual differs from the reference sequence. Some SNPs are associated with disorders like cystic fibrosis or sickle-cell disease. Others may give you red hair or elevated cholesterol in your blood. The human genome tells us that SNPs can be expected to occur at a frequency of about 5 per 1,000 nucleotides, scattered about randomly over the chromosomes. Each of us can be expected to differ from the standard "type sequence" by thousands of nucleotide SNPs.

Microarrays Raise Critical Issues of Personal Privacy

Humans are thought to contain some 10 million different SNPs, all of which could reside on a small library of gene microarrays. When your DNA is flushed over a SNP microarray, the sequences that light up will instantly reveal your SNP profile, the genetic characteristics that make up who you are. Genes that might affect your health, your behavior, your future potential—all are there to be read. Your SNP profile will reflect all of this variation: a table of contents of your chromosomes, a molecular window to who you are.

When millions of such SNP profiles have been gathered over the coming years, computers will be able to identify other individuals with profiles like yours, and, by examining health records, standard personality tests, and the like, correlate parts of your profile with particular traits. Even behavioral characteristics involving many genes, which until now have been thought too complex to ever analyze, cannot resist a determined assault by a computer comparing SNP profiles. This raises issues of privacy—who should have access to this information and how should it be used?

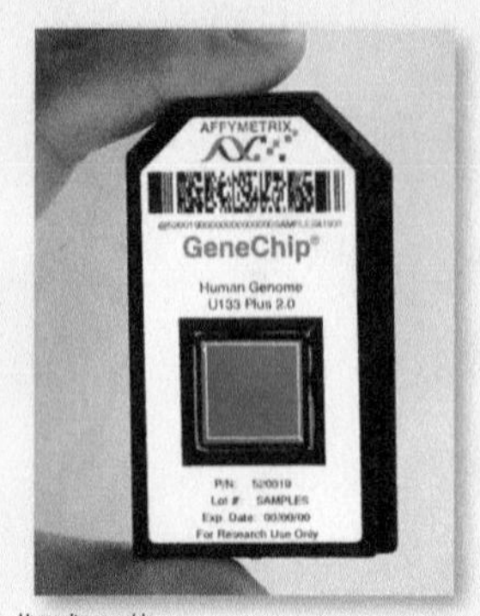

Humanity on a chip.
Microarrays such as this Affymetrix GeneChip now include all known human genes.

224

- Added more information on RNA-level control in chapter 12, as this is an area of active research and medical interest. Also added a new "Biology and Staying Healthy" feature on "Silencing Genes to Treat Disease," showing medical applications of RNA interference.
- Added two new "Biology and Staying Healthy" features in chapter 13, "Putting Your Genome to Work" and "DNA and the Innocence Project."
- Expanded information on adult stem cell therapies in chapter 13, including the possibility of using adult cells with embryonic stem cell-like properties.

Acknowledgments

I have for several years enjoyed and profited from collaborations with Jonathan Losos of Harvard University, a friend of long standing and a delight to work with. My coauthor on the previous edition, Jonathan had to relinquish that role on this edition. A coauthor on *Biology*, classroom teacher, and active researcher, this text has proven one load too many. I miss the fun of working with him.

Every author knows that he or she labors on the shoulders of many others; the text you see is the result of hard work by an army of "behind-the-scenes" editors, spelling and grammar checkers, photo researchers, and artists that perform their magic on our manuscript; and an even larger army of production managers and staff that then transform this manuscript into a bound book. I cannot thank them all. Michael Hackett, Rose Koos, and Kris Tibbetts were my editorial team, with whom I worked every day. Publisher Janice Roerig-Blong solved the many management problems her author inadvertently created in his excess of enthusiasm, and provided valuable advice and support. Marty Lange, the editor-in-chief, oversaw all of this with humor and consistent support. Sheila Frank spearheaded our production team, which for several editions now has made a habit of working miracles with a tight schedule. The photo program was carried out by Lori Hancock, who as always did a super job. The art program, conceived several editions ago by William Ober, M.D., and Claire Garrison, R.N., continues to develop with the clarity and excitment they had envisioned. Laurie Janssen did a great job with the design—she really seems to love frogs. This edition was produced by Electronic Publishing Services Inc.

My long-time, off-site developmental editors and right arms Liz Sievers and Megan Berdelman have again played an invaluable role in overseeing every detail of a complex revision. Their intelligence and perseverance continue to play a major role in the quality of this book.

The marketing of this new edition was planned and supervised by Tamara Maury, a battle-wise general not afraid to fight in the trenches alongside the many able sales reps that present our book to instructors.

Last but not least, I would like to extend a special thanks to Michael Lange, vice president–new product launches at McGraw-Hill, for his continued strong support of this project.

George Johnson

Reviewers

I have authored other texts, and all of my writing efforts have taught me the great value of reviewers in improving my texts. Scientific colleagues from around the country have provided numerous suggestions on how to improve the content of the third edition of *Essentials,* and many instructors and students using the second edition have suggested ways to clarify explanations, improve presentations, and expand on important topics. The instructors listed below provided detailed comments. I have tried to listen carefully to all of you. Everyone of you has my thanks!

Sylvester Allred
Northern Arizona University
Lena Ballard
Rock Valley College
Dennis Bell
University of Louisiana–Monroe
Linda L. Bergen-Losee
Saint Leo University
Lisa L. Boggs
Southwestern Oklahoma State University
Cheryl Boice
Lake City Community College

Nancy Bowers
Park University
Carol A. Britson
University of Mississippi
Steven G. Brumbaugh
Green River Community College
Lisa Bryant
Arkansas State University
Matthew Burnham
Jones County Junior College
Chantae M. Calhoun
Lawson State Community College
Jocelyn Cash
Central Piedmont Community College
Bane W. Cheek
Polk Community College
Denise L. Chung
Long Island University–Brooklyn Campus
Craig W. Clifford
Northeastern State University
Yvonne E. Cole
Florissant Valley Community College
George R. Davis
Minnesota State University–Moorhead
Chris Davison
Long Beach City College
Buffany DeBoer
Wayne State College
Kristiann Dougherty
Valencia Community College
Michael J. Dougherty
Hampden–Sydney College
William E. Dunscombe
Union County College
Bruce Edinger
West Liberty State College
Marirose T. Ethington
Genesee Community College
Tracy M. Felton
Union County College
Tullio Ferretti
Hinds Community College
Victor Fet
Marshall University
Teresa G. Fischer
Indian River College
Melanie Florence
Dixie State College
Brandon L. Foster
Wake Technical Community College
Debra L. Foster
Park University
Nancy A. Freeman
El Camino Community College
Dennis W. Fulbright
Michigan State University
Michael D. Gottlieb
LaGuardia Community College
Tammy Greene
Arkansas State University–Beebe
Carla Guthridge
Cameron University
Sue Habeck
Tacoma Community College
Richard Hanke
Rose State College
Nixie Hnetkovsky
Frontier Community College
Michael E. S. Hudspeth
Northern Illinois University
Amy G. Hurst
Rose State College
Jeremiah N. Jarrett
Central Connecticut State University
Adeline Jasinski
Bristol Community College
Angela Jones
California State University–Long Beach
Robyn Jordan
University of Louisiana–Monroe
Judy Kaufman
Monroe Community College
Ronald Keiper
Valencia Community College
Amy Kennedy
Central Carolina Community College
Amine Kidane
Columbus State Community College
Karl Kleiner
York College of Pennsylvania
Roger C. Klockziem
Martin Luther College
Mary Lehman
Longwood University
Susan Lewandowski
Westmoreland County Community College
Suzanne Long
Monroe Community College
Eric Lovely
Arkansas Tech University
Richard Maloof
County College of Morris
Mark Manteuffel
St. Louis Community College
Roy J. Marler
Cascade College
Kamau W. Mbuthia
Bowling Green State University
Melissa Meador
Arkansas State University–Beebe
Linda Meeks
Lake Michigan College
Judith Megaw
Indian River State College
Eric R. Myers
South Suburban College
Steven Mark Norris
California State University–Channel Islands
Igor V. Oksov
Union County College
Theodore J. O'Tanyi
Widener University
Joe Petti
Albertus Magnus College
Mary Phillips
Tulsa Community College
Crystal Pietrowicz
Southern Maine Community College
Karen Plucinski
Missouri Southern State University
Wendy M. Rappazzo
Harford Community College
Pamela Riddell
Macomb Community College
Carlton Rockett
Bowling Green State University
Robert J. Schodorf
Lake Michigan College
Roy D. Schodtler
Lake Land College
Roger Seeber, Jr.
West Liberty State College
William A. Shear
Hampden–Sydney College
Greg Sievert
Emporia State University
William Simcik
Lone Star College–Tomball
Beatrice Sirakaya
Pennsylvania State University
Erika Stephens
Arkansas State University–Beebe
Judith L. Stewart
College of Southern Nevada
Irina Stroup
Shasta College
George E. Veomett
University of Nebraska–Lincoln
Adil M. Wadia
The University of Akron Wayne College
Timothy S. Wakefield
John Brown University
Suzanne Wakim
Butte–Glenn Community College District
Jamie Welling
South Suburban College
Jennifer Wiatrowski
Pasco–Hernando Community College
Daniece Williams
Hinds Community College–Rankin Campus
David Williams
Valencia Community College
Harry E. Womack
Salisbury University
Calvin Young
Fullerton College
Kevin V. Young
Utah State University–Brigham City

Supplements

Dedicated to providing high-quality and effective supplements for instructors and students, the following supplements were developed for *Essentials of The Living World.*

For Instructors

Connect Biology

McGraw-Hill Connect Biology is a web-based assignment and assessment platform that gives students the means to better connect with their coursework, with their instructors, and with the important concepts that they will need to know for success now and in the future. With Connect Biology, instructors can deliver assignments, quizzes, and tests easily online. Students can practice important skills at their own pace and on their own schedule.

Companion Web Site www.mhhe.com/esstlw3

The companion Web site contains the following resources for instructors:

Presentation Tools Everything you need for outstanding presentations in one place! This easy-to-use table of assets includes:

- Animation PowerPoints—numerous full-color animations illustrating important processes are also provided. Harness the visual impact of concepts in motion by importing these files into classroom presentations or online course materials.
- Lecture PowerPoints—with animations fully embedded
- Labeled and unlabeled JPEG images—full-color digital files of all illustrations that can be readily incorporated into presentations, exams, or custom-made classroom materials.
- Tables—tables from the text are available in electronic format.

Presentation Center In addition to the images from your book, this online digital library contains photos, artwork, animations, and other media from an array of McGraw-Hill textbooks that can be used to create customized lectures, visually enhanced tests and quizzes, compelling course Web sites, or attractive printed support materials. All assets are copyrighted by McGraw-Hill Higher Education, but can be used by instructors for classroom purposes.

Instructor's Manual The instructor's manual contains chapter outlines, lecture enrichment ideas, and critical thinking questions.

Computerized Test Bank A comprehensive bank of test questions is provided within a computerized test bank powered by McGraw-Hill's flexible electronic testing program EZ Test Online.

EZ Test Online allows you to create paper and online tests or quizzes in this easy-to-use program! Imagine being able to create and access your test or quiz anywhere, at any time, without installing the testing software. Now, with EZ Test Online, instructors can select questions from multiple McGraw-Hill test banks or author their own, and then either print the test for paper distribution or give it online.

Test Creation

- Author/edit questions online using the 14 different question-type templates.
- Create question pools to offer multiple versions online—great for practice.
- Export your tests for use in WebCT, Blackboard, PageOut, and Apple's iQuiz.
- Sharing tests with colleagues, adjuncts, TAs is easy.

Online Test Management

- Set availability dates and time limits for your quiz or test.
- Assign points by question or question type with dropdown menu.
- Provide immediate feedback to students or delay feedback until all finish the test.
- Create practice tests online to enable student mastery.
- Your roster can be uploaded to enable student self-registration.

Online Scoring and Reporting

- Automated scoring for most of EZ Test's numerous question types.
- Allows manual scoring for essay and other open-response questions.
- Manual rescoring and feedback are also available.
- EZ Test's grade book is designed to easily export to your grade book.
- View basic statistical reports.

Support and Help

- Flash tutorials for getting started on the support site.
- Support Web site: **www.mhhe.com/eztest**
- Product specialist available at 1-800-331-5094.
- Online training: **http://auth.mhhe.com/mpss/workshops**

Virtual Labs

A complete set of more than 20 online introductory biology laboratory exercises are available on this text's companion Web site. Each exercise is self-contained with all instructions and assessment for students. For use either to stand-alone or as a supplement to a traditional lab course, this interactive learning tool will help students understand key biological concepts and processes.

McGraw-Hill: Biology Digitized Video Clips

McGraw-Hill is pleased to offer an outstanding presentation tool to text-adopting instructors—digitized biology video clips on DVD! Licensed from some of the highest-quality science video producers in the world, these brief segments range from about five seconds to just under three minutes in length and cover all areas of general biology from cells to ecosystems. Engaging and informative, McGraw-Hill's digitized videos will help capture students' interest while illustrating key biological concepts and processes such as mitosis, how cilia and flagella work, and how some plants have evolved into carnivores.

Student Response System

Wireless technology brings interactivity into the classroom or lecture hall. Instructors and students receive immediate feedback through wireless response pads that are easy to use and engage students. This system can be used by instructors to take attendance, administer quizzes and tests, create a lecture with intermittent questions, manage lectures and student comprehension through the use of the grade book, and integrate interactivity into their PowerPoint presentations.

For Students

Companion Web Site www.mhhe.com/esstlw3

The Johnson: *Essentials of The Living World* companion Web site is an electronic study system that offers students a digital portal of knowledge. Students can readily access a variety of digital learning objects that include:

- Chapter-level quizzing
- Bio Tutorial animations with quizzing
- Vocabulary flashcards
- Virtual labs

Biology Prep, also available on the companion Web site, helps students prepare for their upcoming coursework in biology. This Web site enables students to perform self-assessments, conduct self-study sessions with tutorials, and perform a postassessment of their knowledge in the following areas:

- Introductory Biology Skills
- Basic Math Review I and II
- Chemistry
- Metric System
- Lab Reports and Referencing

Electronic Book

If you or your students are ready for an alternative version of the traditional textbook, McGraw-Hill has partnered with CourseSmart and VitalSource to bring you innovative and inexpensive electronic textbooks. Students can save up to 50% off the cost of a print book, reduce their impact on the environment, and gain access to powerful Web tools for learning including full-text search, notes and highlighting, and e-mail tools for sharing notes between classmates. eBooks from McGraw-Hill are smart, interactive, searchable, and portable.

To review comp copies or to purchase an eBook, go to either www.CourseSmart.com or www.VitalSource.com.

How to Study Science

This workbook offers students helpful suggestions for meeting the considerable challenges of a science course. It gives practical advice on such topics as how to take notes, how to get the most out of laboratories, and how to overcome science anxiety.

Photo Atlas for General Biology

This atlas was developed to support our numerous general biology titles. It can be used as a supplement for a general biology lecture or laboratory course.

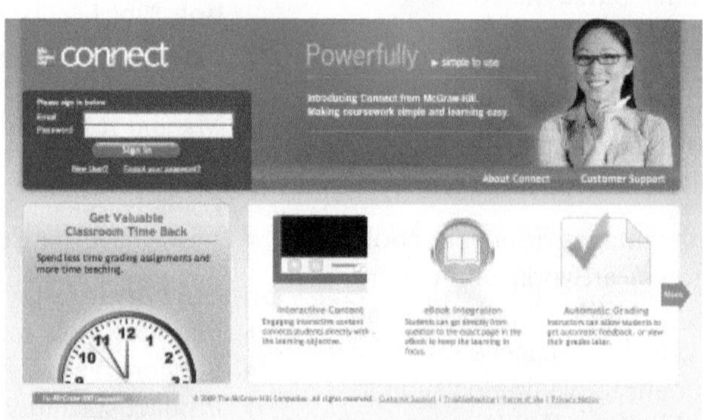

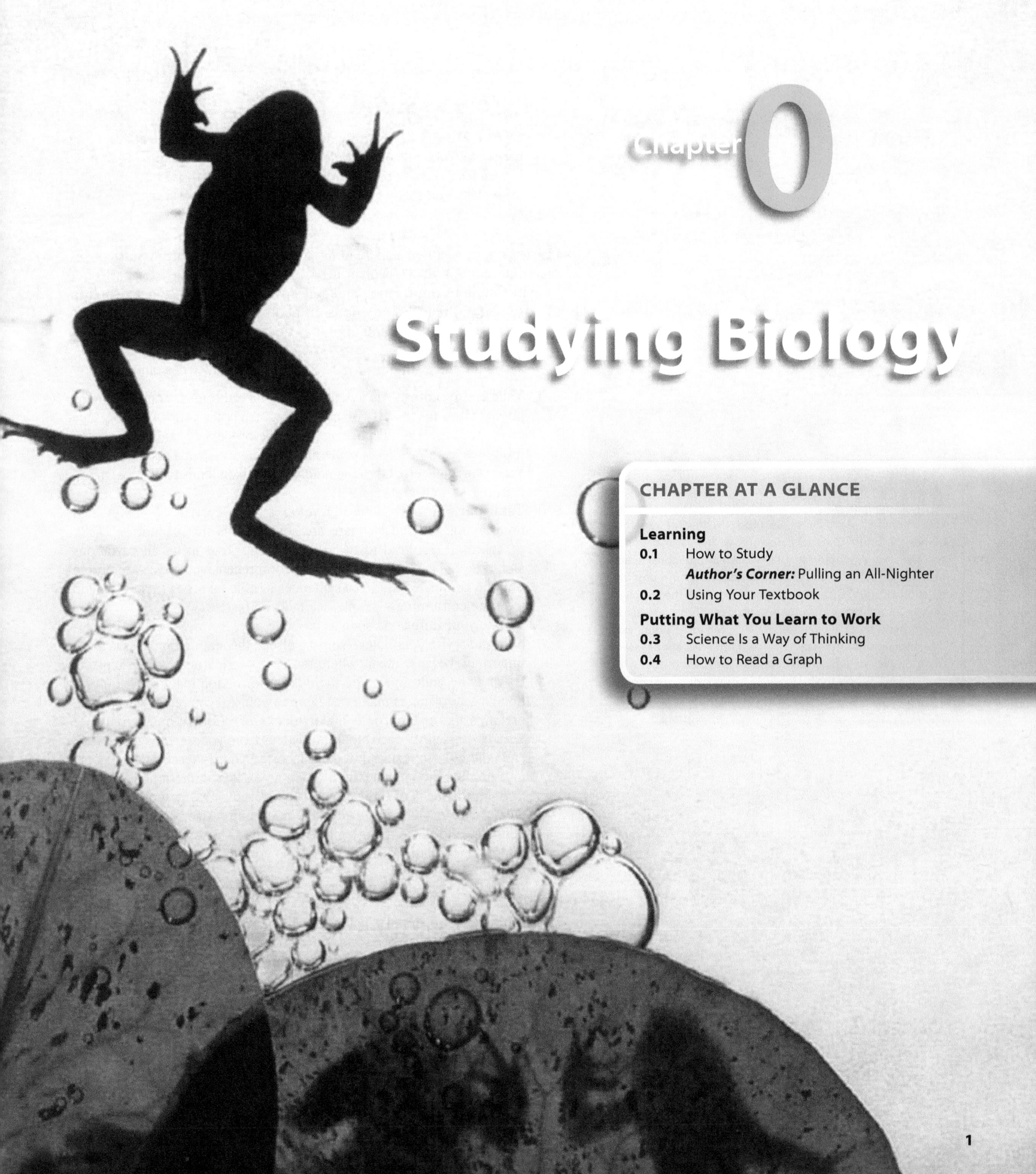

Chapter 0

Studying Biology

CHAPTER AT A GLANCE

Learning

0.1 How to Study

CONCEPT PREVIEW: Studying biology successfully is an active process. To do well, you should attend lectures, do assigned readings before lecture, take complete class notes, rewrite those notes soon after class, and study for exams in short, focused sessions.

Taking Notes

Listening to lectures and reading the text are only the first steps in learning enough to do well in a biology course. The key to mastering the mountain of information and concepts you are about to encounter is to take careful notes. Studying from poor-quality notes that are sparse, disorganized, and barely intelligible is not a productive way to approach preparing for an exam.

There are three simple ways to improve the quality of your notes:

1. **Take many notes.** Always attempt to take the most complete notes possible during class. If you miss class, take notes yourself from a tape of the lecture, if at all possible. It is the process of taking notes that promotes learning. Using someone else's notes is but a poor substitute. When someone else takes the notes, that person tends to do most of the learning as well.
2. **Take paraphrased notes.** Develop a legible style of abbreviated note taking. Obviously, there are some things that cannot be easily paraphrased (referred to in a simpler way), but using abbreviations and paraphrasing will permit more comprehensive notes. Attempting to write complete organized sentences in note taking is frustrating and too time consuming—people just talk too fast!
3. **Revise your notes.** As soon as possible after lecture, you should decipher and revise your notes. Nothing else in the learning process is more important, because this is where most of your learning will take place. By revising your notes, you meld the information together, and put it into a context that is understandable to you. As you revise your notes, organize the material into major blocks of information with simple "heads" to identify each block. Add ideas from your reading of the text, and note links to material in other lectures. Clarify terms and concepts that might be confusing with short notes and definitions. Thinking through the ideas of the lecture in this organized way will crystallize them for you, which is the key step in learning. Also, simply rewriting your notes to make them legible, neat, and tidy can be a tremendous improvement that will further enhance your ease of learning.

BIOLOGY & YOU

Improving Memory. There is an active market on the internet for commercial products that claim to improve your memory. Many of these products involve repetitive games or other gimmicks; few have any lasting impact on memory. Psychologists have carried out considerable research on this subject, and have found that the best way to improve memory seems to be to increase the supply of oxygen to the brain. How do you do this? These researchers recommend aerobic exercise. Walking for three hours each week significantly increases brain oxygen levels, as does swimming or cycling. One study found that chewing gum while studying will supply the brain with enough oxygen to improve memorizing items simply because of the muscle movement.

Remembering and Forgetting

Learning is the process of placing information in your memory. Just as in your computer, there are two sorts of memory. The first, *short-term memory*, is analogous to the RAM (random access memory) of a computer, holding information for only a short period of time. Just as in your computer, this memory is constantly being "written over" as new information comes in. The second kind of memory, *long-term memory*, consists of information that you have stored in your memory banks for future retrieval, like storing files on your computer's hard drive. In its simplest context, learning is the process of transferring information to your hard drive.

Forgetting is the loss of information stored in memory. Most of what we forget when taking exams is the natural consequence of short-term memories not being effectively transferred to long-term memory. Forgetting occurs very rapidly, dropping to below 50% retention within one hour after learning and leveling off at about 20% retention after 24 hours.

There are many things you can do to slow down the forgetting process. Here are two important ones:

1. **Recopy your notes as soon as possible after lecture.** Remember, there is about a 50% memory loss in the first hour. You should use your textbook as well when recopying your notes.
2. **Establish a purpose for reading.** When you sit down to study your textbook, have a definite goal to learn a particular concept. Each chapter begins with a preview of its key concepts—let them be your guides. Do not try and learn the entire contents of a chapter in one session; break it up into small pieces that are "easily digested."

Learning

Learning may be viewed as the efficient transfer of information from your short-term memory to your long-term memory. This transfer is referred to as *rehearsal* by learning strategists. As its name implies, rehearsal always involves some form of repetition. There are four general means of rehearsal in the jargon of education called "critical thinking skills" (figure 0.1).

Repeating. The most obvious form of rehearsal is repetition. To learn facts, the sequence of events in a process, or the names of a group of things, you write them down, say them aloud, and mentally repeat them over and over, until you have "memorized" them. This often is a first step on the road to learning. Many students mistake this as the only step. It is not, as it involves only rote memory, not understanding. If all you do in this course is memorize facts, you will not succeed.

Organizing. It is important to organize the information you are attempting to learn, because the process of sorting and ordering increases retention. For example, if you place a sequence of events in order, like the stages of mitosis, the entire sequence can be recalled if you can remember what gets the sequence started.

Linking. Biology has a natural hierarchy of information, with terms and concepts nested within other terms and concepts. You will learn facts and concepts more easily if you attempt to connect them with something you already know, linking them to some information that is already stored in your memory. Throughout this textbook, you will see arrows, like the one in figure 0.2, indicating such links. Use them to check back over concepts and processes you have already learned. You will be surprised how much doing this will help you learn the new material.

Connecting. You will learn biology much more effectively if you relate what you are learning to the world about you. The many challenges of living in today's world are often related to the information presented in this course, and understanding these relationships will help you learn. In each chapter of this textbook you will encounter several Apps (Application dialogs) in the outer margins (there is a "BIOLOGY & YOU" App on the facing page) that allow you to briefly explore a "real-world" topic related to what you are learning. Read them. You may not be tested on these Apps, but reading them will provide you with another "hook" to help you learn the material on which you will be tested.

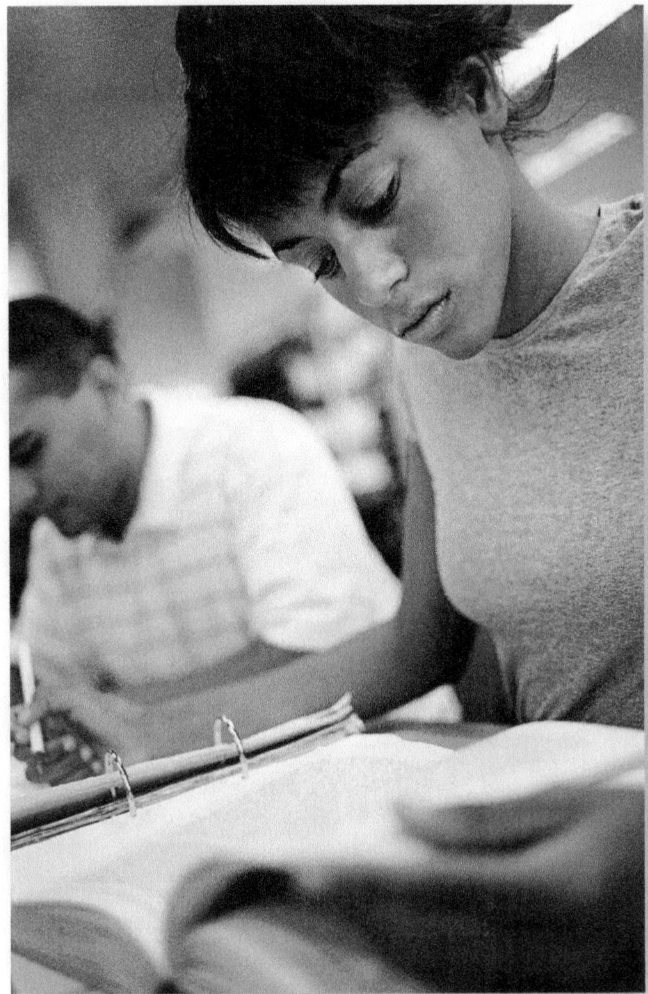

Figure 0.1 Learning requires work.

Learning is something you do, not something that happens to you.

IMPLICATION If you are honest with yourself, how many of the four rehearsal techniques (critical thinking skills) do you use when you take a science course like this one? Do you think they are as important in non-science classes like English or History? Why?

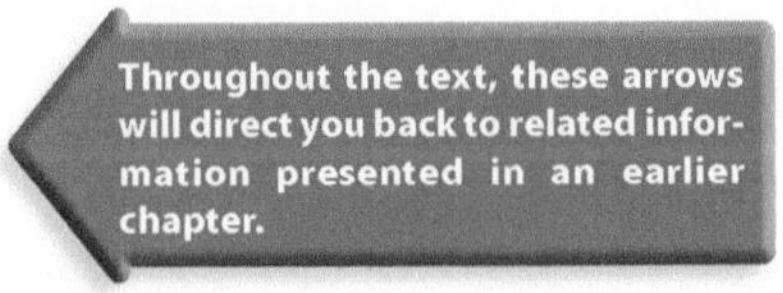

Throughout the text, these arrows will direct you back to related information presented in an earlier chapter.

Figure 0.2 Linking concepts.

These linking arrows, found throughout the text, will help you to form connections between seemingly discrete topics covered earlier in the text.

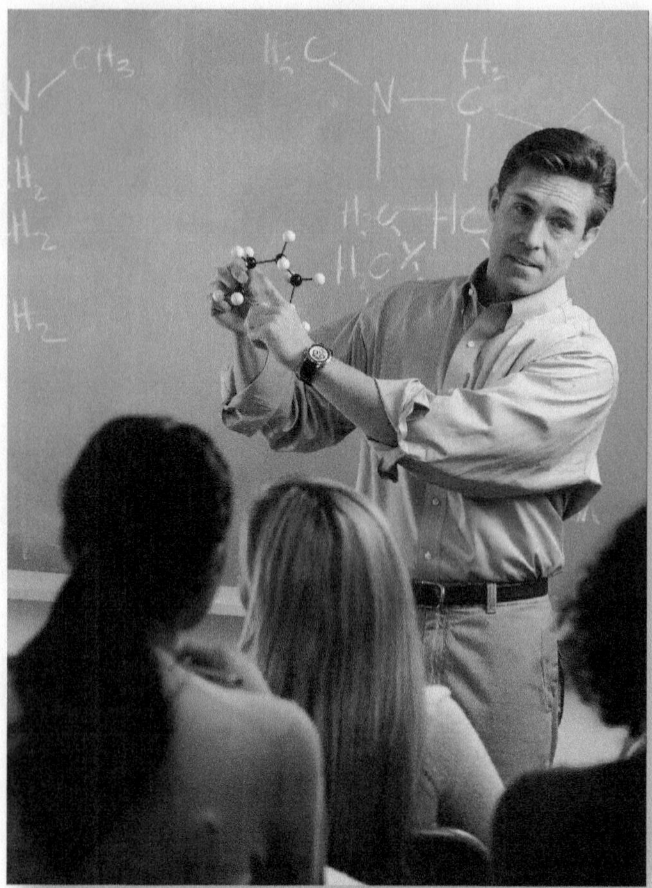

Figure 0.3 Critical learning occurs in the classroom.

Learning occurs in at least four distinct stages: attending class; doing assigned textbook readings before lecture; listening and taking notes during lecture; and recopying notes shortly after lecture. If you are diligent in these steps, then studying lecture notes and text assignments before exams is much more effective. Skipping any of these stages makes successful learning far less likely.

Studying to Learn

If I have heard it once, I have heard it a thousand times, "Gee, Professor Johnson, I studied for 20 hours straight and I still got a D." By now, you should be getting the idea that just throwing time at the material does not necessarily ensure a favorable outcome. Many students treat studying for biology like penance: If you do it, you will be rewarded for having done so. Not always.

The length of time spent studying and the spacing between study or reading sessions directly affects how much you learn. If you had 10 hours to spend studying, you would be better off if you broke it up into 10 one-hour sessions than to spend it all in one or two sessions. There are two good reasons for this:

First, we know from formal cognition research (as well as from our everyday life experiences) that we remember "beginnings" and "endings" but tend to forget "middles." Thus, the learning process can benefit from many "beginnings" and "endings."

Second, unless you are unusual, after 30 minutes or an hour your ability to concentrate is diminished. Concentration is a critical component of studying to learn. Many short, topic-focused study sessions maximize your ability to concentrate effectively. For most of us, effective concentration also means a comfortable, quiet environment with no outside distractions like loud music or conversations.

Learning Is an Active Process

It is important to realize that learning biology is not something you can do passively. Many students think that simply possessing a lecture video or a set of class notes will get them through. In and of themselves, videos and notes are no more important than the Nautilus machine an athlete works out on. It is not the machine *per se*, but what happens when you use it effectively that is of importance.

Common sense will have a great deal to do with your success in learning biology, as it does in most of life's endeavors. Your success in this biology course will depend on simple, obvious things (figure 0.3):

- *Attend class.* Go to all the lectures and be on time.
- *Read the assigned readings before lecture.* If you have done so, you will hear things in lecture that will be familiar to you, a recognition that is a vital form of learning reinforcement. Later you can go back to the text to check details.
- *Take comprehensive notes.* Recognizing and writing down lecture points is another form of recognition and reinforcement. Later, studying for an exam, you will have already forgotten lecture material you did not record, and so even if you study hard you will miss exam questions on this material.
- *Revise your notes soon after lecture.* Actively interacting with your class notes while you still hold much of the lecture in short-term memory provides perhaps the most powerful form of reinforcement, and will be a key to your success.

As you proceed through this textbook, you will encounter a blizzard of terms and concepts. Biology is a field rich with ideas and the technical jargon needed to describe them. What you discover reading this textbook is intended to support the lectures that provide the core of your biology course. Integrating what you learn here with what you learn in lecture will provide you with the strongest possible tool for successfully mastering the basics of biology. The rest is just hard work.

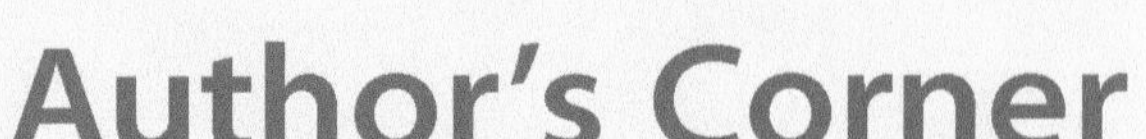

Author's Corner

Pulling an All-Nighter

At some point in the next months you will face that scary rite, the first exam in this course. As a university professor I get to give the exams rather than take them, but I can remember with crystal clarity when the shoe was on the other foot. I didn't like exams a bit as a student—what student does? But in my case I was often practically paralyzed with fear. What scared me about exams was the possibility of unanticipated questions. No matter how much I learned, there was always something I didn't know, some direction from which my teacher could lob a question I had no chance of answering.

I lived and died by the all-nighter. Black coffee was my closest friend in final exam week, and sleep seemed a luxury I couldn't afford. My parents urged me to sleep more, but I was trying to cram enough in to meet any possible question, and couldn't waste time sleeping.

Now, driven by time (often kicking and screaming), I find I did it all wrong. In work published over the last few years, researchers at Harvard Medical School have demonstrated that our memory of newly-learned information improves only after sleeping at least six hours. If I wanted to do well on final exams, I could not have chosen a poorer way to prepare. The gods must look after the ignorant, as I usually passed.

Learning is, in its most basic sense, a matter of forming memories. The Harvard researchers' experiments showed that a person trying to learn something does not improve his or her knowledge until after they have had more than six hours of sleep (preferably eight). It seems the brain needs time to file new information and skills away in the proper slots so they can be retrieved later. Without enough sleep to do all this filing, new information does not get properly encoded into the brain's memory circuits.

To sort out the role of sleep in learning, the Harvard Medical School researchers used Harvard undergrads as guinea pigs. The undergraduates were trained to look for particular visual targets on a computer screen, and to push a button as soon as they were sure they had seen one. At first, responses were relatively sluggish—it typically took 400 milliseconds for a target to reach a student's conscious awareness. With an hour's training, however, many students were hitting the button correctly in 75 milliseconds.

How well had they learned? When retested from 3 to 12 hours later on the same day, there was no further improvement past a student's best time in the training session. If the researchers let a student get a little sleep, but less than six hours, then retested the next day, the student still showed no improvement in performing the target identification.

For students who slept more than six hours, the story was very different. Sleep greatly improved performance. Students who achieved 75 milliseconds in the training session would reliably perform the target identification in 62 milliseconds after a good night's sleep! After several nights of ample sleep, they often got even more proficient.

Why six or eight hours, and not four or five? The sort of sleeping you do at the beginning of a night's sleep and the sort you do at the end are different, and both, it appears, are required for efficient learning.

The first two hours of sleeping are spent in deep sleep, what psychiatrists call slow wave sleep. During this time, certain brain

chemicals become used up, which allows information that has been gathered during the day to flow out of the memory center of the brain, the hippocampus, and into the cortex, the outer covering of the brain where long-term memories are stored. Like moving information in a computer from active memory to the hard drive, this process preserves experience for future reference. Without it, long-term learning cannot occur.

Over the next hours, the cortex sorts through the information it has received, distributing it to various locations and networks. Particular connections between nerve cells become strengthened as memories are preserved, a process that is thought to require the time-consuming manufacturing of new proteins.

If you halt this process before it is complete, the day's memories do not get fully "transcribed," and you don't remember all that you would have, had you allowed the process to continue to completion. A few hours are just not enough time to get the job done. Four hours, the Harvard researchers estimate, is a minimum requirement.

The last two hours of a night's uninterrupted sleep are spent in rapid-eye-movement (rem) sleep. This is when dreams occur. The brain shuts down the connection to the hippocampus and runs through the data it has stored over the previous hours. This process is also important to learning, as it reinforces and strengthens the many connections between nerve cells that make up the new memory. Like a child repeating a refrain to memorize it, the brain goes over what it has learned, till practice makes perfect.

That's why my college system of getting by on three or four hours of sleep during exam week and crashing for 12 hours on weekends didn't work. After a few days, all of the facts I had memorized during one of my "all-nighters" faded away. Of course they did. I had never given them a chance to integrate properly into my memory circuits.

As I look back, I now see that how well I did on my exams probably had far less to do with how hard I studied than with how much I slept. It doesn't seem fair that after all these years, with my own kids now in college pulling all-nighters, I have to admit that my parents were right all along.

0.2 Using Your Textbook

CONCEPT PREVIEW: Your text is a tool to reinforce and clarify what you learn in lecture. Your use of it will only be effective if coordinated with your development of recopied lecture notes.

A Textbook Is a Tool

A student enrolled in an introductory biology course as you are, almost never learns everything from the textbook. Your text is a tool to explain and amplify what you learn in lecture. No textbook is a substitute for attending lectures, taking notes, and studying them. Success in your biology course is like a stool with three legs: lectures, class notes, and text reading—all three are necessary. Used together, they will take you a long way towards success in the course.

When to Use Your Text. While you can glance at your text at any time to refresh your memory or answer a question that pops into your mind, your use of your text as a learning tool should focus on providing support for the other two "legs" of course success, lectures and class notes.

Do the Assigned Reading. Many instructors assign reading from the text, reading that is supposed to be done before lecture. The timing here is very important: If you already have a general idea of what is being discussed in lecture, it is much easier to follow the discussion and take better notes.

Link the Text to Your Lecture Notes. Few lectures cover exactly what is in the text, and much of what is in the text may not be covered in lecture. That said, much of what you will hear in lecture is covered in your text. This coverage provides you with a powerful tool to reinforce ideas and information you encounter in lecture. Text illustrations and detailed explanations can pound home an idea quickly grasped in lecture, and answer any questions that might occur to you as you sort through the logic of an argument. Thus it is absolutely essential that you follow along with your text as you recopy your lecture notes, keying your notes to the textbook as you go. Annotating your notes in this way will make them far better learning tools as you study for exams later.

Review for Exams. It goes without saying that you should review your recopied lecture notes to prepare for an exam. But that is not enough. What is often missed in gearing up for an exam is the need to also review that part of the text that covers the same material. Reading the chapter again, one last time, helps place your lecture notes in perspective, so that it will be easier to remember key points when a topic explodes at you off the page of your exam.

How to Use Your Text. The single most important way to use your text is to read it. As your biology course proceeds and you move through the text, read each assigned chapter all the way through at one sitting. This will give you valuable perspective. Then, guided by your lecture notes, go back through the chapter one topic at a time, and focus on learning that one topic as you recopy your notes. Pay attention to the "linking" arrows in the text, as using them will reinforce what you are learning. As discussed earlier, building a bridge between text and lecture notes is a very powerful way to learn. Remember, your notes don't take the exam, and neither does the textbook; you do, and the learning that occurs as you integrate text pages and lecture notes in your mind will go a long way toward your taking it well.

Learning Tools at Your Disposal

A textbook is more than just words. What do you see when you flip through the pages of this text? Pictures, lots of them. And questions, scattered through each chapter and clustered at chapter's end. The pictures and quiz questions you will encounter within each chapter can be an important part of your learning experience.

Let the Illustrations Teach You. All introductory biology texts are rich with colorful photographs and diagrams. They are not there to decorate, but to aid your comprehension of ideas and concepts. When the text refers you to a specific figure, look at it—the visual link will help you remember the idea much better than restricting yourself to cold words on a page.

Three sorts of illustrations offer particularly strong reinforcement:

Essential Biological Process Illustrations. While you will be asked to learn many technical terms in this course, learning the names of things is not your key goal. Your goal is to master a small set of concepts. There are several essential biological processes that explain how organisms work the way they do. When you have understood these processes, much of the heavy lifting in learning biology is done. Every time you encounter one of these essential biological processes in the text, you will be provided with an illustration to help you better understand. These *Essential Biological Process* illustrations break the process down into easily-understood stages, so that you can grasp how the overall process works without being lost in a forest of details (figure 0.4*a*).

Bubble Links. Illustrations teach best when they are simple. Unfortunately, some of the structures and processes being illustrated just aren't simple. Every time you encounter a complex diagram in the text, it will be "predigested" for you, the individual components of the diagram are each identified with a number in a colored circle, or bubble. This same number is also placed in the text narrative right where that component is discussed. These bubble links allow the text to step you through the illustration, explaining what is going on at each stage—the illustration is a feast you devour one bite at a time.

Phylum Facts. Not all of what you will learn are concepts. Sometimes you will need to soak up a lot of information, painting a picture with facts. Nowhere is this more true than when you study animal diversity. In chapter 18 you will encounter a train of animal phyla (a phylum is a major category of organisms) with which you must become familiar. In such a sea of information, what should you learn? Every time you encounter a phylum in chapter 18, you will be provided with a *Phylum Facts* illustration that selects the key bits of information about the body and lifestyle of that kind of animal (figure 0.4*b*). If you learned and understood only the items highlighted there, you would have mastered much of what you need to know.

Check What You Know. As you move through a chapter, addressing first one topic and then another, it will be important that you monitor your progress—not only what you have read, but how well you have understood it.

Concept Checks. At the end of each segment of a chapter you will encounter Concept Checks, a few questions you can use to assess how you are doing. They are not comprehensive, but rather representative. If you miss any of them, you should go back and have another go at that section.

End-of Chapter Questions. When you complete a chapter, you can gauge how well you have learned the material by answering the "Self-Test" and "Visual Understanding" questions at the end of the chapter. If you get a question wrong, that indicates where you need to go to finish the job. If you don't get any wrong, you have probably done your job well. You can further test your knowledge with the "Challenge Questions."

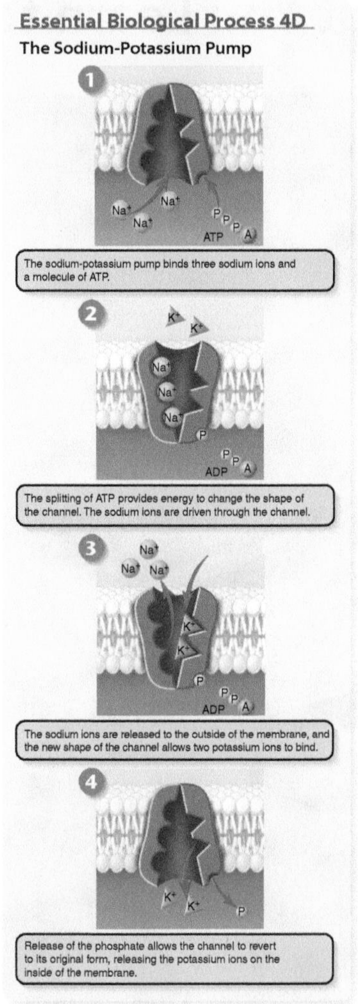

(a)

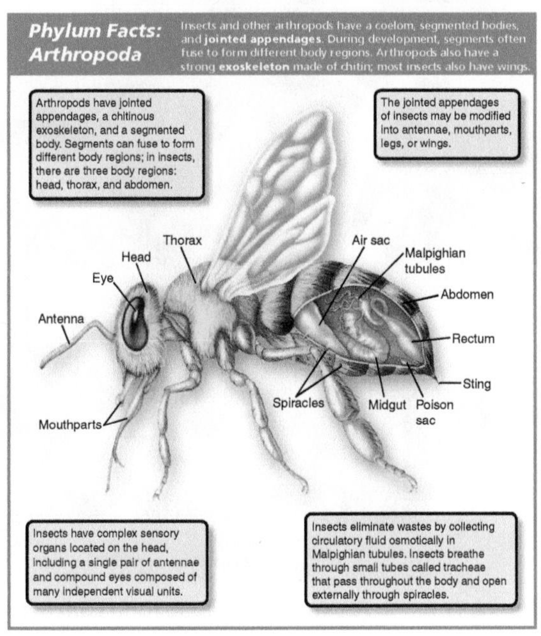

(b)

Figure 0.4 Visual learning tools.

(a) An example of an *Essential Biological Process* illustration.
(b) An example of a Phylum Facts illustration.

Putting What You Learn to Work

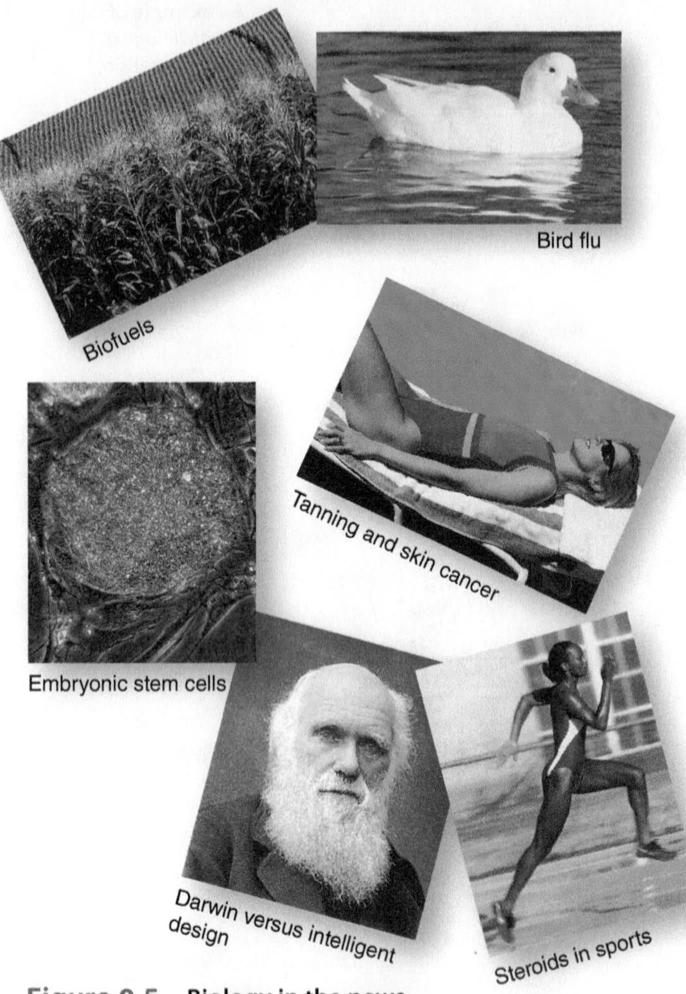

Figure 0.5 Biology in the news.

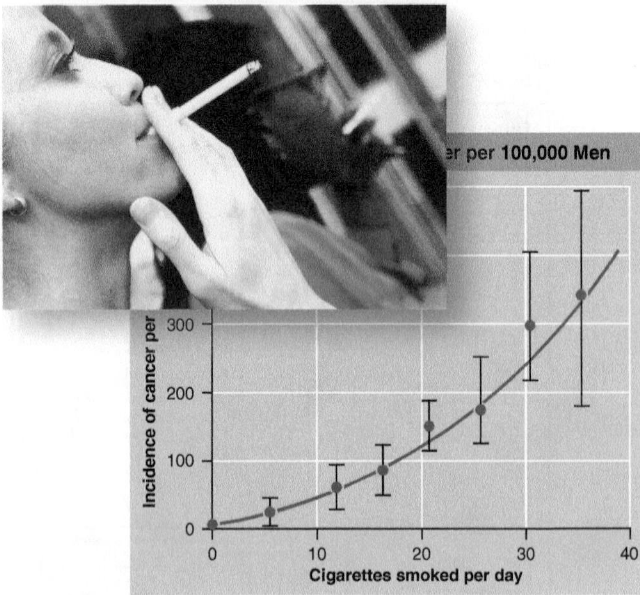

Figure 0.6 Does smoking cause lung cancer?

0.3 Science Is a Way of Thinking

CONCEPT PREVIEW: Scientists investigate by gathering data and analyzing it to form possible explanations they can test.

In the study of biology you will encounter a great deal of information, a forest of new terms and definitions, and a lot of descriptions of how things work—body processes, evolutionary relationships, interactions within ecosystems, and many others. In all of this, you will be asked to accept that what you are being taught is "true," that it accurately reflects reality. In fact, what it accurately reflects is what we know about reality. Of the things that you learn in this course, some will be altered by future scientists as they learn more. As we will discuss in chapter 1, our knowledge of science is always incomplete, the picture of reality we construct always a rough draft.

One of the most important things you can learn in a biology course is how these adjustments are made. Long after this class is completed, you will be making decisions that involve biology, and they will be better, more informed decisions if you have acquired the skill to evaluate scientific claims for yourself. Because it is printed in the newspaper or cited on a web site doesn't make a scientific claim valid. Figure 0.5 illustrates the sorts of biology you encounter today in the news—and this is just a small sample. They are, all of them, important issues that will affect your own life. How do you reach informed opinions about them?

You do it by asking the question, "How do we know this?" Science is a way of thinking that demands to see the evidence, that challenges the validity of every claim. If you can learn to do this, to apply this skill in the future to personal decisions about biology as it impacts your life, you will have taken from this course a valuable lesson.

How Do We Know What We Know?

A useful way to learn how scientists think, how they constantly check and question what they know, is to look at real cases. What follows are four instances where biologists have come to a conclusion. These conclusions will be taught in this textbook, reflecting the world about us as best as science can determine. All four of these cases will be treated at length in later chapters—here they serve only to introduce the process of scientific questioning.

Does Cigarette Smoking Cause Lung Cancer? According to the American Cancer Society, 564,830 Americans died of cancer in 2006. Fully one in four of the students using this textbook can be expected to die of it. Twenty-nine percent of these cancer victims, almost a third, die of lung cancer.

As you might imagine, something that kills so many of us has been the subject of much research. The first step biologists took was to ask a simple question: "Who gets lung cancer?" The answer came back loud and clear: Fully 87% of lung cancer deaths are cigarette smokers. Delving into this more closely, researchers looked to see if the incidence of lung cancer (that is, how many people contract it per 100,000 people) can be predicted by how many cigarettes a person smokes each day. As you can see in the graph in figure 0.6 (which is shown again on page 590), it can. The more cigarettes smoked, the higher the occurrence of lung cancer. Based on this study, and lots of others like it, examined in more detail on pages 194 and 498, biologists concluded that smoking cigarettes causes lung cancer.

Does Carbon Dioxide Cause Global Warming? Our world is getting warmer—a lot warmer. The great ice caps that cover Antarctica and Greenland are melting, and sea levels are rising. Looking for the cause, atmospheric scientists soon began to suspect what might at first seem an unlikely culprit: carbon dioxide (CO_2), a gas that is a minor component (0.03%) of the air we breathe. As you will learn in this course, burning coal and other fossil fuels releases CO_2 into the atmosphere. Problems arise because CO_2 traps heat. As the modern world industrializes, more and more CO_2 is released. Does this lead to a hotter earth? To find out, researchers looked to see if the rise in global temperature reflected a rise in the atmosphere's CO_2. As you can see in the graph in figure 0.7 (which is shown again on page 436), it does. After these and other careful studies we will explore in detail on pages 436 and 452, scientists concluded that rising CO_2 levels are indeed the cause of global warming.

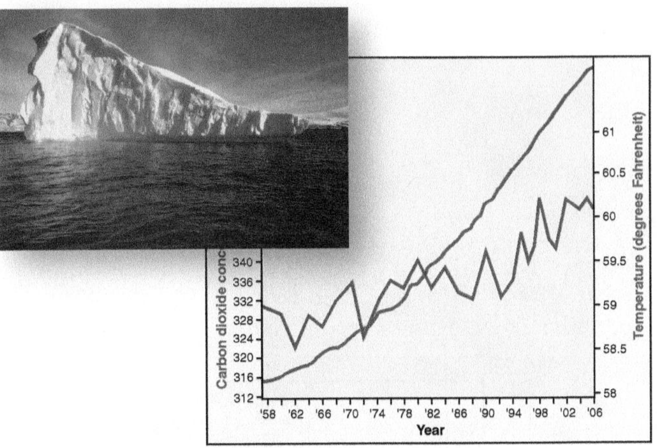

Figure 0.7 **Does carbon dioxide cause global warming?**

Does Obesity Lead to Type 2 Diabetes? The United States is in the midst of an obesity epidemic. Over the last 16 years, the percentage of Americans who are obese has almost tripled, from 12% to over 34%. Coincidentally (or is it a coincidence?), the number of Americans suffering from type 2 diabetes (a disorder in which the body loses its ability to regulate glucose levels in the blood, often leading to blindness and amputation of limbs) has more than tripled over the same 16 year period, from 7 million to more than 23 million (that's one in every fourteen Americans!).

What is going on here? When researchers compared obesity levels with type 2 diabetes levels, they found a marked correlation, clearly visible in the graph in figure 0.8 (which is shown again on page 585). Investigating more closely, the researchers found that an estimated 80% of people who develop type 2 diabetes are obese. Detailed investigations described on page 585 have now confirmed the relationship that these early studies hinted at: Overeating triggers changes in the body that lead to type 2 diabetes.

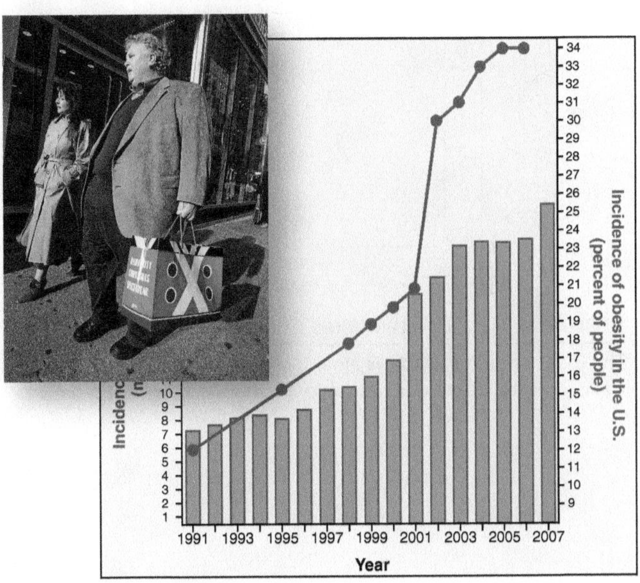

Figure 0.8 **Does obesity lead to type 2 diabetes?**

What Causes the Ozone Hole? Twenty five years ago, atmospheric scientists first reported a loss of ozone (O_3 gas) high in the atmosphere over Antarctica. This was scary, because ozone in the upper atmosphere absorbs ultraviolet radiation from the sun, protecting the earth's surface from these harmful rays. Trying to understand the reason for this "ozone hole," researchers considered many possibilities, and one of them seemed a good candidate: chlorofluorocarbons, or CFCs. CFCs are supposedly inert chemicals that are widely used as heat exchangers in air conditioners. However, further studies, detailed on pages 20 and 21, indicated that CFCs are not inert after all—in the intense cold temperatures high over Antarctica, they cause O_3 to be converted to O_2. Scientists concluded that CFCs were indeed causing the ozone hole over Antarctica. This finding led to international treaties beginning in 1990 blocking the further manufacture of CFC chemicals. As you can see in the graph in figure 0.9 (which is shown again on page 28), the size of the ozone hole soon stopped expanding in size.

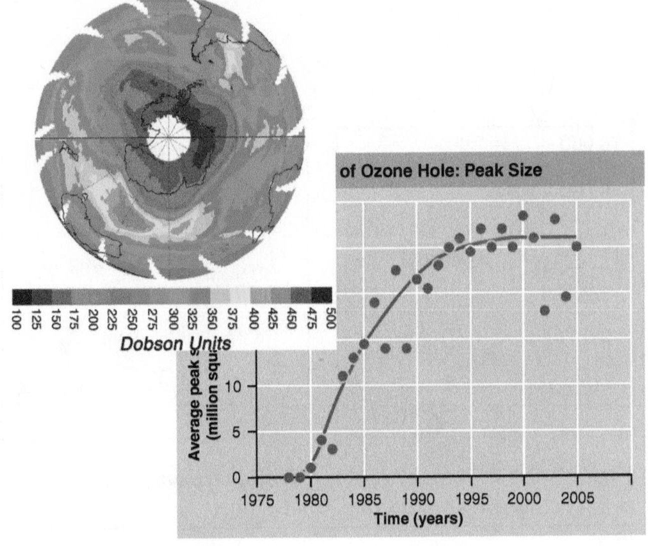

Figure 0.9 **What causes the ozone hole?**

Looking at the Evidence

One thing these four cases have in common is that in each, scientists reached their conclusion not by applying established rules but rather by looking in detail at what was going on and then testing possible explanations. In short, they gathered data and analyzed it. If you are going to think independently about scientific issues in the future, then you will need to learn how to analyze data and understand what it is telling you. In each case above, the data is presented in the form of a graph. Said simply, you will need to learn to read a graph.

0.4 How to Read a Graph

CONCEPT PREVIEW: Scientists often present data in standardized graphs, which portray how a dependent variable changes when an independent variable is changed.

Variables and Graphs

In the previous section, you encountered four graphs illustrating what happened to variables like global temperature, when other variables like atmospheric carbon dioxide change. A **variable,** as its name implies, is something that can change. Variables are the tools of science, and you will encounter many different kinds as you proceed through this text. Many of the variables biologists study are examined in graphs like you saw on the previous pages. A **graph** shows what happens to one variable when another one changes.

There are two types of variables. The first kind, an **independent variable,** is one that a researcher deliberately changes—for example, the concentration of a chemical in a solution, or the number of cigarettes smoked per day. The second kind, a **dependent variable,** is what happens in response to the changes in the independent variable—for example, the intensity of a solution's color, or the incidence of lung cancer. Importantly, the change in a dependent variable that is measured in an experiment is not predetermined by the investigator.

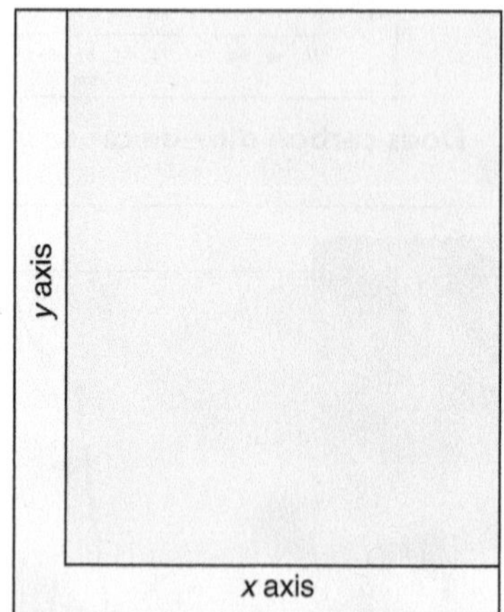

Figure 0.10 The two axes of a graph.

The independent variable is almost always presented along the x axis, and the dependent variable is usually shown along the y axis.

In science, all graphs are presented in a consistent way. The independent variable is always presented and labeled across the bottom, called the *x axis.* The dependent variable is always presented and labeled along the side (usually the left side), called the *y axis* (figure 0.10).

Some research involves examining correlations between sets of variables, rather than the deliberate manipulation of a variable. For example, a researcher who measures both diabetes and obesity levels (as described in the previous section) is actually comparing two dependent variables. While such a comparison can reveal correlations and so suggest potential relationships, ***correlation does not prove causation***. What is happening to one variable may actually have nothing to do with what happens to the other variable. Only by manipulating a variable (making it an independent variable) can you test for causality. Just because people that are obese tend to also have diabetes does not establish that obesity *causes* diabetes. Other experiments are needed to determine causation.

Using the Appropriate Scale and Units

A key aspect of presenting data in a graph is the selection of proper scale. Data presented in a table can utilize many scales, from seconds to centuries, with no problems. A graph, however, typically has a single scale on the *x* axis and a single scale on the *y* axis, which might consist of molecular units (for example, nanometers, microliters, micrograms) or macroscopic units (for example, feet, inches, liters, days, milligrams). In each instance, a scale must be chosen that fits what is being measured. Changes in centimeters would not be obvious in a graph scaled in kilometers. Also, if a variable changes a great deal over the course of the experiment, it is often useful to use an expanding scale. A **log** or **logarithmic scale** is a series of numbers plotted as powers of 10 (1, 10, 100, 1,000,...) rather than in the linear progression seen on most graphs (2,000, 4,000, 6,000...). Consider the two graphs in figure 0.11, where the *y* axis is plotted on a linear scale on the left and on a log scale on the right. You can see that the log scale more clearly displays changes in the dependent variable (the *y* axis) for the upper

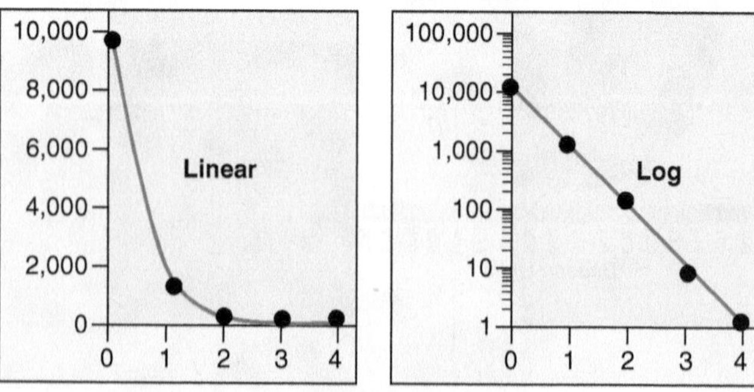

Figure 0.11 Linear and log scale: two ways of presenting the same data.

values of the independent variable (the x axis, values 2, 3, and 4). Notice that the interval *between* each y axis number is not linear either—the interval between each number is itself subdivided on a log scale. Thus, 50 (the fourth tick mark between 10 and 100) is plotted much closer to 100 than to 10.

Individual graphs use different units of measurement, each chosen to best display the experimental data. By international convention, scientific data are presented in **metric units,** a system of units expressed as powers of 10. For example, weight is expressed in units called *grams*. Ten grams make up a decagram, and 1,000 grams is a kilogram. Smaller weights are expressed as a portion of a gram—for example, a centigram is a hundredth of a gram, and a milligram is a thousandth of a gram. The units of measurement employed in a graph are by convention indicated in parentheses next to the independent variable label on the x axis and the dependent variable label on the y axis.

Drawing a Line

Most of the graphs that you will find in this text are **line graphs,** which are graphs composed of data points and one or more lines. Line graphs are typically used to present *continuous data*—that is, data that are discrete samples of a continuous process. An example might be data measuring how quickly the ozone hole develops over Antarctica in August and September of each year. You could in principle measure the area of the ozone hole every day, but to make the project more manageable in time and resources, you might actually take a measurement only once a week. Measurements reveal that the ozone hole increases in area rapidly for about six weeks before shrinking, yielding six data points during its expansion. These six data points are like individual frames from a movie—frozen moments in time. The six data points might indicate a very consistent pattern, or they might not.

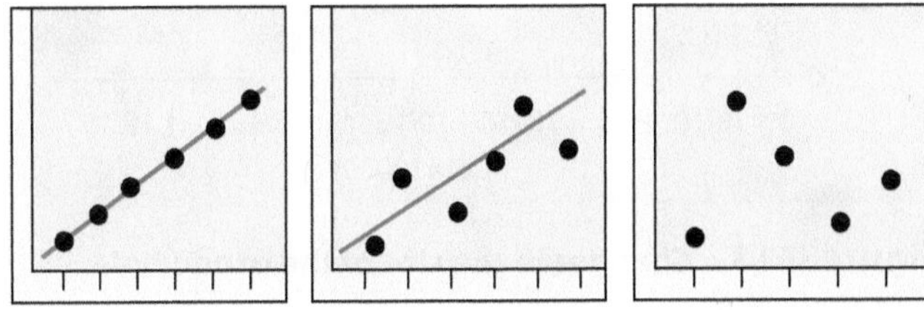

Figure 0.12 Line graphs: hypothetical growth in size of the ozone hole.

Consider the hypothetical data in the graphs of figure 0.12. The data points on the left graph are changing in a very consistent way, with little variation from what a straight line (drawn in red) would predict. The graph in the middle shows more experimental variation, but a straight line still does a good job of revealing the overall pattern of how the data are changing. Such a straight "best-fit line" is called a **regression line** and is calculated by estimating the distance of each point to possible lines, adding the values, and selecting the line with the lowest sum. The data points in the graph on the right are randomly distributed and show no overall pattern, indicating that there is no relationship between the dependent and the independent variables.

Other Graphical Presentations of Data

Sometimes the independent variable for a data set is not continuous but rather represents discrete sets of data. A line graph, with its assumption of continuity, cannot accurately represent the variation occurring in discrete sets of data, where the data sets are being compared with one another. In these cases, the preferred presentation is that of a **histogram,** a kind of bar graph. For example, if you were surveying the heights of pine trees in a park, you might group their heights (the independent variable) into discrete "categories" such as 0 to 5 meters tall, 5 to 10 meters, and so on. These categories are placed on the x axis. You would then count the number of trees in each category and present that dependent variable on the y axis, as shown in figure 0.13.

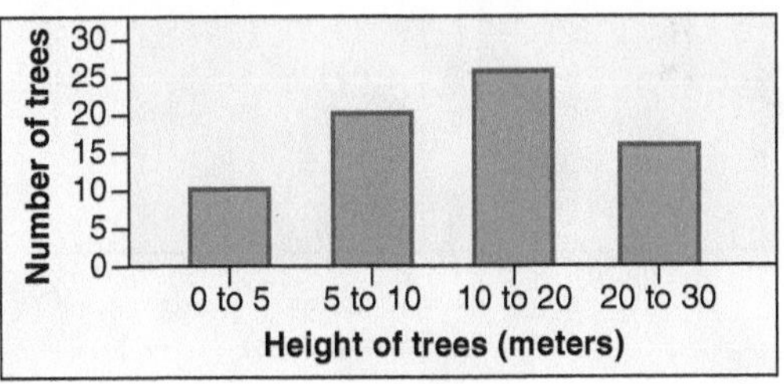

Figure 0.13 Histogram: the frequency of tall trees.

Some data represent proportions of a whole data set, for example the different types of trees in the park as a percentage of all the trees. This type of data is often presented in a **pie chart** (figure 0.14).

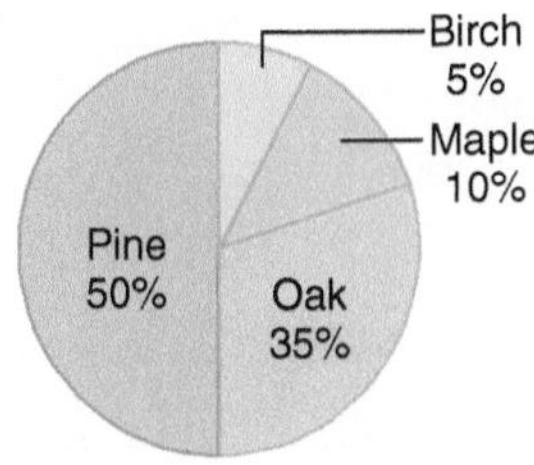

Figure 0.14 Pie chart: the composition of a forest.

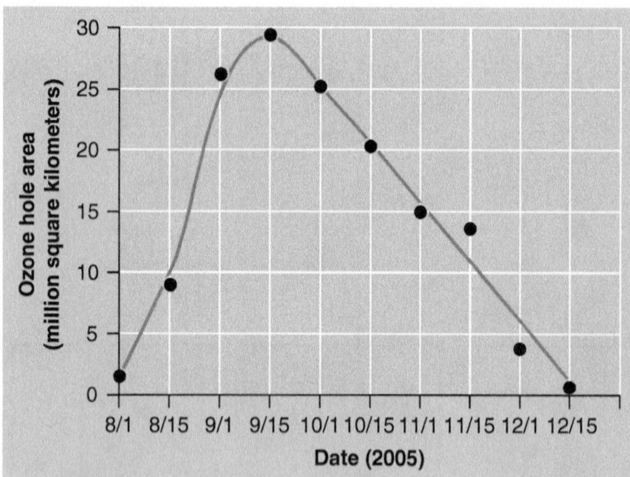

Figure 0.15 Changes in the size of the ozone hole over one year.

This graph shows how the size of the ozone hole changes over time, first expanding in size and then getting smaller.

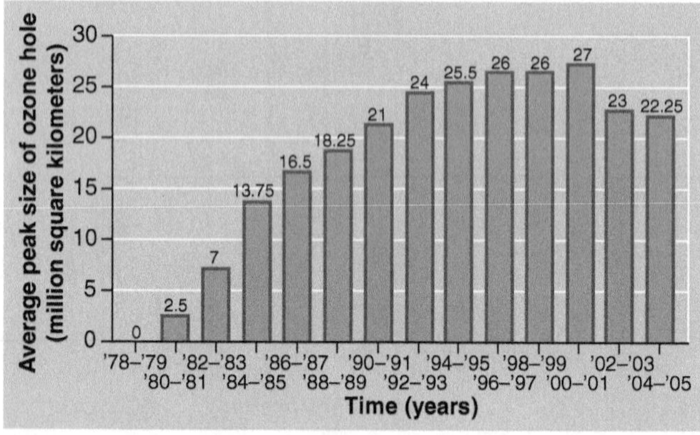

Figure 0.16 The peak sizes of the ozone hole.

This histogram shows how the size of the ozone hole increased in size (determined by its peak size) for 20 years before it then started to decrease.

Putting Your Graph-Reading Skills to Work: Inquiry & Analysis

The sorts of graphs you have encountered here in this brief introduction are all used frequently by scientists in analyzing and presenting their experimental results, and you will encounter them often as you proceed through this text.

Learning to read a graph and understanding what it does and does not tell you is one of the most important things you can take away from a biology course. To help you develop this skill, most of the chapters of this text end with a full-page ***Inquiry & Analysis*** feature. Each of these end-of-chapter features describes a real scientific investigation. You will be introduced to a question, and then given an hypothesis posed by a researcher (a hypothesis is a kind of explanation) to answer that question. The feature will then tell you how the researcher set about evaluating his or her hypothesis with an experiment and will present a graph of the data the researcher obtained. You are then challenged to analyze the data and reach a conclusion about the validity of the hypothesis.

As an example, consider research on the ozone hole, which will be the subject of the *Inquiry & Analysis* feature at the end of chapter 1. What sort of graph might you expect to see? A *line graph* can be used to present data on how the size of the ozone hole changes over the course of one year. Because the dependent variable is the size of the ozone hole measured continuously over a single season, a smooth curve accurately portrays what is actually going on. In this case, the regression line is not a straight line, but rather a curve (figure 0.15).

Can line graphs and histograms be used to present the same data? In some cases, yes. The mode of its presentation does not alter the data; it only serves to emphasize the point being investigated. The *histogram* in figure 0.16 presents data on how the peak size of the ozone hole has changed in two-year intervals over the past 26 years. However, this same data could also have been presented as a line graph—as in the *Inquiry & Analysis* of chapter 1 (also shown in figure 0.9).

Presented with a graph of the data obtained in the investigation of the *Inquiry & Analysis*, it will be your job to analyze it. Every analysis of a graph involves four distinct steps, some more complex than others but all essential to the process.

Applying Concepts. Your first task is to make sure you understand the nature of the variables, and the scale at which they are being presented in the graph. As a self-test, it is always a good idea to ask yourself to identify the dependent variable.

Interpreting Data. Look at the graph. What is changing? How much? How quickly? Is the change continuous? Progressive? What in fact has happened?

Making Inferences. Looking at what has happened, can you logically infer that the independent variable has caused the change you see in the dependent variable?

Drawing Conclusions. Does the inference you were able to make support the hypothesis that the experiment set out to test?

This process of inquiry and analysis is the nuts and bolts of science, and by mastering it, you will go a long way toward learning how a scientist thinks.

Chapter 1

The Science of Biology

CHAPTER AT A GLANCE

Biology and the Living World

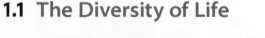

What are these? Throughout this text you will encounter blue and green linking arrows. These "Flash-back" and "Flash-forward" concept links will direct you to related material in earlier chapters or in later chapters. Using them will help you master the interconnected nature of concepts in biology.

1.1 The Diversity of Life

CONCEPT PREVIEW: The living world is very diverse, but all organisms share key properties.

In its broadest sense, biology is the study of living things—the science of life. The living world is teeming with a breathtaking variety of creatures—whales, algae, mushrooms, bacteria, pine trees—all of which can be categorized into six groups, or **kingdoms,** of organisms (figure 1.1). Organisms that are placed into a kingdom possess similar characteristics with all other organisms in that same kingdom and are very different from organisms in the other kingdoms.

Biologists study the diversity of life in many different ways. They live with gorillas, collect fossils, and listen to whales. They isolate bacteria, grow mushrooms, and examine the structure of fruit flies. They read the messages encoded in the long molecules of heredity. In the midst of all this diversity, it is easy to lose sight of the key lesson of biology, which is that all living things have much in common.

Figure 1.1 The six kingdoms of life.

Biologists assign all living things to six major categories called *kingdoms*. Each kingdom is profoundly different from the others.

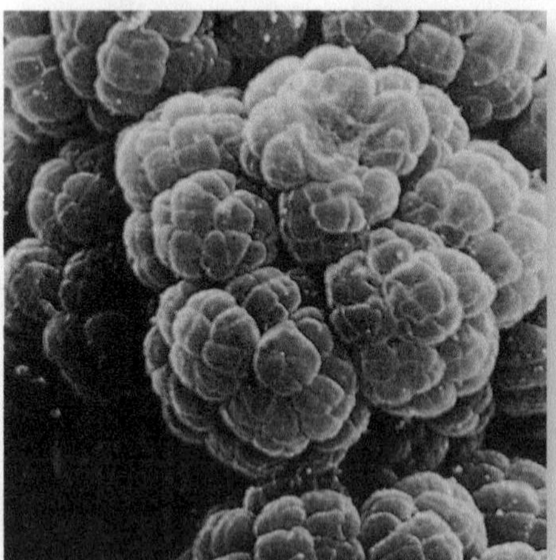

Archaea. This kingdom of prokaryotes (simple cells that do not have nuclei) includes this methanogen, which manufactures methane.

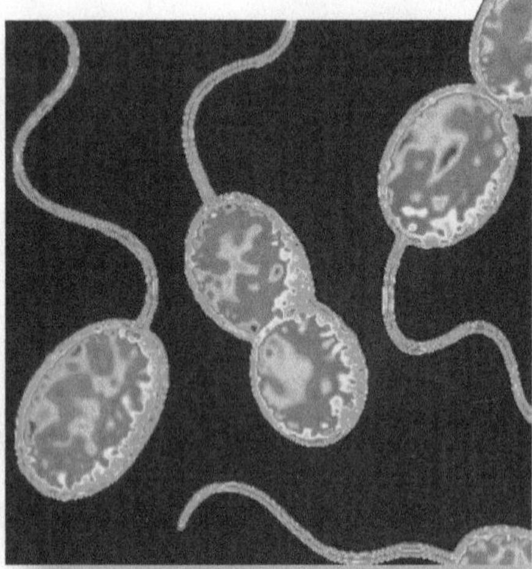

Bacteria. This group is the second of the two prokaryotic kingdoms. Shown here are purple sulfur bacteria, which are able to convert light energy into chemical energy.

Protista. Most of the unicellular eukaryotes (those whose cells contain a nucleus) are grouped into this kingdom, and so are the multicellular algae pictured here.

Fungi. This kingdom contains nonphotosynthetic organisms, mostly multicellular, that digest their food externally, such as these mushrooms.

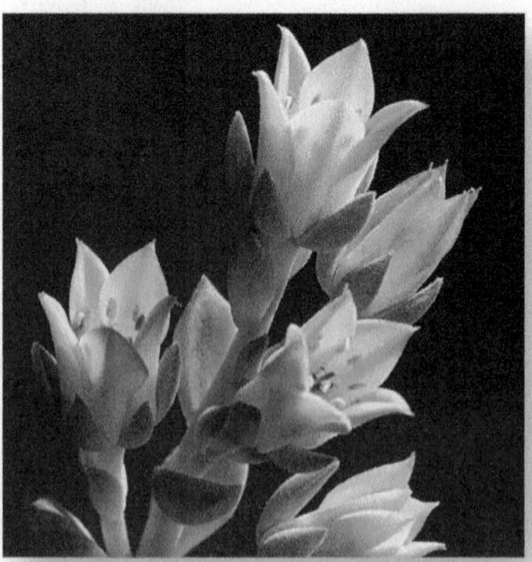

Plantae. This kingdom contains photosynthetic multicellular organisms that are primarily terrestrial, such as the flowering plant pictured here.

Animalia. Organisms in this kingdom are nonphotosynthetic multicellular organisms that digest their food internally, such as this ram.

1.2 Properties of Life

CONCEPT PREVIEW: All living things possess cells that carry out metabolism, maintain stable internal conditions, reproduce, and use DNA to transmit hereditary information to offspring.

Biology is the study of life—but what does it mean to be alive? What are the properties that define a living organism? This is not as simple a question as it seems because some of the most obvious properties of living organisms are also properties of many nonliving things—for example, *complexity* (a computer is complex), *movement* (clouds move in the sky), and *response to stimulation* (a soap bubble pops if you touch it). To appreciate why these three properties, so common among living things, do not help us define life, imagine a mushroom standing next to a television: The television seems more complex than the mushroom, the picture on the television screen is moving while the mushroom just stands there, and the television responds to a remote control device while the mushroom continues to just stand there—yet it is the mushroom that is alive. All living things share five basic properties:

1. **Cellular organization.** All living things are composed of one (figure 1.2) or more cells. A cell is a tiny compartment with a thin covering called a *membrane.* Some cells have simple interiors, while others are complexly organized, but all are able to grow and reproduce. A human body contains about 10–100 trillion cells (depending on how big you are)—that is a lot, a string 100 trillion centimeters long could wrap around the world 1,600 times!
2. **Metabolism.** All living things use energy. Moving, growing, thinking—everything you do requires energy. Where does all this energy come from? It is captured from sunlight by plants, algae, and certain bacteria through photosynthesis. To get the energy that powers our lives, we extract it from plants or from animals that eat plants or that eat plant-eating animals (figure 1.3). The transfer of energy from one form to another in cells is an example of *metabolism.* All organisms transfer energy from one place to another within cells using a special energy-carrying molecule called ATP.
3. **Homeostasis.** All living things maintain stable internal conditions so that their complex processes can be better coordinated. While the environment often varies a lot, organisms act to keep their interior conditions relatively constant, a process called *homeostasis.* For example, your body acts to maintain an internal temperature of approximately 37°C (98.6°F), regardless of how hot or cold the weather might be.
4. **Growth and reproduction.** All living things grow and reproduce. Bacteria increase in size and simply split in two, as often as every 15 minutes. More complex organisms grow by increasing the number of cells and reproduce sexually by producing gametes that combine giving rise to offspring (some, like the bristlecone pine of California, have reproduced after 4,600 years).
5. **Heredity.** All organisms possess a genetic system that is based on a long molecule called *DNA (deoxyribonucleic acid).* The information that determines what an individual organism will be like is contained in a code that is dictated by the order of the subunits making up the DNA molecule, just as the order of letters on this page determines the sense of what you are reading. Each set of instructions within the DNA is called a *gene.* DNA is faithfully copied from one generation to the next, and so any change in a gene is preserved and passed on to future generations. The transmission of characteristics from parent to offspring is a process called *heredity.*

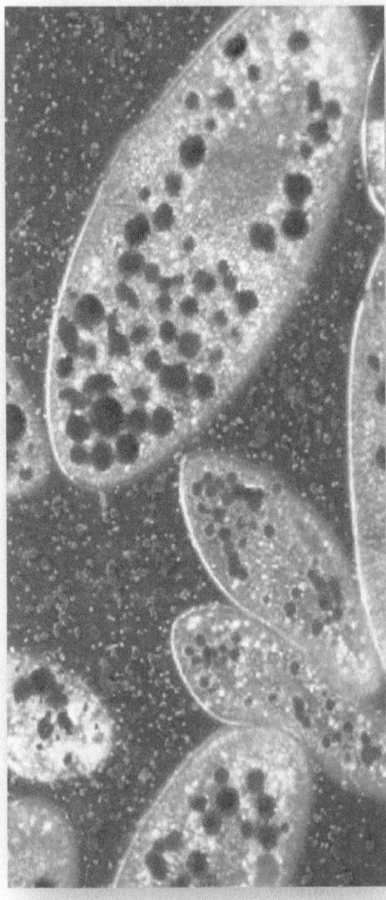

Figure 1.2 Cellular organization.

These paramecia are complex single-celled protists that have just ingested several yeast cells. Like these paramecia, many organisms consist of just a single cell, while others are composed of trillions of cells.

IMPLICATION In your body, bacterial cells outnumber the body's own cells by a 10 to 1 ratio. What do you imagine these bacteria are doing?

Figure 1.3 Metabolism.

This kingfisher obtains the energy it needs to move, grow, and carry out its body processes by eating fish that eat algae. The bird metabolizes this food using chemical processes that occur within cells.

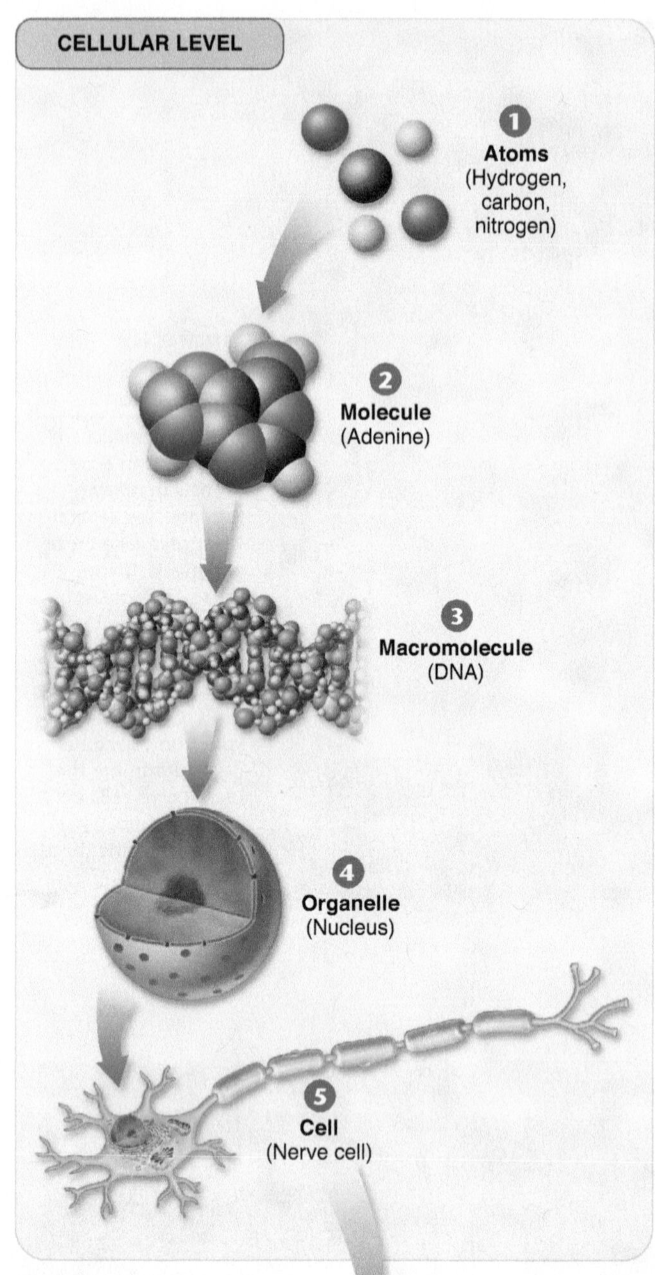

1.3 The Organization of Life

CONCEPT PREVIEW: Cells, multicellular organisms, and ecological systems each are organized in a hierarchy of increasing complexity. Life's hierarchical organization is responsible for the emergent properties that characterize the living world.

A Hierarchy of Increasing Complexity

A key factor in organizing living things is the degree of complexity. We will examine the complexity of life at three levels: cellular, organismal, and populational.

This text follows this hierarchy of increasing complexity. The cellular level is discussed in chapters 2 through 13; the organismal level is discussed in chapters 23 through 33; and the population level is discussed in chapters 14 through 22.

Cellular Level. Following down the first section of figure 1.4, you can see that structures within cells get more and more complex—that there is a *hierarchy* of increasing complexity within cells.

1. **Atoms.** The fundamental elements of matter are atoms.
2. **Molecules.** Atoms are joined together into complex clusters called molecules.
3. **Macromolecules.** Large complex molecules are called macromolecules, such as DNA that stores hereditary information.
4. **Organelles.** Complex biological molecules are assembled into tiny compartments within cells called organelles, such as the nucleus within which the cell's DNA is stored.
5. **Cells.** Organelles and other elements are assembled into membrane-bounded units we call cells. Cells are the smallest level of organization that can be considered alive.

Figure 1.4 Levels of organization.

A traditional and very useful way to sort through the many ways in which the organisms of the living world interact is to organize them in terms of levels of organization, proceeding from the very small and simple to the very large and complex. Here we examine organization within the cellular, organismal, and populational levels.

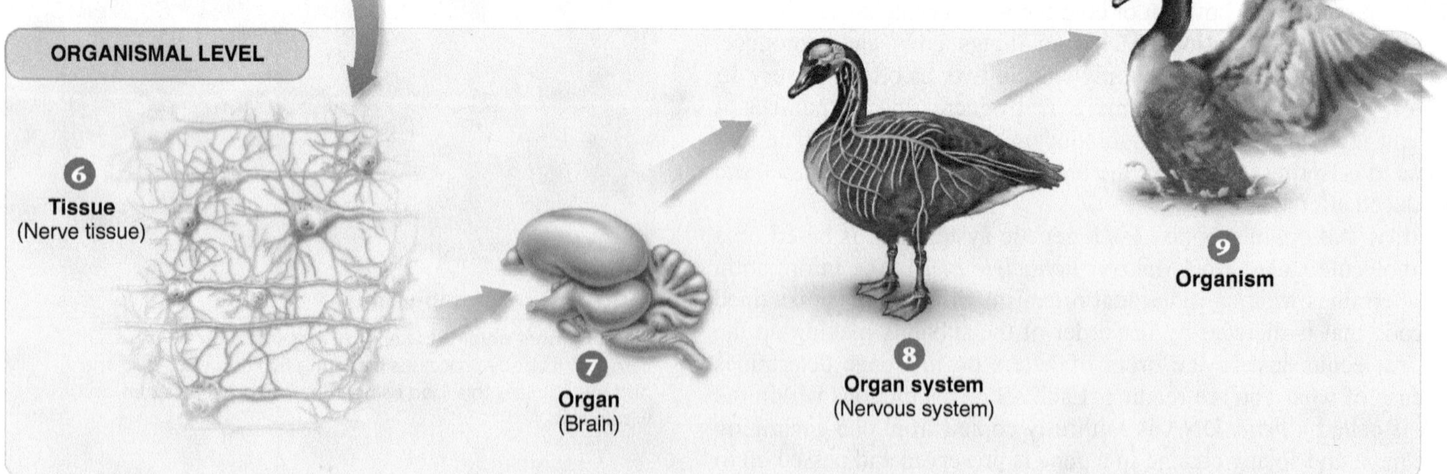

Organismal Level. At the organismal level, in the second section of figure 1.4, cells are organized into four levels of complexity.

6 **Tissues.** The most basic level is that of tissues, which are groups of similar cells that act as a functional unit. Nerve tissue is one kind of tissue, composed of cells called neurons that carry electrical signals.

7 **Organs.** Tissues, in turn, are grouped into organs, which are body structures composed of several different tissues that form a structural and functional unit. Your brain is an organ composed of nerve cells and a variety of connective tissues that form protective coverings and distribute blood.

8 **Organ systems.** At the third level of organization, organs are grouped into organ systems. The nervous system, for example, consists of sensory organs, the brain and spinal cord, neurons that convey signals throughout the body, and supporting cells.

9 **Organism.** Organ systems function together to form an organism.

Populational Level. Organisms are further organized into several hierarchical levels within the living world, as you can see to the right.

10 **Population.** The most basic of these is the population, which is a group of organisms of the same species living in the same place. A flock of geese living together on a pond is a population.

11 **Species.** All the populations of a particular kind of organism together form a species, its members similar in appearance and able to interbreed. All Canada geese, whether found in Canada, Minnesota, or Missouri, are basically the same, members of the species *Branta canadensis.* Sandhill cranes are a different species.

12 **Community.** At a higher level of biological organization, a community consists of all the populations of different species living together in one place. Geese, for example, may share their pond with ducks, fish, grasses, and many kinds of insects. All interact in a single pond community.

13 **Ecosystem.** At the highest tier of biological organization, a biological community and the soil and water within which it lives together constitute an ecological system, or ecosystem.

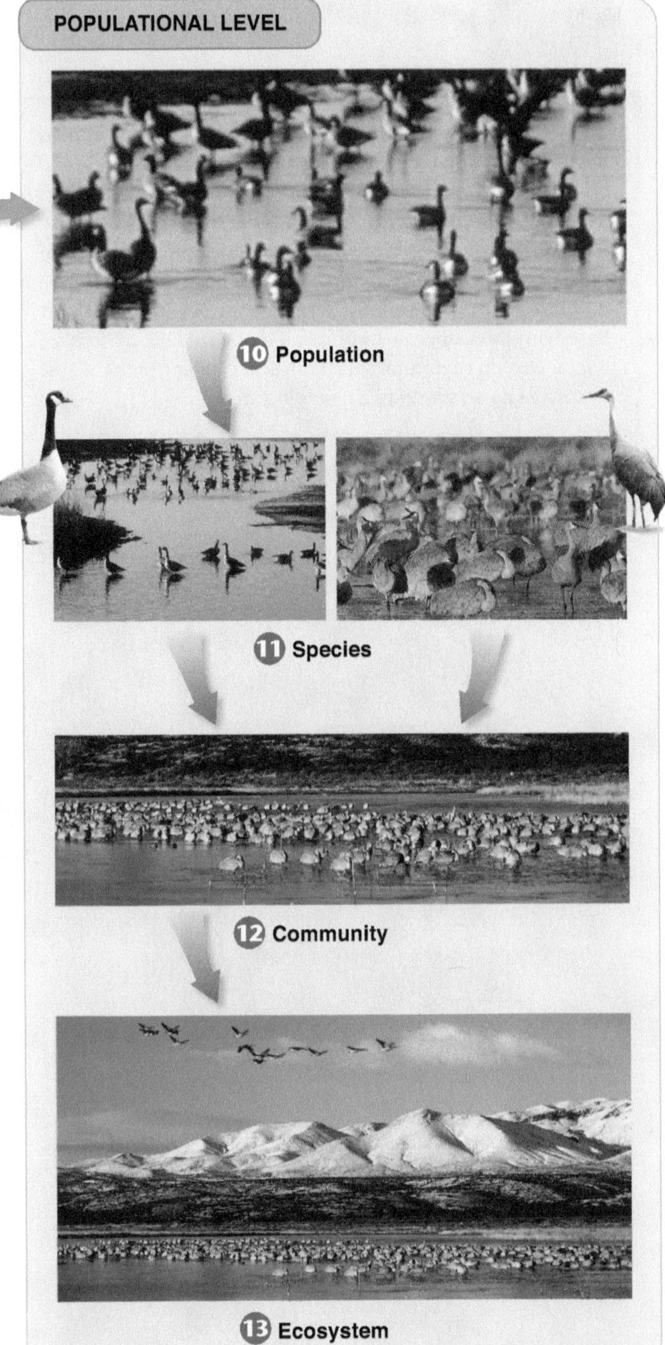

Emergent Properties

At each higher level in the living hierarchy, novel properties emerge, properties that were not present at the simpler level of organization. These **emergent properties** result from the way in which components interact, and often cannot be guessed just by looking at the parts themselves. Humans have the same array of cell types as a giraffe, for example, yet, examining a collection of its individual cells gives little clue of what your body is like.

The emergent properties of life are not magical or supernatural. They are the natural consequence of the hierarchy or structural organization which is the hallmark of life. Water, which makes up 50–75% of your body's weight, and ice are both made of H_2O molecules, but one is liquid and the other solid because the H_2O molecules in ice are more organized.

Functional properties emerge from more complex organization. Metabolism is an emergent property of life. The chemical reactions within a cell arise from interactions between molecules that are orchestrated by the orderly environment of the cell's interior. Consciousness is an emergent property of the brain that results from the interactions of many neurons in different parts of the brain.

EVOLUTION

Computer Games Evolve. In 2008 the designer of the best-selling video game of all time (THE SIMS) unveiled his new creation, SPORE. In this computer game, players experience life unfolding across billions of years, its course guided by evolutionary biology. The game starts with single-celled bacteria living in the ocean, and follows their evolution into intelligent multicelled creatures that populate the land. Based on the mathematics of game theory, SPORE performs a digital version of natural selection, and challenges the player to survive by adapting to a changing world.

1.4 Biological Themes

CONCEPT PREVIEW: The five general themes of biology are (1) evolution, (2) the flow of energy, (3) cooperation, (4) structure determines function, and (5) homeostasis.

Just as a house is organized into thematic areas such as bedroom, kitchen, and bathroom, so the living world is organized by major *themes,* such as how energy flows within the living world from one part to another. As you study biology in this text, five general themes will emerge repeatedly, themes that serve to both unify and explain biology as a science.

Evolution

Evolution is genetic change in a species over time. Charles Darwin was an English naturalist who, in 1859, proposed the idea that this change is a result of a process called **natural selection.** Simply stated, those organisms whose characteristics make them better able to survive the challenges of their environment live to reproduce, passing their favorable characteristics on to their offspring. Darwin was thoroughly familiar with variation in domesticated animals (in addition to many nondomesticated organisms). He knew that varieties of pigeons could be selected by breeders to exhibit exaggerated characteristics, a process called *artificial selection.* You can see some of these extreme-looking pigeons pictured here. We now know that the characteristics selected are passed on through generations because DNA is transmitted from parent to offspring. Darwin visualized how selection in nature could be similar to that which had produced the different varieties of pigeons. Thus, the many forms of life we see about us on earth today, and the way we ourselves are constructed and function, reflect a long history of natural selection.

The Flow of Energy

All organisms require energy to carry out the activities of living—to build bodies and do work and think thoughts. All of the energy used by most organisms comes from the sun and is passed in one direction through ecosystems. The simplest way to understand the flow of energy through the living world is to look at who uses it. The first stage of energy's journey is its capture by green plants, algae, and some bacteria by the process of photosynthesis. This process uses energy from the sun to synthesize sugars that photosynthetic organisms like plants store in their bodies. Plants then serve as a source of life-driving energy for animals that eat them. Other animals, like the eagle shown here, may then eat the plant eaters. At each stage, some energy is used for the processes of living, some is transferred, and much is lost primarily as heat. The flow of energy is a key factor in shaping ecosystems, affecting how many and what kinds of organisms live in a community.

Cooperation

The ants cooperating in the photo on the facing page protect the plant on which they live from predators and shading by other plants, while this plant returns the favor by providing the ants with nutrients (the yellow structures at the tips of the leaves). This type of cooperation between different kinds of organisms has played a critical role in the evolution of life on earth. For example, organisms of two different species that live in direct contact, like the ants and the plant on which they live, form a type of relationship called **symbiosis.** Many types of cells possess organelles that are the descendants of symbiotic bacteria, and symbiotic fungi helped plants first invade land from the sea. The coevolution of flowering plants and insects—where changes in flowers influenced insect evolution and in turn, changes in insects influenced flower evolution—has been responsible for much of life's great diversity.

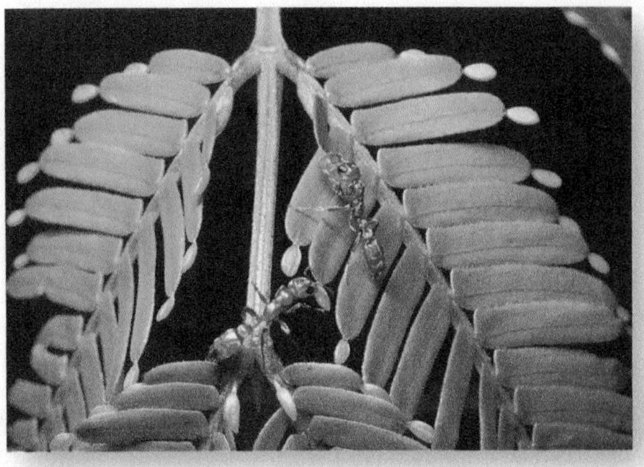

Structure Determines Function

One of the most obvious lessons of biology is that biological structures are very well suited to their functions. You will see this at every level of organization: Enzymes, which are macromolecules that cells use to carry out chemical reactions, are precisely structured to match the shapes of the chemicals the enzymes must manipulate. Within the many kinds of organisms in the living world, body structures seem carefully designed to carry out their functions—the long tongue with which the moth to the right sucks nectar from deep inside a flower is one example. The superb fit of structure to function in the living world is no accident. Life has existed on earth for over 2 billion years, a long time for evolution to favor changes that better suit organisms to meet the challenges of living. It should come as no surprise to you that after all this honing and adjustment, biological structures carry out their functions well.

Homeostasis

The high degree of specialization we see among complex organisms is only possible because these organisms act to maintain a relatively stable internal environment, a process introduced earlier called homeostasis. Without this constancy, many of the complex interactions that need to take place within organisms would be impossible, just as a city cannot function without rules to maintain order. Maintaining homeostasis in a body as complex as yours requires a great deal of signaling back-and-forth between cells. For example, homeostasis often involves water balance to maintain proper blood chemistry. All complex organisms need water—some, like this hippo, luxuriate in it. Others, like the kangaroo rat that lives in arid conditions where water is scarce, obtain water from food and never actually drink. But, they both need to maintain water balance in their bodies.

As already stated, you will encounter these biological themes repeatedly in this text. But just as a budding architect must learn more than the parts of buildings, so your study of biology should teach you more than a list of themes, concepts, and parts of organisms. Biology is a dynamic science that will affect your life in many ways, and that lesson is one of the most important you will learn.

Concept Check

1. What five basic life properties does a mushroom have that a television lacks?
2. Name one emergent property of life.
3. Identify a function in your body where maintaining homeostasis is important.

The Scientific Process

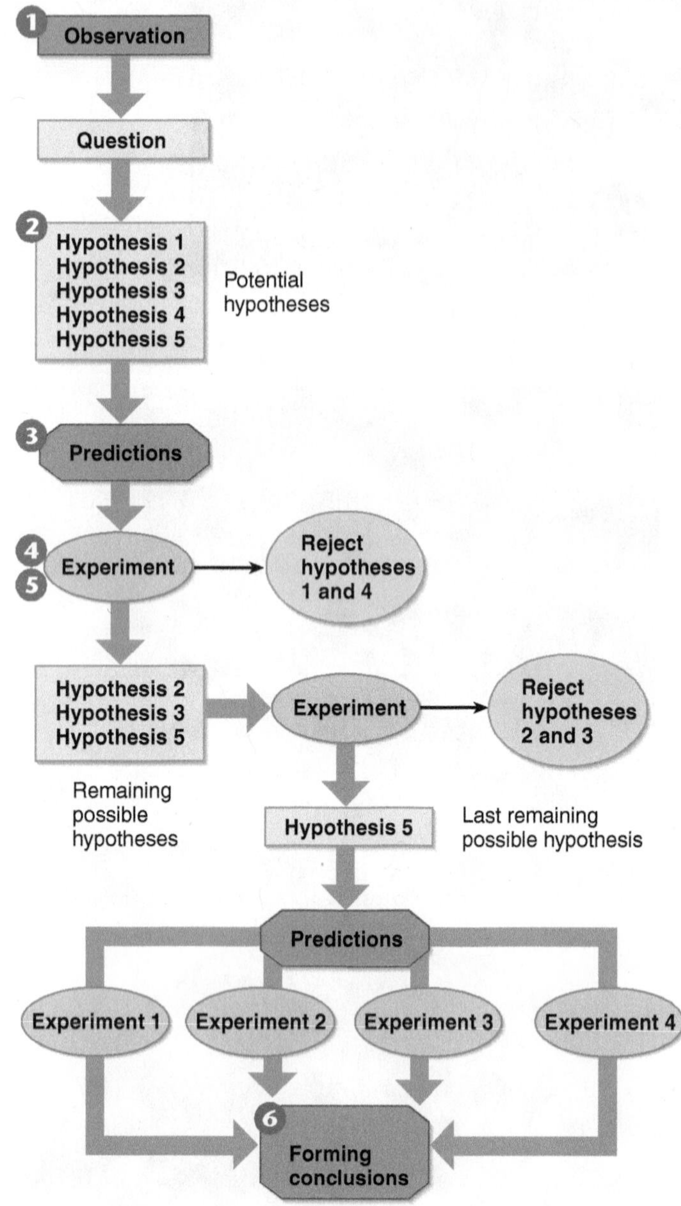

Figure 1.5 The scientific process.

This diagram illustrates the stages of a scientific investigation. First, observations are made that raise a particular question. Then a number of potential explanations (hypotheses) are suggested to answer the question. Next, predictions are made based on the hypotheses, and several rounds of experiments (including control experiments) are carried out in an attempt to eliminate one or more of the hypotheses. Finally, any hypothesis that is not eliminated is retained. Further predictions can be made based on the accepted hypothesis and tested with experiments. If a hypothesis is validated by numerous experiments and stands the test of time, it may eventually become a theory.

1.5 Stages of a Scientific Investigation

CONCEPT PREVIEW: Science progresses by systematically eliminating hypotheses that are not consistent with observation.

How Science Is Done

Scientists establish general principles as a way to explain the world around us, but how do scientists determine which general principles are true from among the many that might be? They do this by systematically testing alternative proposals. If these proposals prove inconsistent with experimental observations, they are rejected as untrue. After making careful observations concerning a particular area of science, scientists construct a hypothesis, which is a suggested explanation that accounts for those observations, an "educated guess." A hypothesis is a proposition that might be true. Those hypotheses that have not yet been disproved are retained. They are useful because they fit the known facts, but they are always subject to future rejection in the light of new information.

We call the test of a hypothesis an experiment. To evaluate alternative hypotheses, you would conduct an experiment designed to eliminate one or more of the hypotheses. Note that this does not prove that any of the other hypotheses are true; it merely demonstrates that one of them is not. A successful experiment is one in which one or more of the alternative hypotheses is demonstrated to be inconsistent with the results and is thus rejected.

In this text, you will encounter a great deal of information, often accompanied by explanations. These explanations are hypotheses that have withstood the test of experiment. Many will continue to do so; others will be revised as new observations are made. Biology, like all science, is in a constant state of change, with new ideas appearing and replacing old ones.

The Scientific Process

Science is a particular way of investigating the world, of forming general rules about why things happen by observing particular situations. A scientist is an observer, someone who looks at the world to understand how it works.

Scientific investigations can be said to have six stages as illustrated in figure 1.5: ❶ observing what is going on; ❷ forming a set of hypotheses; ❸ making predictions; ❹ testing them and ❺ carrying out controls, until one or more of the hypotheses have been eliminated; and ❻ forming conclusions based on the remaining hypothesis. To better understand how a scientist progresses through these stages, let's examine an actual scientific investigation, the discovery and analysis of the ozone hole.

1. **Observation.** The key to any successful scientific investigation is careful *observation.* Scientists had studied the skies over the Antarctic for many years, noting a thousand details about temperature, light, and levels of chemicals. You can see an example of these types of observations in figure 1.6, which is a recording of the levels of ozone in the atmosphere (the purple areas represent the lowest levels of ozone). Had these scientists not kept careful records of what they observed, they might not have noticed that ozone levels were dropping.
2. **Hypothesis.** When the unexpected drop in ozone was reported, scientists made a guess why—perhaps something was destroying

the ozone; maybe the culprit was chlorofluorocarbons (CFCs), an industrial chemical used as a coolant in air conditioners, propellants in aerosols, and foaming agents in making Styrofoam. Of course, this was not a guess in the true sense; scientists had some working knowledge of CFC and what it might be doing in the upper atmosphere. We call such a guess a **hypothesis.** What the scientists guessed was that chlorine from the breakdown of CFCs was reacting chemically with ozone over the Antarctic, converting ozone (O_3) into oxygen gas (O_2), removing the ozone shield from our earth's atmosphere. Often, scientists will form *alternative hypotheses* if they have more than one guess about what they observe. In this case, there were several other hypotheses advanced to explain the ozone hole. One suggestion explained it as a normal consequence of the spinning of the earth, the ozone spinning away from the polar regions much as water spins away from the center as a clothes washer moves through its spin cycle. Another hypothesis was that the ozone hole was simply due to sunspots, and would soon disappear.

3. **Predictions.** If the CFC hypothesis is correct, then several consequences can reasonably be expected. We call these expected consequences *predictions.* A prediction is what you expect to happen if a hypothesis is true. The CFC hypothesis predicts that if CFCs are responsible for producing the ozone hole, then it should be possible to detect CFCs in the upper Antarctic atmosphere as well as the chlorine released from CFCs that attack the ozone.
4. **Testing.** Scientists set out to test the CFC hypothesis by attempting to verify some of its predictions. We call the test of a hypothesis an *experiment.* To test the hypothesis, atmospheric samples were collected from the stratosphere over 6 miles up by a high-altitude balloon. Analysis of the samples revealed the presence of CFCs, as predicted. Were the CFCs interacting with the ozone? The samples contained free chlorine and fluorine, confirming the breakdown of CFC molecules. The results of the experiment thus support the hypothesis.
5. **Controls.** Events in the upper atmosphere can be influenced by many factors. We call each factor that might influence a process a **variable.** To evaluate alternative hypotheses about one variable, all the other variables must be kept constant so that we do not get misled or confused by these other influences. This is done by carrying out two experiments in parallel: In the first experimental test, we alter one variable in a known way to test a particular hypothesis; in the second, called a *control experiment,* we do *not* alter that variable. In all other respects, the two experiments are the same. To further test the CFC hypothesis, scientists carried out control laboratory experiments in which they detected no drop in ozone levels in the absence of CFCs. The result of the control was consistent with the predictions of the hypothesis.
6. **Conclusion.** A hypothesis that has been tested and not rejected is tentatively accepted. The hypothesis that CFCs released into the atmosphere are destroying the earth's protective ozone shield is now supported by a great deal of experimental evidence and is widely accepted. A collection of related hypotheses that have been tested many times and not rejected is called a **theory.** A theory indicates a higher degree of certainty; however, in science, nothing is "certain." For example, the theory of the ozone shield—that ozone in the upper atmosphere shields the earth's surface from harmful UV rays by absorbing them—is supported by a wealth of observation and experimentation and is widely accepted.

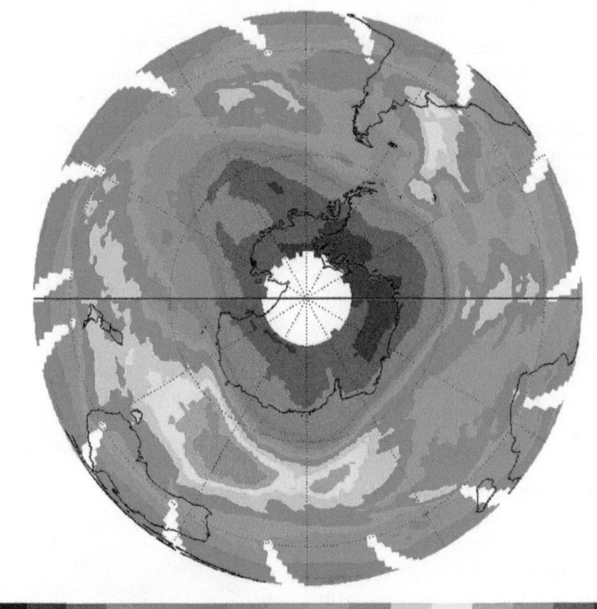

Figure 1.6 The ozone hole.

The swirling colors represent different concentrations of ozone over the South Pole as viewed from a satellite on September 15, 2001. As you can easily see, there is an "ozone hole" (the *purple* areas) over Antarctica covering an area about the size of the United States. (The color *white* indicates areas where no data were available.)

IMPLICATION If the ozone hole indicated by the purple area only extends over Antarctica (and sometimes the tip of South America), why should people living in North America worry about it?

BIOLOGY & YOU

Ozone Therapy. Ozone is claimed by some to have remarkable healing properties and holistic health benefits. For example, it is asserted that ozone inhibits the growth of lung and breast cancer cells. Like other claims of health benefits, this claim is widely discounted by the medical community. Most states prohibit the medical use of ozone and consider the marketing of ozone generators as dangerous (ozone has toxic effects on the lungs) and providing no medical benefit.

The theory that the Earth was flat—the idea that the Earth was flat was generally accepted until about 330 B.C. when Aristotle provided observational evidence for a spherical Earth using constellations. About 100 years later Eratosthenes provided quantitative evidence by estimating the circumference of the Earth.

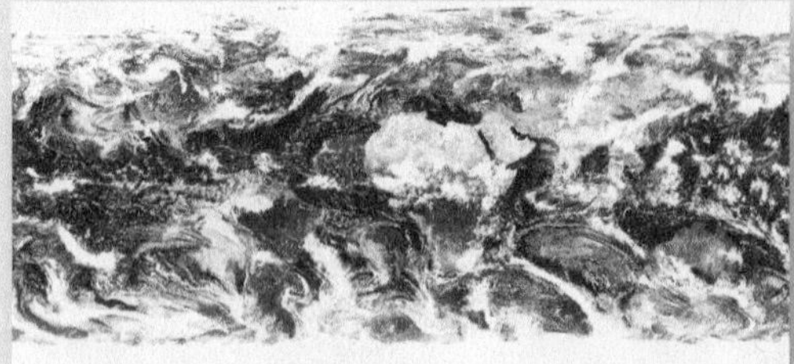

The theory that the sun circles Earth—this geocentric view of the universe was accepted as fact until Copernicus first proposed a sun-centered solar system in the 16th century, which was supported by quantitative evidence in the early 1600s by Galileo.

The theory of creationism—this explanation of the origin and diversity of life on Earth following the account presented in the Bible was widely accepted, although other explanations that proposed that life evolved on Earth were also put forth. The theory of creationism was questioned and then dispelled in 1859, when Charles Darwin proposed an explanation for evolution, a process called natural selection, which is the widely accepted scientific explanation of the origin and diversity of life on Earth.

The theory of acquired traits—Jean-Baptiste Lamarck, a predecessor of Darwin, proposed an explanation of evolution. He stated that traits were acquired during one's life and were then passed on to offspring. Darwin later proposed the explanation of natural selection as the driving force of evolution.

The hypothesis of cold nuclear fusion—the experimental results that led to this hypothesis, that nuclear reactions could be performed at near room temperature and pressure, were presented in 1989. The results could have revolutionized the energy industry, but the results could not be duplicated and widespread support for the hypothesis never developed.

Figure 1.7 Rejected theories.

To illustrate how experimentation changes scientific thought, consider these scientific theories that were once accepted as true, but have since been rejected.

IMPLICATION The theory of global warming was controversial when first proposed, but has gained widespread support in recent years. How has the acceptance of this theory affected your own life, or has it?

1.6 Theory and Certainty

CONCEPT PREVIEW: A scientist does not follow a fixed method to form hypotheses but relies also on judgment and intuition.

A theory is a unifying explanation for a broad range of observations. Thus we speak of the theory of gravity, the theory of evolution, and the theory of the atom. Theories are the solid ground of science, that of which we are the most certain. However, there is no absolute truth in science, only varying degrees of uncertainty. A scientist's acceptance of a theory is always provisional, because the possibility always remains that future evidence will cause a theory to be revised; some "once-accepted" theories are discussed in figure 1.7.

The word "theory" is thus used very differently by scientists than by the general public. To a scientist, a theory represents that of which he or she is most certain; to the general public, the word theory implies a *lack* of knowledge or a guess. How often have you heard someone say, "It's only a theory!"? As you can imagine, confusion often results. In this text the word theory will always be used in its scientific sense, in reference to a generally accepted scientific principle.

The Scientific "Method"

It was once fashionable to claim that scientific progress is the result of applying a series of steps called the *scientific method;* that is, a series of logical "either/or" predictions tested by experiments to reject one alternative. The assumption was that trial-and-error testing would inevitably lead one through the maze of uncertainty that always slows scientific progress. If this were indeed true, a computer would make a good scientist—but science is not done this way! If you ask successful scientists how they do their work, you will discover that without exception they design their experiments with a pretty fair idea of how they will come out. Environmental scientists understood the chemistry of chlorine and ozone when they formulated the CFC hypothesis, and they could imagine how the chlorine in CFCs would attack ozone molecules. A hypothesis that a successful scientist tests is not just any hypothesis. Rather, it is a "hunch" or educated guess in which the scientist integrates all that he or she knows, in an attempt to get a sense of what *might* be true. It is because insight and imagination play such a large role that some scientists are so much better at science than others—just as Beethoven and Mozart stand out among composers.

The Limitations of Science

Scientific study is limited to organisms and processes that we are able to observe and measure. Supernatural and religious hypotheses are beyond the realm of scientific analysis because they cannot be scientifically studied, analyzed, or explained. Supernatural hypotheses can be used to explain any result, and cannot be disproven by experiment or observation. Scientists in their work are limited to objective interpretations of observable phenomena.

Concept Check

1. What laboratory control experiment did scientists carry out to test the CFC hypothesis?
2. Why don't computers, which are good at trial-and-error testing, make good scientists?
3. What is the difference between a hypothesis and a theory?

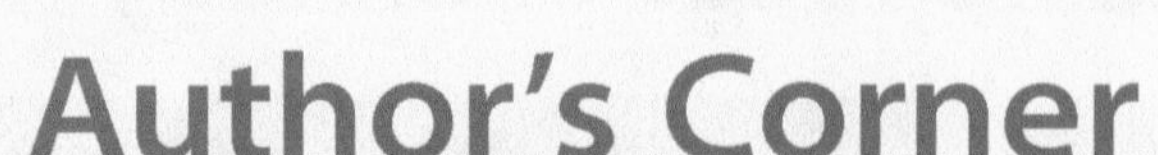

Where Are All My Socks Going?

All my life, for as far back as I can remember, I have been losing socks. Not pairs of socks, mind you, but single socks. I first became aware of this peculiar phenomenon when as a young man I went away to college. When Thanksgiving rolled around that first year, I brought an enormous duffle bag of laundry home. My mother, instead of braining me, dumped the lot into the washer and dryer, and so discovered what I had not noticed—that few of my socks matched anymore.

That was over forty years ago, but it might as well have been yesterday. All my life, I have continued to lose socks. This last Christmas I threw out a sock drawer full of socks that didn't match, and took advantage of sales to buy a dozen pairs of brand-new ones. Last week, when I did a body count, three of the new pairs had lost a sock!

Enough. I set out to solve the mystery of the missing socks. How? The way Sherlock Holmes would have, scientifically. Holmes worked by eliminating those possibilities that he found not to be true. A scientist calls possibilities "hypotheses" and, like Sherlock, rejects those that do not fit the facts. Sherlock tells us that when only one possibility remains unrejected, then—however unlikely—it must be true.

Hypothesis 1: It's the socks. I have four pairs of socks bought as Christmas gifts but forgotten until recently. Deep in my sock drawer, they have remained undisturbed for five months. If socks disappear because of some intrinsic property (say the manufacturer has somehow designed them to disappear to generate new sales), then I could expect at least one of these undisturbed ones to have left the scene by now. However, when I looked, all four pairs were complete. Undisturbed socks don't disappear. Thus I reject the hypothesis that the problem is caused by the socks themselves.

Hypothesis 2: Transformation, a fanciful suggestion by science fiction writer Avram Davidson in his 1958 story "Or All the Seas with Oysters" that I cannot get out of the quirky corner of my mind. I discard the socks I have worn each evening in a laundry basket in my closet. Over many years, I have noticed a tendency for socks I have placed in the closet to disappear. Over that same long period, as my socks are disappearing, there is something in my closet that seems to multiply—COAT HANGERS! Socks are larval coat hangers! To test this outlandish hypothesis, I had only to move the laundry basket out of the closet. Several months later, I was still losing socks, so this hypothesis is rejected.

Hypothesis 3: Static cling. The missing single socks may have been hiding within the sleeves of sweat shirts or jackets, inside trouser legs, or curled up within seldom-worn garments. Rubbing around in the dryer, socks can garner quite a bit of static electricity, easily enough to cause them to cling to other garments. Socks adhering to the outside of a shirt or pant leg are soon dislodged, but ones that find themselves within a sleeve, leg, or fold may simply stay there, not "lost" so much as misplaced. However, after a diligent search, I did not run across any previously lost socks hiding in the sleeves of my winter garments or other seldom-worn items, so I reject this hypothesis.

Hypothesis 4: I lose my socks going to or from the laundry. Perhaps in handling the socks from laundry basket to the washer/dryer and back to my sock drawer, a sock is occasionally lost. To test this hypothesis, I have pawed through the laundry coming into the washer. No single socks. Perhaps the socks are lost after doing the laundry, during folding or transport from laundry to sock drawer. If so, there should be no single socks coming out of the dryer. But there are! The singletons are first detected among the dry laundry, before folding. Thus I eliminate the hypothesis that the problem arises from mishandling the laundry. It seems the problem is in the laundry room.

Hypothesis 5: I lose them during washing. Perhaps the washing machine is somehow "eating" my socks. I looked in the washing machine to see if a sock could get trapped inside, or chewed up by the machine, but I can see no possibility. The clothes slosh around in a closed metal container with water passing in and out through little holes no wider than a pencil. No sock could slip through such a hole. There is a thin gap between the rotating cylinder and the top of the washer through which an errant sock might escape, but my socks are too bulky for this route. So I eliminate the hypothesis that the washing machine is the culprit.

Hypothesis 6: I lose them during drying. Perhaps somewhere in the drying process socks are being lost. I stuck my head in our clothes dryer to see if I could see any socks, and I couldn't. However, as I look, I can see a place a sock could go—behind the drying wheel! A clothes dryer is basically a great big turning cylinder with dry air blowing through the middle. The edges of the turning cylinder don't push hard against the side of the machine. Just maybe, every once in a while, a sock might get pulled through, sucked into the back of the machine.

To test this hypothesis, I should take the back of the dryer off and look inside to see if it is stuffed with my missing socks. My wife, knowing my mechanical abilities, is not in favor of this test. Thus, until our dryer dies and I can take it apart, I shall not be able to reject hypothesis 6. Lacking any other likely hypothesis, I take Sherlock Holmes' advice and tentatively conclude that the dryer is the culprit.

Core Ideas of Biology

Figure 1.8 Life in a drop of pond water.

All organisms are composed of cells. Some organisms, including these protists, are single celled, while others, such as plants, animals, and fungi, consist of many cells.

1.7 Four Theories Unify Biology as a Science

CONCEPT PREVIEW: The theories uniting biology state that cellular organisms store hereditary information in DNA. Sometimes DNA alterations occur, which when preserved result in evolutionary change. Today's biological diversity is the product of a long evolutionary journey.

The Cell Theory: Organization of Life

All organisms are composed of cells, life's basic units. Cells were discovered by Robert Hooke in England in 1665. Hooke was using one of the first microscopes, one that magnified 30 times. Looking through a thin slice of cork, he observed many tiny chambers, which reminded him of monks' cells in a monastery. Not long after that, the Dutch scientist Anton van Leeuwenhoek used microscopes capable of magnifying 300 times, and discovered an amazing world of single-celled life in a drop of pond water like you see in figure 1.8. He called the bacterial and protist cells he saw "wee animalcules." However, it took almost two centuries before biologists fully understood their significance. In 1839, the German biologists Matthias Schleiden and Theodor Schwann, summarizing a large number of observations by themselves and others, concluded that all living organisms consist of cells. Their conclusion forms the basis of what has come to be known as the *cell theory.* Later, biologists added the idea that all cells come from other cells. The cell theory, one of the basic ideas in biology, is the foundation for understanding the reproduction and growth of all organisms. You will learn much more about cells in chapter 4.

The Gene Theory: Molecular Basis of Inheritance

Even the simplest cell is incredibly complex, more intricate than a computer. The information that specifies what a cell is like—its detailed plan—is encoded in a long cablelike molecule called **DNA (deoxyribonucleic acid)**. Researchers James Watson and Francis Crick discovered in 1953 that each DNA molecule is formed from two long chains of building blocks, called nucleotides, wound around each other. You can see in figure 1.9 that the two chains face each other, like two lines of people holding hands. The chains contain information in the same way this sentence does—as a sequence of letters. There are four different nucleotides in DNA (symbolized as A, T, C, and G in the figure), and the sequence in which they occur encodes the information. Specific sequences of several hundred to many thousand nucleotides make up a *gene,* a discrete unit of hereditary information. A gene might encode a particular protein, or a different kind of unique molecule called RNA, or a gene might act to regulate other genes. All organisms on earth encode their genes in strands of DNA. This prevalence of DNA led to the development of the *gene theory.* Illustrated in figure 1.10, the gene theory states that the proteins and RNA molecules encoded by an organism's genes determine what it will be like. How genes function is the subject of chapter 12. In chapter 13 you will explore how detailed knowledge of genes is revolutionizing biology and having an impact on the lives of all of us.

How DNA functions in the cell is directly related to its structure and is discussed in detail in chapter 3, pages 52 and 53 and again in chapter 11, page 186.

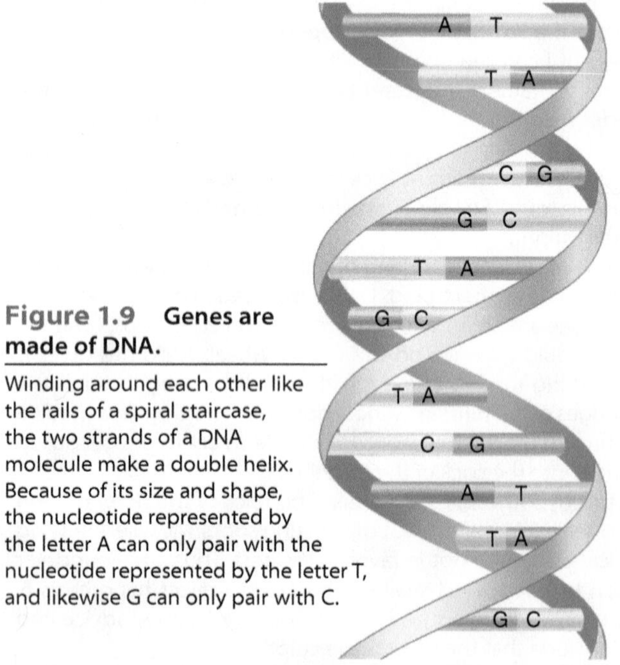

Figure 1.9 Genes are made of DNA.

Winding around each other like the rails of a spiral staircase, the two strands of a DNA molecule make a double helix. Because of its size and shape, the nucleotide represented by the letter A can only pair with the nucleotide represented by the letter T, and likewise G can only pair with C.

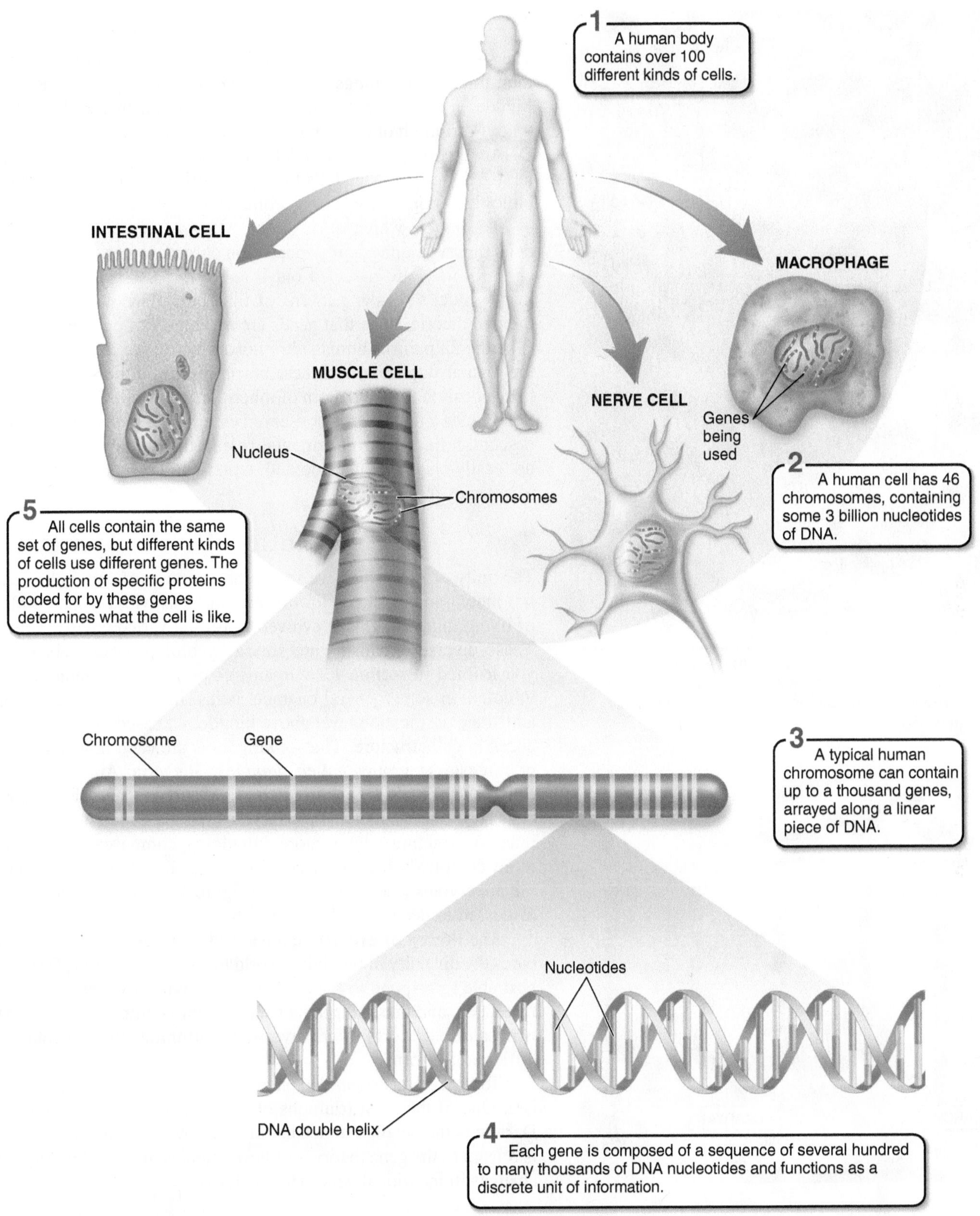
1
A human body contains over 100 different kinds of cells.
INTESTINAL CELL
MACROPHAGE
MUSCLE CELL
NERVE CELL
Genes being used
Nucleus
Chromosomes
2
A human cell has 46 chromosomes, containing some 3 billion nucleotides of DNA.
5
All cells contain the same set of genes, but different kinds of cells use different genes. The production of specific proteins coded for by these genes determines what the cell is like.
Chromosome
Gene
3
A typical human chromosome can contain up to a thousand genes, arrayed along a linear piece of DNA.
Nucleotides
DNA double helix
4
Each gene is composed of a sequence of several hundred to many thousands of DNA nucleotides and functions as a discrete unit of information.

Figure 1.10 The gene theory.

The gene theory states that what an organism is like is determined in large measure by its genes. Here you see how the many kinds of cells in the body of each of us are determined by which genes are used in making each particular kind of cell.

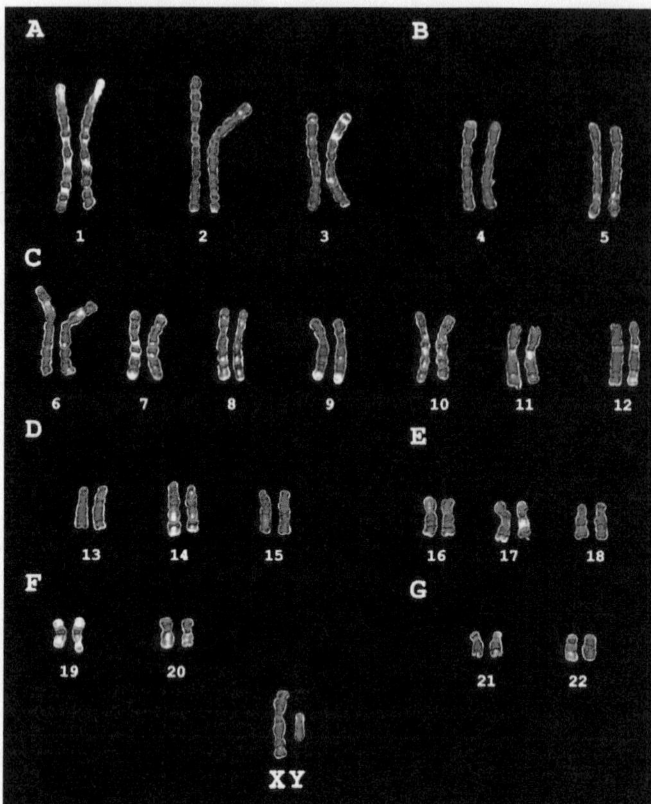

Figure 1.11 Human chromosomes.

The chromosomal theory of inheritance states that genes are located on chromosomes. This human karyotype (an ordering of chromosomes) shows banding patterns on chromosomes that represent clusters of genes.

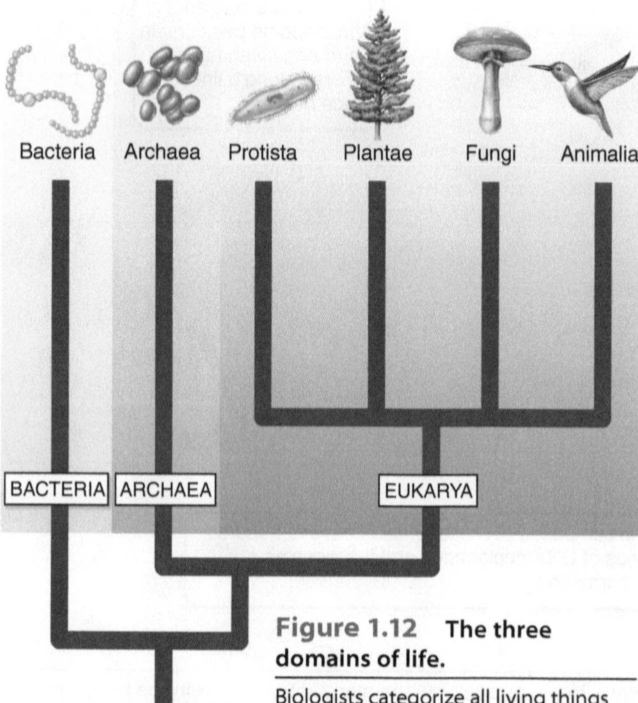

Figure 1.12 The three domains of life.

Biologists categorize all living things into three overarching groups called domains: Bacteria, Archaea, and Eukarya. Domain Bacteria contains the kingdom Bacteria, and domain Archaea contains the kingdom Archaea. Domain Eukarya is composed of four more kingdoms: Protista, Plantae, Fungi, and Animalia.

The Theory of Heredity: Unity of Life

The storage of hereditary information in genes composed of DNA is common to all living things. The *theory of heredity* first advanced by Gregor Mendel in 1865 states that the genes of an organism are inherited as discrete units. A triumph of experimental science developed long before genes and DNA were understood, Mendel's theory of heredity is the subject of chapter 10. Soon after Mendel's theory gave rise to the field of genetics, other biologists proposed what has come to be called the *chromosomal theory of inheritance,* which in its simplest form states that the genes of Mendel's theory are physically located on chromosomes, and that it is because chromosomes are parceled out in a regular manner during reproduction that Mendel's regular patterns of inheritance are seen. In modern terms, the two theories state that genes are a component of a cell's chromosomes (like the 23 pairs of human chromosomes you see in figure 1.11), and that the regular duplication of these chromosomes during sexual reproduction is responsible for the pattern of inheritance we call Mendelian segregation. Sometimes a character is conserved essentially unchanged in a long line of descent, reflecting a fundamental role in the biology of the organism, one not easily changed once adopted. Other characters might be modified due to changes in DNA.

The Theory of Evolution: Diversity of Life

The unity of life, which we see in the retention of certain key characteristics among many related life-forms, contrasts with the incredible diversity of living things that have evolved to fill the varied environments of earth. These diverse organisms are sorted by biologists into six kingdoms, as you learned in section 1.1. Organisms placed in the same kingdom have in common some general characteristics. In recent years, biologists have added a classification level above kingdoms, based on fundamental differences in cell structure. The six kingdoms are each now assigned into one of three great groups called *domains:* Bacteria, Archaea, and Eukarya. Bacteria (the yellow zone in figure 1.12) and Archaea (the pink zone) each consist of one kingdom of prokaryotes (single-celled organisms with little internal structure). Four more kingdoms composed of organisms with more complexly-organized cells are placed within the domain Eukarya, the eukaryotes (the purple zone in figure 1.12). The kingdoms of life are discussed in detail in chapter 15.

The **theory of evolution,** advanced by Charles Darwin in 1859, attributes the diversity of the living world to natural selection. Those organisms best able to respond to the challenges of living will leave more offspring, he argued, and thus their traits become more common in the population. It is because the world offers diverse opportunities that it contains so many different life-forms.

Today scientists can decipher all the genes (the genome) of an organism. One of the great triumphs of science in the century and a half since Darwin is the detailed understanding of how Darwin's theory of evolution is related to the gene theory—of how changes in life's diversity result from changes in individual genes (figure 1.13).

Concept Check

1. Why was it not possible to develop the cell theory until the end of the 17th century?
2. How is the gene theory related to the theory of heredity?
3. The theory of heredity is closely related to the chromosomal theory of inheritance. Explain the relationship between these two theories.

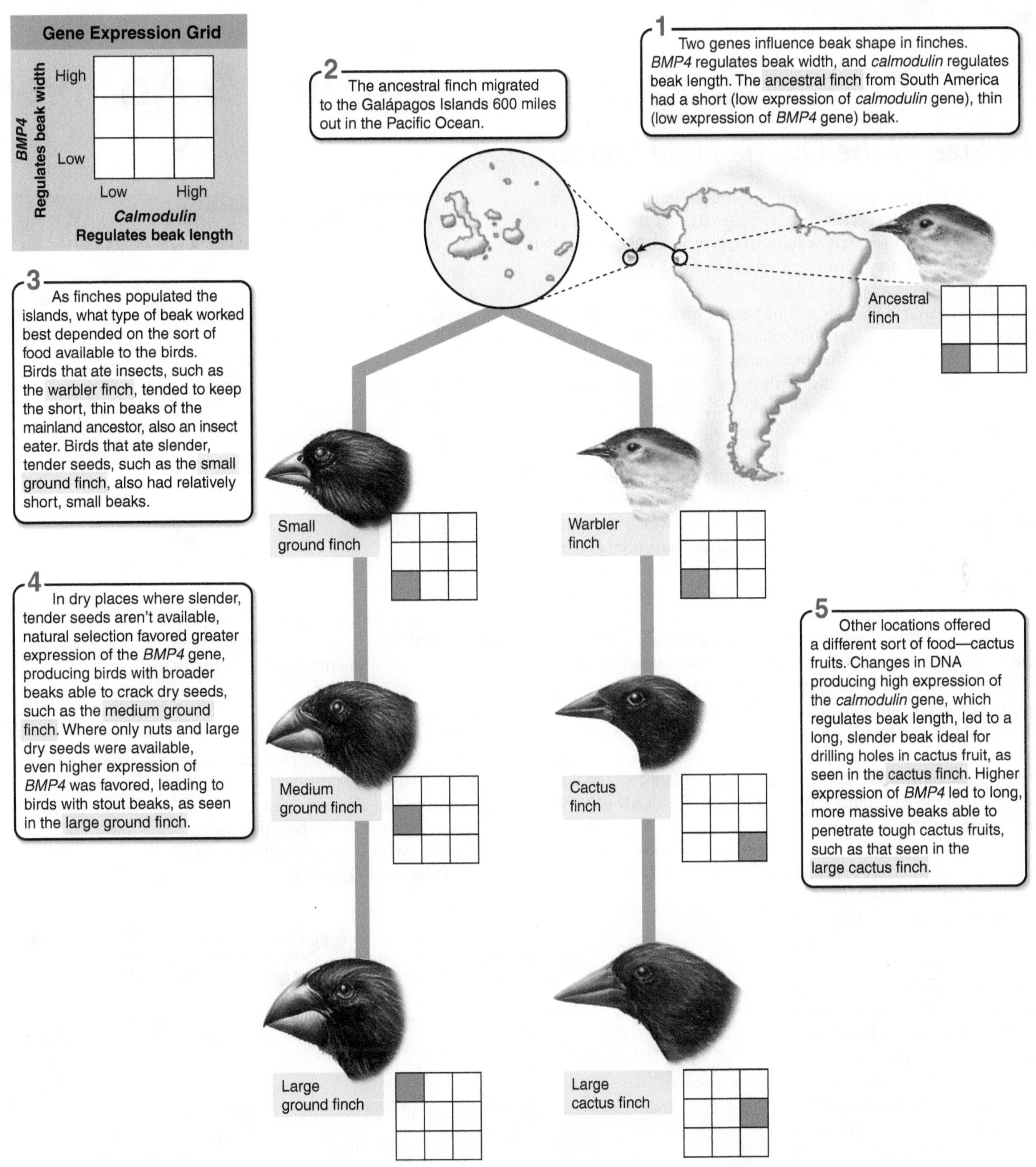

Gene Expression Grid
High
Low
BMP4
Regulates beak width
Low
High
Calmodulin
Regulates beak length
1
Two genes influence beak shape in finches. BMP4 regulates beak width, and calmodulin regulates beak length. The ancestral finch from South America had a short (low expression of calmodulin gene), thin (low expression of BMP4 gene) beak.
2
The ancestral finch migrated to the Galápagos Islands 600 miles out in the Pacific Ocean.
3
As finches populated the islands, what type of beak worked best depended on the sort of food available to the birds. Birds that ate insects, such as the warbler finch, tended to keep the short, thin beaks of the mainland ancestor, also an insect eater. Birds that ate slender, tender seeds, such as the small ground finch, also had relatively short, small beaks.
4
In dry places where slender, tender seeds aren't available, natural selection favored greater expression of the BMP4 gene, producing birds with broader beaks able to crack dry seeds, such as the medium ground finch. Where only nuts and large dry seeds were available, even higher expression of BMP4 was favored, leading to birds with stout beaks, as seen in the large ground finch.
5
Other locations offered a different sort of food—cactus fruits. Changes in DNA producing high expression of the calmodulin gene, which regulates beak length, led to a long, slender beak ideal for drilling holes in cactus fruit, as seen in the cactus finch. Higher expression of BMP4 led to long, more massive beaks able to penetrate tough cactus fruits, such as that seen in the large cactus finch.
Ancestral finch
Small ground finch
Warbler finch
Medium ground finch
Cactus finch
Large ground finch
Large cactus finch

Figure 1.13 The theory of evolution.

Darwin's theory of evolution proposes that many forms of a gene may exist among members of a population, and that those members with a form better suited to their particular habitat will tend to reproduce more successfully, and so their traits become more common in the population, a process Darwin dubbed "natural selection." Here you see how this process is thought to have worked on two pivotal genes that helped generate the diversity of finches on the Galápagos Islands, visited by Darwin in 1831 on his round-the-world voyage on HMS *Beagle*. This example of evolution was a key to Darwin's thinking. The way in which modern knowledge of genes has expanded our understanding of evolution among Darwin's finches is examined in greater detail in chapter 14.

Inquiry & Analysis

Is the Size of the Ozone Hole Increasing?

In 1985 Joseph Farman, a British atmospheric scientist working in Antarctica, made an unexpected discovery. Analyzing the Antarctic sky, he found far less ozone (O_3, a form of oxygen gas) than should be there—a 30% drop from a reading recorded five years earlier in the Antarctic!

At first it was argued that this thinning of the ozone (soon dubbed the "ozone hole") was an as-yet-unexplained weather phenomenon. Evidence soon mounted, however, implicating synthetic chemicals as the culprit. Detailed analysis of chemicals in the Antarctic atmosphere revealed a surprisingly high concentration of chlorine, a chemical known to destroy ozone. The source of the chlorine was a class of chemicals called **chlorofluorocarbons (CFCs).** CFCs have been manufactured in large amounts since they were invented in the 1920s, largely for use as coolants in air conditioners, propellants in aerosols, and foaming agents in making Styrofoam. CFCs were widely regarded as harmless because they are chemically unreactive under normal conditions. But in the atmosphere over Antarctica, CFCs break down and produce chlorine, which acts as a catalyst, attacking and destroying ozone, as shown in the figure below.

The thinning of the ozone layer in the upper atmosphere 25 to 40 kilometers above the surface of the earth is a serious matter. The ozone layer protects life from the harmful ultraviolet (UV) rays of the sun that bombard the earth continuously. Like invisible sunglasses, the ozone layer filters out these dangerous rays. So when ozone is destroyed, the UV rays are able to pass through to the earth. When UV rays damage the DNA in skin cells, it can lead to skin cancer. It is estimated that every 1% drop in the atmospheric ozone concentration leads to a 6% increase in skin cancers.

As scientific observations have become widely known, governments have rushed to correct the situation. By 1990, worldwide agreements to phase out production of CFCs by the end of the century had been signed. Production of CFCs declined by 86% in the following 10 years. The world currently produces less than 200,000 tons of CFCs annually, down from 1986 levels of 1.1 million tons.

While ozone depletion is still producing major ozone holes over the Antarctic, researchers' models predict that the situation should gradually improve as less CFCs are produced, with the period of maximum ozone depletion peaking now and beginning to fall in the next few years.

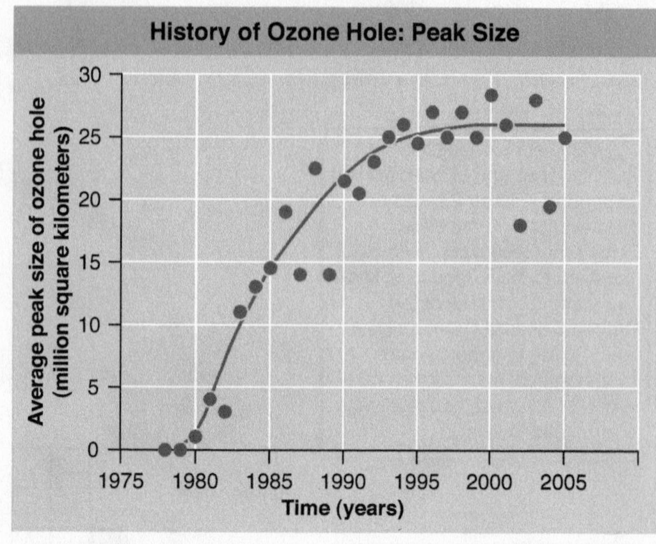

Are they right? The graph above presents measurements of the average peak size of the ozone hole centered over Antarctica, data collected by atmospheric scientists since 1976.

Analysis

1. **Making Inferences** Did the size of the ozone hole increase from 1980 to 1990? from 1995 to 2005?
2. **Drawing Conclusions** Does the graph support the conclusion that the size of the ozone hole over Antarctica is presently increasing? Explain. What might account for the difference you observe between 1980–90 and 1995–2005?

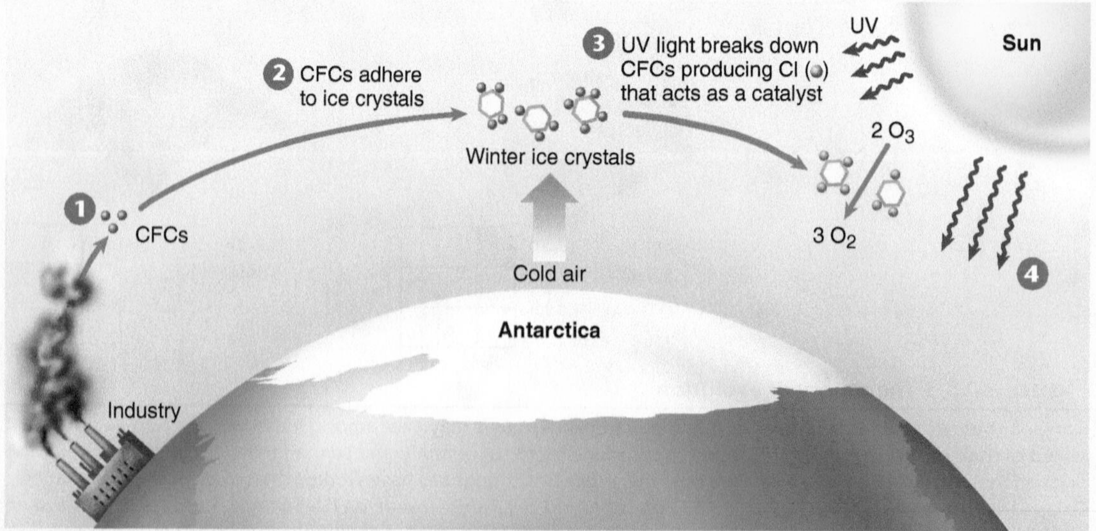

Concept Summary

Biology and the Living World

1.1 The Diversity of Life

- Biology is the study of life. All living organisms share common characteristics, but they are also diverse and are categorized into six groups called kingdoms. The six kingdoms are Bacteria, Archaea, Protista, Fungi, Plantae, and Animalia (**figure 1.1**).

1.2 Properties of Life

- All living organisms share five basic properties: cellular organization, metabolism, homeostasis, growth and reproduction, and heredity. Cellular organization indicates that all living organisms are composed of cells. Metabolism means that all living organisms, like the kingfisher shown here from **figure 1.3,** use energy. Homeostasis is the process whereby all living organisms maintain stable internal conditions. The properties of growth and reproduction indicate that all living organisms grow in size and reproduce. The property of heredity describes how all living organisms possess genetic information in DNA that determines how each organism looks and functions, and this information is passed on to future generations.

1.3 The Organization of Life

- Living organisms exhibit increasing levels of complexity within their cells (cellular level), within their bodies (organismal level), and within ecosystems (population level) (**figure 1.4**).
- Novel properties that appear in each level of the hierarchy of life are called emergent properties. These properties are the natural consequences of ever more complex structural organization.

1.4 Biological Themes

- Five themes emerge from the study of biology: evolution, the flow of energy, cooperation, structure determines function, and homeostasis. These themes are used to examine the similarities and differences among organisms.

The Scientific Process

1.5 Stages of a Scientific Investigation

- Scientists use observations to formulate hypotheses. Hypotheses are possible explanations that are used to form predictions. These predictions are tested experimentally. Some hypotheses are rejected based on experimental results, while others are tentatively accepted.
- Scientific investigations often use a series of stages, called the scientific process, to study a scientific question. These stages are observations, forming hypotheses, making predictions, testing, establishing controls, and drawing conclusions (**figure 1.5**).
- The discovery of the hole in the ozone required careful observations of data collected from the atmosphere. Based on these observations (**figure 1.6**), scientists proposed an explanation of what caused a decrease in the levels of ozone over the Antarctic. This explanation is called a hypothesis. They then formed predictions and tested the hypothesis against controls. The hypothesis that CFCs released into the atmosphere were causing the breakdown of ozone to oxygen gas was supported by the data. Further experimentation allowed scientists to form the conclusion that CFCs were responsible for the loss of ozone over the Antarctic.

1.6 Theory and Certainty

- Hypotheses that hold up to testing over time are combined into statements called theories. Theories carry a higher degree of certainty, although no theory in science is absolute.
- The process of science was once viewed as a series of "either/or" predictions that were tested experimentally. This process, referred to as the "scientific method," did not take into account the importance of insight and imagination that are necessary to good scientific investigations.
- Science can only study what can be tested experimentally. A hypothesis can only be established through science if it can be tested and potentially disproven.

Core Ideas of Biology

1.7 Four Theories Unify Biology as a Science

- There are four unifying theories in biology: cell theory, gene theory, the theory of heredity, and the theory of evolution.
- The cell theory states that all living organisms are composed of cells, which grow and reproduce to form other cells (**figure 1.8**).
- The gene theory states that long molecules of DNA carry instructions for producing cellular components. These instructions are encoded in the nucleotide sequences in the strands of DNA, like this section of DNA from **figure 1.9.** The nucleotides are organized into discrete units called genes, and the genes determine how an organism looks and functions (**figure 1.10**).
- The theory of heredity states that the genes of an organism are passed as discrete units from parent to offspring (**figure 1.11**).
- Organisms are organized into kingdoms based on similar characteristics. The organisms within a kingdom show similarities but exhibit differences from those of other kingdoms. The kingdoms are further organized into three major groups called domains based on their cellular characteristics. The three domains are Bacteria, Archaea, and Eukarya (**figure 1.12**).
- The theory of evolution states that modifications in genes that are passed from parent to offspring result in changes in future generations. These changes lead to greater diversity among organisms over time, ultimately leading to the formation of new groups of organisms (**figure 1.13**).

Self-Test

1. Biologists categorize all living things based on related characteristics into large groups, called
   a. kingdoms. c. populations.
   b. species. d. ecosystems.
2. Living things can be distinguished from nonliving things because they have
   a. complexity. c. cellular organization.
   b. movement. d. response to a stimulus.
3. Living things are organized. Choose the answer that illustrates this organization and that is arranged from smallest to largest.
   a. cell, atom, molecule, tissue, organelle, organ, organ system, organism, population, species, community, ecosystem
   b. atom, molecule, organelle, cell, tissue, organ, organ system, organism, population, species, community, ecosystem
   c. atom, molecule, organelle, cell, tissue, organ, organ system, organism, community, population, species, ecosystem
   d. atom, molecule, cell wall, cell, organ, organelle, organism, species, population, community, ecosystem
4. At each level in the hierarchy of living things, properties occur that were not present at the simpler levels. These properties are referred to as
   a. novelistic properties. c. incremental properties.
   b. complex properties. d. emergent properties.
5. The five general biological themes include
   a. evolution, energy flow, competition, structure determines function, and homeostasis.
   b. evolution, energy flow, cooperation, structure determines function, and homeostasis.
   c. evolution, growth, competition, structure determines function, and homeostasis.
   d. evolution, growth, cooperation, structure determines function, and homeostasis.
6. When trying to figure out explanations for observations, you usually construct a series of possible hypotheses. Then you make predictions of what will happen if each hypothesis is true, and
   a. test each hypothesis, using appropriate controls, to determine which hypothesis is true.
   b. test each hypothesis, using appropriate controls, to rule out as many as possible.
   c. use logic to determine which hypothesis is most likely true.
   d. reject those that seem unlikely.
7. Which of the following statements is correct regarding a hypothesis?
   a. After sufficient testing, you can conclude that it is true.
   b. If it explains the observations, it doesn't need to be tested.
   c. After sufficient testing, you can accept it as probable, being aware that it may be revised or rejected in the future.
   d. You never have any degree of certainty that it is true; there are too many variables.
8. Cell theory states that
   a. all organisms have cell walls and all cell walls come from other cells.
   b. all cellular organisms undergo sexual reproduction.
   c. all living organisms use cells for energy, either their own or they ingest cells of other organisms.
   d. all living organisms consist of cells, and all cells come from other cells.
9. The gene theory states that all the information that specifies what a cell is and what it does
   a. is different for each cell type in the organism.
   b. is passed down, unchanged, from parents to offspring.
   c. is contained in a long molecule called DNA.
   d. All of the above.
10. The theory of evolution is based on the hypothesis put forth by
    a. Mendel. c. Darwin.
    b. Watson and Crick. d. Schleiden and Schwann.

Visual Understanding

1. For over two centuries global temperatures have been warming, and over this same period of time the number of pirate ship attacks has steadily decreased. Does this graph support the conclusion that the number of pirate ship attacks has decreased because of warmer temperatures? [Hint: Read section 0.4 in chapter 0 to help answer the question.]

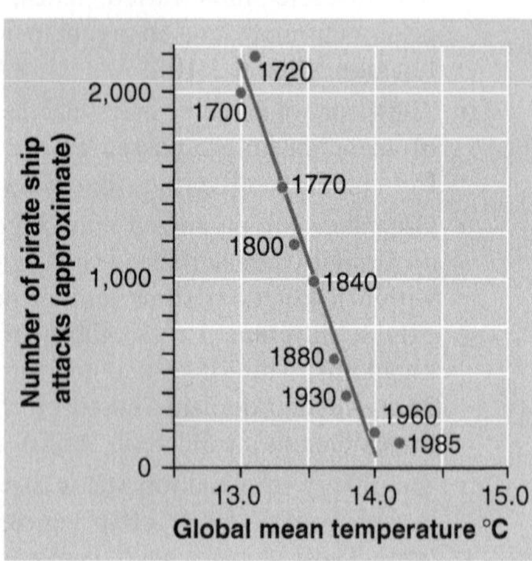

2. **Figure 1.6** Scientists identified the hole in the ozone layer through observations, by analyzing data collected over time. What other step in the scientific process involves the collection of data?

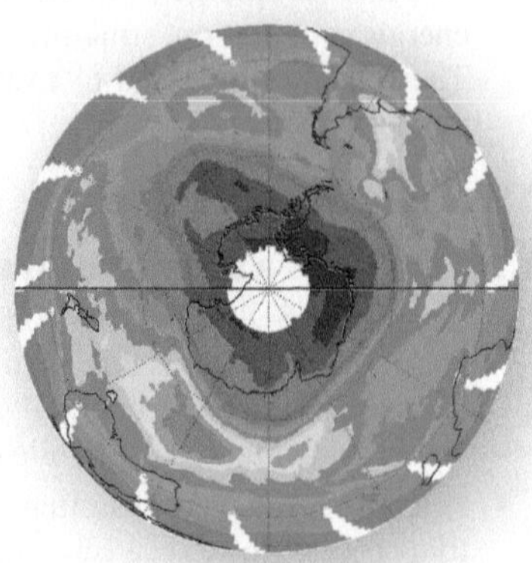

Challenge Questions

1. You are the biologist in a group of scientists who have traveled to a distant star system and landed on a planet. You see an astounding array of shapes and forms. You have three days to take samples of living things before returning to earth. How do you decide what is alive?
2. St. John's wort is an herb that has been used for hundreds of years as a remedy for mild depression. How might a modern-day scientist research its effectiveness?

Chapter 2

The Chemistry of Life

CHAPTER AT A GLANCE

Some Simple Chemistry

Figure 2.1 Replacing electrolytes.

During extreme exercise, athletes will often consume drinks that contain "electrolytes," chemicals such as calcium, potassium, and sodium that play an important role in muscle contraction. Electrolytes can also be depleted in other types of dehydration.

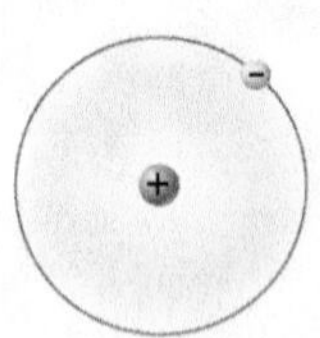

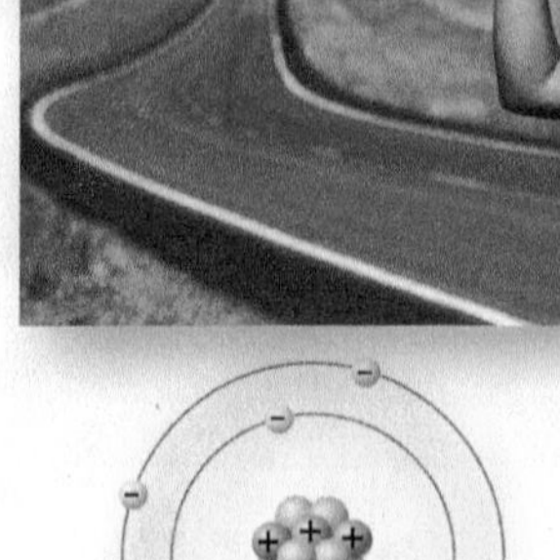

Figure 2.2 Basic structure of atoms.

All atoms have a nucleus consisting of protons and neutrons, except hydrogen, the smallest atom, which has only one proton and no neutrons in its nucleus. Carbon, for example, has six protons and six neutrons in its nucleus. Electrons spin around the nucleus in orbitals a far distance away from the nucleus. The electrons determine how atoms react with each other.

TABLE 2.1 Elements Common in Living Organisms

Element	Symbol	Atomic Number	Mass Number
Hydrogen	H	1	1.008
Carbon	C	6	12.011
Nitrogen	N	7	14.007
Oxygen	O	8	15.999
Sodium	Na	11	22.989
Phosphorus	P	15	30.974
Sulfur	S	16	32.064
Chlorine	Cl	17	35.453
Potassium	K	19	39.098
Calcium	Ca	20	40.080
Iron	Fe	26	55.847

2.1 Atoms

CONCEPT PREVIEW: Atoms, the smallest particles into which a substance can be divided, are composed of electrons orbiting a nucleus that contains protons and neutrons. Electrons determine the chemical behavior of atoms.

Biology is the science of life, and all life, in fact even all nonlife, is made of substances. Chemistry is the study of the properties of these substances. So, while it may seem tedious or unrelated to examine chemistry in a biology text, it is essential. Organisms are chemical machines (figure 2.1), and to understand them we must learn a little chemistry.

Any substance in the universe that has mass and occupies space is defined as matter. All matter is composed of extremely small particles called **atoms.** An atom is the smallest particle into which a substance can be divided and still retain its chemical properties.

Every atom has the same basic structure you see in figure 2.2. At the center of every atom is a small, very dense nucleus formed of two types of subatomic particles, **protons** (illustrated by purple balls) and **neutrons** (the pink balls in the figure). Whizzing around the nucleus is an orbiting cloud of a third kind of subatomic particle, the **electron** (depicted by yellow balls on concentric rings). Neutrons have no electrical charge, whereas protons have a positive charge and electrons have a negative one. In each atom, there is an orbiting electron for every proton in the nucleus. The electron's negative charge balances the proton's positive charge so that the atom is electrically neutral.

An atom is typically described by the number of protons in its nucleus or by the overall mass of the atom. The terms *mass* and *weight* are often used interchangeably, but they have slightly different meanings. Mass refers to the amount of a substance, whereas weight refers to the force gravity exerts on a substance. Hence, an object has the same mass whether it is on the earth or the moon, but its weight will be greater on the earth, because the earth's gravitational force is greater than the moon's. For example, an astronaut weighing 180 pounds on earth will weigh about 30 pounds on the moon. He didn't lose any significant mass during his flight to the moon, there is just less gravitational pull on his mass.

The number of protons in the nucleus of an atom is called the **atomic number.** For example, the atomic number of carbon is 6 because it has six protons. Atoms with the same atomic number (that is, the same number of protons) have the same chemical properties and are said to belong to the same **element.** Formally speaking, an element is any substance that cannot be broken down into any other substance by ordinary chemical means.

Neutrons are similar to protons in mass, and the number of protons and neutrons in the nucleus of an atom is called the **mass number.** A carbon atom that has six protons and six neutrons has a mass number of 12. An electron's contribution to the overall mass of an atom is negligible. The atomic numbers and mass numbers of some of the most common elements in living organisms are shown in table 2.1.

Electrons Determine What Atoms Are Like

Electrons have very little mass (only about 1/1,840 the mass of a proton). Of all the mass contributing to your weight, the portion that is contributed by electrons is less than the mass of your eyelashes. And yet electrons determine the chemical behavior of atoms because they are the parts of atoms that come close enough to each other in nature to interact. Almost all the volume of an atom is empty space. Protons and neutrons lie at the core of this space, while orbiting electrons are very far from the nucleus. If the nucleus of an atom were the size of an apple, the orbit of the nearest electron would be more than a mile out!

Electrons Carry Energy

Because electrons are negatively charged, they are attracted to the positively charged nucleus, but they also repel the negative charges of each other. It takes work to keep them in orbit, just as it takes work to hold an apple in your hand when gravity is pulling the apple down toward the ground. The apple in your hand is said to possess **energy,** the ability to do work, because of its position—if you were to release it, the apple would fall. Similarly, electrons have energy of position, called *potential energy*. It takes work to oppose the attraction of the nucleus, so moving the electron farther out away from the nucleus, as shown by the set of arrows on the right side of figure 2.3, requires an input of energy and results in an electron with greater potential energy. Moving an electron in toward the nucleus has the opposite effect (the set of arrows on the left side); energy is released, and the electron has less potential energy. Consider again an apple held in your hand. If you carry the apple up to a second-story window, it has a greater potential energy when you drop it, compared to six inches from the ground. Cells use the potential energy of atoms to drive chemical reactions.

Potential energy is discussed in more detail on page 88 and examples of how the potential energy from electrons is used in biological systems are described in chapters 6 and 7.

While the energy levels of an atom are often visualized as well-defined circular orbits around a central nucleus as was shown in figure 2.2, such a simple picture is not accurate. These energy levels, called *electron shells,* often consist of complex three-dimensional shapes, and the exact location of an individual electron at any given time is impossible to specify. However, some locations are more probable than others, and it is often possible to say where an electron is *most likely* to be located. The volume of space around a nucleus where an electron is most likely to be found is called the *orbital* of that electron.

Each electron shell has a specific number of orbitals, and each orbital can hold up to two electrons. The first shell in any atom contains one orbital. Helium, shown in figure 2.4*a*, has one electron shell with one orbital that corresponds to the lowest energy level. The orbital contains two electrons, shown above and below the nucleus. In atoms with more than one electron shell, the second shell contains four orbitals and holds up to eight electrons. Nitrogen, shown in figure 2.4*b*, has two electron shells; the first one is completely filled with two electrons, but three of the four orbitals in the second electron shell are not filled because nitrogen's second shell contains only five electrons (openings in orbitals are indicated with dotted circles). In atoms with more than two electron shells, subsequent shells also contain up to four orbitals with a maximum of eight electrons. Atoms with unfilled electron orbitals tend to be more reactive because they lose, gain, or share electrons in order to fill their outermost electron shell. An atom with a completely filled outermost shell is more stable. Losing, gaining, or sharing electrons is the basis for chemical reactions in which chemical bonds form between atoms.

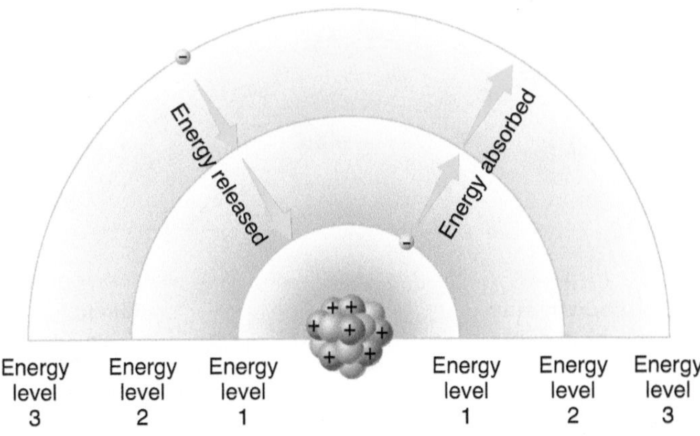

Figure 2.3 The electrons of atoms possess potential energy.

Electrons that circulate rapidly around the nucleus contain energy, and depending on their distance from the nucleus, they may contain more or less energy. Energy level 1 is the lowest potential energy level because it is closest to the nucleus. When an electron absorbs energy, it moves from level 1 to the next higher energy level (level 2). When an electron loses energy, it falls to a lower energy level closer to the nucleus.

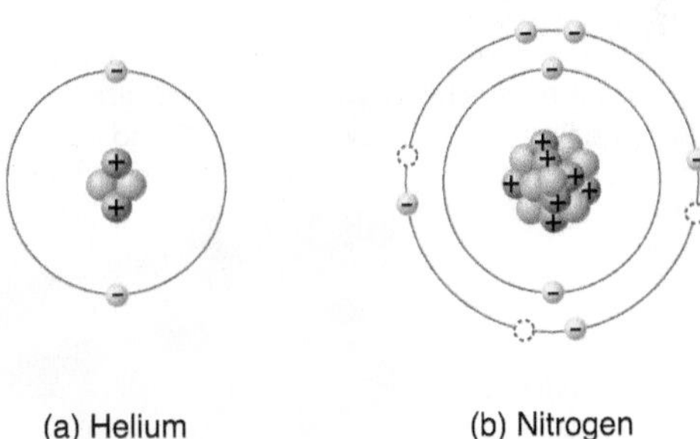

Figure 2.4 Electrons in electron shells.

(a) An atom of helium has two protons, two neutrons, and two electrons. The electrons fill the one orbital in its one electron shell, the lowest energy level. (b) An atom of nitrogen has seven protons, seven neutrons, and seven electrons. Two electrons fill the orbital in the innermost electron shell, and five electrons occupy orbitals in the second electron shell (the second energy level). The orbitals in the second electron shell can hold up to eight electrons; therefore there are three vacancies in the outer electron shell of a nitrogen atom.

IMPLICATION Helium gas is often used to inflate party balloons, and if you release these balloons they rise up into the air. If you fill the party balloons with nitrogen gas, they don't rise. Why this difference in party balloon behavior?

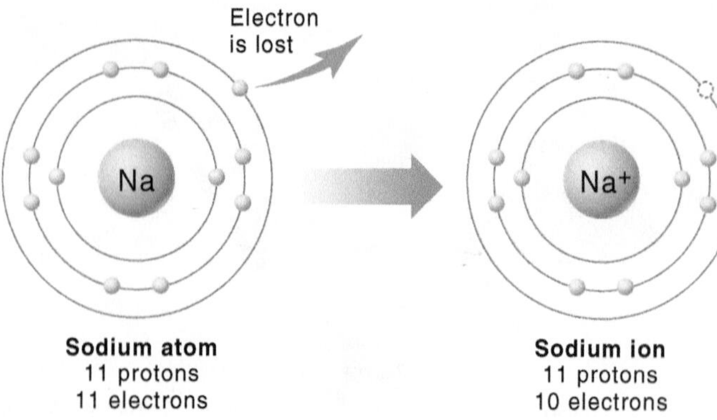

Figure 2.5 Making a sodium ion.

An electrically neutral sodium atom has 11 protons and 11 electrons. Sodium ions bear a positive charge when they ionize and lose one electron. Sodium ions have 11 protons and only 10 electrons.

2.2 Ions and Isotopes

CONCEPT PREVIEW: Ions, which are electrically-charged, result when an atom gains or loses electrons. Isotopes of an element differ in the number of neutrons they contain, but all have the same chemical properties.

Ions

Sometimes an atom may gain or lose an electron from its outer shell (we will look at why this happens in the next section). Atoms in which the number of electrons does not equal the number of protons because they have gained or lost one or more electrons are called **ions.** All ions are electrically charged. For example, an atom of sodium (on the left in figure 2.5) becomes a positively charged ion (Na^+), called a *cation*, when it loses an electron (on the right); one proton in the nucleus is left with an unbalanced charge (11 positively charged protons and only 10 negatively charged electrons). Negatively charged ions, called *anions*, form when an atom gains one or more electrons from another atom.

Isotopes

The number of neutrons in an atom of a particular element can vary without changing the chemical properties of the element. Atoms that have the same number of protons but different numbers of neutrons are called **isotopes.** Isotopes of an atom have the same atomic number but differ in their mass number. Most elements in nature exist as mixtures of different isotopes. For example, there are three isotopes of the element carbon, all of which possess six protons (the purple balls in figure 2.6). The most common isotope of carbon (99% of all carbon) has six neutrons (the pink balls). Because its mass number is 12 (six protons plus six neutrons), it is referred to as carbon-12 (on the left). The isotope carbon-14 (on the right) is rare (1 in 1 trillion atoms of carbon) and unstable, such that its nucleus tends to break up into particles with lower atomic numbers, a process called **radioactive decay.** Radioactive isotopes are used in dating fossils, as discussed in the *Inquiry & Analysis* at the end of the chapter, and in medicine.

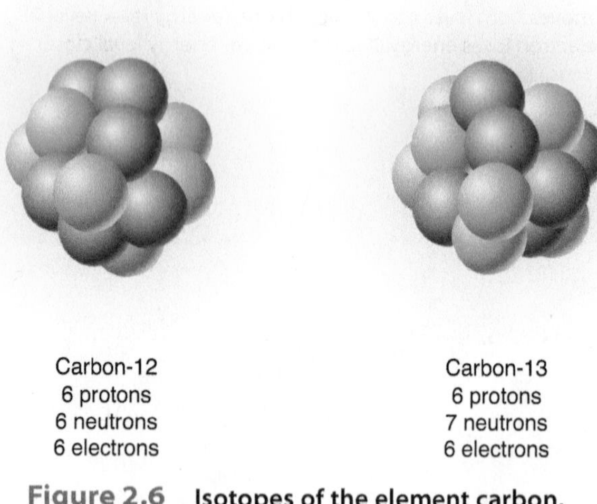

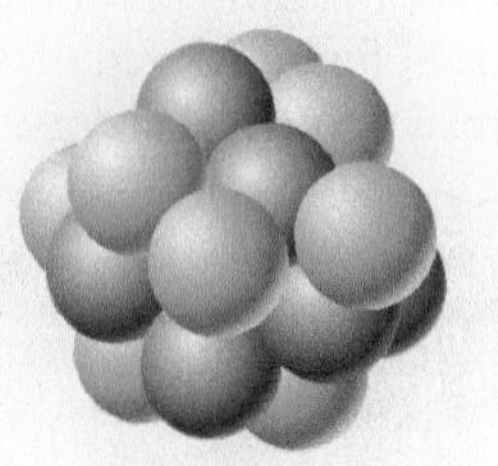

Figure 2.6 Isotopes of the element carbon.

The three most abundant isotopes of carbon are carbon-12, carbon-13, and carbon-14. The yellow "clouds" in the diagrams represent the orbiting electrons, whose numbers are the same for all three isotopes. Protons are shown in purple, and neutrons are shown in pink.

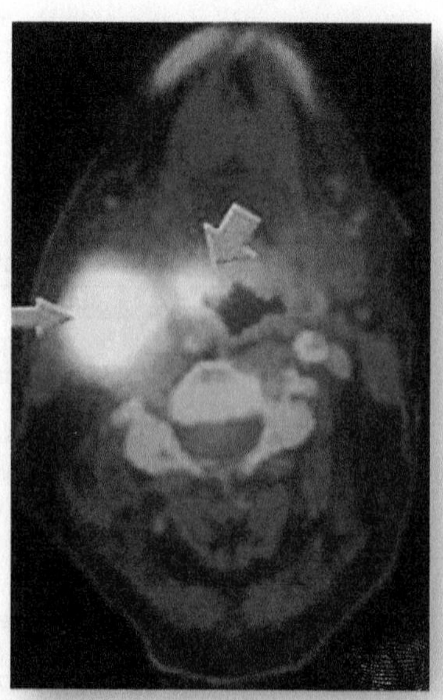

Figure 2.7 Using a radioactive tracer to identify cancer.

In certain medical imaging procedures, the patient is injected intravenously with a radioactive tracer that is absorbed in greater amounts by cancer cells. The tracer emits radioactivity that is detected using PET and PET/CT equipment. A cancerous area in the neck is seen as bright yellow glowing areas.

Medical Uses of Radioactive Isotopes

Radioactive isotopes are used in many medical procedures. Short-lived isotopes, those that decay fairly rapidly and produce harmless products, are commonly used as tracers in the body. A *tracer* is a radioactive substance that is taken up and used by the body. Emissions from the radioactive isotope tracer are detected using special laboratory equipment, and can reveal key diagnostic information about the functioning of the body. For example, PET and PET/CT (positron emission tomography/computerized tomography) imaging procedures can be used to identify a cancerous area in the body. First, a radioactive tracer is injected into the body. This tracer is taken up by all cells, but it is taken up in larger amounts in cells with higher metabolic activities, such as cancer cells. Images are then taken of the body, and areas emitting greater amounts of the tracer can be seen. For example, in the image in figure 2.7, the radioactive-emitting cancer site appears as yellow glowing areas. There are many other uses of radioactive isotopes in medicine both in detection and treatment of disorders.

2.3 Molecules

CONCEPT PREVIEW: Molecules are atoms linked together by chemical bonds. Ionic bonds, covalent bonds, and hydrogen bonds are the three principal types of bonds; van der Waals forces are weaker interactions.

A **molecule** is a group of atoms held together by energy. The energy acts as "glue," ensuring that the various atoms stick to one another. The energy or force holding two atoms together is called a **chemical bond.** There are three principal kinds of chemical bonds: ionic bonds, where the force is generated by the attraction of oppositely charged ions; covalent bonds, where the force results from the sharing of electrons; and hydrogen bonds, where the force is generated by the attraction of opposite partial electrical charges. Another type of chemical attraction called van der Waals forces will be discussed later, but keep in mind that this type of interaction is not considered a chemical bond.

Ionic Bonds

Chemical bonds called **ionic bonds** form when atoms are attracted to each other by opposite electrical charges. Just as the positive pole of a magnet is attracted to the negative pole of another, so an atom can form a strong link with another atom if they have opposite electrical charges. Because an atom with an electrical charge is an ion, these bonds are called ionic bonds.

Everyday table salt is built of ionic bonds. The sodium and chlorine atoms that make up table salt are ions. The sodium you see in the yellow panels of figure 2.8*a* gives up the sole electron in its outermost shell (leaving a filled outer shell) and chlorine, in the light green panels, gains an electron to complete its outermost shell. Recall from section 2.1 that an atom is more stable when its outermost electron shell is filled. As a result of this electron hopping, sodium atoms in table salt are positive sodium ions and chlorine atoms are negative chloride ions. Because each ion is electrically attracted to all surrounding ions of opposite charge, they form an elaborate matrix of ionic bonds between alternating sodium and chloride ions—a crystal (figure 2.8*b*). That is why table salt is composed of tiny crystals and is not a powder.

The two key properties of ionic bonds that make them form crystals are that they are strong (although not as strong as covalent bonds) and that they are *not* directional. An ion is attracted to the electrical field contributed by all nearby ions of opposite charge. Ionic bonds do not play an important part in most biological molecules because of this lack of directionality. They require the more specific associations made possible by directional bonds.

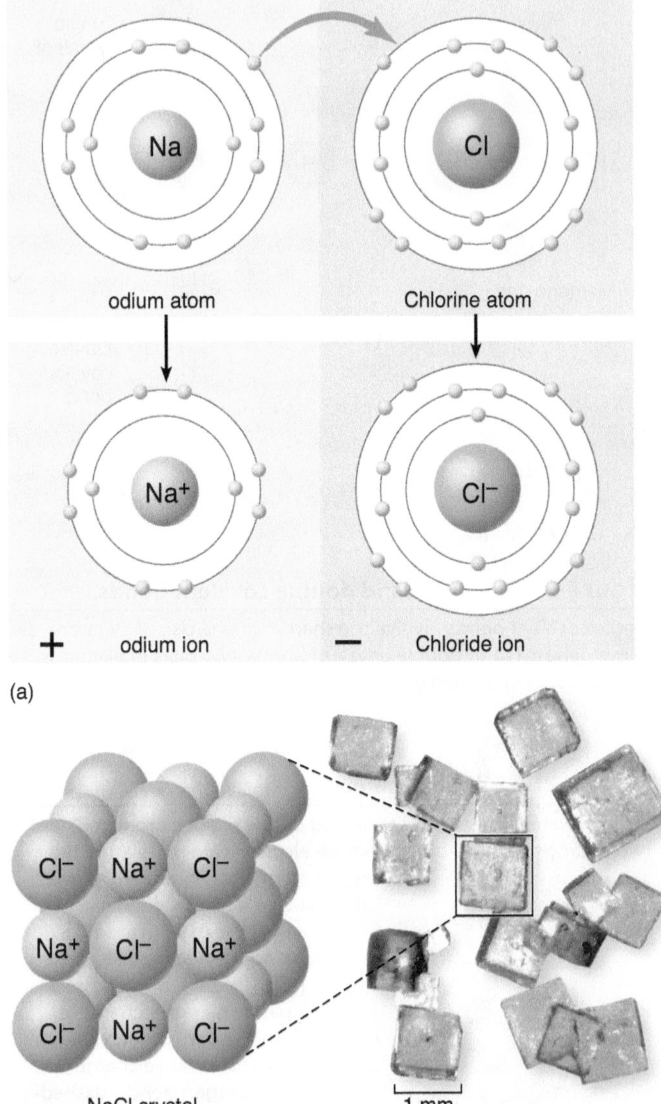

Figure 2.8 The formation of ionic bonds in table salt.
(a) When a sodium atom donates an electron to a chlorine atom, the sodium atom, lacking that electron, becomes a positively charged sodium ion. The chlorine atom, having gained an extra electron, becomes a negatively charged chloride ion. (b) Sodium chloride forms a highly regular lattice of alternating sodium ions and chloride ions. You are familiar with these crystals as everyday table salt.

Covalent Bonds

Strong chemical bonds called **covalent bonds** form between two atoms when they share electrons (figure 2.9). Most of the atoms in your body are linked to other atoms by covalent bonds. Why do atoms in molecules share electrons? Remember, all atoms seek to fill up their outermost shell of orbiting electrons, which in all atoms (except tiny hydrogen and helium) takes eight electrons. For example, an atom with six outer shell electrons seeks to share them with an atom that has two outer shell electrons or with two atoms that have single outer shell electrons. The carbon atom has four electrons in its outermost shell, and so carbon can form as many as four covalent bonds in its attempt to fully populate its outermost shell of electrons. Because there are many ways four covalent bonds can form, carbon atoms participate in many different kinds of molecules. The strength of covalent bonds increases as more electrons are

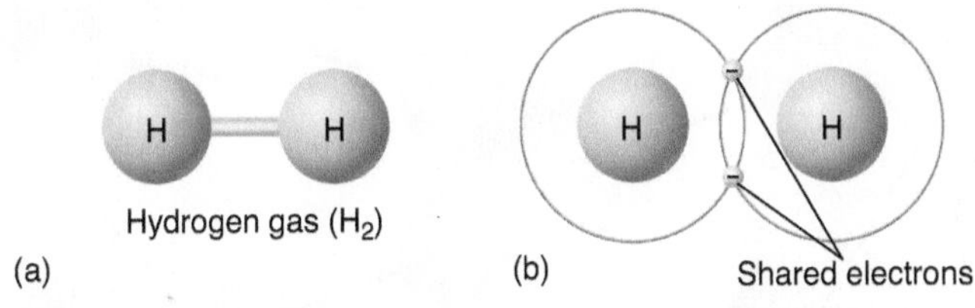

Figure 2.9 Covalent bonds.
Covalent bonds involve the sharing of electrons, indicated by the blur bar in (a). Hydrogen gas consists of two atoms of hydrogen, each having one electron. The covalent bond forms when the two atoms share the two electrons, as shown in (b).

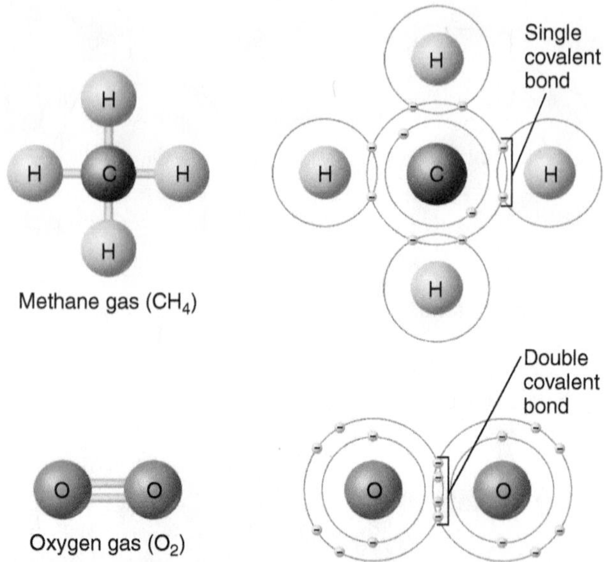

Figure 2.10 Single and double covalent bonds.

Single covalent bonds involve the sharing of one pair of electrons, as in methane (CH_4). In double covalent bonds, two pairs of electrons are shared, as in oxygen gas.

Figure 2.11 Water molecules.

(a) Each water molecule is composed of one oxygen atom (red) and two hydrogen atoms (blue). Because electrons are more attracted to oxygen atoms than hydrogen atoms, the shared electrons spend more time near the oxygen atom, making the water molecule polar. (b) Each oxygen has a partial negative charge (δ−), and each hydrogen has a partial positive charge (δ+). Hydrogen bonds (dashed lines) form between the positive end of one water molecule and the negative end of another water molecule.

Oxygen
8+
8n
+
Hydrogen
Hydrogen
Electrons from hydrogen

(a) Electron shells in a water molecule

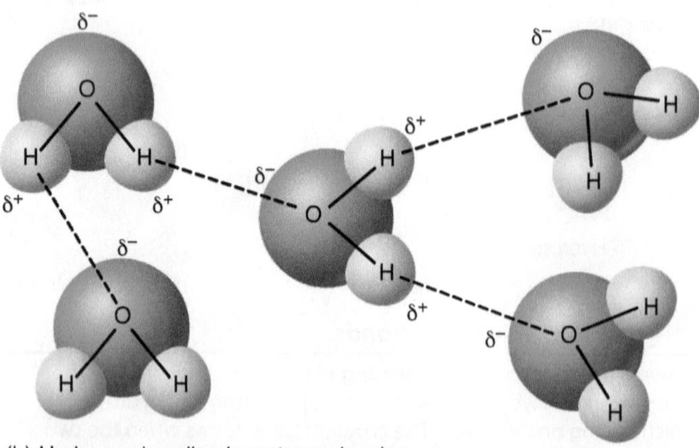

(b) Hydrogen bonding in water molecules

shared. If only one pair of electrons is shared between two atoms (as in the carbon-hydrogen bonds in the methane molecule in figure 2.10), the covalent bond is called a *single covalent bond.* If two pairs of electrons are shared (as in oxygen gas in figure 2.10), it is a stronger bond, called a *double covalent bond;* and if three pairs of electrons are shared it is a very strong *triple covalent bond.*

> **The atoms in nitrogen gas (N_2) are held together by a very strong triple covalent bond. As described on page 394, only a few kinds of bacteria are able to break this bond and make the nitrogen available to other organisms.**

The two key properties of covalent bonds that make them ideal for their molecule-building role in living systems are that (1) they are strong, involving the sharing of lots of energy; and (2) they are very directional—allowing bonds to form between two specific atoms, rather than creating a generalized attraction of one atom for its neighbors. For example, compare the methane molecule in figure 2.10 with the NaCl crystal in figure 2.8.

Polar and Nonpolar Covalent Bonds. When a covalent bond forms between two atoms, one nucleus may be much better at attracting the shared electrons than the other. In water, for example, the shared electrons are much more strongly attracted to the oxygen atom than to the hydrogen atoms. When this happens, shared electrons spend more time in the vicinity of the oxygen atom, making it somewhat negative in charge; they spend less time in the vicinity of the hydrogens, and these become somewhat positive in charge (figure 2.11). The charges are not full electrical charges, as in ions, but rather tiny *partial charges.* What you end up with is a sort of molecular magnet, with positive and negative ends, or "poles." Molecules like this are said to be **polar molecules.**

Hydrogen Bonds

Polar molecules like water are attracted to one another through a special type of weak chemical bond called a **hydrogen bond** (figure 2.11*b*). Hydrogen bonds occur when the positive end of one polar molecule is attracted to the negative end of another, like two magnets drawn to each other. Two key properties of hydrogen bonds cause them to play an important role in the molecules found in organisms. First, hydrogen bonds are highly directional. Second, they are weak and so are not effective over long distances like more powerful covalent and ionic bonds. Too weak to actually form stable molecules, they act more like Velcro, forming a tight bond by the additive effects of many weak interactions.

van der Waals Forces

A kind of weak chemical attraction (not a bond) is a nondirectional attractive force called **van der Waals forces.** These chemical forces come into play only when two atoms are very close to one another. The attraction is very weak, and disappears if the atoms move even a little apart. It becomes significant when numerous atoms in one molecule simultaneously come close to numerous atoms of another molecule—that is, when their shapes match precisely.

Concept Check

1. The three common isotopes of carbon all have the same chemical behavior, meaning that they form the same types of chemical bonds. Explain why they are able to do this?
2. Of the attractive forces discussed here, which is not a chemical bond?
3. Both ionic and covalent bonds are strong. Why are molecules in living organisms usually made of covalent but not ionic bonds?

How Tropical Lizards Climb Vertical Walls

Science is most fun when it tickles your imagination. This is particularly true when you see something you know just can't be true. A few years ago, my wife, Barbara, and I were on a tropical vacation, and I was lying on the bed when a little lizard walked up the wall beside me and across the ceiling, stopping right over my head, and looked down at me.

This was no special effect, no trick with mirrors. I was seeing it with my own eyes, real as day, right there above me. The lizard, a green gecko about the size of a toothbrush, stood upside down on the ceiling and seemed to laugh at me for several minutes before trotting over to the far wall and down.

How did my gecko friend perform this gripping feat? Investigators have puzzled over the adhesive properties of geckos for decades. What force prevented gravity from dropping the gecko on my nose?

The most reasonable hypothesis seemed suction—salamanders' feet form suction cups that let them climb walls, so maybe geckos' do too. The way to test this is to see if the feet adhere in a vacuum, with no air to create suction. Salamander feet don't adhere, but gecko feet do. It's not suction.

How about friction? Cockroaches climb using tiny hooks that grapple onto irregularities in the surface, much as rock climbers use crampons. Geckos, however, happily run up walls of smooth polished glass that no cockroach can climb. It's not friction.

Electrostatic attraction? Clothes in a dryer stick together because of electrical charges created by their rubbing together. You can stop this by adding a "static remover" that is itself heavily ionized. But a gecko's feet still adhere in ionized air. It's not electrostatic attraction.

Could it be glue? Many insects use adhesive secretions from glands in their feet to aid climbing. But there are no gland cells in gecko feet, no secreted chemical. It's not glue.

There was one tantalizing clue, however, the kind that experimenters love. Gecko feet seem to get stickier on surfaces with highly ordered molecules. This suggests that geckos are tapping directly into the molecular structure of the surfaces they walk on!

Tracking down this clue, Robert Full of the University of California, Berkeley, and his research team took a closer look at gecko feet. Geckos have rows of tiny hairs on the bottoms of their feet, like the bristles of a toothbrush. There are about half a million of these hairs on each foot, pointed toward the heel.

When you look at these hairs under a microscope, the end of each hair is divided into between 400 and 1,000 fine projections, the projections sticking out from the tip like tiny stiff brushes.

When a gecko takes a step, it drives the sole of its foot onto the surface and pushes it backward. This shoves the forest of tips directly against the surface. The atoms of each gecko tip become closely engaged with the atoms of the surface, and *that* is the force that defies gravity. When two atoms approach each other very closely—closer than the diameter of an atom—a subtle nuclear attraction called "van der Waals forces" comes into play. These forces are individually very weak, but when lots of atoms add their little bits, the sum can add up to quite a lot.

Full and his team used microelectrical mechanical sensors, originally designed to be used with atomic force microscopes that map a surface by "feeling" it with a mechanical probe. Using the sensors, they were able to measure the force exerted by a single hair removed from a gecko's foot. It was 200 micronewtons, a tiny force but stupendous for a single hair. Enough to hold up an ant. A million hairs could support a small child. My little gecko, ceiling-walking with 2 million of them, could have carried an 80-pound backpack—talk about being overengineered!

If they stick that well, how do geckos ever become unstuck? For a gecko's foot to stick, each hair projection must butt up squarely against the surface, so the hair's individual atoms can come into play. Tipped past a critical angle—30 degrees—the attractive forces between hair and surface atoms weaken to nothing. The trick is to tip the foot hairs until the projections let go. Geckos release their feet by curling up each toe and peeling it off, sort of like undoing Velcro.

Now I can laugh with my little gecko friend, should I see it again, for I know its secret.

Water: Cradle of Life

TABLE 2.2	**The Properties of Water**
Property	**Explanation**
Heat storage	Hydrogen bonds require considerable heat before they break, minimizing temperature changes.
Ice formation	Water molecules in an ice crystal are spaced relatively far apart because of hydrogen bonding.
High heat of vaporization	Many hydrogen bonds must be broken for water to evaporate, which requires considerable heat.
Cohesion	Hydrogen bonds hold molecules of water together.
High polarity	Water molecules are attracted to ions and other polar compounds.

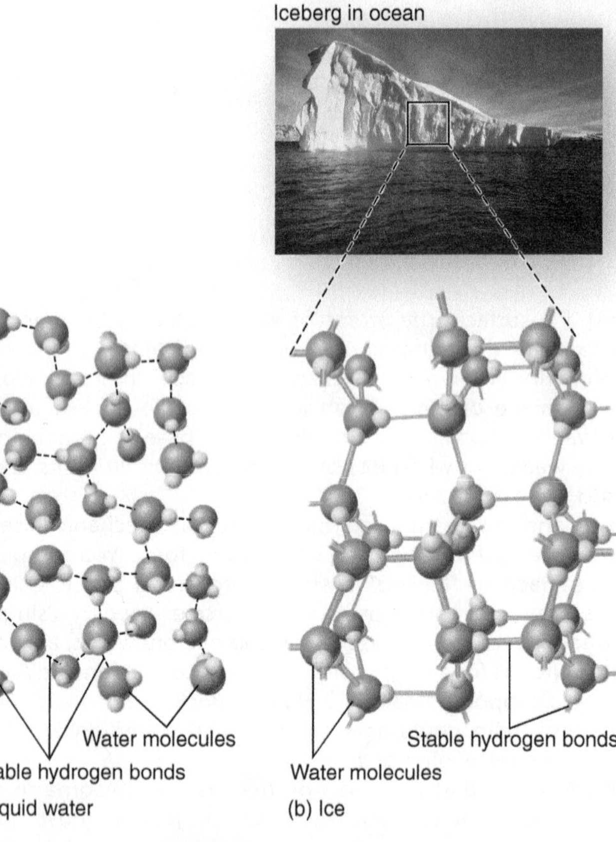

Figure 2.12 Ice formation.

When water (a) cools below 0°C, it forms a regular crystal structure (b) that floats. The individual water molecules are spaced apart and held in position by hydrogen bonds.

IMPLICATION: Will the melting of the polar ice cap (ice floating in the ocean) due to global warming raise sea level? [Hint: If you leave a glass of ice water on the table, does the level of water in the glass change as the ice melts?]

2.4 Hydrogen Bonds Give Water Unique Properties

CONCEPT PREVIEW: Water molecules form a network of hydrogen bonds in liquid and dissolve other polar molecules. Many of the key properties of water arise because it takes considerable energy to break liquid water's many hydrogen bonds.

Three-fourths of the earth's surface is covered by liquid water. About two-thirds of your body is water, and you cannot exist long without it. All other organisms also require water. It is no accident that tropical rain forests are bursting with life, whereas dry deserts seem almost lifeless except after it rains. The chemistry of life, then, is water chemistry.

Water has a simple atomic structure, an oxygen atom linked to two hydrogen atoms by single covalent bonds (see figure 2.11). The chemical formula for water is thus H_2O. It is because the oxygen atom attracts the shared electrons more strongly than the hydrogen atoms that water is a *polar molecule* and so can form *hydrogen bonds.* Water's ability to form hydrogen bonds is responsible for much of the organization of living chemistry, from the structure of membranes that encase every cell to how large molecules, called proteins, fold.

The weak hydrogen bonds that form between a hydrogen atom of one water molecule and the oxygen atom of another produce a lattice of hydrogen bonds within liquid water. Each of these bonds is individually very weak and short-lived—a single bond lasts only 1/100,000,000,000 of a second. However, like the grains of sand on a beach, the cumulative effect of large numbers of these bonds is enormous and is responsible for many of the important physical properties of water (table 2.2).

Heat Storage

The temperature of any substance is a measure of how rapidly its individual molecules are moving. Because of the many hydrogen bonds that water molecules form with one another, a large input of thermal energy is required to disrupt the organization of liquid water and raise its temperature. Because of this, water heats up more slowly than almost any other compound and holds its temperature longer. That is a major reason why your body, which is mostly water, is able to maintain a relatively constant internal temperature.

Ice Formation

If the temperature is low enough, very few hydrogen bonds between water molecules will break. Instead, the lattice of these bonds assumes a crystal-like structure, forming a solid we call ice. Interestingly, ice is less dense than water—that is why icebergs and ice cubes float. Why is ice less dense? This is best understood by comparing the molecular structures of water and ice that you see in figure 2.12. At temperatures above freezing (0°C or 32°F), water molecules in figure 2.12*a* move around each other with hydrogen bonds breaking and forming. As temperatures drop, the movement of water molecules decreases, allowing hydrogen bonds to stabilize, holding individual molecules farther apart, as in figure 2.12*b*, making the ice structure less dense.

High Heat of Vaporization

If the temperature is high enough, many hydrogen bonds between water molecules will break, with the result that the liquid is changed into vapor (a gas). A considerable amount of heat energy is required to do this—every gram of water that evaporates from your skin removes 2,452 joules of heat from your body, which is equal to the energy released by lowering the temperature of 586 grams of water 1°C (which is quite a lot of heat). That is why sweating cools you off; as the sweat evaporates (vaporizes) it takes energy with it, in the form of heat, cooling the body.

Cohesion

Because water molecules are very polar, they are attracted to other polar molecules—hydrogen bonds bind polar molecules to each other. When the other polar molecule is another water molecule, the attraction is called **cohesion.** The surface tension of water is created by cohesion. Surface tension is the force that causes water to bead, like on the spider web in figure 2.13, or supports the weight of the water strider. When the other polar molecule is a different substance, the attraction is called **adhesion.** Capillary action—such as water moving up into a paper towel—is created by adhesion. Water clings to any substance, such as paper fibers, with which it can form hydrogen bonds. Adhesion is why things get "wet" when they are dipped in water and why waxy substances do not—they are composed of nonpolar molecules that don't form hydrogen bonds with water molecules.

Cohesion and adhesion are properties of water that are necessary for the movement of water in plants, from the roots to the leaves as described on page 627.

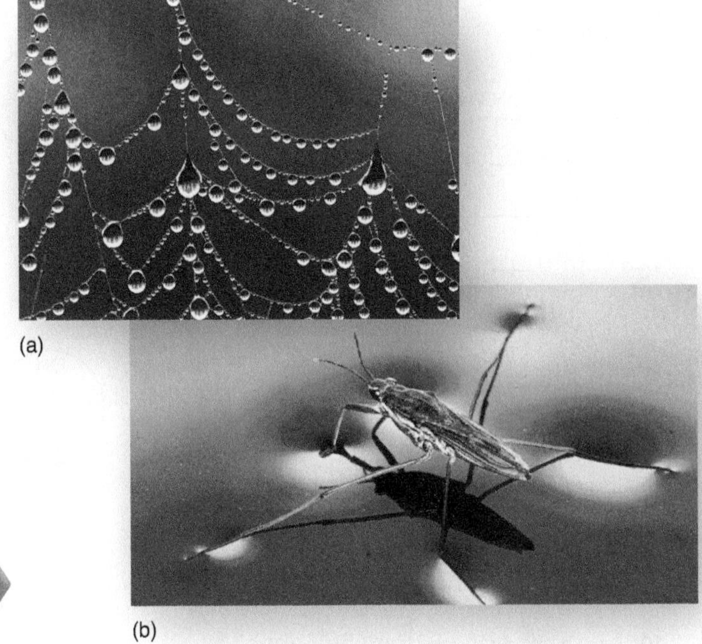

Figure 2.13 Cohesion.

(a) Cohesion allows water molecules to stick together and form droplets. (b) Surface tension is a property derived from cohesion—that is, water has a "strong" surface due to the force of its hydrogen bonds. Some insects, such as this water strider, literally walk on water.

IMPLICATION If you were to devise very large footpads made of lightweight film, would you be able to walk on water like this water strider? Why would you have to wear footpads and not just bare feet?

High Polarity

Water molecules in solution always tend to form the maximum number of hydrogen bonds possible. Polar molecules form hydrogen bonds and are attracted to water molecules. Polar molecules are called **hydrophilic** (from the Greek *hydros,* water, and *philic,* loving). Water molecules gather closely around any molecule that exhibits an electrical charge, whether a full charge (ion) or partial charge (polar molecule). When a salt crystal dissolves in water as you see happening in figure 2.14, what really happens is that individual ions break off from the crystal and become surrounded by water molecules. The partial positive charge of blue hydrogen atoms of water are attracted to the negative charge of the chloride ions and the partial negative charge of the red oxygen atoms are attracted to the positive charge of the sodium ions. Water molecules orient around each ion like a swarm of bees attracted to honey, and this shell of water molecules, called a *hydration shell,* prevents the ions from reassociating with the crystal. Similar shells of water form around all polar molecules, and polar molecules that dissolve in water in this way are said to be **soluble** in water.

Nonpolar molecules like oil do not form hydrogen bonds and are not water-soluble. When nonpolar molecules are placed in water, the water molecules shy away, instead forming hydrogen bonds with other water molecules. The nonpolar molecules are forced into association with one another, crowded together to minimize their disruption of the hydrogen bonding of water. It seems almost as if the nonpolar compounds shrink from contact with water, and for this reason they are called **hydrophobic** (from the Greek *hydros,* water, and *phobos,* fearing). Many biological structures are shaped by such hydrophobic forces, as will be discussed in chapter 3.

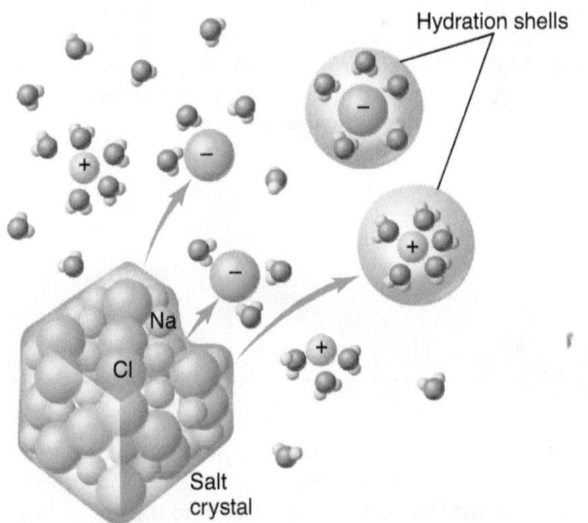

Figure 2.14 How salt dissolves in water.

Salt is soluble in water because the partial charges on water molecules are attracted to the charged sodium and chloride ions. The water molecules surround the ions, forming what are called hydration shells. When all of the ions have been separated from the crystal, the salt is said to be dissolved.

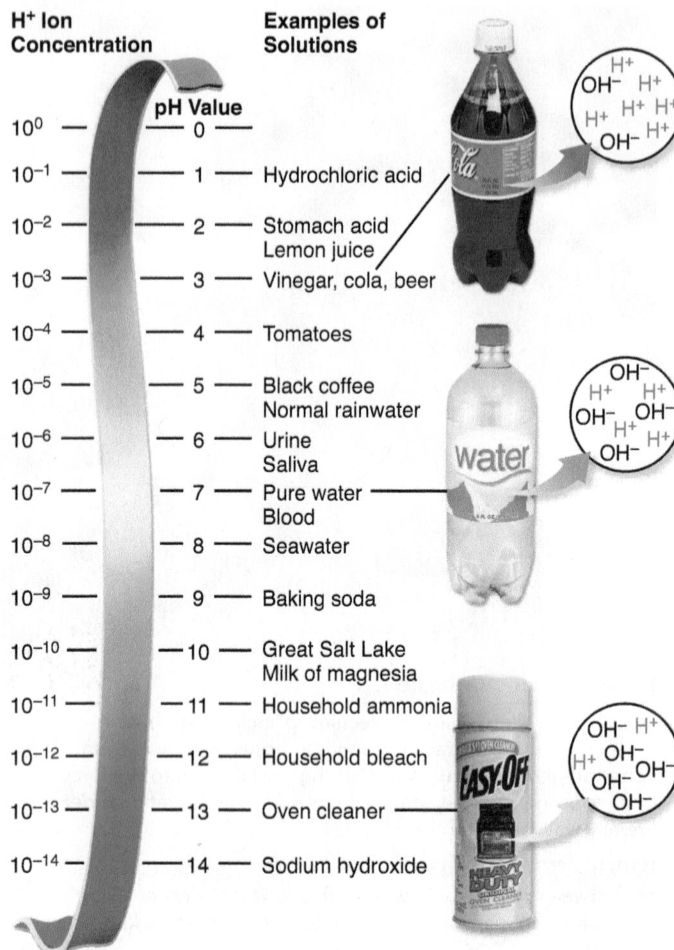

Figure 2.15 The pH scale.

A fluid is assigned a value according to the number of hydrogen ions present in a liter of that fluid. The scale is logarithmic, so that a change of only 1 means a 10-fold change in the concentration of hydrogen ions; thus lemon juice with a pH of 2 is 100 times more acidic than tomatoes with a pH of 4, and seawater is 10 times more basic than pure water.

BIOLOGY & YOU

Heartburn. Your stomach contains large amounts of hydrochloric acid, used to digest food. Sometimes this acid backs up from the stomach into the esophagus (the food pipe) stretching up from the stomach to the throat. This escape of acid from the stomach, called acid reflux, causes a painful burning sensation as the acid attacks the inner lining of the esophagus. Because the esophagus lies just behind the heart, the burning sensation is informally referred to as "heartburn." Nearly one-third of the adult population of the U.S. experiences acid reflux to some degree at least once a month. For minor heartburn you might take an antacid, such as Tums, which is a base that counteracts stomach acidity.

2.5 Water Ionizes

CONCEPT PREVIEW: A tiny fraction of water molecules spontaneously ionize at any moment, forming H^+ and OH^-. The pH of a solution is a measure of its H^+ concentration. Low pH values indicate high H^+ concentrations (acids), and high pH values indicate low H^+ concentrations (bases).

The covalent bonds within a water molecule sometimes break spontaneously. When it happens, a proton (hydrogen atom nuclei) dissociates from the molecule as a positively charged ion, *hydrogen ion* (H^+). The rest of the dissociated water molecule, which has retained the shared electron from the covalent bond, is a negatively charged *hydroxide ion* (OH^-).

$$\underset{\text{water}}{H_2O} \longleftrightarrow \underset{\text{hydroxide ion}}{OH^-} + \underset{\text{hydrogen ion}}{H^+}$$

pH

A convenient way to express the hydrogen ion concentration of a solution is to use the **pH scale** (figure 2.15). This scale ranges from 0 (highest hydrogen ion concentration) to 14 (lowest hydrogen ion concentration). Pure water has a pH of 7. Each pH unit represents a 10-fold change in hydrogen ion concentration. This means that a solution with a pH of 4 has *10 times* the H^+ concentration of one with a pH of 5, and *100 times* the H^+ concentration of one with a pH of 6.

Acids. Any substance that dissociates in water to increase the concentration of H^+ is called an **acid.** Acidic solutions have pH values below 7. The stronger an acid, the more H^+ and so the lower its pH. For example, hydrochloric acid (HCl), which is abundant in your stomach, ionizes completely in water, giving the solution a pH of 1.

Bases. A substance that combines with H^+ when dissolved in water is called a **base.** By combining with H^+, a base lowers the H^+ concentration in the solution. Basic (or alkaline) solutions, therefore, have pH values above 7. Very strong bases, such as sodium hydroxide (NaOH), have pH values of 12 or more.

Buffers

The pH inside almost all living cells, and in the fluid surrounding cells in multicellular organisms, is fairly close to 7. The many proteins that govern metabolism are all extremely sensitive to pH, and slight alterations in pH can cause the molecules to take on different shapes that disrupt their activities. For this reason, it is important that a cell maintain a constant pH level. The pH of your blood, for example, is 7.4, and you would survive only a few minutes if it were to fall to 7.0 or rise to 7.8.

What keeps an organism's pH constant? Cells contain chemical substances called **buffers** that minimize changes in concentrations of H^+ and OH^- by taking up or releasing hydrogen ions into solution as the hydrogen ion concentration of the solution changes. As the "Today's Biology" feature on the facing page explains, when acid in rain or snow exceeds the buffering capacity of a tree or other organism, death may result.

Concept Check

1. What is the difference between cohesion and adhesion?
2. What property of water makes it advantageous for an athlete to sweat?
3. When you drink a coke you are consuming an acid. Why doesn't your body's pH go down as a result?

Acid Rain

As you study biology, you will learn that hydrogen ions play many roles in the chemistry of life. When conditions become overly acidic—too many hydrogen ions—serious damage to organisms often results. One important example of this is acid precipitation, more informally called **acid rain.** Acid precipitation is just what it sounds like, the presence of acid in rain or snow. Where does the acid come from? Tall smokestacks from coal-burning power plants send smoke high into the atmosphere through these stacks, each of which is over 65 meters tall. The smoke the stacks belch out contains high concentrations of sulfur dioxide (SO_2), because the coal that the plants burn is rich in sulfur. The sulfur-rich smoke is dispersed and diluted by winds and air currents. Since the 1950s, such tall stacks have become popular in the United States and Europe—there are now over 800 of them in the United States alone.

In the 1970s, 20 years after the stacks were introduced, ecologists began to report evidence that the tall stacks were not eliminating the problems associated with the sulfur, just exporting the ill effects elsewhere. The lakes and forests of the Northeast suffered drastic drops in biodiversity, forests dying and lakes becoming devoid of life. It turned out that the SO_2 introduced into the upper atmosphere by high smokestacks combines with water vapor to produce sulfuric acid (H_2SO_4). When this water later falls back to earth as rain or snow, it carries the sulfuric acid with it. When schoolchildren measured the pH of natural rainwater as part of a nationwide project in 1989, rain and snow in the Northeast often had a pH as low as 2 or 3—more acidic than vinegar.

After accumulating in soils for over 50 years, the effects of acid rain are now only too evident. The impact of acid rain on forests first became apparent in the Northeast. Some 15% of the lakes in New England have become chronically acidic and are dying biologically as their pH levels fall to below 5.0. Many of the forests of the northeastern United States and Canada have also been seriously damaged. The trees in this photo show the ill effects of acid precipitation. In the last decades, acid added to forest soils has caused the loss from these soils of over half the essential plant nutrients, calcium and magnesium. Researchers blame excess acids for dissolving Ca^{++} and Mg^{++} ions into drainage waters much faster than weathering rocks can replenish them. Without them, trees stop growing and die.

Now, some 30 years later, acid rain effects are becoming apparent in the Southeast as well. Researchers suggest the reason for the delay is that southern soils are generally thicker than northern ones and thus able to sponge up far more acid. But now that southern forest soils are becoming saturated, they too are beginning to die. In a third of the southeastern streams studied, fish are declining or already gone.

The solution is straightforward: capture and remove the emissions instead of releasing them into the atmosphere. Progressively tougher pollution laws over the past three decades have reduced U.S. emissions of sulfur dioxide by about 40% from its 1973 peak of 28.8 metric tons a year. Despite this significant progress, much remains to be done. Unless levels are cut further, researchers predict forests may not recover for centuries.

An informed public will be essential. While textbook treatments have in the past tended to minimize the impact of this issue on students ("the vast majority of North American forests are not suffering substantially from acid precipitation"), it is important that we face the issue squarely and support continued efforts to address this serious problem.

Inquiry & Analysis

Using Radioactive Decay to Date the Iceman

In the fall of 1991, sticking out of the melting snow on the crest of a high pass near the mountainous border between Italy and Austria, two Austrian hikers found a corpse. Right away it was clear the body was very old, frozen in an icy trench where he had sought shelter long ago and only now released as the ice melted. In the years since this startling find, scientists have learned a great deal about the dead man, who they named Ötzi. They know his age, his health, the clothing he wore, what he ate, and that he died from an arrow that ripped through his back. Its tip is still embedded in the back of his left shoulder. From the distribution of chemicals in his teeth and bones, we know he lived his life within 60 kilometers of where he died.

When did this Iceman die? Scientists answered this key question by measuring the degree of decay of the short-lived carbon isotope ^{14}C in Ötzi's body. While most carbon atoms are the stable isotope ^{12}C, a tiny proportion are the unstable radioactive isotope ^{14}C, created by the bombardment of nitrogen-14 (^{14}N) atoms with cosmic rays. This proportion of ^{14}C is captured by plants in photosynthesis and is present in the carbon molecules of the animal's body that eats the plant. After the plant or animal dies, it no longer accumulates any more carbon, and the ^{14}C present at the time of death decays over time back to ^{14}N. Over time the ratio of ^{14}C to ^{12}C decreases. It takes 5,730 years for half of the ^{14}C present to decay, a length of time called the **half-life** of the ^{14}C isotope. Because the half-life is a constant that never changes, the extent of radioactive decay allows you to date a sample. Thus a sample that had one quarter of its original proportion of ^{14}C remaining would be approximately 11,460 years old (two half-lives).

The graph to the right displays the radioactive decay curve of the carbon isotope ^{14}C. Scientists know it takes 5,730 years for half of the ^{14}C present in a sample to decay to nitrogen-14 (^{14}N). When Ötzi's carbon isotopes were analyzed, researchers determined that the ratio of ^{14}C to ^{12}C (a **ratio** is the size of one variable relative to another), also written as the fraction $^{14}C/^{12}C$, in Ötzi's body was 0.435 of the fraction found in tissues of a person who has recently died.

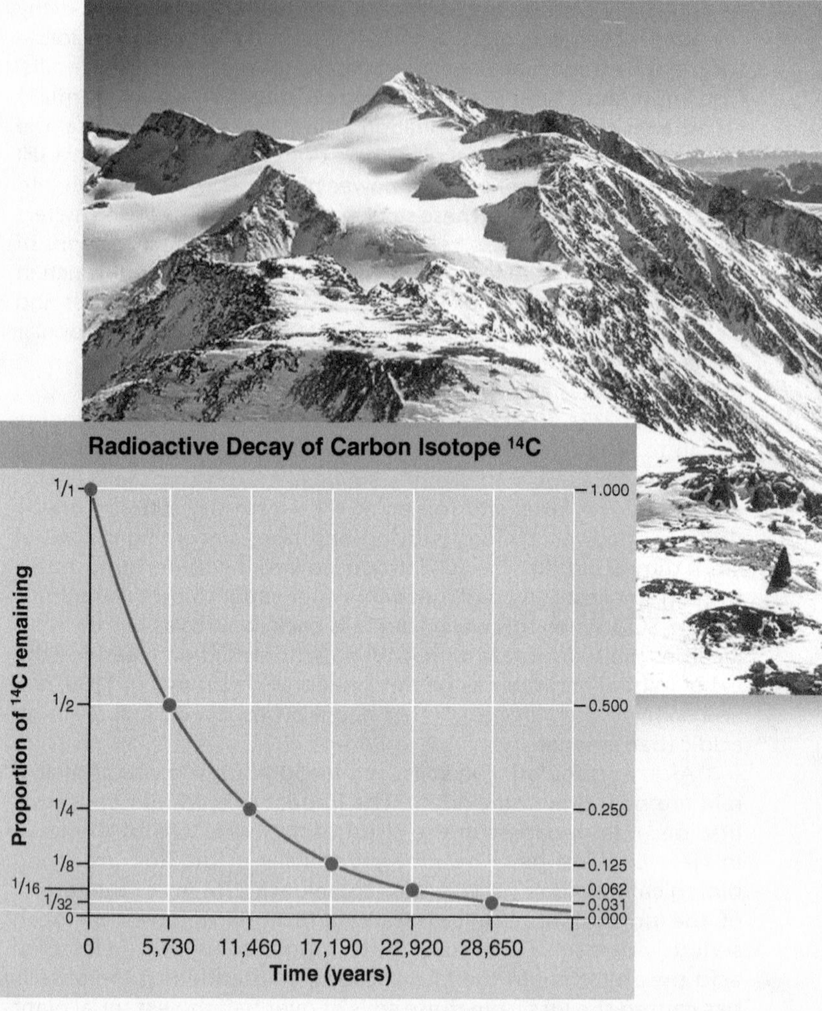

Analysis

1. **Applying Concepts** What proportion (a **proportion** is the size of a variable relative to the whole) of the ^{14}C present in Ötzi's body when he died is still there today? When he died, it would have been 1.0.
2. **Interpreting Data** Plot this proportion on the ^{14}C radioactive decay curve above. How many half-lives does this point represent?
3. **Making Inferences** If Ötzi were indeed a recent corpse, made to look old by the harsh weather conditions found on the high mountain pass, what would you expect the ratio of ^{14}C to ^{12}C to be, relative to that in your own body?
4. **Drawing Conclusions** When did Ötzi the Iceman die?

Concept Summary

Some Simple Chemistry

2.1 Atoms

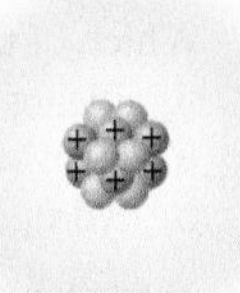

- An atom is the smallest particle that retains the chemical properties of its substance. Atoms contain a core nucleus of protons and neutrons; electrons spin around the nucleus (**figure 2.2**). The number of electrons equals the number of protons in an atom.
- The number of protons in an atom is called its atomic number. The mass that is contributed by the protons and neutrons is called the atom's mass number. All atoms that have the same atomic number are said to be the same element.
- Protons are positively charged particles and neutron particles carry no charge. Electrons are negatively charged particles that orbit around the nucleus at different energy levels. Electrons determine the chemical behavior of an atom because they are the subatomic particles that interact with other atoms.
- It takes energy to hold the electrons in their orbits; this energy of position is called potential energy. The amount of potential energy of an electron is based on its distance from the nucleus (**figure 2.3**).
- Most electron shells hold up to eight electrons and atoms will undergo chemical reactions in order to fill the outermost electron shell, either by gaining, losing, or sharing electrons (**figure 2.4**).

2.2 Ions and Isotopes

- Ions are atoms that have either gained one or more electrons (negative ions called anions) or lost one or more electrons (positive ions called cations) (**figure 2.5**).
- Isotopes are atoms that have the same number of protons but differing numbers of neutrons (**figure 2.6**). Isotopes tend to be unstable and break up into other elements through a process called radioactive decay. Some isotopes have applications in medicine (**figure 2.7**).

2.3 Molecules

- Molecules form when atoms are held together with energy. The force holding atoms together is called a chemical bond. There are three main types of chemical bonds.
- Ionic bonds form when ions of opposite charge are attracted to each other. Table salt is formed by ionic bonds between positive sodium ions and negative chloride ions (**figure 2.8**).
- Covalent bonds form when two atoms share electrons, attempting to fill empty electron orbitals (**figure 2.9**). Covalent bonds are stronger when more electrons are shared. The sharing of two pairs of electrons in a double covalent bond, shown here from **figure 2.10,** is stronger then a single covalent bond, and a triple bond is even stronger.

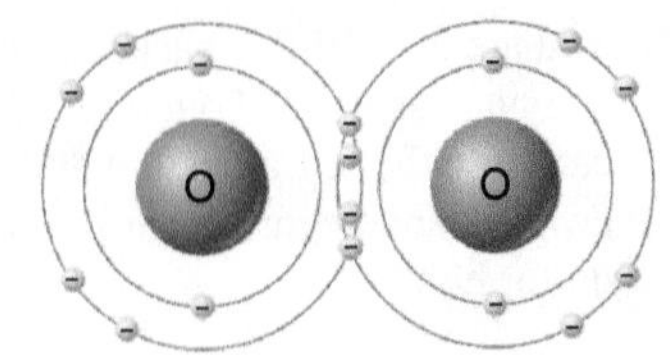

- Hydrogen bonds form between polar molecules. The atoms in a polar molecule are held together by covalent bonds in which the shared electrons are unevenly distributed around their nuclei, giving the molecule a slightly positive end and a slightly negative end. Hydrogen bonds form when the positive end of one molecule is attracted to the negative end of another (**figure 2.11**).
- Weak chemical attractions, called van der Waals forces, can hold two atoms together temporarily when they come into contact. However, van der Waals forces are not considered chemical bonds.

Water: Cradle of Life

2.4 Hydrogen Bonds Give Water Unique Properties

- Water molecules are polar molecules that form hydrogen bonds with each other and with other polar molecules. Many of the physical properties of water are attributed to hydrogen bonding.
- Water molecules held together through hydrogen bonding are more difficult to separate, and as a result a significant amount of heat energy is needed to pull the molecules apart. For this reason, water heats up slowly and holds it temperature longer.
- The hydrogen bonds that hold water molecules together become more stable at lower temperatures and as a result they lock water molecules into place in solid crystal structures called ice, such as that shown here from **figure 2.12.** Individual water molecules maintain a set distance from neighboring molecules due to the stable formation of the hydrogen bonds. In liquid water, hydrogen bonds break and reform, allowing individual water molecules more movement, bringing them into closer proximity to each other. This results in a substance that is more dense than ice.
- In order for water to vaporize into a gas, a significant input of heat energy is needed to break the hydrogen bonds. This high heat of vaporization is a property of water used by our bodies in regulating body temperature.
- Because water molecules are polar molecules, they will form hydrogen bonds with other polar molecules. If the other polar molecules are water molecules, the process is called cohesion (**figure 2.13**). If the other polar molecules are some other substance, the process is called adhesion.
- When water molecules form hydrogen bonds with other polar molecules, water molecules will tend to surround other polar molecules, forming a barrier around them called a hydration shell. Polar molecules are said to be hydrophilic and are water-soluble (**figure 2.14**). Nonpolar molecules do not form hydrogen bonds and will cluster together when placed in water. They are said to be hydrophobic and are water-insoluble.

2.5 Water Ionizes

- Water molecules dissociate forming negatively charged hydroxide ions (OH^-) and positively charged hydrogen ions (H^+). This property of water is significant because the concentration of H^+ in a solution determines its pH and effects its chemical properties.
- A solution with a higher H^+ concentration is an acid and has a pH below 7. A solution with a lower H^+ concentration is a base and has a pH above 7 (**figure 2.15**). A buffer is a chemical substance that minimizes changes in pH by taking up excess H^+ in acidic solution, or releasing H^+ in basic solutions.

Self-Test

1. The smallest particle into which a substance can be divided and still retain all of its chemical properties is
   a. matter.
   b. an atom.
   c. a molecule.
   d. mass.
2. An atom that has gained or lost one or more electrons is
   a. an isotope.
   b. a neutron.
   c. an ion.
   d. radioactive.
3. Atoms are held together by a force called a bond. The three types of bonds are
   a. positive, negative, and neutral.
   b. hydrophobic, hydrophilic, and van der Waals interactions.
   c. magnetic, electric, and radioactive.
   d. ionic, covalent, and hydrogen.
4. Carbon has four electrons in its outer electron shell, therefore
   a. it has a completely filled outer electron shell.
   b. it can form four single covalent bonds.
   c. it does not react with any other atom.
   d. it has a positive charge.
5. The partial separation of charge in the water molecule
   a. results from the electrons' greater attraction to the oxygen atom.
   b. means the molecule has a positive end and a negative end.
   c. indicates that the water molecule is a polar molecule.
   d. All of these are correct.
6. Water has some very unusual properties. These properties occur because of the
   a. hydrogen bonds between the individual water molecules.
   b. covalent bonds between the individual water molecules.
   c. hydrogen bonds within each individual water molecule.
   d. ionic bonds between the individual water molecules.
7. Which of the following properties are somehow related to the need for significant heat energy to break hydrogen bonds?
   a. cohesion and adhesion
   b. hydrophobic and hydrophilic
   c. heat storage and heat of vaporization
   d. ice formation and high polarity
8. The attraction of water molecules to other water molecules is called
   a. cohesion.
   b. capillary action.
   c. solubility.
   d. adhesion.
9. Water sometimes ionizes, a single molecule breaking apart into a hydrogen ion and a hydroxide ion. Other materials may dissociate in water, resulting in either (1) an increase of hydrogen ions or (2) decrease of hydrogen ions in the solution. We call the results
   a. (1) acids and (2) bases.
   b. (1) bases and (2) acids.
   c. (1) neutral solutions and (2) neutronic solutions.
   d. (1) hydrogen solutions and (2) hydroxide solutions.
10. Which of the following is *not* true about buffers?
    a. A buffer takes up H^+ from the solution.
    b. A buffer keeps the pH relatively constant.
    c. A buffer stops water from ionizing.
    d. A buffer releases H^+ into the solution.

Visual Understanding

1. **Figure 2.11*a*** This figure shows an oxygen atom forming covalent bonds with two hydrogen atoms. A carbon atom, like oxygen, has two electrons in its innermost shell, but only four electrons in its outermost shell. Using this water molecule and figure 2.10 as guides, draw a diagram showing how carbon forms covalent bonds with two oxygen atoms in a carbon dioxide (CO_2) molecule.

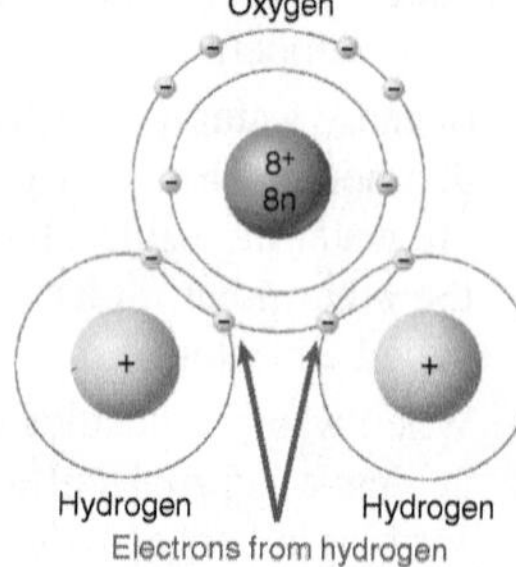

2. **Figure 2.13** How can these things—drops of water clinging to a web and insects walking on water—occur?

Challenge Questions

1. What results if an atom gains or loses electrons? What results if an atom gains or loses neutrons? What results if an atom gains or loses protons?
2. You are on a 10-day backpacking trip with a small group of friends. Yvonne has washed out a set of water bottles with bleach. Before she can rinse them, Carlos, hot and thirsty, picks one up and drinks it, drops it, and begins to choke. What is the problem, and what can you do for him?

Chapter 3

Molecules of Life

CHAPTER AT A GLANCE

Forming Macromolecules

Nutrition Facts

Serving Size 2 tbsp (33g) (makes 3.5 cups popped)
Servings Per Bag about 3
Servings Per Box about 9

Amount Per Serving	2 tbsp (33g) Unpopped	Per 1 cup Popped
Calories	170	35
Calories from Fat	90	20
	% Daily Value**	
Total Fat 10g*	15%	3%
Saturated Fat 2g	10%	0%
Trans Fat 3.5g		
Cholesterol 0mg	0%	0%
Sodium 440mg	18%	4%
Total Carbohydrate 19g	6%	1%
Dietary Fiber 3g	12%	4%
Sugars 0g		
Protein 3g		
Iron	6%	0%

Figure 3.1 What's in a nutritional label?

Fats, cholesterol, carbohydrates, and proteins are just some of the molecules found in popcorn and in other foods and are discussed in this chapter.

Group	Structural Formula	Ball-and-Stick Model	Found In
Hydroxyl	—OH	O–H	Carbohydrates
Carbonyl	>C=O	C=O	Lipids
Carboxyl	—C(=O)OH	C, O, O–H	Proteins
Amino	—N(H)H	N, H, H	Proteins
Phosphate	—O—P(O⁻)(=O)—O⁻	O, P, O⁻, O⁻, O	DNA, ATP

Figure 3.2 Five principal functional groups.

These functional groups can be transferred from one molecule to another and are common in organic molecules.

IMPLICATION: Which chemical elements appear to be common in organic molecules, based on these functional groups?

3.1 Polymers Are Built of Monomers

CONCEPT PREVIEW: Macromolecules are formed by linking subunits together into long chains. The chemical reaction involves removing a water molecule as each link is formed. Macromolecules are broken down into their subunits by adding the water molecules back.

The bodies of organisms contain thousands of different kinds of molecules and atoms. Organisms obtain many of these molecules from their surroundings and from what they consume. You might be familiar with some of the substances listed on nutritional labels, such as the one shown in figure 3.1. But what do the words on these labels mean? Some of them are names of minerals, such as calcium and iron (discussed in chapters 23, 25, 32). Others are vitamins, which are discussed in chapter 26. Still others are the subject of this chapter: large molecules that are found in our food and that make up the bodies of organisms, such as proteins, carbohydrates (including sugars), and lipids (including, fats, trans fats, saturated fats, and cholesterol). These molecules, called *organic molecules,* are formed by living organisms and consist of a carbon-based core with special groups attached. These groups of atoms have special chemical properties and are referred to as *functional groups.* Functional groups, like those listed in figure 3.2, tend to act as units during chemical reactions and confer specific chemical properties on the molecules that possess them.

The bodies of organisms contain thousands of different kinds of organic molecules, but much of the body is made of just four kinds: *proteins, nucleic acids, carbohydrates,* and *lipids.* Called **macromolecules** because they can be very large, these four are the building materials of cells, the "bricks and mortar" that make up the body of a cell and the machinery that runs within it.

Macromolecules are assembled by sticking smaller bits, called **monomers,** together much as a train is built by linking rail-cars together. A molecule built up of long chains of similar subunits is called a **polymer.**

Making (and Breaking) Macromolecules

The four different kinds of macromolecules (proteins, nucleic acids, carbohydrates, and lipids) are built from different monomers, as shown in figure 3.3, but all have their subunits put together in the same way. A covalent bond is formed between two subunits in which a hydroxyl group (OH) is removed from one subunit and a hydrogen (H) is removed from the other. This process, illustrated in figure 3.4*a*, is called *dehydration synthesis* because, in effect, the removal of the OH and H groups (highlighted by the blue oval) constitutes removal of a molecule of water—the word *dehydration* means "taking away water." This process requires the help of a special class of proteins called **enzymes** to facilitate the positioning of the molecules so that the correct chemical bonds are stressed and broken. The process of tearing down a molecule

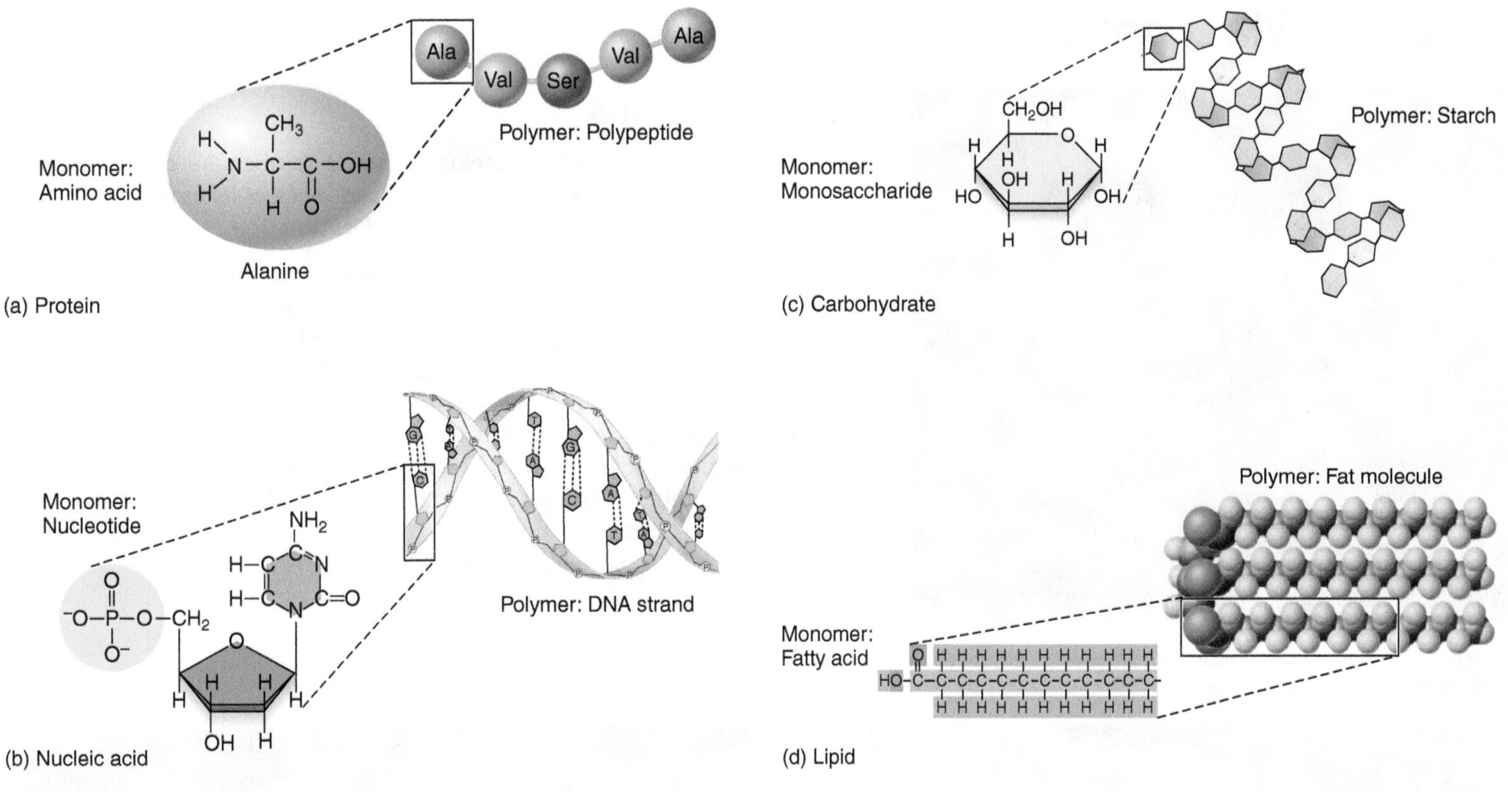

Figure 3.3 Polymers are built from monomers.

Each macromolecule polymer is built from different monomers. (a) A protein polymer, called a polypeptide, is built from amino acid monomers. (b) A nucleic acid polymer, such as a strand of DNA, is built from nucleotide monomers. (c) A carbohydrate polymer, such as a starch molecule, is built from monosaccharide monomers. (d) A lipid polymer, such as a fat molecule, is built from fatty acids.

such as the protein or fat contained in the food you eat is essentially the reverse of dehydration synthesis: instead of removing a water molecule, one is added. When a water molecule comes in, as shown in figure 3.4*b*, a hydrogen becomes attached to one subunit and a hydroxyl to another, and the covalent bond is broken. The breaking up of a polymer in this way is called **hydrolysis.**

Recall from page 40 that water molecules will undergo a process of ionization, where the molecule dissociates into H^+ and OH^- ions. Enzymes can help facilitate this process thereby facilitating dehydration and hydrolysis reactions in the cell.

Concept Check

1. What type of atom makes up the core in all organic molecules?
2. Which functional group is not present in either proteins or carbohydrates?
3. When subunits link together to form a polymer, what molecule is produced as a by-product?

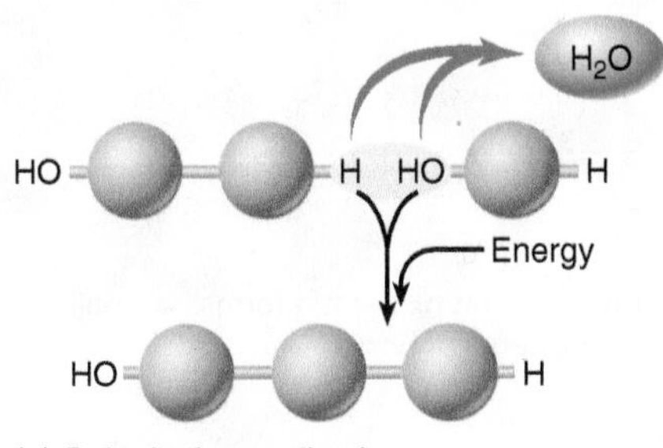

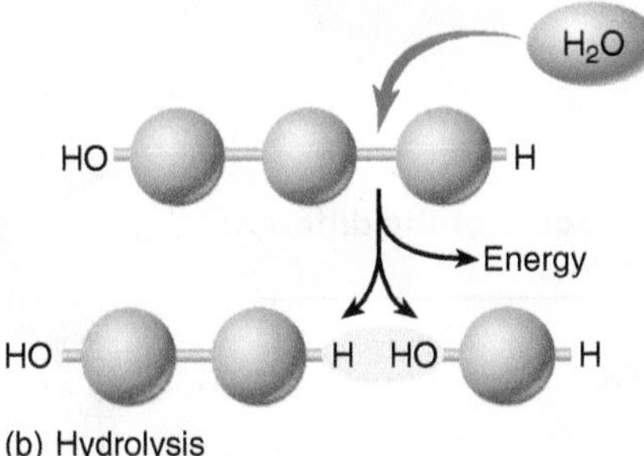

Figure 3.4 Dehydration and hydrolysis.

(a) Biological molecules are formed by linking subunits with a covalent bond in a dehydration synthesis, during which a water molecule is released. (b) Breaking such a bond requires the addition of a water molecule, a reaction called hydrolysis.

Types of Macromolecules

3.2 Proteins

CONCEPT PREVIEW: Proteins are made up of chains of amino acids that fold into complex shapes. The sequence of its amino acids determines a protein's structure and its function.

Complex macromolecules called **proteins** are important biological macromolecules within the bodies of all organisms. One of the most important types of proteins are *enzymes,* which have the key role in cells of helping to carry out particular chemical reactions. Other proteins play structural roles. Cartilage, bones, and tendons all contain a structural protein called collagen. Keratin, another structural protein, forms hair, the horns of a rhinoceros, and feathers. Still other proteins act as chemical messengers within the brain and throughout the body. Figure 3.5 presents an overview of the wide-ranging functions of proteins.

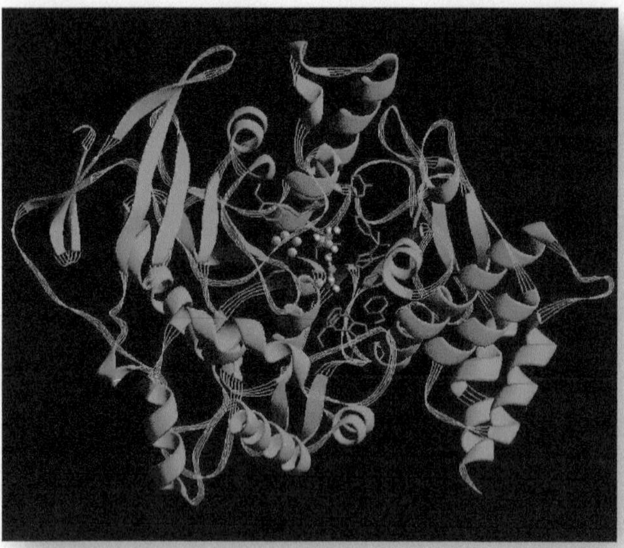

(a) Enzymes: Globular proteins called enzymes play a key role in many chemical reactions. This is a computer model of an enzyme.

(b) Structural proteins (keratin): Keratin forms hair, nails, feathers, and components of horns.

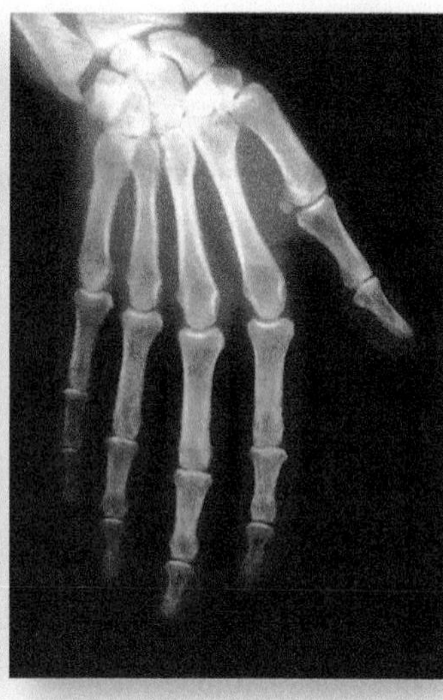

(c) Structural proteins (collagen): Collagen is present in bones, tendons, and cartilage.

(d) Contractile proteins: Proteins called actin and myosin are present in muscles.

Figure 3.5 Some of the different types of proteins.

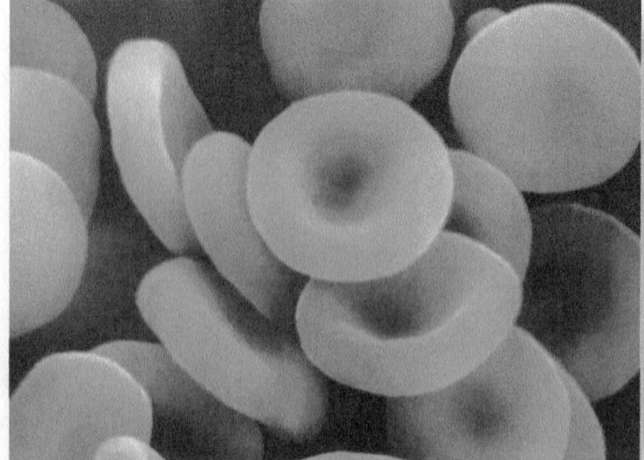

(e) Transport proteins: Red blood cells contain the protein hemoglobin, which transports oxygen in the body.

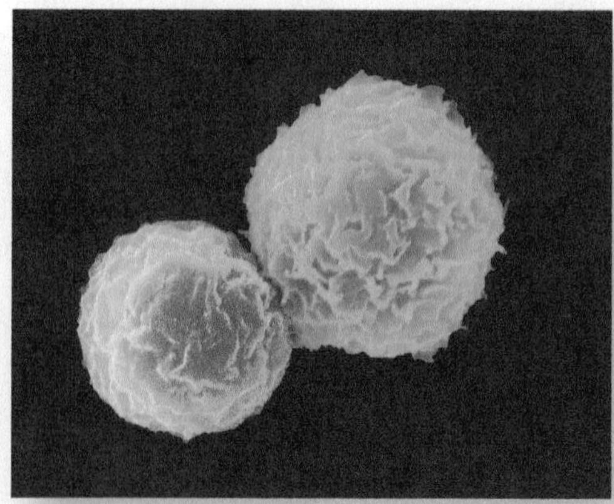

(f) Defensive proteins: White blood cells destroy foreign cells in the body and make antibody proteins that attack invaders.

Amino Acids

Despite their diverse functions, all proteins have the same basic structure: a long polymer chain made of subunits called amino acids. Amino acids are small molecules with a simple basic structure: a central carbon atom attached to an amino group (—NH_2), a carboxyl group (—COOH), a hydrogen atom (H), and a functional group, designated "R" (figure 3.6).

Amino acid

Amino group

Carboxyl group

Figure 3.6 Basic structure of an amino acid.

There are 20 common amino acids that differ from one another by the identity of their functional R group. The R group of an amino acid largely determines its chemical properties. Some amino acid R groups are polar, interacting with water; some are nonpolar, shying away from water; and others have special chemical groups that are important in forming links between protein chains or in forming kinks in their shapes.

Linking Amino Acids

An individual protein is made by linking specific amino acids together in a particular order, just as a word is made by putting letters of the alphabet together in a particular order. The covalent bond linking two amino acids together is called a **peptide bond.** You can see in figure 3.7 that a water molecule is released as the peptide bond forms. Long chains of amino acids linked by peptide bonds are called **polypeptides.** Functional polypeptides are more commonly called proteins. The keratin in human hair is a kind of protein.

A peptide bond, like all covalent bonds discussed on page 35, involves the sharing of electrons between atoms. The carbon atom from the carboxyl group of one amino acid shares electrons with the nitrogen atom from the amino group of another amino acid.

IN THE NEWS

Deadly Baby Food. Babies the world over live on milk, rich in proteins, fats, and other nutrients. In China in 2008 thousands of babies became critically ill from the formula they were fed. Why did they get sick? The manufacturer of the baby formula purchased the milk used to make the formula from milk traders. The milk traders buy raw milk from small farmers and mix it together to resell. In order to maximize their profits, some traders were adding water to the milk to increase their volumes. Manufacturers in China routinely check the protein level of milk by measuring the amount of nitrogen the milk contains. Protein is the only significant source of nitrogen in milk and so nitrogen is an indicator of the levels of protein. Diluted milk would reveal lower than normal amounts of nitrogen and so would be rejected. To get around this, some traders added the chemical melamine to their diluted milk. Used in making plastics and fertilizers, melamine ($C_3H_6N_6$) is rich in nitrogen, allowing the diluted milk to fool the manufacturers' test. Tragically, melamine causes kidney failure in infants. In the United States commercial milk is checked more carefully. In the future it will be checked in China as well.

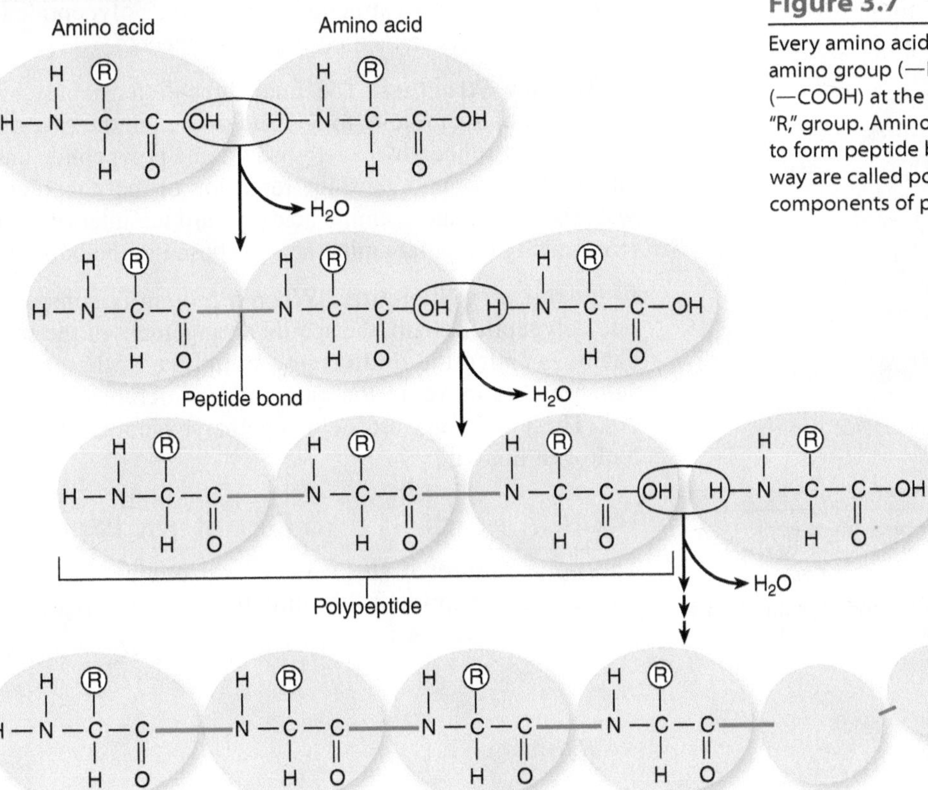

Figure 3.7 The formation of a peptide bond.

Every amino acid has the same basic structure, with an amino group (—NH_2) at one end and a carboxyl group (—COOH) at the other. The only variable is the functional, or "R," group. Amino acids are linked by dehydration synthesis to form peptide bonds. Chains of amino acids linked in this way are called polypeptides and are the basic structural components of proteins, such as keratin in human hair.

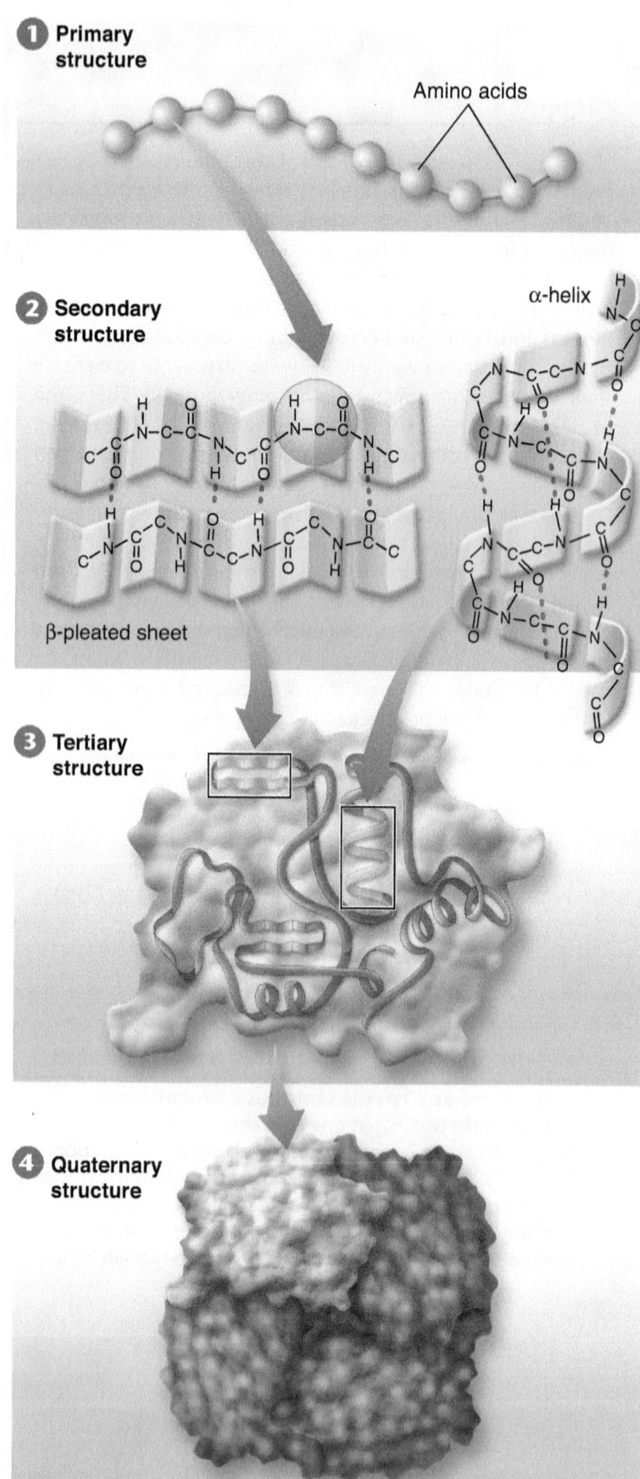

Figure 3.8 Levels of protein structure.

The *primary structure* of a protein is its sequence of amino acids. Twisting or pleating of the chain of amino acids, called *secondary structure*, is due to the formation of localized hydrogen bonds (the *red* dotted lines) within the chain. More complex folding of the chain is referred to as *tertiary structure*. Two or more polypeptide chains associated together form a *quaternary structure*.

Protein Structure

Some proteins form long, thin fibers, whereas others are globular, with the long strands of polypeptides coiled up and folded back on themselves or intertwined with other polypeptides. The shape of a protein is very important because it determines the protein's function. If we picture a polypeptide as a long strand similar to a strand of yarn, a protein might be the sweater knitted from it. Importantly, the sequence of amino acids in a polypeptide determines the protein's structure. There are four general levels of protein structure: primary, secondary, tertiary, and quaternary (figure 3.8).

❶ **Primary Structure.** The sequence of amino acids of a polypeptide chain is termed the polypeptide's **primary structure.** The amino acids are linked together by peptide bonds, forming long chains like the "beaded strand" at the top of figure 3.8. The primary structure of a protein, the sequence of its amino acids, determines all other levels of protein structure.

❷ **Secondary Structure.** Because some of the amino acids are nonpolar and others are polar, a polypeptide chain folds up in solution as the nonpolar regions are forced together. To understand this, recall the polar properties of water. Water is a polar molecule that is attracted to and forms hydrogen bonds with other polar molecules but repels nonpolar molecules. This polar attraction and repulsion will push nonpolar amino acid functional groups away from the watery environment, leaving the polar amino acid functional groups to interact with water molecules and each other. Hydrogen bonds forming between different parts of the chain then stabilize the folding of the polypeptide. As you can see in ❷, these stabilizing hydrogen bonds do not involve the R groups themselves, but rather the polypeptide backbone. This initial folding is called the **secondary structure** of a protein. Hydrogen bonding within this secondary structure can fold the polypeptide into coils, called α-helices, and sheets, called β-pleated sheets.

Hydrogen bonding, as discussed on page 36, occurs between polar molecules. The polar portions of the amino acids that are in close proximity are held in place with hydrogen bonds.

❸ **Tertiary Structure.** The final three-dimensional shape, or **tertiary structure,** of the protein, folded and twisted in the case of a globular molecule, is determined by exactly where in a polypeptide chain the nonpolar amino acids occur. Again, the repulsion of the nonpolar amino acids by water will force these amino acids toward the interior of the globular protein, leaving the polar amino acids exposed to the outside.

❹ **Quaternary Structure.** When a protein is composed of more than one polypeptide chain, the spatial arrangement of the several component chains is called the **quaternary structure** of the protein, like the four subunits that make up the quaternary structure of the protein in figure 3.8. These subunits are held together by noncovalent forces, such as hydrogen bonding.

Protein Folding and Denaturation

The polar nature of the watery environment in the cell influences how the polypeptide folds into the functional protein. The protein in figure 3.9 is folded in such a way that allows it to carry out its function. If the polar nature of the protein's environment changes by either increasing temperature or lowering pH, both of which alter hydrogen bonding, the protein may unfold, as in the lower right of the figure. When this happens the protein is said to be *denatured.* When proteins are denatured, they usually lose their ability to function properly. When the polar nature of the solvent is reestablished, some proteins may spontaneously refold, but most don't. Cooking an egg is an example of denaturing proteins that do not refold. The egg proteins denature as temperature increases, but do not refold as the egg cools down—they are permanently denatured. Protein denaturation is also the rationale behind traditional methods of preserving food. Prior to the ready availability of refrigerators and freezers, a practical way to keep microorganisms from growing in food was to keep the food in a solution containing a high concentration of vinegar, a treatment called pickling. The low pH of the vinegar denatures proteins in microorganisms and so keeps them from growing on the food.

You will discover on page 92 how enzyme function is affected by temperature and pH. Most enzymes have optimal ranges of temperature and pH. Conditions above or below their ranges can interfere with enzyme function.

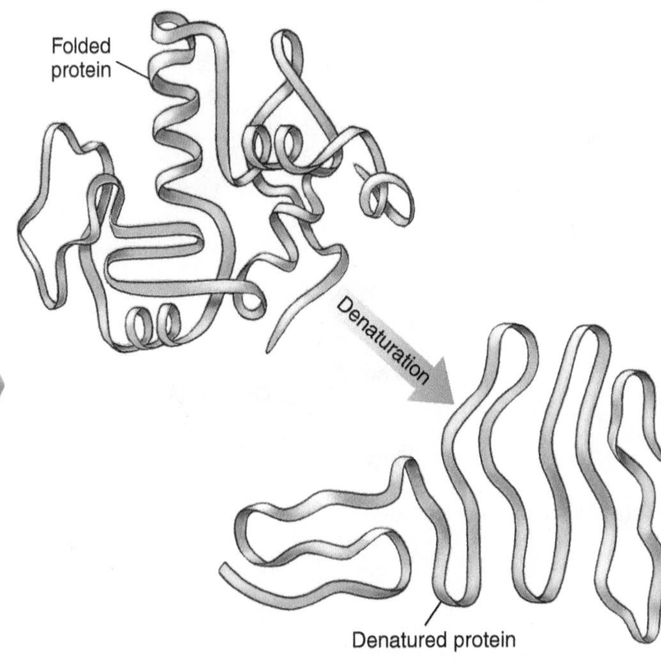

Figure 3.9 Protein denaturation.

Changes in a protein's environment, such as variations in temperature or pH, can cause a protein to unfold and lose its shape in a process called denaturation. In this denatured state, proteins are biologically inactive.

IMPLICATION A tiger can eat raw meat with relish, but most of us humans prefer our steak cooked. Is this just a matter of taste, or does cooking meat before eating it have any benefit?

Protein Structure Determines Function

The three dimensional shape of a protein determines its function. For example, many structural proteins assume long cable-like shapes that let them play architectural roles within cells. The spiderweb-like structures you see in figure 3.10*a* are such structural proteins, tagged so that they are visible through a microscope. The cables that these proteins form within the cell help maintain the cell's shape, and also function as rails through the interior used to rapidly transport materials from one area to another.

Globular proteins are polypeptides that fold and twist into complex three-dimensional shapes, and for them to function properly they need to fold correctly. *Enzymes* are globular proteins that help particular chemical reactions to occur in the cell. When the polypeptide folds correctly the enzyme surface has a groove or depression that precisely fits a particular molecule. For example, the red molecule binding to the groove on the surface of the enzyme in figure 3.10*b* is a sugar. Once within the groove, the molecule is induced to undergo a chemical reaction, such as the formation or breaking of one of its covalent bonds. By bringing two atoms close together, an enzyme can make it easier for them to share electrons and form covalent bonds. Other enzymes function by positioning a molecule so that there is stress on a particular bond so that it breaks. To better understand this, consider a high-heel shoe or boot. It is structured so that your foot fits into it, but (as anyone who has worn one knows) the foot is stressed by the shape of the shoe. An enzyme chemically stresses a molecule lying within a groove on its surface.

Because the primary structure of a protein (its sequence of amino acids) determines how the protein folds into its functional shape, a change in the identity of even one amino acid can have profound effects on a protein's ability to function properly.

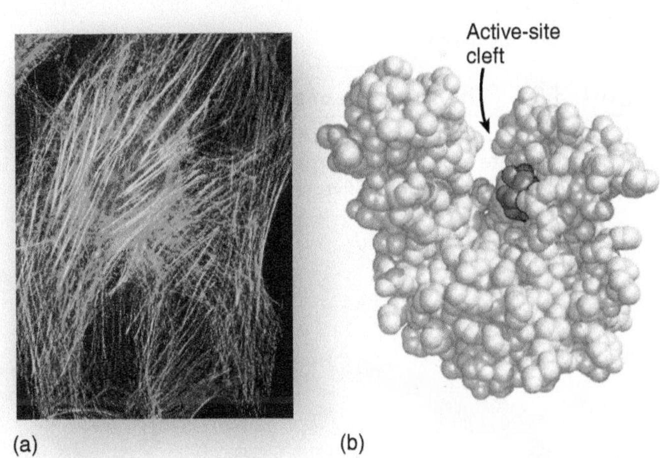

Figure 3.10 Protein structure determines function.

(a) Fluorescently-labeled structural proteins within a cell.
(b) Enzymes are globular proteins that aid chemical reactions in the cell. This enzyme (*blue*) has a deep groove that binds a specific chemical (*red*) at a site on the enzyme called the active site.

Nitrogenous base

Phosphate group

OH in RNA

H in DNA

Sugar

(a) Structure of nucleotide

Adenine

Guanine

Cytosine

Thymine (DNA only)

Uracil (RNA only)

(b) Nitrogenous bases

Figure 3.11 The structure of a nucleotide.

(a) Nucleotides are composed of three parts: a five-carbon sugar, a phosphate group, and an organic nitrogenous base. The nitrogenous base can be one of five, shown in (b).

3.3 Nucleic Acids

CONCEPT PREVIEW: Nucleic acids like DNA are composed of long chains of nucleotides. The sequence of nucleotides in a DNA molecule specifies the amino acid sequence of proteins.

Very long polymers called nucleic acids serve as the genetic information storage devices of cells, just as DVDs or hard drives store the information that computers use. Nucleic acids are long polymers of repeating subunits called **nucleotides.** Each nucleotide is a complex organic molecule composed of three parts shown in figure 3.11*a:* a five-carbon sugar (in blue), a phosphate group (in yellow, PO_4), and an organic nitrogen-containing base (in orange). In the formation of a nucleic acid, the individual sugars are linked through dehydration reactions with the phosphate groups forming very long polynucleotide chains. The nitrogenous bases extend out from the backbone of the chain.

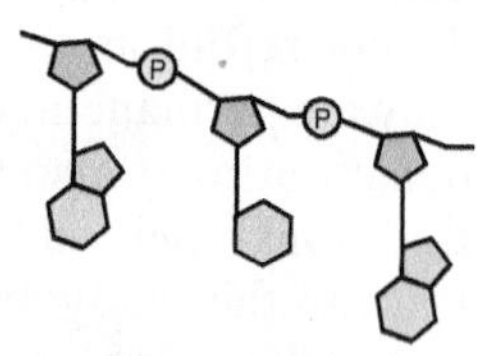

How does the long, chainlike structure of a nucleic acid permit it to store the information necessary to specify what an organism is like? If nucleic acids were simply a monotonous repeating polymer, it could not encode the message of life. Imagine trying to write a story using only the letter *E* and no spaces or punctuation. All you could ever say is "EEEEEEE. . . ." You need more than one letter to communicate—the English alphabet uses 26 letters. Nucleic acids can encode information because they contain more than one kind of nucleotide. There are five different nucleotides found in nucleic acids: two larger ones that contain the nitrogenous bases adenine and guanine (shown in the top row of figure 3.11*b*), and three smaller ones (in the bottom row) that contain the nitrogenous bases cytosine, thymine, and uracil. Nucleic acids encode information by varying the identity of the nucleotide at each position in the polymer.

DNA and RNA

Nucleic acids come in two varieties, **deoxyribonucleic acid (DNA)** and **ribonucleic acid (RNA),** both are polymers of nucleotides but they have different functions in the cell and they differ in their structures. RNA is similar to DNA, but with two major chemical differences. First, RNA molecules contain the sugar ribose in which four of the five carbons bond to a hydroxyl group (—OH). In DNA, one of the hydroxyl groups is replaced with a hydrogen atom (this is the carbon labeled 2′ in figure 3.11*a*). Second, DNA contains the thymine nucleotide, RNA molecules do not; they

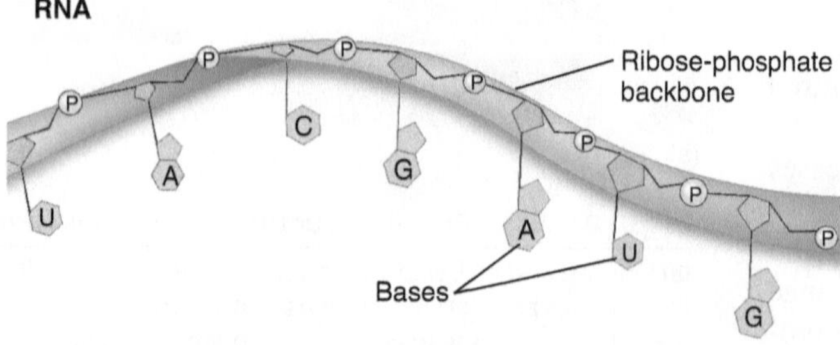

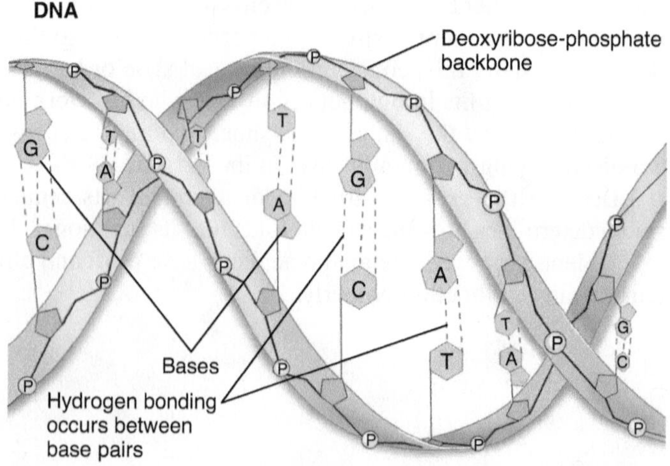

Figure 3.12 How DNA structure differs from RNA.

RNA is a single-strand of nucleotides (*left*), while DNA (*right*) contains two polynucleotide strands wrapped around each other.

contain the uracil nucleotide instead. Structurally, RNA is also different. RNA is a long, single strand of nucleotides (on the left in figure 3.12) while DNA consists of *two* polynucleotide chains wound around each other in a double helix, like strands of a pearl necklace twisted together (shown on the right in figure 3.12). They also have different roles to play in the cell. DNA stores the genetic information that determines what a cell is like. The sequence of nucleotides in DNA determines the order of amino acids in the primary structure of the protein. However, the DNA doesn't convey this information directly, rather RNA carries this information from the DNA to the protein-making machinery in the cell.

The Double Helix

How does DNA form a double helix? When scientists looked carefully at the structure of DNA, they found that the bases of each chain point inward toward the other (like the DNA strands shown in figure 3.13). The bases of the two chains are linked in the middle of the molecule by hydrogen bonds (the dotted lines between the two strands), like two columns of people holding hands across. The key to understanding the double helix structure of DNA is revealed by looking at the nucleotide bases: *only two base pairs are possible.* Because the distance between the two strands is consistent, this suggests that two big bases cannot pair together—the combination is simply too bulky to fit; similarly, two little ones cannot pair, as they would pinch the helix inward too much. To form a double helix, it is necessary to pair a big base with a little one. *In every DNA double helix, adenine (A) pairs with thymine (T) and guanine (G) pairs with cytosine (C).* The reason A doesn't pair with C and G doesn't pair with T is that these base pairs cannot form proper hydrogen bonds—the electron-sharing atoms are not aligned with each other.

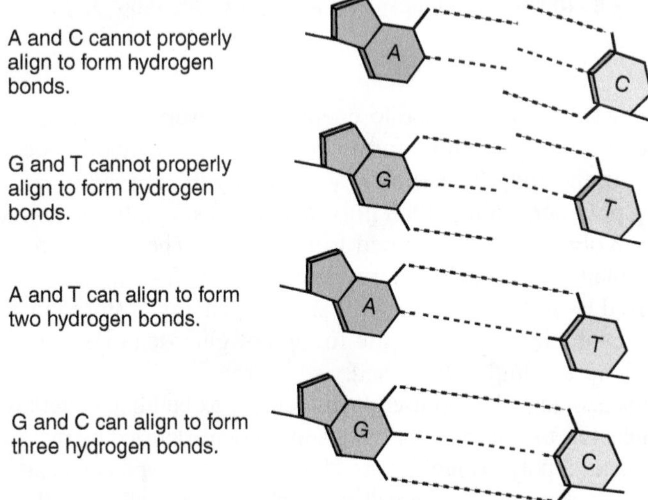

A and C cannot properly align to form hydrogen bonds.
A
C
G and T cannot properly align to form hydrogen bonds.
G
T
A and T can align to form two hydrogen bonds.
A
T
G and C can align to form three hydrogen bonds.
G
C

The simple A–T, G–C base pairs within the DNA double helix allow the cell to copy the information in a very simple way. It just unzips the helix and adds the nucleotides with complementary bases to each strand! That is the great advantage of a double helix—it actually contains two copies of the information, one the mirror image of the other. If the sequence of one chain is ATTGCAT, the sequence of its partner in the double helix *must* be TAACGTA. The fidelity with which hereditary information is passed from one generation to the next is a direct result of this simple double-entry bookkeeping, which makes accurate copying of the genetic message possible.

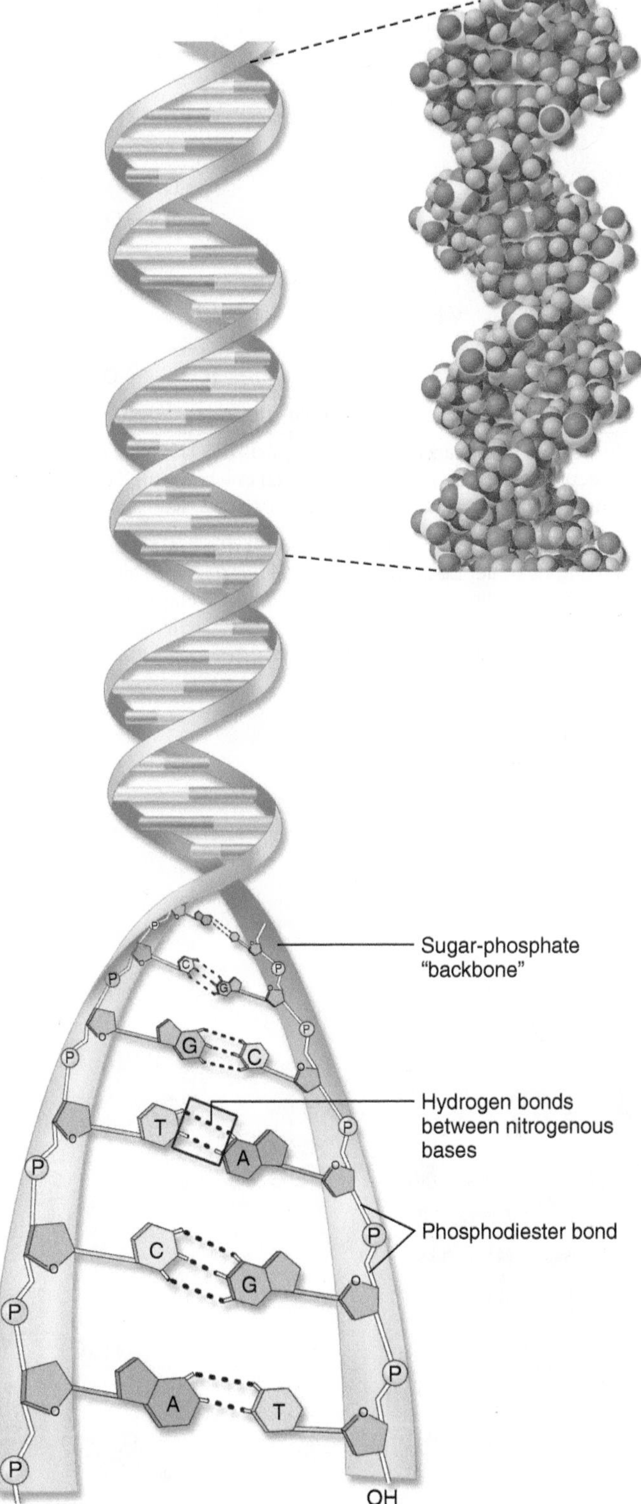

Figure 3.13 The DNA double helix.

The DNA molecule is composed of two polynucleotide chains twisted together to form a double helix. The two chains of the double helix are joined by hydrogen bonds between the A–T and G–C base pairs. The section of DNA on the upper right is a space-filling model of DNA, where atoms are indicated by colored balls.

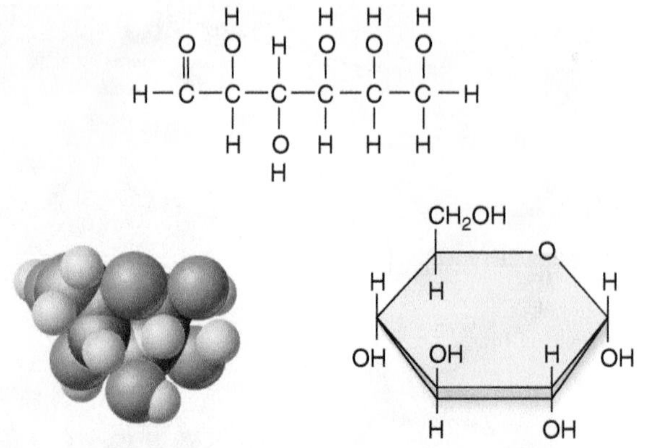

Figure 3.14 The structure of glucose.

Glucose is a monosaccharide and consists of a linear six-carbon molecule that forms a ring when placed in water. This illustration shows three ways glucose can be pictured in a diagram.

IMPLICATION Many vitamin and fruit drinks are marketed as being healthier because they are "all natural," with "no refined sugars." Yet reading the nutrition facts label reveals that a single 12oz bottle typically contains 29 grams of sugar. In what way do you think "natural" sugar is different from "refined" sugar?

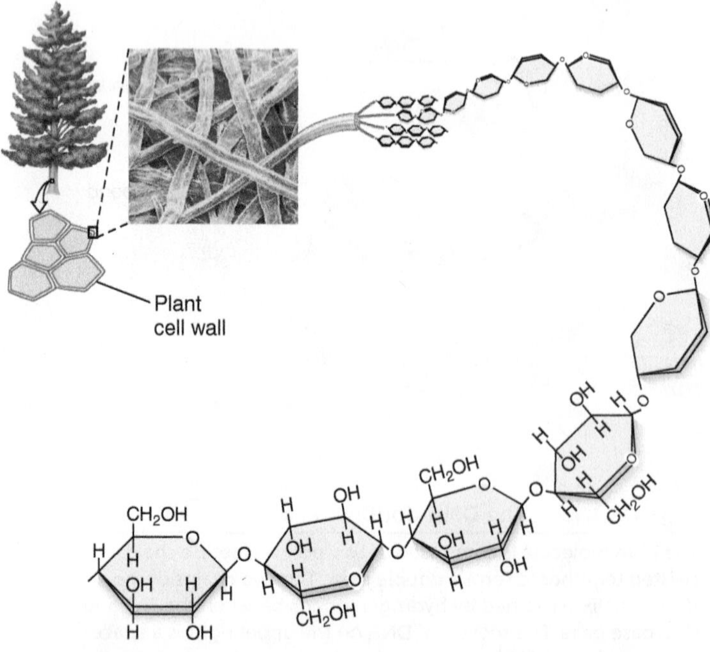

Figure 3.15 A polysaccharide: cellulose.

The polysaccharide cellulose is found in the cell walls of plant cells and is composed of glucose subunits.

3.4 Carbohydrates

CONCEPT PREVIEW: Carbohydrates are molecules made of C, H, and O atoms. As sugars they store energy in C—H bonds, and as long chains, they can provide structural support in some types of organisms.

Polymers called **carbohydrates** make up the structural framework of certain cells and play a critical role in energy storage. A carbohydrate is any molecule that contains carbon, hydrogen, and oxygen in the ratio 1:2:1. Some carbohydrates are simple, small monomers or dimers and are called simple carbohydrates. Others are long polymers and are called complex carbohydrates. Because they contain many carbon-hydrogen (C—H) bonds, carbohydrates are well-suited for energy storage. Such C—H bonds are the ones most often broken by organisms to obtain energy. Table 3.1 on the facing page shows some examples of carbohydrates.

Simple Carbohydrates

The simplest carbohydrates are the *simple sugars* or **monosaccharides** (from the Greek *monos,* single, and *saccharon,* sweet). These molecules consist of one subunit. For example, glucose, the sugar that carries energy to the cells of your body, is made of six carbons and has the chemical formula $C_6H_{12}O_6$. A molecule of glucose is pictured in several ways in figure 3.14. The long chain of carbon atoms at the top of the figure is its formal chemical structure. When placed in water, the chain folds into the ring structure shown on the lower right. The individual atoms are depicted in the "3-D" space-filling model you see in the lower left. Another type of simple carbohydrate is a **disaccharide,** which forms when two monosaccharides link together through a dehydration reaction. Table sugar is a disaccharide, sucrose, made by linking two six-carbon sugars together, a glucose and a fructose (see table 3.1).

Complex Carbohydrates

Organisms store their metabolic energy by converting sugars, which are water-soluble, into insoluble forms that can be deposited in specific storage areas in the body. This trick is achieved by linking the sugars together into long polymer chains called **polysaccharides.** Plants and animals store energy in polysaccharides formed from glucose. The glucose polysaccharide that plants use to store energy is called *starch*—that is why potatoes are referred to as "starchy" food. In animals, energy is stored in *glycogen,* a highly insoluble macromolecule formed of glucose polysaccharides that are very long and highly branched.

Plants and animals also use glucose chains as building materials, linking the subunits together in different orientations not recognized by most enzymes. These structural polysaccharides are chitin in animals and *cellulose* in plants. The cellulose deposited in the cell walls of the plant cells, like the cellulose strand shown in figure 3.15, cannot be digested by humans and makes up the fiber in our diets. Microbes in the digestive tracts of cows and horses, however, have the cellulose-digesting enzymes we humans lack. The microbial enzyme breaks the bonds holding the glucose molecules together so that they can be used by the animal cells for energy. These animals can thrive on a diet of grass, but you can't. Termites have these enzymes too, which is why a termite can eat wood while you would starve on a diet of tree limbs or lumber.

As discussed on page 307, fungi possess enzymes that can break down cellulose, which is why fungi often grow on dead trees. Some bacteria are also able to break down cellulose and live in the digestive system of certain animals as described on page 507.

TABLE 3.1 Carbohydrates and Their Functions

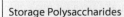

Carbohydrate	Example	Description
Transport Disaccharides		
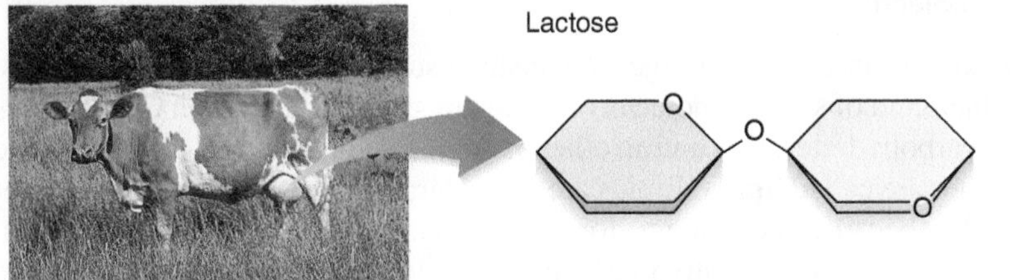	Lactose	Glucose is transported within some organisms as a disaccharide. In this form, it is less readily metabolized because the normal glucose-utilizing enzymes of the organism cannot break the bond linking the two monosaccharide subunits. One type of disaccharide is called lactose. Many mammals supply energy to their young in the form of lactose, which is found in milk. Another transport disaccharide is sucrose. Many plants transport glucose throughout the plant in the form of sucrose, which is harvested from sugarcane to make granulated sugar.
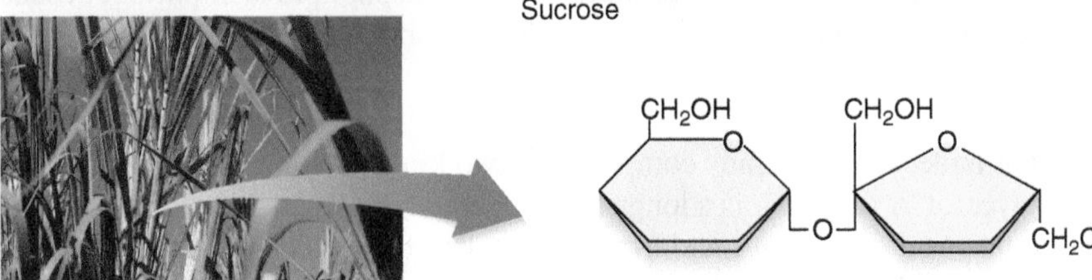	Sucrose	
Storage Polysaccharides		
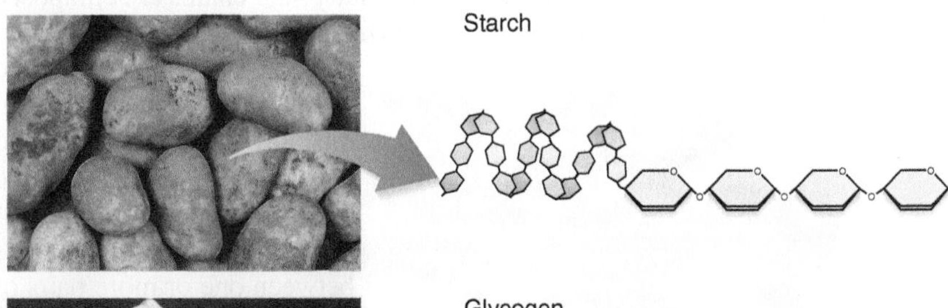	Starch	Organisms store energy in long chains of glucose molecules called polysaccharides. The chains tend to coil up in water, making them insoluble and ideal for storage. The storage polysaccharides found in plants are called starches, which can be branched or unbranched. Starch is found in potatoes and in grains, such as corn and wheat.
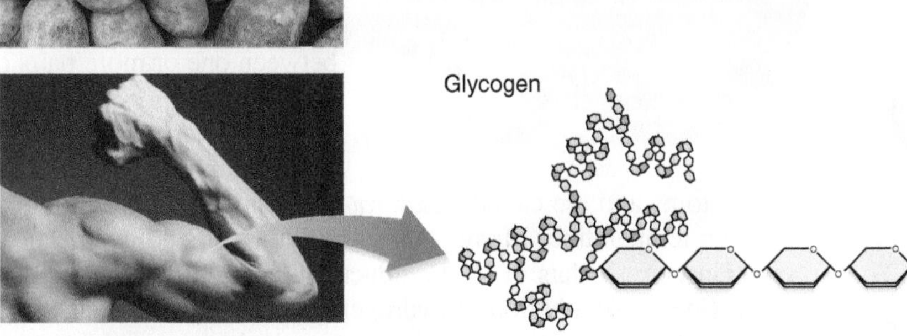	Glycogen	In animals, glucose is stored as glycogen. Glycogen is similar to starch in that it consists of long chains of glucose that coil up in water and are insoluble. But glycogen chains are much longer and highly branched. Glycogen can be stored in muscles and the liver.
Structural Polysaccharides		
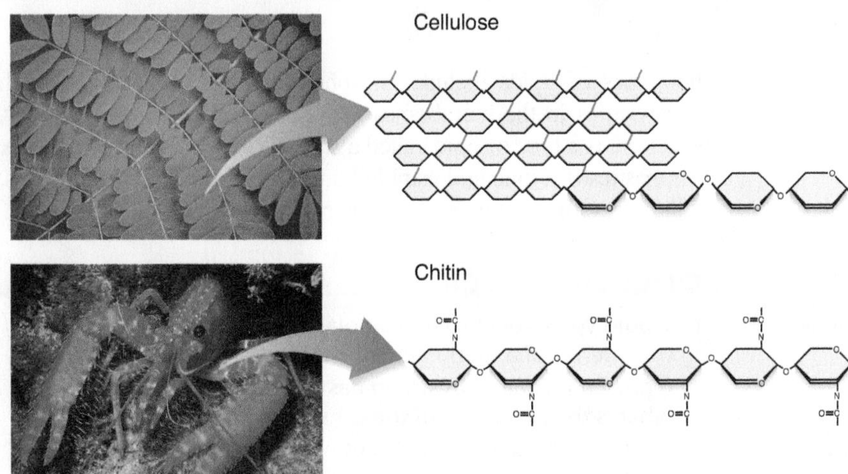	Cellulose	Cellulose is a structural polysaccharide found in the cell walls of plants; its glucose subunits are joined in a way that cannot be broken down readily. Cleavage of the links between the glucose subunits in cellulose requires an enzyme most organisms lack. Some animals, such as cows, are able to digest cellulose by means of bacteria and protists they harbor in their digestive tract, which provide the necessary enzymes.
	Chitin	Chitin is a type of structural polysaccharide found in the external skeletons of many invertebrates, including insects and crustaceans, and in the cell walls of fungi. Chitin is a modified form of cellulose with a nitrogen group added to the glucose units. When cross-linked by proteins, it forms a tough, resistant surface material.

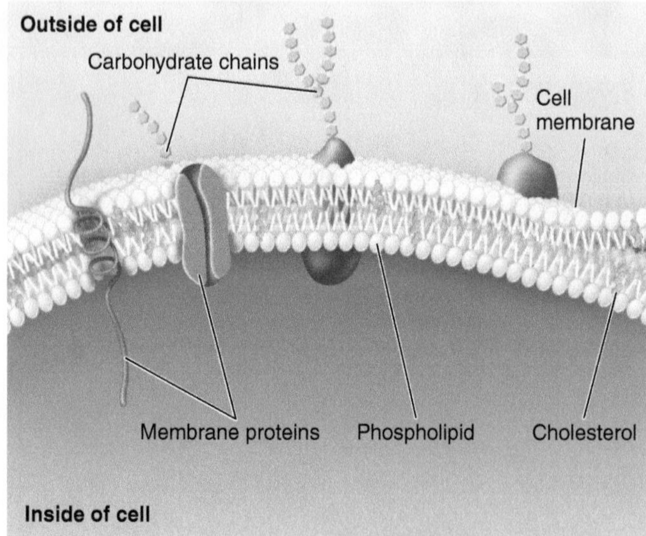

Figure 3.16 Lipids are a key component of biological membranes.

Lipids are one of the most common molecules in the human body, because the membranes of all cells are composed of phospholipids. Membranes also contain cholesterol, another type of lipid.

3.5 Lipids

CONCEPT PREVIEW: Lipids are not water-soluble. A type of lipid called a fat contains chains of fatty acid subunits that store energy. Other lipids include phospholipids, steroids, rubber, and pigment molecules.

For long-term energy storage, organisms usually convert glucose into fats, another kind of storage molecule that contains more energy-rich C—H bonds than carbohydrates. Fats and all other biological molecules that are not soluble in water are called **lipids.** Lipids are nonpolar; in water, fat molecules cluster together because they cannot form hydrogen bonds with water molecules. This is why oil forms into a layer on top of water when the two substances are mixed. A special type of lipid called a phospholipid is important because it forms boundary layers in cells called membranes (figure 3.16).

Fats

Fat molecules are lipids composed of two kinds of subunits: fatty acids and glycerol. A *fatty acid* is a long chain of carbon and hydrogen atoms. Glycerol contains three carbons and forms the backbone to which three fatty acids are attached through dehydration reactions.

The chemical composition of the fatty acids that make up a fat molecule can affect its physical properties. Fats whose fatty acid chains are composed of the maximum number of hydrogen atoms (figure 3.17*b*) are said to be *saturated.* Saturated fats are solid at room temperature. Animal fats are often saturated and occur as hard fats. On the other hand, fats composed of fatty acids with double bonds between one or more pairs of carbon atoms (figure 3.17*c*) contain fewer than the maximum number of hydrogen atoms and are called *unsaturated.* Unsaturated fats are liquid at room temperature. Many plant fats are unsaturated and occur in oils. Unsaturated fats in food products may be artificially *hydrogenated* (industrial addition of hydrogens), extending the shelf life of products like peanut butter. In some cases, the hydrogenation creates *trans fats,* a type of unsaturated fat linked to heart disease.

Covalent bonds, as discussed on page 35, form when atoms share electrons. The single covalent bonds in saturated fats result when the carbons share one pair of electrons. The double covalent bonds in unsaturated fats result when two pairs of electrons are shared between carbon atoms.

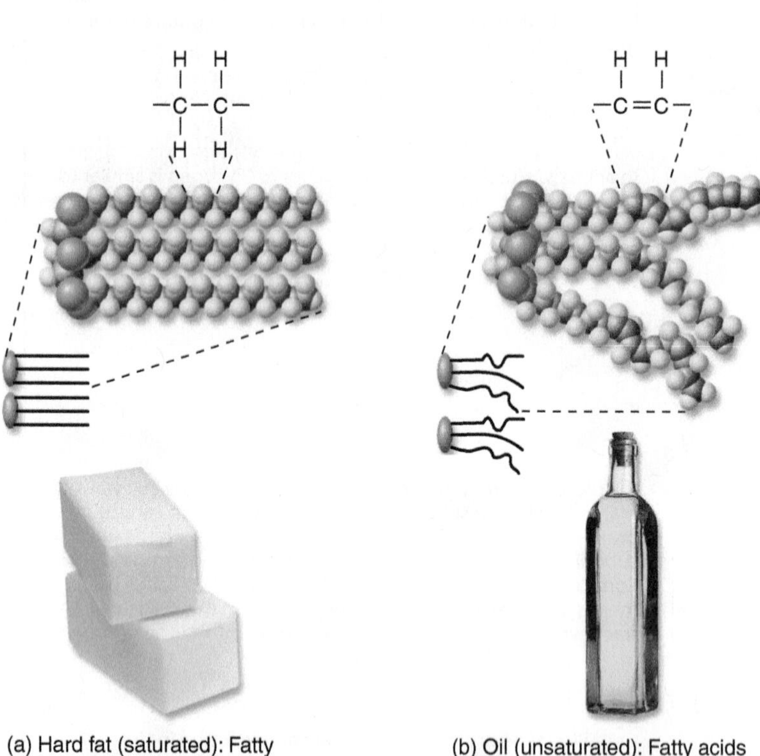

(a) Hard fat (saturated): Fatty acids with single bonds between all carbon pairs

(b) Oil (unsaturated): Fatty acids that contain double bonds between one or more pairs of carbon atoms

Figure 3.17 Saturated and unsaturated fats.

Fat molecules each contain a three-carbon glycerol to which is attached three fatty acid tails. (a) Most animal fats are "saturated" (every carbon atom carries the maximum load of hydrogens). Their fatty acid chains fit closely together and form immobile arrays called hard fats. (b) Most plant fats are unsaturated, which prevents close association between chains and so results in oils.

Other Types of Lipids

Other types of lipids include phospholipids and cholesterol, which play key roles in the membranes that encase all cells of your body. Cholesterol is a type of lipid called a *steroid.* The male and female sex hormones testosterone and estradiol are also steroids. Rubber, waxes, and light-absorbing pigments are other important biological lipids.

Concept Check

1. Would you expect to find a polar or nonpolar amino acid in the interior of a globular protein? Why?
2. If one chain of a DNA strand has the sequence ACCTGGAAT, what is the sequence of the other strand?
3. Why can you digest starch but not cellulose?
4. Which fat is liquid at room temperature, a saturated or unsaturated fat?

Anabolic Steroids in Sports

Among the most notorious of lipids in recent years has been the class of synthetic hormones known as anabolic steroids. Since the 1950s some athletes have been taking these chemicals to build muscle and so boost athletic performance. Both because of the intrinsic unfairness of this and because of health risks, the use of anabolic steroids has been banned in sports for decades. Controversy over their use in professional baseball has recently returned anabolic steroids to the nation's front pages.

Anabolic steroids were developed in the 1930s to treat hypogonadism, a condition in which the male testes do not produce sufficient amounts of the hormone testosterone for normal growth and sexual development. Scientists soon discovered that by slightly altering the chemical structure of testosterone, they could produce synthetic versions that facilitated the growth of skeletal muscle in laboratory animals. The word "anabolic" means growing or building. Further tweaking reduced the added impact of these new chemicals on sexual development. More than 100 different anabolic steroids have been developed, most of which have to be injected to be effective. All require a prescription to be used legally in the United States, and all are banned in professional, college, and high school sports.

Homerun slugger Barry Bonds was involved in a steroid controversy in 2006.

Another way to increase the body's level of testosterone is to use a chemical which is not itself anabolic but one that the body converts to testosterone. One such chemical is 4-androstenedione, more commonly called "andro." It was first developed in the 1970s by East German scientists to try to enhance their athletes' Olympic performances. Because andro does not have the same side effects as anabolic steroids, it was legally available until 2004. It was used by Mark McGwire, but it is now banned in all sports, and possession of andro is a federal crime.

Anabolic steroids work by signalling muscle cells to make more protein. They bind to special "androgenic receptor" proteins within the cells of muscle tissue. Like jabbing these proteins with a poker, the binding prods the receptors into action, causing them to activate genes on the cell's chromosomes that produce muscle tissue proteins, triggering an increase in protein synthesis. At the same time, the anabolic steroid molecules bind to so-called "cortisol receptor" proteins in the cell, preventing these receptors from doing their job of causing protein breakdown, the muscle cell's way of suppressing inflammation and promoting the use of proteins for fuel during exercise. By increasing protein production and inhibiting the breakdown of proteins in muscle cells after workouts, anabolic steroids significantly increase the mass of an athlete's muscle tissue.

If the only effect of anabolic steroids on your body was to enhance your athletic performance by increasing your muscle mass, using them would still be wrong, for one very simple and important reason: fairness. To gain advantage in competition by concealed use of anabolic steroids—"doping"—is simply cheating. That is why these drugs are banned in sports.

The use of anabolic steroids by athletes and others is not only wrong, but also illegal, because increased muscle mass is not the only effect of using these chemicals. Among adolescents, anabolic steroids can also lead to premature termination of the adolescent growth spurt, so that for the rest of their lives, users remain shorter than they would have been without the drugs. Adolescents and adults are also affected by steroids in the following ways. Anabolic steroids can lead to potentially fatal liver cysts and liver cancer (the liver is the organ of the body that attempts to detoxify the blood), cholesterol changes and hypertension (both of which can promote heart attack and stroke), and acne. Other signs of steroid use in men include reduced size of testicles, balding, and development of breasts. In women, signs include the growth of facial hair, lowering of the voice, and cessation of menstruation.

In the fall of 2003, athletic organizations learned that some athletes were using a new performance-enhancing anabolic steroid undetectable by standard antidoping tests, tetrahydrogestrinone (THG). The use of THG was only discovered because an anonymous coach sent a spent syringe to U.S. antidoping officials. THG's chemical structure is similar to gestrinone, a drug used to treat a form of pelvic inflammation, and can be made from it by simply adding four hydrogen atoms, an easy chemical task. THG tends to break down when prepared for analysis by standard means, which explains why antidoping tests had failed to detect it. New urine tests for THG that were developed in 2004 have been used to catch several well-known sports figures, including British athlete Dwain Chambers and baseball slugger Rafael Palmeiro.

How Does pH Affect a Protein's Function?

The red blood cells you see to the lower right carry oxygen to all parts of your body. These cells are red because they are chock full of a large iron-rich protein called *hemoglobin.* The iron atoms in each hemoglobin molecule provide a place for oxygen gas molecules to stick to the protein. When oxygen levels are highest (in the lungs), oxygen atoms bind to hemoglobin tightly, and a large percent of the hemoglobin molecules in a cell possess bound oxygen atoms. When oxygen levels are lower (in the tissues of the body), hemoglobin doesn't bind oxygen atoms as tightly, and as a consequence hemoglobin releases its oxygen to the tissues. What causes this difference between lungs and tissues in how hemoglobin loads and unloads oxygen? Oxygen concentration is not the only factor that might be responsible. A protein's function can be affected by pH, and blood pH, for example, also differs between lungs and body tissues (**pH** is a measure of how many H^+ ions a solution contains). Tissues are slightly more acidic (that is, they have more H^+ ions and a lower pH). Their metabolic activities release CO_2 into the blood, which quickly becomes converted to carbonic acid and lowers the pH.

The graph to the right displays so-called "oxygen loading curves" that reveal the effectiveness with which hemoglobin binds oxygen. The more effective the binding, the less oxygen required before hemoglobin becomes fully loaded, and the further to the left a loading curve is shifted. To assess the impact of pH on this process, O_2 loading curves were carried out at three different blood pH values. In the graph, oxygen levels in the blood are presented on the *x* axis, and for each data point the corresponding % hemoglobin saturation (a %, or **percent,** is the numerator [top part] of a fraction whose denominator [bottom part] is 100—in this case, a measure of the fraction of the hemoglobin that is bound to oxygen) is presented on the *y* axis. The oxygen-loading curve was repeated at pH values of 7.6, 7.4, and 7.2, corresponding to the blood pH that might be expected in resting, exercising, and very active muscle tissue, respectively.

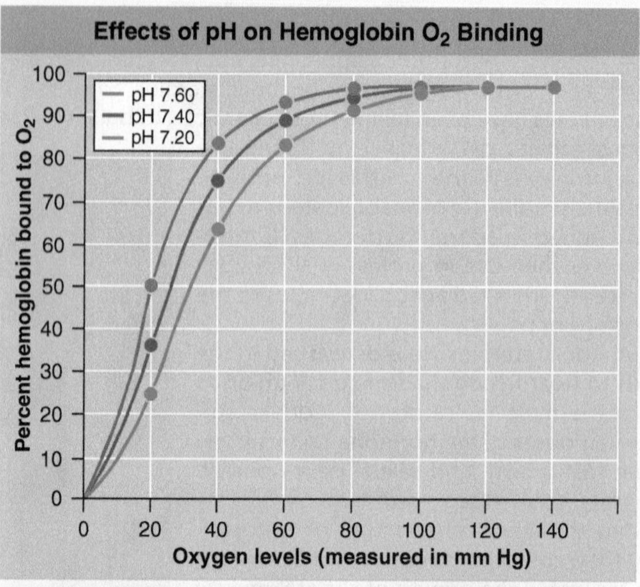

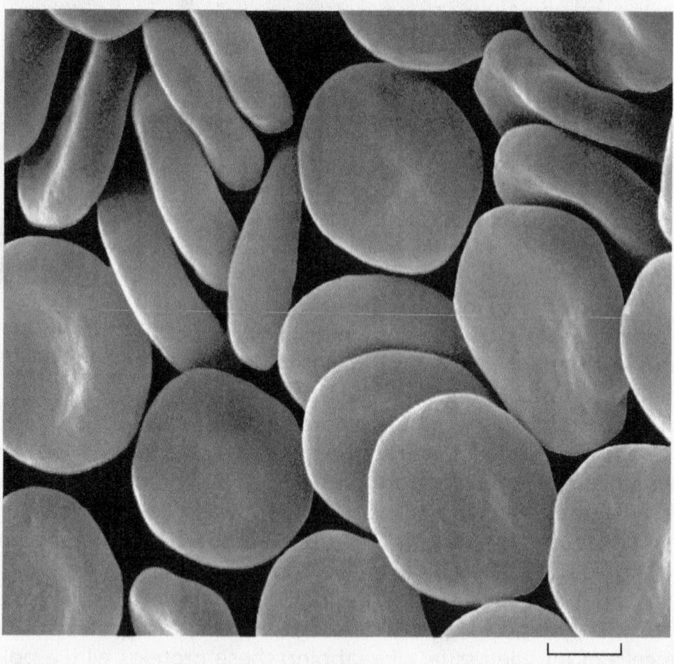

Analysis

1. **Applying Concepts** Which of the three pH values represents the highest concentration of hydrogen ions? (The **concentration** of a substance is the amount of that substance present in a given volume.) Is this value more acidic or more basic than the other two?
2. **Interpreting Data** What is the percent hemoglobin bound to O_2 for each of the three pH concentrations at saturation (where the lines flatten out)? at an oxygen level of 20 mm Hg? at 40 mm Hg? at 60 mm Hg?
3. **Making Inferences** At an oxygen level of 40 mm Hg, would hemoglobin bind oxygen more tightly at a pH of 7.8 or 7.0?
4. **Drawing Conclusions** How does pH affect the release of oxygen from hemoglobin?

Concept Summary

Forming Macromolecules

3.1 Polymers Are Built of Monomers

- Living organisms produce organic macromolecules, which are large carbon-based molecules. The chemical properties of these molecules are due to unique functional groups that are attached to the carbon core (**figure 3.2**).
- Macromolecules are formed by the linking together of subunits, called monomers, to form larger polymers. Amino acids are the subunits that link together to form polypeptides. Nucleotide monomers link together to form nucleic acids. Monosaccharide monomers link together to form carbohydrates. Fatty acids are the monomers that link together to form a type of lipid called fats (**figure 3.3**).
- Polymers are formed by dehydration reactions, like the reaction shown here from **figure 3.4*a*.** Dehydration reactions produce covalent bonds that link monomers together. The reaction is called a dehydration reaction because a water molecule is a product of the reaction.
- The breakdown of macromolecule involves hydrolysis reactions, where a water molecule is broken down into H^+ and OH^-. These ions disrupt the covalent bonds that hold two monomers together, causing the bond to break (**figure 3.4*b***).

Types of Macromolecules

3.2 Proteins

- Proteins are macromolecules that carry out many functions in the cell (**figure 3.5**). They are produced by the linking together of amino acid subunits that form a chain called a polypeptide.
- There are 20 different amino acids found in proteins. All amino acids have the same basic core structure (**figure 3.6**). They differ in the type of functional group attached to the core. The functional groups are referred to as R groups. Some functional groups are polar, some are nonpolar, and still others give the amino acid unique chemical properties.
- Amino acids are linked together with covalent bonds referred to as peptide bonds (**figure 3.7**).
- The sequence of amino acids within the polypeptide is the primary structure of the protein (**figure 3.8**). The chain of amino acids can twist into a secondary structure, where hydrogen bonding holds portions of the polypeptide in a coiled shape, called an α-helix, or in sheets called β-pleated sheets. Further bending and folding of the polypeptide results in its tertiary structure. When two or more polypeptides are present in a protein, the interaction of these polypeptide subunits is its quaternary structure.
- Changes in environmental conditions that disrupt hydrogen bonding can cause a protein to unfold, a process called denaturation (**figure 3.9**). Globular proteins, like the enzyme shown here from **figure 3.10,** cannot function if they are denatured. Some denatured proteins can refold back into their functional shapes. The structure of the protein determines its function.

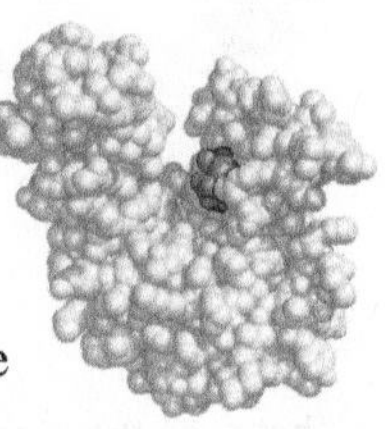

3.3 Nucleic Acids

- Nucleic acids, such as DNA and RNA, are long chains of nucleotides. Nucleotides contain three parts: a 5-carbon sugar, a phosphate group, and a nitrogenous base (**figure 3.11**). DNA and RNA function in information storage and retrieval in the cell, carrying the information needed to build proteins. The information is stored as different sequences of nucleotides that determine the order of amino acids in proteins.
- DNA and RNA differ chemically in that the sugar found in DNA is deoxyribose and in RNA it is ribose. The nitrogenous bases in DNA are cytosine, adenine, guanine, and thymine, and the same are found in RNA except for thymine, which is substituted in RNA with uracil (**figure 3.11*b***).
- DNA and RNA also differ structurally. DNA contains two strands of nucleotides wound around each other, called a double helix. RNA, as shown here from **figure 3.12,** is a single strand of nucleotides.

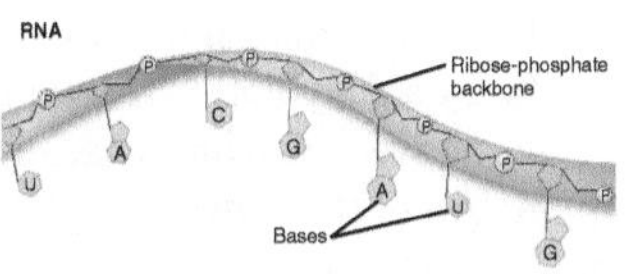

- The two nucleotide strands of the DNA double helix are held together through hydrogen bonding between nitrogenous bases: adenine (A) pairs with thymine (T), and cytosine (C) pairs with guanine (G) (**figure 3.13**).

3.4 Carbohydrates

- Carbohydrates, also referred to as sugars, are macromolecules that serve two primary functions in the cell: structural framework and energy storage.
- Carbohydrates that consist of only one or two monomers are called simple carbohydrates, such as the glucose monosaccharide shown here from **figure 3.14,** and disaccharides. Carbohydrates that consist of long chains of monomers are called complex carbohydrates or polysaccharides (**figure 3.15**).
- Polysaccharides such as starch and glycogen provide a means of storing energy in the cell. They are broken down in the cells when energy is needed. Carbohydrates such as cellulose and chitin provide structural integrity (**table 3.1**) and are not broken down by animals because they lack the enzyme necessary. Certain microbes in the guts of some animals are able to breakdown cellulose.

3.5 Lipids

- Lipids are large nonpolar molecules that are insoluble in water. Lipids called phospholipids are components of biological membranes. Fats that function in long-term energy storage include saturated fats, as shown here from **figure 3.17,** and unsaturated fats. Saturated fats are solid at room temperature and are found in animals, while unsaturated fats are liquid (oils) at room temperature and are found in plants.

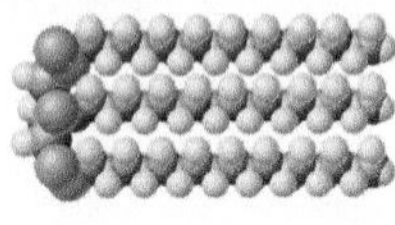

- Other lipids include the steroids (including the sex steroids and cholesterol), rubber, and pigments.

Self-Test

1. The four kinds of organic macromolecules are
   a. hydroxyls, carboxyls, aminos, and phosphates.
   b. proteins, carbohydrates, lipids, and nucleic acids.
   c. DNA, RNA, simple sugars, and amino acids.
   d. carbon, hydrogen, oxygen, and nitrogen.
2. Organic molecules are made up of monomers. Which of the following is *not* considered a monomer of organic molecules?
   a. amino acids **c.** polypeptides
   b. simple sugars **d.** nucleotides
3. Your body is filled with many types of proteins. Each type has a distinctive sequence of amino acids that determines both its unique _____ and its specialized _____.
   a. number, weight **c.** structure, function
   b. length, mass **d.** charge, pH
4. A peptide bond forms
   a. by the removal of a water molecule.
   b. by a dehydration reaction.
   c. between two amino acids.
   d. All of the above.
5. Nucleic acids
   a. are the energy source for our bodies.
   b. act on other molecules, breaking them apart or building new ones to help us function.
   c. are only found in a few, specialized locations within the body.
   d. are information storage devices found in body cells.
6. The two strands of a DNA molecule are held together through hydrogen bonds between nucleotide bases. Which of the following best describes this base pairing in DNA?
   a. Adenine forms hydrogen bonds with thymine.
   b. Adenine forms hydrogen bonds with cytosine.
   c. Cytosine forms hydrogen bonds with thymine.
   d. Guanine forms hydrogen bonds with adenine.
7. Carbohydrates are used for
   a. structure and energy. **c.** fat storage and hair.
   b. information storage. **d.** hormones and enzymes.
8. Which of the following carbohydrates is *not* found in plants?
   a. glycogen **c.** starch
   b. cellulose **d.** All are found in plants.
9. A characteristic common to fat molecules is
   a. that they contain long chains of C—H bonds.
   b. that they are insoluble in water.
   c. that they have a glycerol backbone.
   d. All of these are characteristics of fat molecules.
10. Lipids are used for
   a. motion and defense.
   b. information storage.
   c. energy storage and for some hormones.
   d. enzymes and for some hormones.

Visual Understanding

1. **Figure 3.7 and table 3.1** The molecule below, on the left, is a peptide made from monomers of amino acids. The molecule below, on the right, is a disaccharide made from monomers of simple sugars. Both molecules were synthesized using a common chemical reaction. What is the chemical reaction that formed these molecules and what is the common by-product of both these reactions?

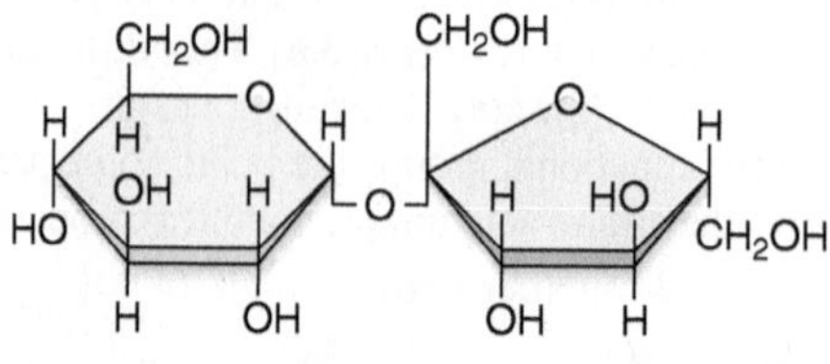

Sucrose

2. **Figure 3.17** The following are two lipid molecules. The lipid on the left is a saturated fat and the one on the right is an unsaturated fat. What is the difference in the chemical structure of their fatty acid tails and how does this affect their physical properties?

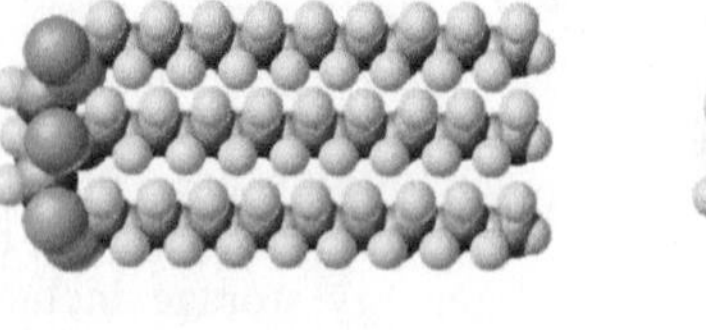

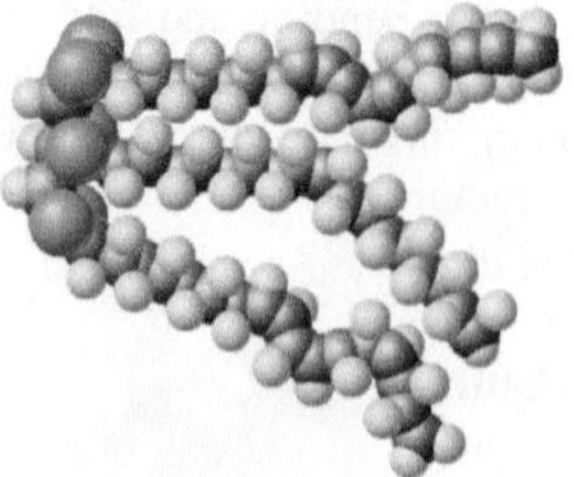

Challenge Questions

1. How many molecules of water are used up in the breakdown of a polypeptide that is 15 amino acids in length?
2. The enzyme present in the cells of your body can break the bonds between the glucose monomers in starch but it cannot break the bonds between the glucose monomers in cellulose. Enzymes are very specific in what molecules they bind to. After examining the chemical structures of starch and cellulose in table 3.1, explain why the same enzyme that breaks down starch cannot break down cellulose.

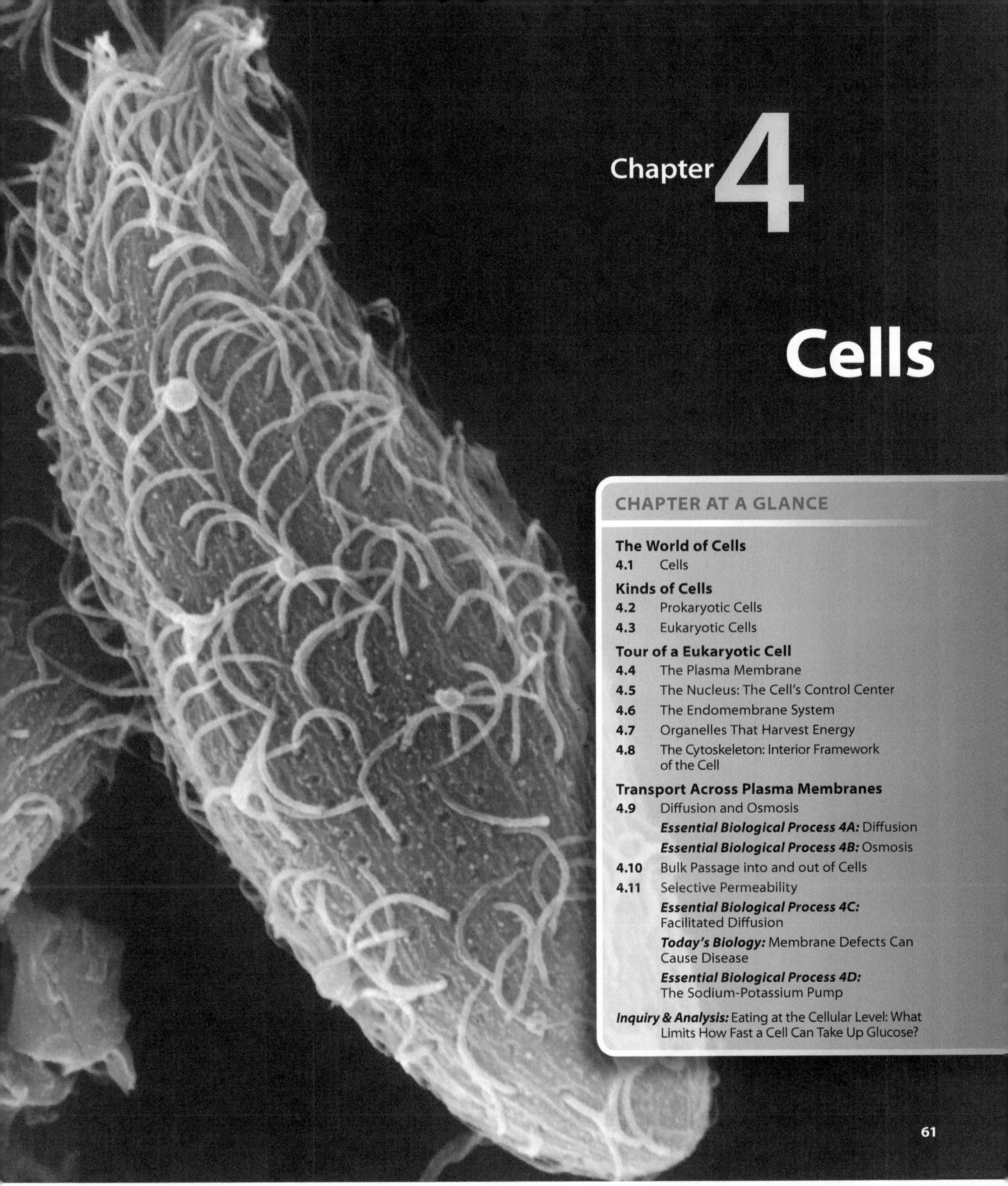

Chapter 4

Cells

CHAPTER AT A GLANCE

The World of Cells

4.1 Cells

CONCEPT PREVIEW: All living things are composed of one or more cells. Most cells and their components are so small they can only be viewed using microscopes.

Hold your finger up and look at it closely. What do you see? Skin. It looks solid and smooth, creased with lines and flexible to the touch. But if you were able to remove a bit and examine it under a microscope, it would look very different. Figure 4.1 takes you on a journey into your fingertip. The crammed bodies you see in panels 3 and 4 are skin cells, laid out like a tiled floor. As your journey continues, you travel inside one of the cells and see organelles, structures in the cell that perform specific functions. Proceeding even further inward, you encounter the molecules of which the structures are made, and finally the atoms shown in panels 8 and 9. While some organisms are composed of a single cell, your body is composed of many cells. A human body has as many cells as there are stars in a galaxy, between 10 and 100 trillion, depending on your size. In this chapter we look more closely at cells and learn something of their internal structure and how they communicate with their environment.

Figure 4.1 The size of cells and their contents.

This diagram shows the size of human skin cells, organelles, and molecules. In general, the diameter of a human skin cell is a little less than 20 micrometers (μm), a mitochondrion is 2 μm, a ribosome is 20 nanometers (nm), a protein molecule is 2 nm, and an atom is 0.2 nm.

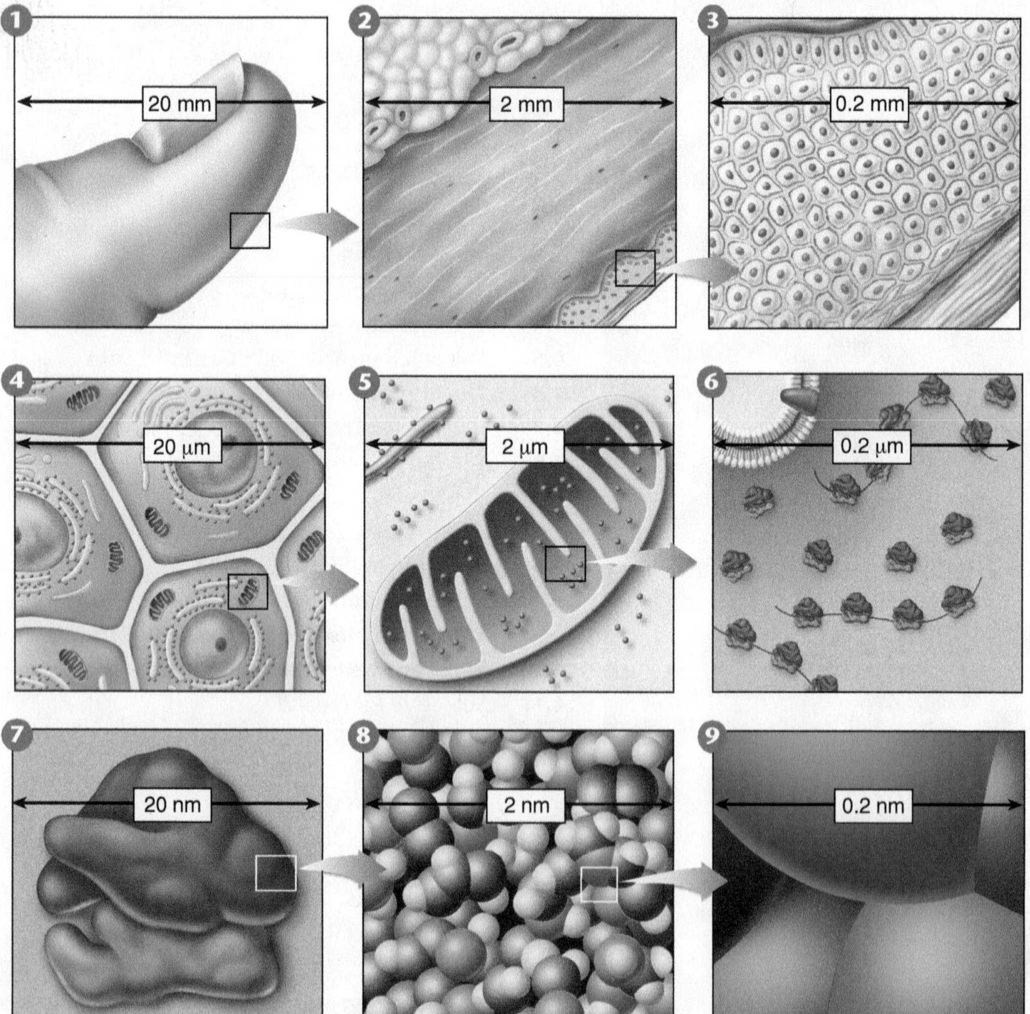

The Cell Theory

Cells are small, so small that no one observed them until microscopes were invented in the mid-seventeenth century. Robert Hooke first described cells in 1665, when he used a microscope he had built to examine a thin slice of nonliving plant tissue called cork. Hooke observed a honeycomb of tiny, empty (because the cells were dead) compartments. He called the compartments in the cork *cellulae* (Latin, small rooms), and the term has come down to us as **cells.** For another century and a half, however, biologists failed to recognize the importance of cells. In 1838, botanist Matthias Schleiden made a careful study of plant tissues and developed the first statement of the cell theory. He stated that all plants "are aggregates of fully individualized, independent, separate beings, namely the cells themselves." In 1839, Theodor Schwann reported that all animal tissues also consist of individual cells.

The idea that all organisms are composed of cells is called the cell theory. In its modern form, the cell theory includes three principles:

1. All organisms are composed of one or more cells, within which the processes of life occur.

2. Cells are the smallest living things. Nothing smaller than a cell is considered alive.
3. Cells arise only by division of a previously existing cell. Although life likely evolved spontaneously in the environment of the early earth, biologists have concluded that no additional cells are originating spontaneously at present. Rather, life on earth represents a continuous line of descent from those early cells.

Most Cells Are Very Small

Cells are not all the same size. Individual marine alga cells, for example, can be up to 5 centimeters long—as long as your little finger. In contrast, the cells of your body are typically from 5 to 20 micrometers (μm) in diameter, too small to see with the naked eye. It would take anywhere from 100 to 400 human cells to span the diameter of the head of a pin. The cells of bacteria are even smaller than your cells, only a few micrometers thick (figure 4.2).

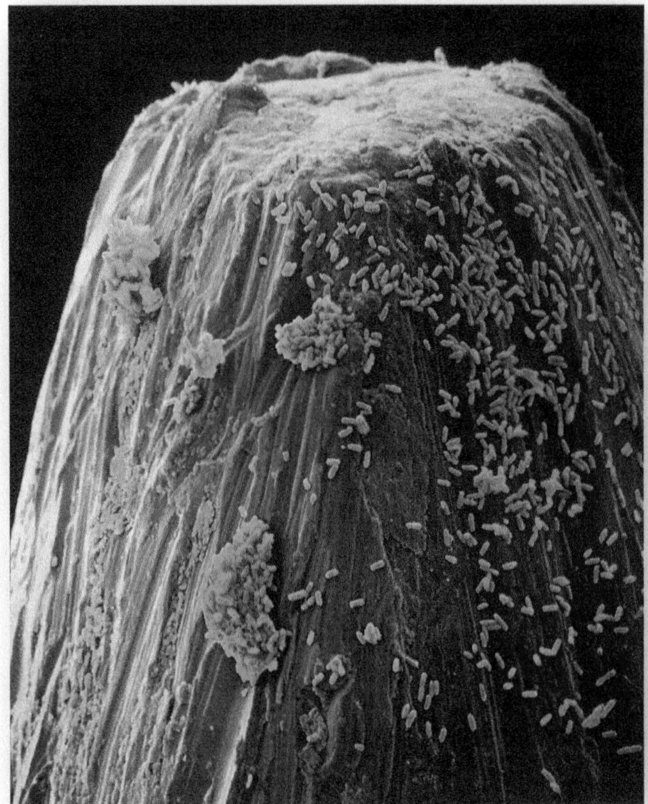

Figure 4.2 Bacteria on the point of a pin (175×).

Why Aren't Cells Larger?

Why are most cells so tiny? Most cells are small because larger cells do not function as efficiently. In the center of every cell is a command center that must issue orders to all parts of the cell, directing the synthesis of certain enzymes, the entry of ions and molecules from the exterior, and the assembly of new cell parts. These orders must pass from the core to all parts of the cell, and it takes them a very long time to reach the periphery of a large cell. For this reason, an organism made up of relatively small cells has an advantage over one composed of larger cells.

Another reason cells are not larger is the advantage of having a greater surface area. A cell's surface provides the interior's only opportunity to interact with the environment, as its surface provides the only way for substances to pass into and out of the cell. As cells grow larger, their interior volume increases much more than their surface area, and as a result there is far less surface available to service each unit of volume. In the same way, before airplanes and trains were invented the size of cities was limited because the surrounding countryside could not support all the people living in a big city—only so many roads could be built into the city, only so many farms were close enough to the city to use them.

Visualizing Cells

How many cells are big enough to see with the unaided eye? Not many (see figure 4.3). Most are less than 50 micrometers in diameter, far smaller than the period at the end of this sentence.

The Resolution Problem. How do we study cells if they are too small to see? The key is to understand why we can't see them. The reason we can't see such small objects is the limited resolution of the human eye. *Resolution* is defined as the minimum distance two points can be apart and still be distinguished as two separated points. The limit of resolution of the human eye is about 100 micrometers. This limit occurs because when two objects are closer together than about 100 micrometers, the light reflected from each strikes the same "detector" cell at the rear of the eye. Only when the objects are farther apart than 100 micrometers will the light from each strike different cells, allowing your eye to resolve them as two objects rather than one.

IN THE NEWS

High Resolution TV. A new generation of "high definition" televisions is providing remarkable pictures of very high resolution. Computer and television engineers define resolution very simply as the number of individual points of color (or "pixels") you can see. A traditional 15-inch television displays 640 dots on each of 480 vertical lines, so-called 480 resolution. Until recently, DVD discs provided the best resolution for a TV picture. DVDs use red-laser light beams to read and project 720 vertical lines. This was as many dots per line as you could get without two dots being read by adjacent red-laser beams overlapping. With the invention of the much narrower blue laser, it became possible to squeeze dots much more closely together on a true high-resolution HD TV screen—1,080 vertical lines, yielding over 2 million dots of color. This produces an image of vivid clarity difficult to distinguish from what your eye would deliver.

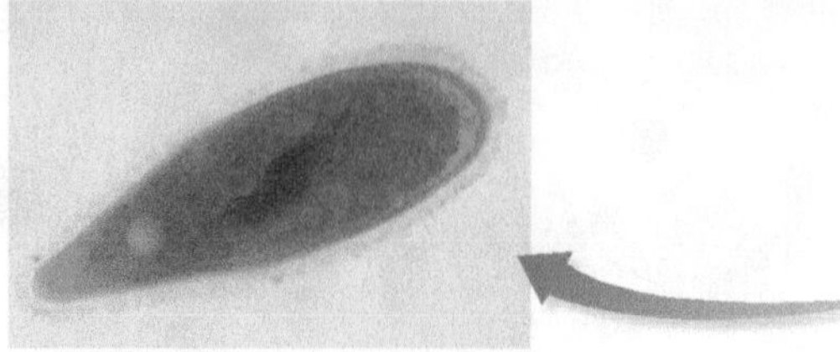

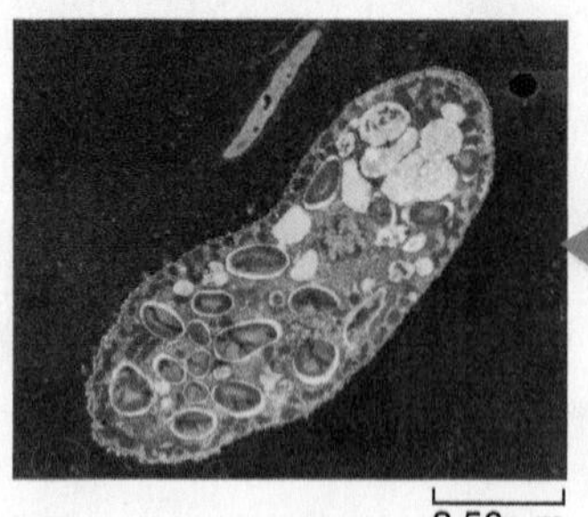

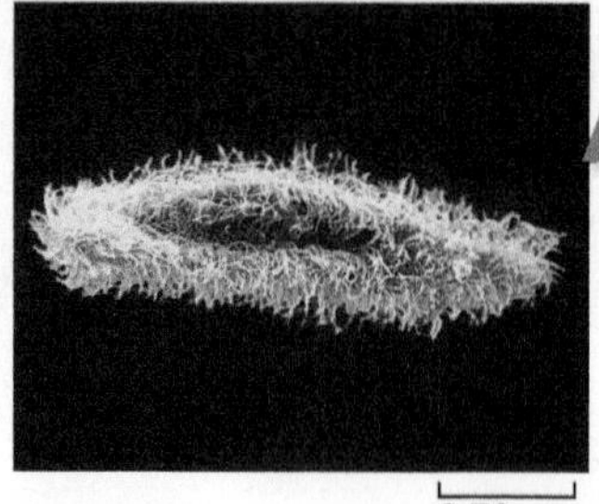

Microscopes. One way to increase resolution is to increase magnification, so that small objects appear larger. Modern *light microscopes* use two magnifying lenses (and a variety of correcting lenses) to achieve very high magnification and clarity (figure 4.3). The first lens focuses the image of the object on the second lens, which magnifies it again and focuses it on the receptor cells that line the inside of back of the eye. Microscopes that magnify in stages using several lenses are called **compound microscopes.** They can resolve structures that are separated by as little as 200 nanometers (nm).

Increasing Resolution. Light microscopes, even compound ones, are not powerful enough to resolve many structures within cells. For example, a membrane is only 5 nanometers thick. Why not just add another magnifying stage to the microscope and so increase its resolving power? Because when two objects are closer than a few hundred nanometers, the light beams reflecting from the two images start to overlap. The only way two light beams can get closer together and still be resolved is if their wavelengths are shorter.

One way to avoid overlap is by using a beam of electrons rather than a beam of light. Electrons have a much shorter wavelength, and a microscope employing electron beams has 1,000 times the resolving power of a light microscope. A **transmission electron microscope (TEM),** so called because the electrons used to visualize the specimens are transmitted through the material, is capable of resolving objects only 0.2 nanometers apart—just twice the diameter of a hydrogen atom!

A second kind of electron microscope, the **scanning electron microscope (SEM),** beams the electrons onto the surface of the specimen. The electrons reflect back, are amplified, and the image created is transmitted to a screen and photographed, producing an often striking three-dimensional picture.

Concept Check

1. All of the cells in your body developed from a single fertilized egg cell. Which principle of the cell theory relates to this fact?
2. Why is it advantageous for your body to be made up of small cells?
3. Why can your eye not see two objects as different if closer than 100 micrometers?

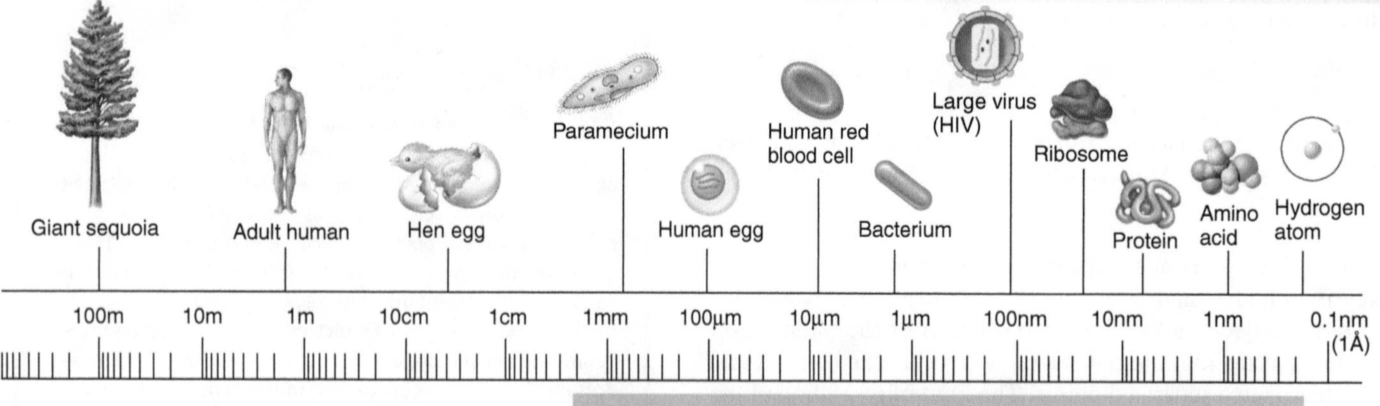

Figure 4.3 A scale of visibility.

Most cells are microscopic in size, although many vertebrate eggs can be seen with the unaided eye. Prokaryotic cells are generally 1 to 2 micrometers (µm) across.

Kinds of Cells

4.2 Prokaryotic Cells

CONCEPT PREVIEW: Prokaryotic cells lack a nucleus and do not have an extensive system of interior membranes. They are encased in a cell wall and may contain external structures such as a capsule, flagellum, or pili.

Recall from the discussion of the diversity of life on page 26, that all organisms are classified based on their characteristics into three domains and further divided into six kingdoms. Two of the three domains contain prokaryotic organisms: Bacteria and Archaea.

There are two major kinds of cells: prokaryotes and eukaryotes. **Prokaryotes** have a relatively uniform interior that is not subdivided by internal membranes into separate compartments. They do not, for example, have special membrane-bounded compartments, called *organelles,* or a *nucleus* (a membrane-bounded compartment that holds hereditary information). All *bacteria* and *archaea* are prokaryotes; all other organisms are eukaryotes.

Prokaryotes are the simplest cellular organisms. Over 5,000 species are recognized, but doubtless many times that number actually exist and have not yet been described. Although these species are diverse in form, their organization is fundamentally similar: They are single-celled organisms, with small cells typically about 2 micrometers thick; the cells are enclosed by a plasma membrane but have no distinct interior compartments. Outside of almost all bacteria is a *cell wall,* a framework of carbohydrates cross-linked into a rigid structure. In some bacteria another layer called the *capsule* encloses the cell wall. Archaea are an extremely diverse group that inhabit diverse environments. Bacteria are abundant and play critical roles in many biological processes. Bacteria assume many shapes, like the sausage or spiral shapes shown in figure 4.4*a,b*. They can also adhere in masses or chains, as shown in figure 4.4*c,* but in these cases the individual cells remain functionally separate from one another.

The plasma membrane, as described on page 57, is composed of phospholipids that are arranged to form two layers, where the polar heads are oriented to the outside and the nonpolar tails extend in toward the interior of the membrane.

If you were able to peer into a prokaryotic cell, you would be struck by its simple organization. The entire interior of the cell is one unit, with little or no internal support structure (the rigid wall, the purple layer surrounding the cell in figure 4.5, supports the cell's shape) and no internal compartments bounded by membranes. Scattered throughout the cytoplasm of prokaryotic cells are small structures called *ribosomes,* the small spherical structures you see inside the cell in figure 4.5. Ribosomes are the sites where proteins are made, but they are not considered organelles because they lack a membrane boundary. The DNA is found in a region of the cytoplasm called the *nucleoid region.* Although the DNA is localized in this region of the cytoplasm, it is not considered a nucleus because, as you can see in figure 4.5, the nucleoid region and its associated DNA are not enclosed within an internal membrane.

Some prokaryotes use a **flagellum** (plural, **flagella**) to move. Flagella are long, threadlike structures, made of protein fibers that project from the surface of a cell. They are used in locomotion and feeding. There may be none, one, or more per cell depending on the species. Bacteria can swim at speeds up to 20 cell diameters per second, rotating their flagella like screws.

Some prokaryotic cells contain **pili** (singular, **pilus**), which are short flagella (only several micrometers long, and about 7.5 to 10 nanometers thick). Pili help the prokaryotic cell attach to appropriate substrates and aid in the exchange of genetic information between cells.

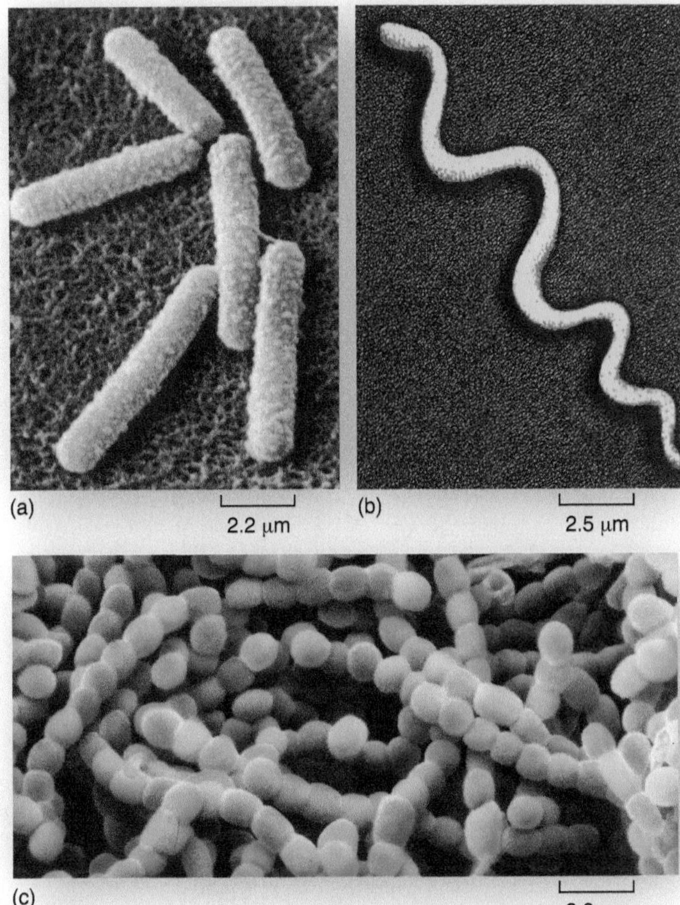

Figure 4.4 Bacterial cells have different shapes.

(a) *Bacillus* is a rod-shaped bacterium. (b) *Treponema* is a coil-shaped bacterium; rotation of internal filaments produces a cork-screw movement. (c) *Streptomyces* is a more or less spherical bacterium in which the individuals adhere in chains.

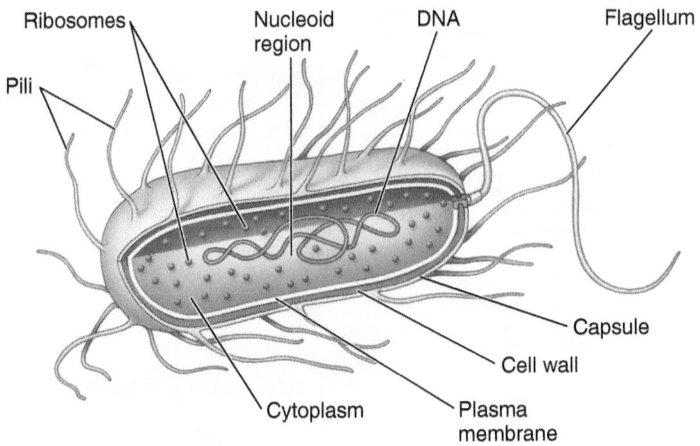

Figure 4.5 Organization of a prokaryotic cell.

Prokaryotic cells lack internal compartments. Not all prokaryotic cells have a flagellum or a capsule like the one illustrated here, but all have a nucleoid region, ribosomes, a plasma membrane, cytoplasm, and a cell wall.

4.3 Eukaryotic Cells

CONCEPT PREVIEW: Eukaryotic cells have a system of interior membranes and membrane-bounded organelles that subdivide the interior into functional compartments.

Eukaryotic cells are much larger and profoundly different from prokaryotic cells, with a complex interior organization. Figures 4.6 and 4.7 present cross-sectional diagrams of idealized animal and plant cells. As you can see, the interior of a eukaryotic cell is much more complex than the prokaryotic cell you encountered in figure 4.5. The **plasma membrane** ❶ encases a semifluid matrix called the **cytoplasm** ❷, which contains within it the nucleus and various cell structures called organelles. An **organelle** is a specialized structure within which particular cell processes occur. Each organelle, such as a **mitochondrion** ❸, has a specific function in the eukaryotic cell. The organelles are anchored at specific locations in the cytoplasm by an interior scaffold of protein fibers, the **cytoskeleton** ❹.

One of the organelles is very visible when these cells are examined with a microscope, filling the center of the cell like the pit of a peach, the **nucleus** ❺ (plural, *nuclei*), from the Latin word for "kernel." Inside the nucleus, the DNA is wound tightly around proteins and packaged into compact units called chromosomes. It is the nucleus that gives **eukaryotes** their name, from the Greek words *eu,* true, and *karyon,* nut; by way of contrast, the earlier-evolving bacteria and archaea are called prokaryotes ("before the nut").

If you examine the organelles in figures 4.6 and 4.7, you can see that most of them form separate compartments within the cytoplasm, bounded by

Figure 4.6 Structure of an animal cell.

In this generalized diagram of an animal cell, the plasma membrane encases the cell, which contains the cytoskeleton and various cell organelles and interior structures suspended in a semifluid matrix called the cytoplasm. Some kinds of animal cells possess fingerlike projections called microvilli. Other types of eukaryotic cells, for example many protist cells, may possess flagella, which aid in movement, or cilia, which can have many different functions.

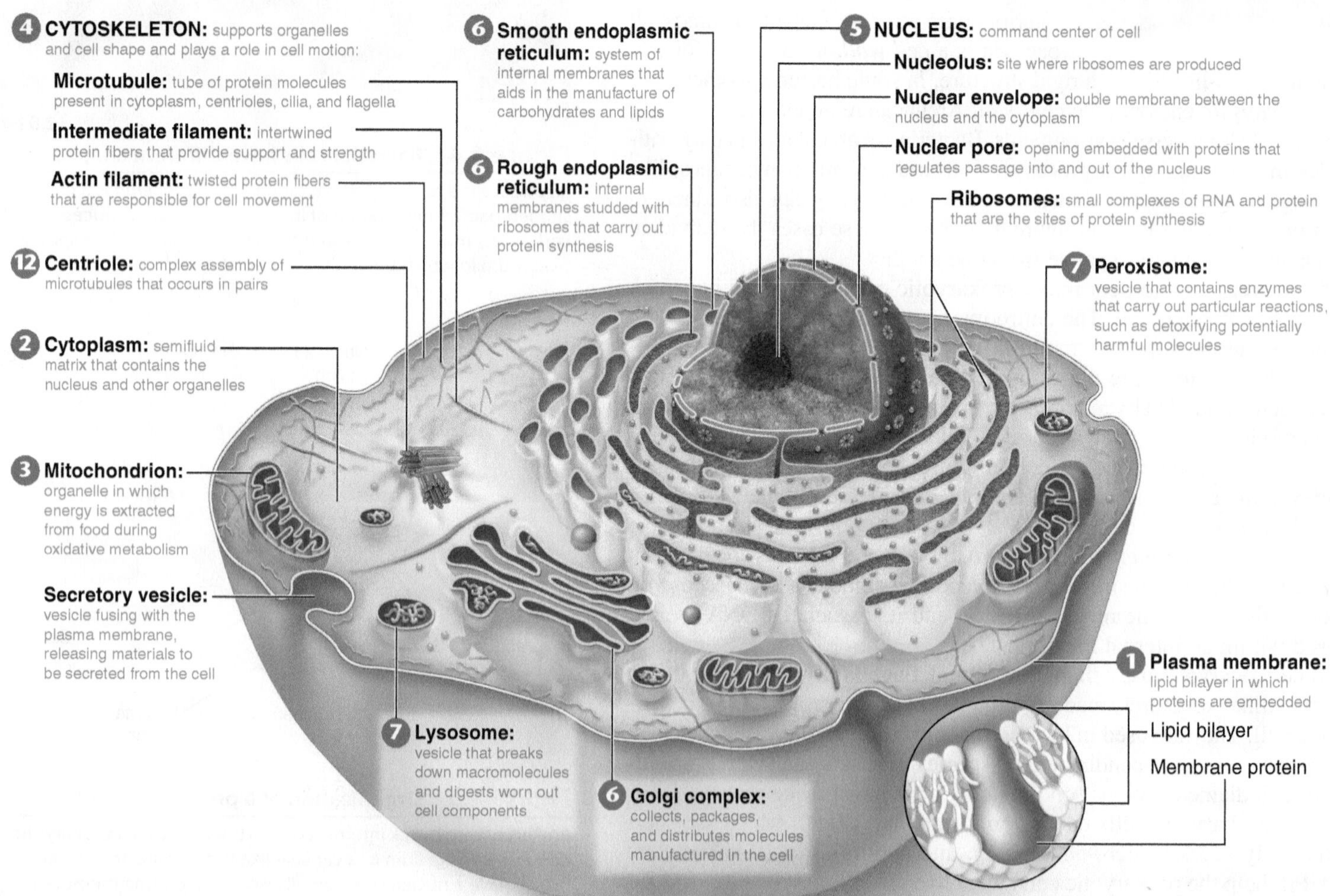
4 CYTOSKELETON: supports organelles and cell shape and plays a role in cell motion:
Microtubule: tube of protein molecules present in cytoplasm, centrioles, cilia, and flagella
Intermediate filament: intertwined protein fibers that provide support and strength
Actin filament: twisted protein fibers that are responsible for cell movement
12 Centriole: complex assembly of microtubules that occurs in pairs
2 Cytoplasm: semifluid matrix that contains the nucleus and other organelles
3 Mitochondrion: organelle in which energy is extracted from food during oxidative metabolism
Secretory vesicle: vesicle fusing with the plasma membrane, releasing materials to be secreted from the cell
6 Smooth endoplasmic reticulum: system of internal membranes that aids in the manufacture of carbohydrates and lipids
6 Rough endoplasmic reticulum: internal membranes studded with ribosomes that carry out protein synthesis
5 NUCLEUS: command center of cell
Nucleolus: site where ribosomes are produced
Nuclear envelope: double membrane between the nucleus and the cytoplasm
Nuclear pore: opening embedded with proteins that regulates passage into and out of the nucleus
Ribosomes: small complexes of RNA and protein that are the sites of protein synthesis
7 Peroxisome: vesicle that contains enzymes that carry out particular reactions, such as detoxifying potentially harmful molecules
1 Plasma membrane: lipid bilayer in which proteins are embedded
Lipid bilayer
Membrane protein
7 Lysosome: vesicle that breaks down macromolecules and digests worn out cell components
6 Golgi complex: collects, packages, and distributes molecules manufactured in the cell

their own membranes. *The hallmark of the eukaryotic cell is this compartmentalization.* This internal compartmentalization is achieved by an extensive **endomembrane system** 6 that weaves through the cell interior.

Vesicles 7 (small membrane-bounded sacs that store and transport materials) form closed-off compartments in the cell, allowing different processes to proceed simultaneously without interfering with one another, just as rooms do in a house. For example, organelles called *lysosomes* are recycling centers that have acidic interiors in which old organelles are broken down and their component molecules recycled. This acid would be very destructive if released into the cytoplasm.

Comparing figure 4.6 with figure 4.7, you will see the same set of organelles, with a few interesting exceptions. For example, the cells of plants, fungi, and many protists have strong exterior **cell walls** 8 composed of cellulose or chitin fibers, while the cells of animals lack cell walls. All plants and many kinds of protists have **chloroplasts** 9, within which photosynthesis occurs. No animal or fungal cells contain chloroplasts. Plant cells also contain a large **central vacuole** 10 that stores water, and **plasmodesmata** 11, which are openings in the cell wall that create cytoplasmic connections between cells. **Centrioles** 12, which will be described later, are present in animal cells but absent in plant and fungal cells.

Concept Check

1. Why can't you see a ribosome with a light microscope?
2. Are there membrane-bounded organelles within a bacterial cell?
3. What important differences are there between plant and animal cells?

Figure 4.7 Structure of a plant cell.

Most mature plant cells contain large central vacuoles that occupy a major portion of the internal volume of the cell and organelles called chloroplasts, within which photosynthesis takes place. The cells of plants, fungi, and some protists have cell walls, although the composition of the walls varies among the groups. Plant cells have cytoplasmic connections through openings in the cell wall called plasmodesmata. Flagella occur in sperm of a few plant species, but are otherwise absent in plant and fungal cells. Centrioles are also absent in plant and fungal cells.

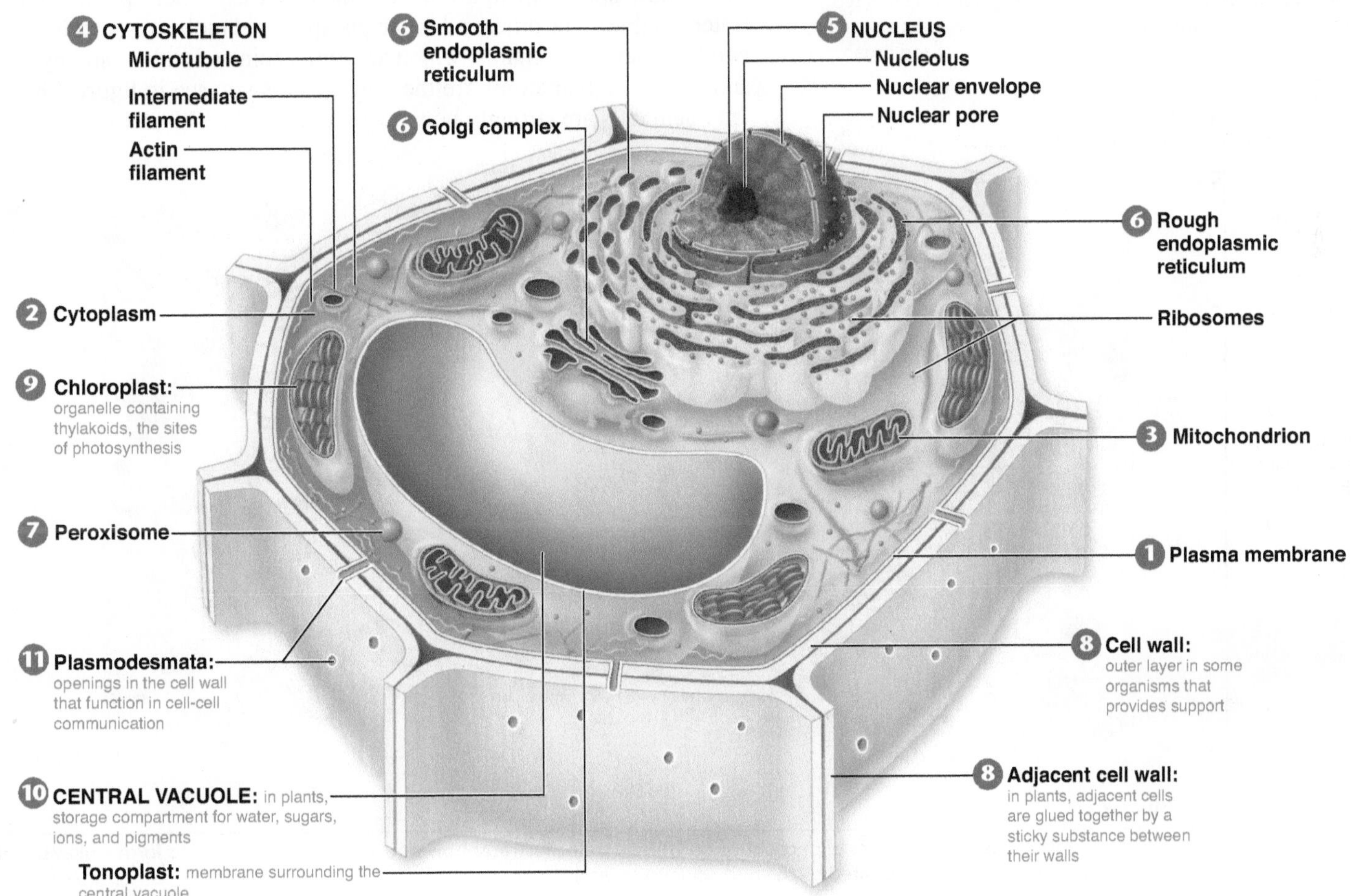

Tour of a Eukaryotic Cell

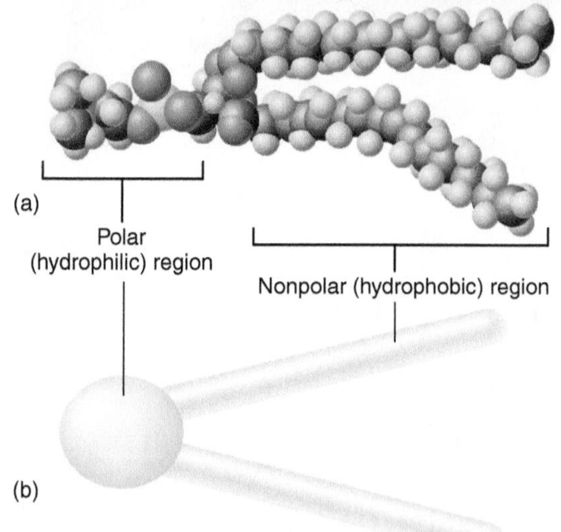

Figure 4.8 Phospholipid structure.

One end of a phospholipid molecule is polar and the other is nonpolar. (a) The molecular structure is shown with colored spheres representing individual atoms (*gray* for carbon, *light blue* for hydrogen, *red* for oxygen, *yellow* for phosphorus, and *blue* for nitrogen). (b) The phospholipid is often depicted diagrammatically as a ball with two tails.

IMPLICATION Sometimes pregnancies end tragically in the second trimester when the mother's immune system unexpectedly attacks fetal membrane phospholipids. Would you expect a specific fetal organ to be primarily affected, or a more generalized organ failure? Explain.

4.4 The Plasma Membrane

CONCEPT PREVIEW: All cells are encased within a delicate lipid bilayer sheet, the plasma membrane, within which are embedded a variety of proteins that act as markers or channels through the membrane.

Encasing all living cells, both prokaryotes and eukaryotes, is a delicate sheet of molecules called the **plasma membrane.** It would take more than 10,000 of these molecular sheets, which are about 5 nanometers thick, piled on top of one another to equal the thickness of this sheet of paper. However, the sheets are not simple in structure, like a soap bubble's skin. Rather, they are made up of a diverse collection of proteins floating within a lipid framework like small boats bobbing on the surface of a pond. Regardless of the kind of cell they enclose, all plasma membranes have the same basic structure of proteins embedded in a sheet of lipids, called the **fluid mosaic model.**

Recall from the discussion of lipids on pages 56 and 57 that a phospholipid is a modified fat molecule where an end carbon in the glycerol backbone forms a chemical bond with a phosphate functional group instead of a third fatty acid tail.

The lipid layer that forms the foundation of a plasma membrane is composed of modified fat molecules called **phospholipids.** A phospholipid molecule can be thought of as a polar head with two nonpolar tails attached to it (figure 4.8). The head of a phospholipid molecule has a phosphate chemical group linked to it—the yellow sphere in figure 4.8*a*—making it extremely polar (and thus water-soluble). The other end of the phospholipid molecule is composed of two long fatty acid chains, which are long chains of carbon and hydrogen atoms. The carbon atoms are the gray spheres you see in figure 4.8*a*. The fatty acid tails are strongly nonpolar and thus water-insoluble.

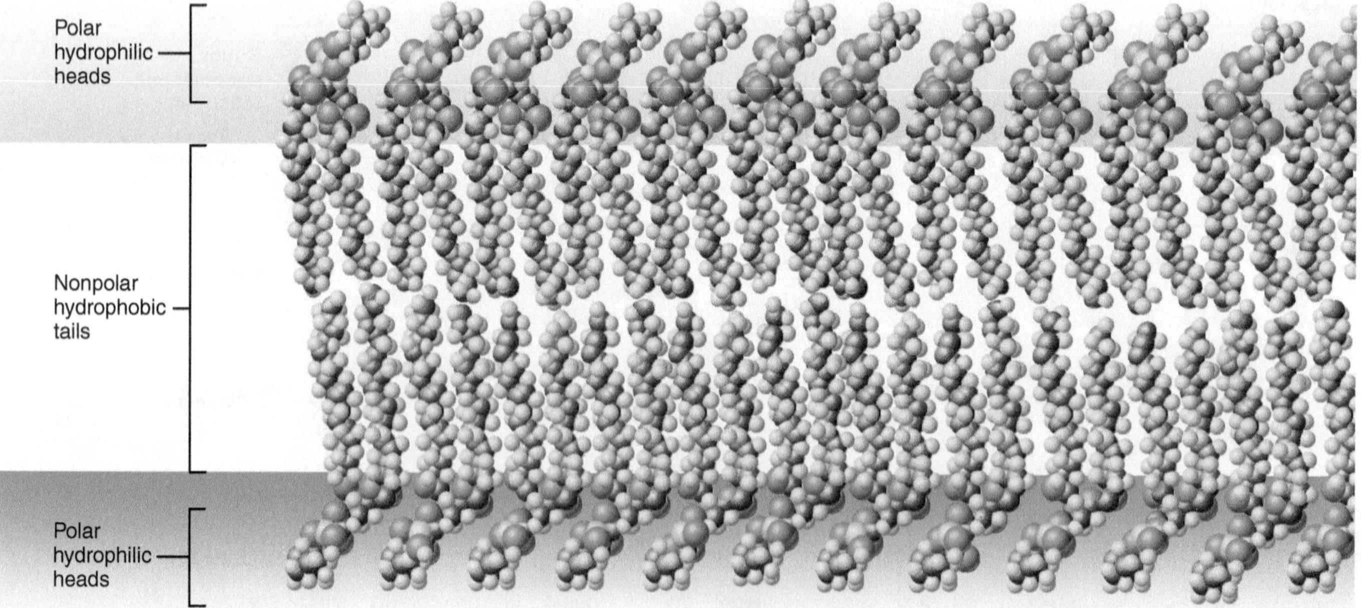

Figure 4.9 The lipid bilayer.

The basic structure of every plasma membrane is a double layer of phospholipids. This diagram illustrates how phospholipids aggregate to form a bilayer with a nonpolar interior when placed in a watery environment (indicated by the blue screened areas).

Imagine what happens when a collection of phospholipid molecules is placed in water. A structure called a **lipid bilayer** forms spontaneously. How does this happen? The long nonpolar tails of the phospholipid molecules are pushed away by the water molecules that surround them, shouldered aside as the water molecules seek partners that can form hydrogen bonds. After much shoving and jostling, every phospholipid molecule ends up with its polar head facing water and its nonpolar tail facing away from water. The phospholipid molecules form a *double* layer, called a bilayer. The shaded blue areas in figure 4.9 represent watery environments inside and outside the plasma membrane that push the nonpolar tails to the interior of the bilayer. Because there are two layers with the tails facing each other, no tails are ever in contact with water. Because the interior of a lipid bilayer is completely nonpolar, it repels any water-soluble molecules that attempt to pass through it, just as a layer of oil stops the passage of a drop of water (that's why ducks do not get wet—oily feathers).

Cholesterol, another nonpolar lipid molecule, resides in the interior portion of the bilayer. Cholesterol is a multiringed molecule that affects the fluid nature of the membrane. Although cholesterol is important in maintaining the integrity of the plasma membrane, it can accumulate in blood vessels, forming plaques that lead to cardiovascular disease.

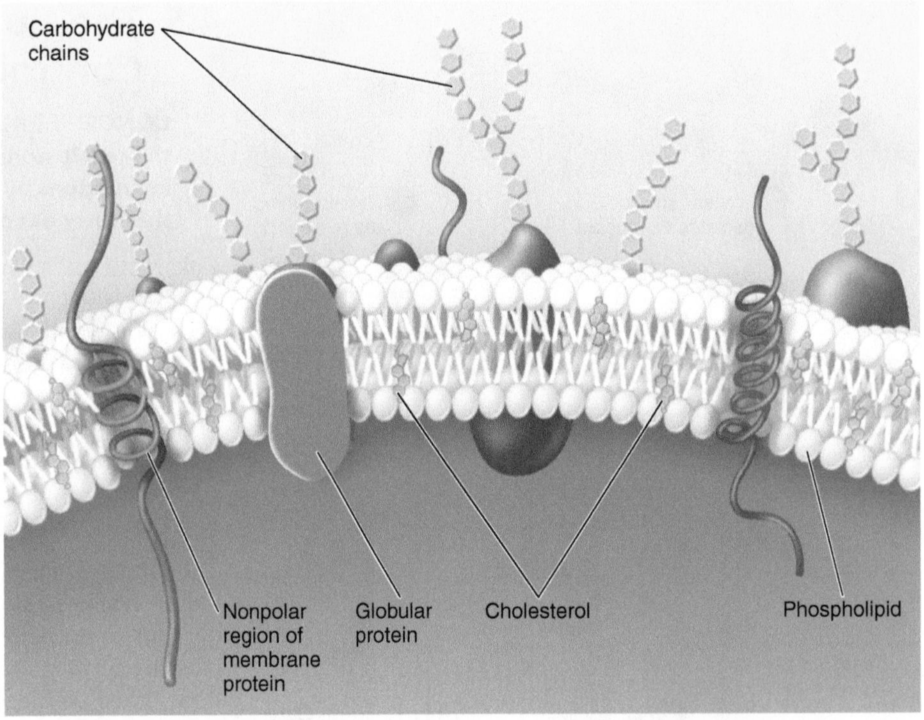

Figure 4.10 Proteins are embedded within the lipid bilayer.

A variety of proteins protrude through the lipid bilayer. Membrane proteins function as channels, receptors, and cell surface markers. Carbohydrate chains are often bound to these proteins and to phospholipids in the membrane. These chains serve as distinctive identification tags, unique to particular types of cells.

Proteins Within the Membrane

The second major component of every biological membrane is a collection of membrane proteins that float within the lipid bilayer. As you can see in figure 4.10, some proteins (the purple structures) pass through the lipid bilayer, providing channels through which molecules and ions pass. While some membrane proteins are fixed into position, others move about freely.

Many membrane proteins project up from the surface of the plasma membrane like buoys, often with carbohydrate chains (the orange chains in figure 4.10) or lipids attached to their tips like flags. These *cell surface proteins* act as markers to identify particular types of cells, or as beacons to bind specific hormones or proteins to the cell.

Cell surface markers called MHC proteins discussed on page 537 identify a person's cells as "self" so the immune system won't attack them. Transmembrane proteins are present in nerve cells and function as ion channels, as discussed on page 554.

Protein channels that extend all the way across the bilayer provide passageways for ions and polar molecules so they can pass into and out of the cell. How do these *transmembrane proteins* manage to span the membrane, rather than just floating on the surface in the way that a drop of water floats on oil? The part of the protein that actually traverses the lipid bilayer is a specially constructed spiral helix of nonpolar amino acids—the red coiled areas of the transmembrane protein you see in figure 4.11. Water responds to these nonpolar amino acids much as it does to nonpolar lipid chains, and as a result the helical spiral is held within the lipid interior of the bilayer, anchored there by the strong tendency of water to avoid contact with these nonpolar amino acids.

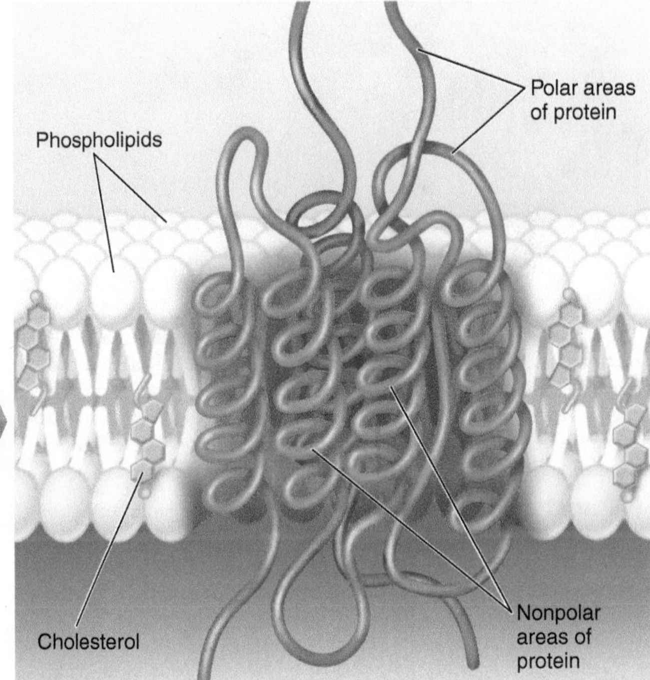

Figure 4.11 Nonpolar regions lock proteins into membranes.

A spiral helix of nonpolar amino acids (*red*) extends across the nonpolar lipid interior, while polar (*purple*) portions of the protein protrude out from the bilayer. The protein cannot move in or out because such a movement would drag polar segments of the protein into the nonpolar interior of the membrane.

4.5 The Nucleus: The Cell's Control Center

CONCEPT PREVIEW: The nucleus is the command center of the cell. It stores the cell's hereditary information and issues instructions by way of RNA to guide the production of the proteins that carry out cell activities.

Eukaryotic cells have many structural components and organelles in common (table 4.1). If you were to journey far into the interior of one of your cells, you would eventually reach the center of the cell. There you would find, cradled within a network of fine filaments like a ball in a basket, the **nucleus** ❶ (figure 4.12). The nucleus is the command and control center of the cell, directing all of its activities. It is also the genetic library where the hereditary information is stored.

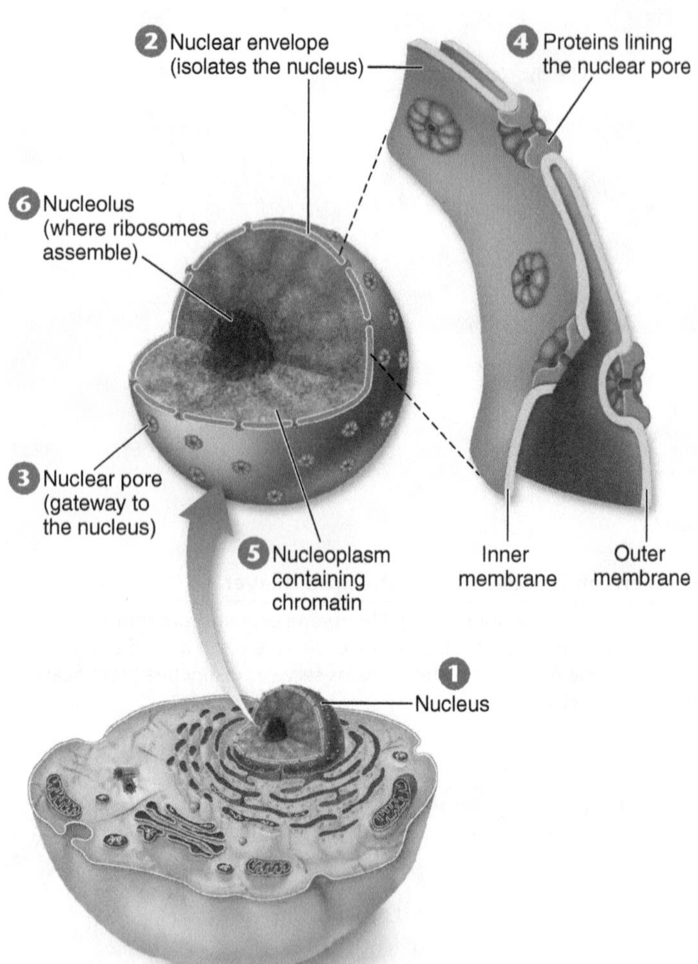

Figure 4.12 The nucleus.

The nucleus is composed of a double membrane, called a nuclear envelope, enclosing a fluid-filled interior containing the chromosomes. In cross section, the individual nuclear pores are seen to extend through the two membrane layers of the envelope. A pore is lined with protein, which acts to control access through the pore.

IMPLICATION A widely held view about the origin of the nucleus explains that the nucleus evolved when an ancient archaea invaded a bacterial cell. Does the fact that the nucleus is bounded by two membranes support this theory?

Nuclear Membrane

The surface of the nucleus is bounded by a special kind of membrane called the **nuclear envelope** ❷. The nuclear envelope is actually *two* membranes, one outside the other, like a sweater over a shirt. The nuclear envelope acts as a barrier between the nucleus and the cytoplasm, but substances need to pass through the envelope. The exchange of materials occurs through openings scattered over the surface of this envelope. Called **nuclear pores** ❸, these openings form when the two membrane layers of the nuclear envelope pinch together. A nuclear pore is not an empty opening, however; rather, it has many proteins embedded within it that permit proteins and RNA to pass into and out of the nucleus ❹.

Chromosomes

In both prokaryotes and eukaryotes, all hereditary information specifying cell structure and function is encoded in DNA. However, unlike prokaryotic DNA that forms an enclosed circle, the DNA of eukaryotes is divided into several segments and associated with protein, forming **chromosomes.** The proteins in the chromosome permit the DNA to wind tightly and condense during cell division. Under a light microscope, these condensed chromosomes are readily seen in dividing cells as densely staining rods. After cell division, eukaryotic chromosomes uncoil and fully extend into threadlike strands called **chromatin** ❺ that can no longer be distinguished individually with a light microscope within the nucleoplasm. Once uncoiled, the chromatin is available for protein synthesis. The process begins when RNA copies of genes are made from the DNA in the nucleus. The RNA molecules leave the nucleus through the nuclear pores and enter the cytoplasm where proteins are synthesized. These proteins, carrying out many different functions, determine what the cell is like.

Ribosomes

To make its many proteins, the cell employs a special structure called a **ribosome,** a kind of platform on which the proteins are built. Ribosomes read the RNA copy of a gene and use that information to direct the construction of a protein. Ribosomes are made up of a special form of RNA called *ribosomal RNA*, or *rRNA*, that is bound up within a complex of several dozen different proteins. Ribosome subunits are assembled in a region within the nucleus called the **nucleolus** ❻.

Protein synthesis is described in detail in chapter 12. The ribosome is the physical structure that holds the RNA in place while it is "read," being translated into the protein encoded by the RNA molecule.

TABLE 4.1 Eukaryotic Cell Structures and Their Functions

Structure	Description	Function
Structural Elements		
Cell wall	Outer layer of cellulose or chitin; absent in animal cells	Protection; support
Cytoskeleton	Network of protein filaments	Structural support; cell movement
Flagella and cilia	Cellular extensions with 9 + 2 arrangement of pairs of microtubules	Motility or moving fluids over surfaces
Plasma Membrane and Endomembrane System		
Plasma membrane	Lipid bilayer in which proteins are embedded	Regulates what passes into and out of cell; cell-to-cell recognition
Endoplasmic reticulum	Network of internal membranes	Forms compartments and vesicles; participates in protein and lipid synthesis
Nucleus	Structure (usually spherical) that contains chromosomes; surrounded by double membrane	Control center of cell; directs protein synthesis and cell reproduction
Golgi complex	Stacks of flattened vesicles	Packages proteins for export from the cell; forms secretory vesicles
Lysosomes	Vesicles derived from Golgi complex that contain hydrolytic digestive enzymes	Digest worn-out organelles and cell debris; play role in cell death
Energy-Producing Organelles		
Mitochondria	Bacteria-like elements with double membrane	Sites of oxidative metabolism; provides ATP for cellular energy
Chloroplasts	Bacteria-like organelles found in plants and algae; complex inner membrane consists of stacked vesicles	Sites of photosynthesis
Elements of Gene Expression		
Chromosomes	Long threads of DNA that form a complex with protein	Contain hereditary information
Nucleolus	Site of genes for rRNA synthesis	Assembles ribosomes
Ribosomes	Small, complex assemblies of protein and RNA, often bound to endoplasmic reticulum	Sites of protein synthesis

4.6 The Endomembrane System

CONCEPT PREVIEW: An extensive system of interior membranes organizes the interior of the cell into functional compartments that manufacture and deliver proteins and carry out a variety of specialized chemical processes.

Surrounding the nucleus within the interior of the eukaryotic cell is a tightly packed mass of membranes. They fill the cell, dividing it into compartments, channeling the transport of molecules through the interior of the cell and providing the surfaces on which enzymes act. The system of internal compartments created by these membranes in eukaryotic cells constitutes the most fundamental distinction between the cells of eukaryotes and prokaryotes.

Figure 4.13 The endoplasmic reticulum (ER).

The endoplasmic reticulum provides the cell with an extensive system of internal membranes for the synthesis and transport of materials. Ribosomes are associated with only one side of the rough ER; the other side is the boundary of a separate compartment within the cell into which the ribosomes extrude newly made proteins destined for secretion. Smooth endoplasmic reticulum has few to no bound ribosomes.

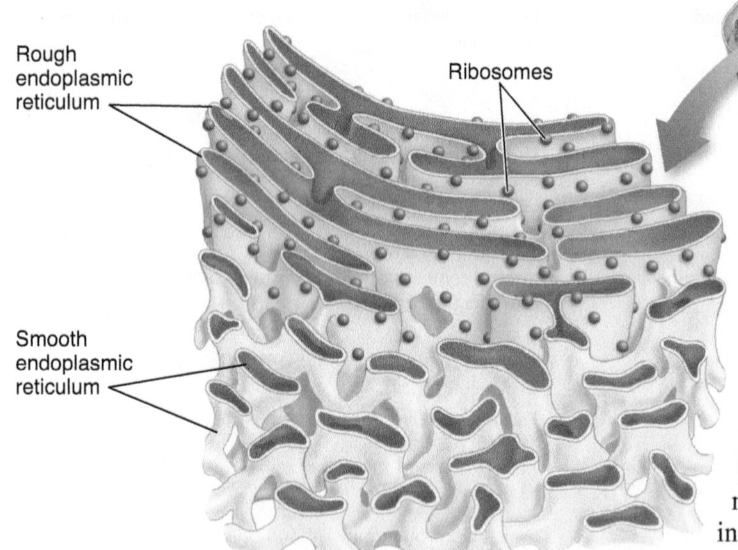

Endoplasmic Reticulum: The Transportation System

The extensive system of internal membranes is called the **endoplasmic reticulum,** often abbreviated **ER.** The term *endoplasmic* means "within the cytoplasm," and the term *reticulum* is a Latin word meaning "little net." Looking at the sheets of membrane weaving through the interior of the cell in figure 4.13, you can see how the ER got its name. The ER creates a series of channels and interconnections, and it also isolates some spaces as membrane-enclosed sacs called **vesicles.**

The surface of the ER is the place where the cell makes proteins intended for export (such as enzymes secreted from the cell surface). The surface of those regions of the ER devoted to the synthesis of such transported proteins is heavily studded with ribosomes and appears pebbly, like the surface of sandpaper, when seen through an electron microscope. For this reason, these regions are called **rough ER.** Regions in which ER-bound ribosomes are relatively scarce are correspondingly called **smooth ER.** The surface of the smooth ER is embedded with enzymes that aid in the manufacture of carbohydrates and lipids.

Figure 4.14 Golgi complex.

This vesicle-forming system, called the Golgi complex after its discoverer, is an integral part of the cell's internal membrane system. The Golgi complex processes and packages materials for transport to another region within the cell and/or for export from the cell. It receives material for processing in transport vesicles on one side and sends the material packaged in secretory vesicles off the other side. (a) Diagram of a Golgi complex. (b) Micrograph of a Golgi complex showing vesicles.

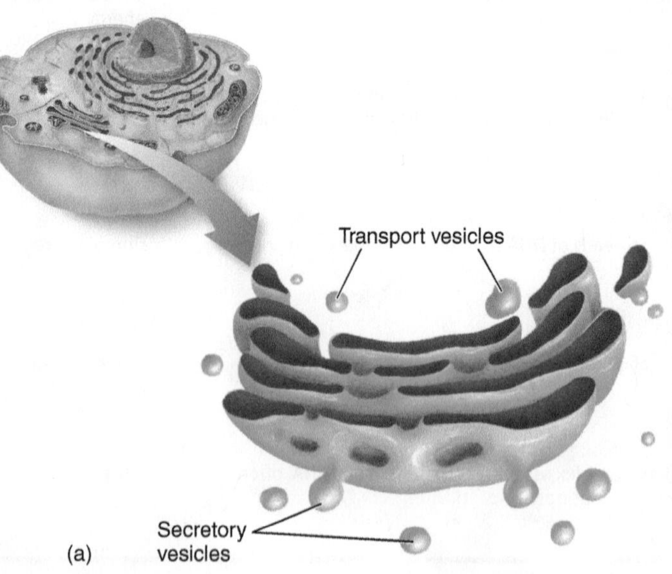

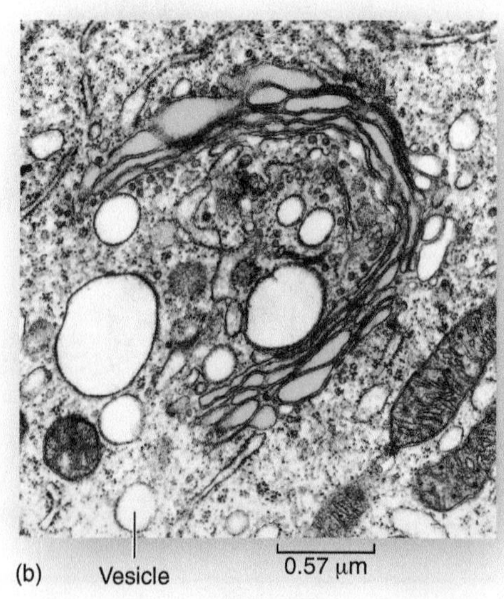

The Golgi Complex: The Delivery System

As new molecules are made on the surface of the ER, they are passed from the ER to flattened stacks of membranes called **Golgi bodies.** These structures, which in figure 4.14 look like pancakes stacked one on top of the other, are named for Camillo Golgi, the nineteenth-century Italian physician who first called attention to them. The number of Golgi bodies a cell contains ranges from 1 or a few in protists, to 20 or more in animal cells and several hundred in certain plant cells. Golgi bodies function in the collection, packaging, and distribution of molecules manufactured in the cell. Scattered through the cytoplasm, Golgi bodies are collectively referred to as the **Golgi complex.**

The rough ER, smooth ER, and Golgi work together as an endomembrane transport system in the cell. Figure 4.15 walks you through the path that molecules take from the ER through the Golgi and out to their final destinations. Proteins and lipids that are manufactured on the ER membranes are transported through the channels of the ER and are packaged into transport vesicles that bud off from the ER ❶. The vesicles fuse with the membrane of the Golgi bodies, dumping their contents into the Golgi ❷. Within the Golgi bodies the molecules may take one of many paths, indicated by the branching arrows in figure 4.15. Many of these molecules become tagged with carbohydrates. The molecules collect at the ends of the membranous folds of the Golgi bodies; these folds are given the special name *cisternae* (Latin, collecting vessels). Vesicles that pinch off from the cisternae carry the molecules to the different compartments of the cell ❸ and ❹, or to the inner surface of the plasma membrane, where molecules to be secreted are released to the outside ❺.

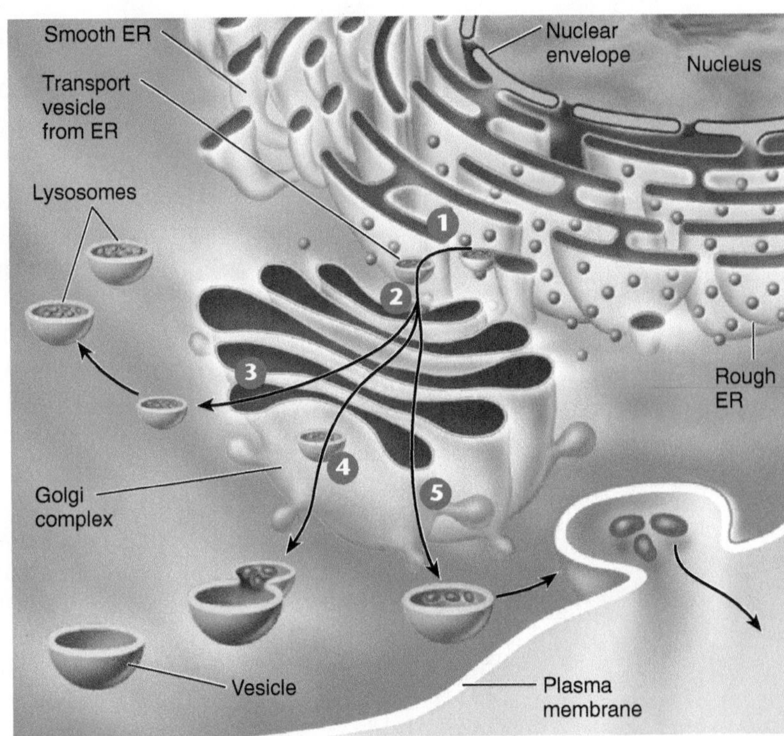

Figure 4.15 How the endomembrane system works.

A highly efficient highway system within the cell, the endomembrane system transports material from the ER to the Golgi and from there to other destinations.

Lysosomes: Recycling Centers

Other organelles called **lysosomes** arise from the Golgi complex (the light orange vesicle budding at ❸) and contain a concentrated mix of the powerful enzymes manufactured in the rough ER that break down macromolecules. Lysosomes are the recycling centers of the cell, breaking down failing organelles and other structures within cells, digesting worn-out cell components, and recycling the proteins and other materials of the old parts.

Vacuoles: Storage Compartments

The interiors of plant and many protist cells contain membrane-bounded storage compartments called **vacuoles.** The center of the plant cell shown in figure 4.16, as in all plant cells, contains a large, apparently empty space, called the *central vacuole.* This vacuole is not really empty; it contains large amounts of water and other materials, such as sugars, ions, and pigments. The central vacuole functions as a storage center for these important substances.

In protists like *Paramecium,* cells contain a *contractile vacuole* near the cell surface that accumulates excess water. This vacuole has a small pore that opens to the outside of the cell. By rhythmic contractions, it pumps accumulated water out through the pore.

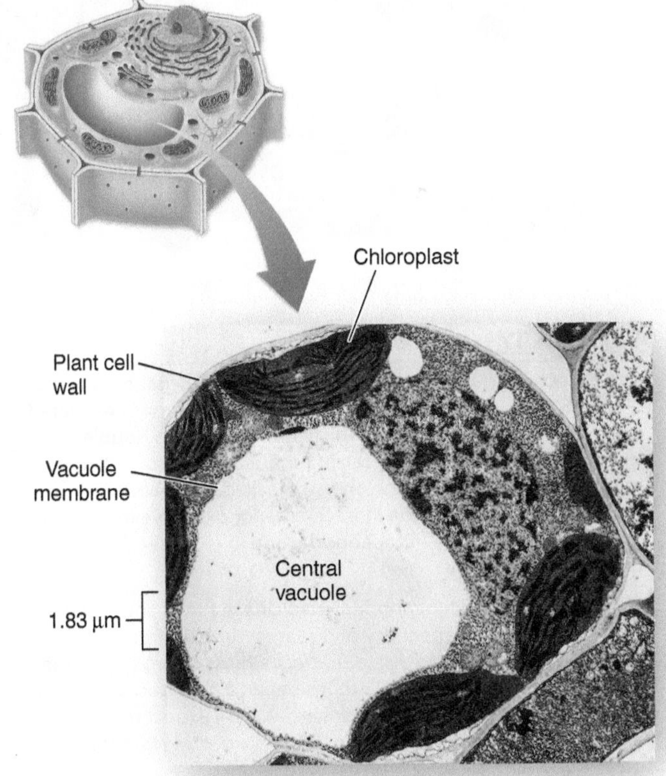

Figure 4.16 A plant central vacuole.

A plant's central vacuole stores dissolved substances and can increase in size to increase the surface area of a plant cell.

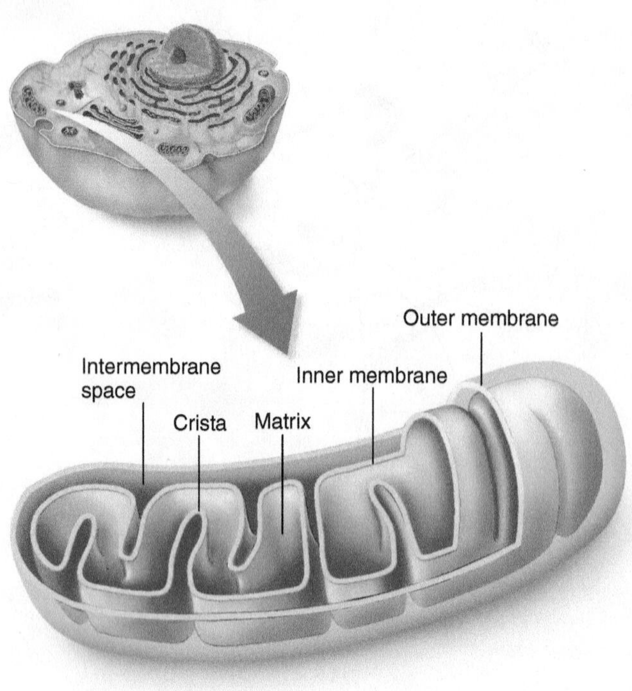

(a)

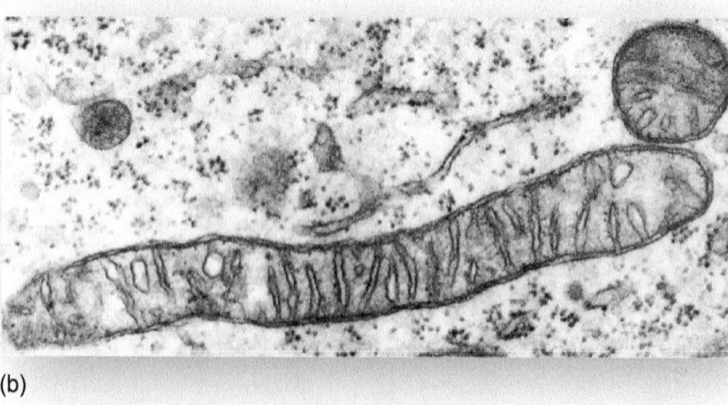

(b)

Figure 4.17 Mitochondria.

The mitochondria of a cell are sausage-shaped organelles within which oxidative metabolism takes place, and energy is extracted from food using oxygen. (a) A mitochondrion has a double membrane. The inner membrane is shaped into folds called cristae. The space within the cristae is called the matrix. The cristae greatly increase the surface area for oxidative metabolism. (b) Micrograph of two mitochondria, one in cross section, the other cut lengthwise.

IMPLICATION Mitochondrial medicine is a new and rapidly developing medical speciality of diseases resulting from failure of the mitochondria. These diseases affect almost all organs, for the simple reason that almost all organs depend on mitochondria for the energy they use. Which organs would you expect to exhibit the most serious mitochondrial diseases? Explain why you chose the organs you did.

4.7 Organelles That Harvest Energy

CONCEPT PREVIEW: Eukaryotic cells contain complex organelles that harvest energy. They have their own DNA and are thought to have arisen by endosymbiosis from ancient bacteria.

Eukaryotic cells contain several kinds of complex, energy harvesting organelles that contain their own DNA and appear to have been derived from ancient bacteria. These bacteria were taken up by ancestral eukaryotic cells in the distant past and remained living inside the host cell, forming a relationship called symbiosis. These organelles include mitochondria (which occur in the cells of all but a very few eukaryotes) and chloroplasts (which occur only in algae and plant cells—they do not occur in animal or fungal cells).

Mitochondria: Powerhouses of the Cell

Eukaryotic organisms extract energy from organic molecules ("food") in a complex series of chemical reactions called **oxidative metabolism,** which takes place only in their mitochondria. **Mitochondria** (singular, **mitochondrion**) are sausage-shaped organelles about the size of a bacterial cell. Mitochondria are bounded by two membranes. The outer membrane, shown partially cut away in figure 4.17, is smooth and apparently derives from the plasma membrane of the host cell that first took up the bacterium long ago. The inner membrane, apparently the plasma membrane of the bacterium that gave rise to the mitochondrion, is bent into numerous folds called **cristae** (singular, **crista**) that resemble the folded plasma membranes in various groups of bacteria. The cutaway view of the figure shows how the cristae partition the mitochondrion into two compartments, an inner **matrix** and an outer compartment, called the **intermembrane space.** As you will learn in chapter 7, this architecture is critical to successfully carrying out oxidative metabolism.

During the 1.5 billion years in which mitochondria have existed in eukaryotic cells, most of their genes have been transferred to the chromosomes of the host cells. But mitochondria still have some of their original genes, contained in a circular, closed, naked molecule of DNA (called *mitochondrial DNA,* or *mtDNA*) that closely resembles the circular DNA molecule of a bacterium. On this mtDNA are several genes that produce some of the proteins essential for oxidative metabolism. In both mitochondria and bacteria, the circular DNA molecule is replicated during the process of division. When a mitochondrion divides, it copies its DNA located in the matrix and splits into two by simple fission, dividing much as bacteria do.

Chloroplasts: Energy-Capturing Centers

All photosynthesis in plants and algae takes place within another bacteria-like organelle, the **chloroplast** (figure 4.18). There is strong evidence that chloroplasts, like mitochondria, were derived from bacteria by symbiosis. A chloroplast is bounded, like a mitochondrion, by two membranes, the inner derived from the original bacterium and the outer resembling the host cell's ER. Chloroplasts are larger than mitochondria, and have a more complex organization. Inside the chloroplast, another series of membranes are fused to form stacks of closed vesicles called **thylakoids,** the green disklike structures visible in the interior of the chloroplast in

The light-dependent reactions of photosynthesis are discussed on pages 104 to 107. Proteins embedded in the thylakoid membrane use energy from the sun to make two molecules, ATP and NADPH. These molecules are used to make sugar molecules.

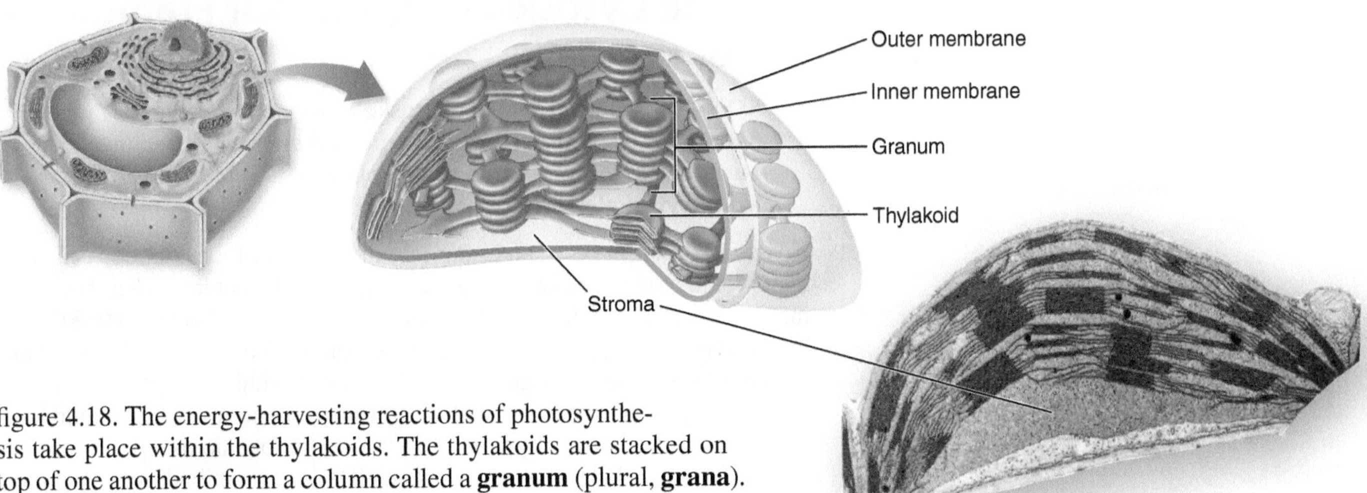

figure 4.18. The energy-harvesting reactions of photosynthesis take place within the thylakoids. The thylakoids are stacked on top of one another to form a column called a **granum** (plural, **grana**). The interior of a chloroplast is bathed with a semiliquid substance called the **stroma.**

Like mitochondria, chloroplasts have a circular DNA molecule. This DNA contains many of the genes coding for the proteins necessary to carry out photosynthesis. Plant cells can contain from one to several hundred chloroplasts, depending on the species. Neither mitochondria nor chloroplasts can be grown in a cell-free culture; they are totally dependent on the cells within which they occur.

Figure 4.18 A chloroplast.

Bacteria-like organelles called chloroplasts are the sites of photosynthesis in photosynthetic eukaryotes. Like mitochondria, they have a complex system of internal membranes on which chemical reactions take place. The internal membranes of a chloroplast are fused to form stacks of closed vesicles called thylakoids. Photosynthesis occurs within these thylakoids. Thylakoids are stacked one on top of the other in columns called grana. The interior of the chloroplast is bathed in a semiliquid substance called the stroma.

Endosymbiosis

Symbiosis is a close, integrated relationship between organisms of different species that live together. The theory of **endosymbiosis** proposes that some of today's eukaryotic organelles evolved by a symbiosis in which one cell of a prokaryotic species was engulfed by and lived inside the cell of another species of prokaryote that was a precursor to eukaryotes. Figure 4.19 shows how this is thought to have occurred. Many cells take up food or other substances through endocytosis, a process whereby the plasma membrane of a cell wraps around the substance, enclosing it within a vesicle inside the cell. Oftentimes, the contents in the vesicle are broken down with digestive enzymes. According to the endosymbiont theory this did not occur; instead, the engulfed prokaryotes provided their hosts with certain advantages associated with their special metabolic abilities. Two key eukaryotic organelles just described are believed to be the descendants of these endosymbiotic prokaryotes: mitochondria, which are thought to have originated as bacteria capable of carrying out oxidative metabolism; and chloroplasts, which apparently arose from photosynthetic bacteria.

The endosymbiont theory is supported by a wealth of evidence. Both mitochondria and chloroplasts are surrounded by two membranes; the inner membrane probably evolved from the plasma membrane of the engulfed bacterium, while the outer membrane is probably derived from the plasma membrane or endoplasmic reticulum of the host cell. Mitochondria are about the same size as most bacteria, and the cristae formed by their inner membranes resemble the folded membranes in various groups of bacteria. Mitochondrial ribosomes are also similar to bacterial ribosomes in size and structure. Both mitochondria and chloroplasts contain circular molecules of DNA similar to those in bacteria. Finally, mitochondria divide by simple fission, splitting in two just as bacterial cells do, and they apparently replicate and partition their DNA in much the same way as bacteria.

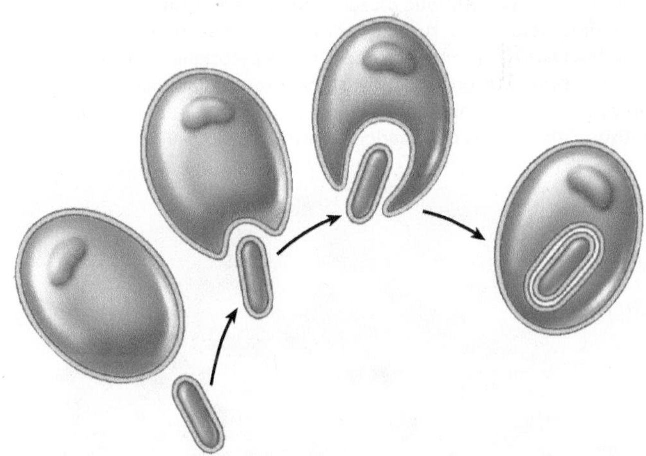

Figure 4.19 Endosymbiosis.

This figure shows how a double membrane may have been created during the symbiotic origin of mitochondria or chloroplasts.

IMPLICATION When first proposed (by Professor Lynn Margulis of Amherst College), the endosymbiosis theory was once widely ridiculed as absurd speculation, until molecular evidence was found to support it. Her more recent Gaia hypothesis that our planet is a super-organism is being similarly discounted. How do you feel about such an idea?

4.8 The Cytoskeleton: Interior Framework of the Cell

CONCEPT PREVIEW: The cytoskeleton is a latticework of protein fibers that determines a cell's shape and anchors organelles to particular locations within the cytoplasm. Cells can move with the aid of cytoskeletal proteins.

If you could shrink down and enter into the interior of a eukaryotic cell, your view would be similar to what you see in figure 4.20, your immediate surroundings dominated by a dense network of protein fibers called the **cytoskeleton.** This framework supports the shape of the cell. It also anchors organelles like the mitochondria in this figure to fixed locations within the cell interior. This fiber network cannot be seen with a light microscope because the individual fibers are single chains of protein, much too fine for microscopes to resolve. To "see" the cytoskeleton, scientists attach fluorescent antibodies to the protein fibers and then photograph them under fluorescent light.

The protein fibers of the cytoskeleton are a dynamic system, constantly being formed and disassembled. There are three different kinds of protein fibers shown as enlargements in the figure: thick ropes of intertwined protein called **intermediate filaments,** hollow tubes called **microtubules** made of the protein tubulin, and long, slender **microfilaments** made of the protein **actin.** The intermediate filaments, microtubules, and microfilaments are anchored to membrane proteins embedded within the plasma membrane.

The cytoskeleton plays a major role in determining the shape of animal cells, which lack rigid cell walls. Because filaments can form and disassemble readily, the shape of an animal cell can change rapidly. If you examine the surface of an animal cell with a microscope, you will often find it alive with motion, projections shooting out from the surface and then retracting, only to shoot out elsewhere moments later.

The cytoskeleton is not only responsible for the cell's shape, but it also provides a scaffold both for ribosomes to carry out protein synthesis and for enzymes to be localized within defined areas of the cytoplasm. By anchoring particular enzymes near one another, the cytoskeleton participates with organelles in organizing the cell's activities.

Figure 4.20 The protein fibers of the cytoskeleton.

Organelles such as mitochondria are anchored to fixed locations in the cytoplasm by the cytoskeleton, a network of protein fibers. *Intermediate filaments* are composed of overlapping proteins that form a ropelike structure, providing tremendous mechanical strength to the cell. *Microtubules* are composed of tubulin protein subunits arranged side by side to form a tube. Microtubules are comparatively stiff cytoskeletal elements that function in intracellular transport and stabilization of cell structure. *Actin microfilaments* are made of two strands of the protein actin twisted together and usually occur in bundles. Actin microfilaments are responsible for cell movement.

IMPLICATION Athletic muscle injuries can result from overstretching before hard running or other activities that extend muscles. Damage appears to occur at the cytoskeleton level, with temporary disorganization of the intermediate filaments. Do you think such injuries are more likely to occur among overenthusiastic joggers or experienced athletes? Explain.

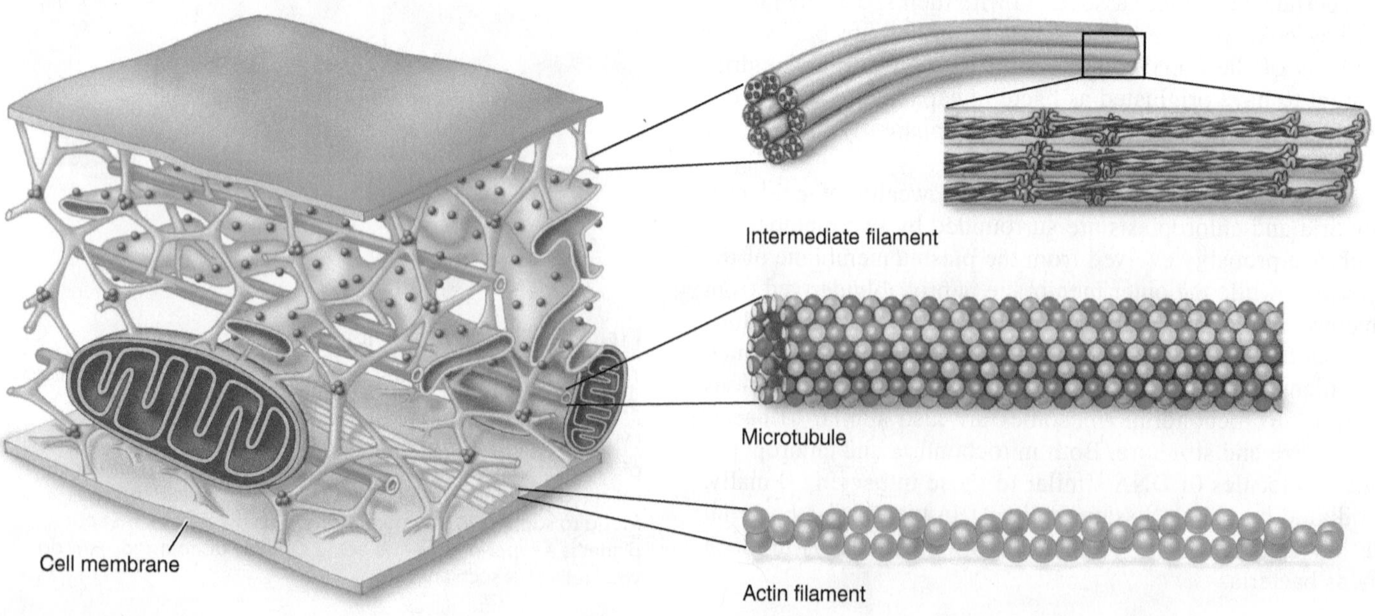

Centrioles

Complex structures called **centrioles** assemble microtubules from tubulin subunits in the cells of animals and most protists. Centrioles occur in pairs within the cytoplasm, usually located at right angles to one another as you can see in figure 4.21. They are usually found near the nuclear envelope and are among the most structurally complex microtubular assemblies of the cell.

Centrioles are involved in assembling a network of microtubules that attach to and separate the chromosomes during cell division. This network of microtubules, called the spindle, is discussed in more detail in chapters 8 and 9.

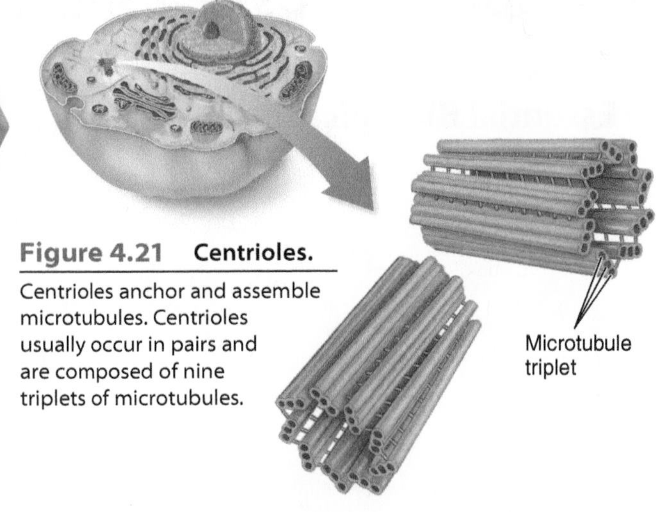

Figure 4.21 Centrioles.

Centrioles anchor and assemble microtubules. Centrioles usually occur in pairs and are composed of nine triplets of microtubules.

Cell Movement

Like a tendon that anchors a muscle to a bone, intermediate filaments act as intracellular tendons, preventing excessive stretching of cells. Actin microfilaments play a major role in determining the shape of cells. Essentially, all cell motion is tied to the movement of actin microfilaments, microtubules, or both. Because actin microfilaments can form and dissolve so readily, they enable some cells to change shape quickly and move from place to place.

Some Cells Crawl. It is the arrangement of actin microfilaments within the cell cytoplasm that allows cells to "crawl," literally! Crawling is a significant cellular phenomenon, essential to inflammation, clotting, wound healing, and the spread of cancer. White blood cells in particular exhibit this ability. Produced in the bone marrow, these cells are released into the circulatory system and eventually crawl out of capillaries and into the tissues to destroy potential pathogens. The crawling mechanism is an exquisite example of cellular coordination.

Swimming with Flagella and Cilia. Some eukaryotic cells contain **flagella** (singular, **flagellum**), fine, long, threadlike organelles protruding from the cell surface. Figure 4.22*a* shows how a flagellum arises from a microtubular structure called a **basal body,** with groups of microtubules arranged in rows of three, shown in the cross-sectional view. Some of these microtubules extend up into the flagellum, which consists of a circle of nine microtubule pairs surrounding two central microtubules. This **9 + 2 arrangement** is a fundamental feature of eukaryotes and apparently evolved early in their history. In humans, we find a single long flagellum on each sperm cell that propels the cell in a swimming motion. If flagella are numerous and organized in dense rows, they are called **cilia.** Cilia do not differ from flagella in their structure, but cilia are usually shorter. The paramecium in figure 4.22*b* is covered with cilia, giving it a furry appearance. In humans, dense mats of cilia project from cells that line our breathing tube, the trachea, to move mucus and dust particles out of the respiratory tract into the throat (where we can expel these contaminants by spitting or swallowing). Eukaryotic flagella serve a similar function as the bacterial flagella discussed in section 4.2, but are very different structurally.

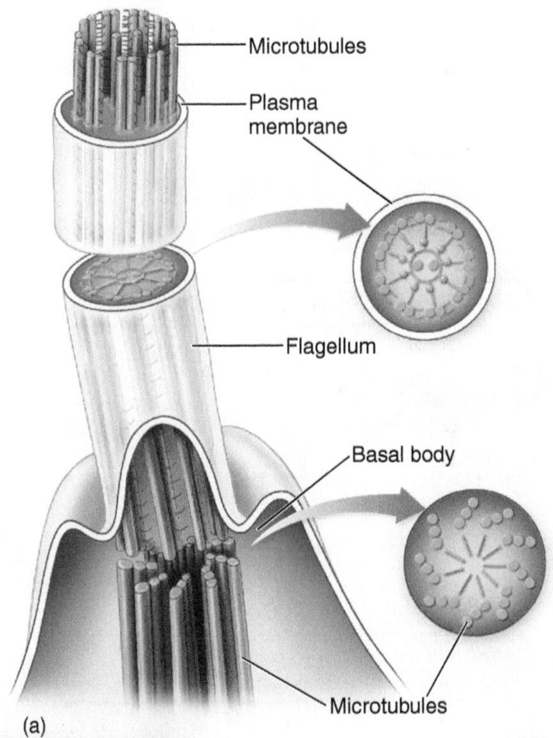

Figure 4.22 Flagella and cilia.

(a) A eukaryotic flagellum springs directly from a basal body and is composed of a ring of nine pairs of microtubules with two microtubules in its core. (b) The surface of this paramecium is covered with a dense forest of cilia.

Concept Check

1. How are proteins able to insert into the plasma membrane?
2. How is smooth ER different from rough ER?
3. What is the evidence that mitochondria evolved from ancient bacteria?
4. Which element of the cytoskeleton is active in the crawling of white blood cells?

Transport Across Plasma Membranes

Essential Biological Process 4A

Diffusion

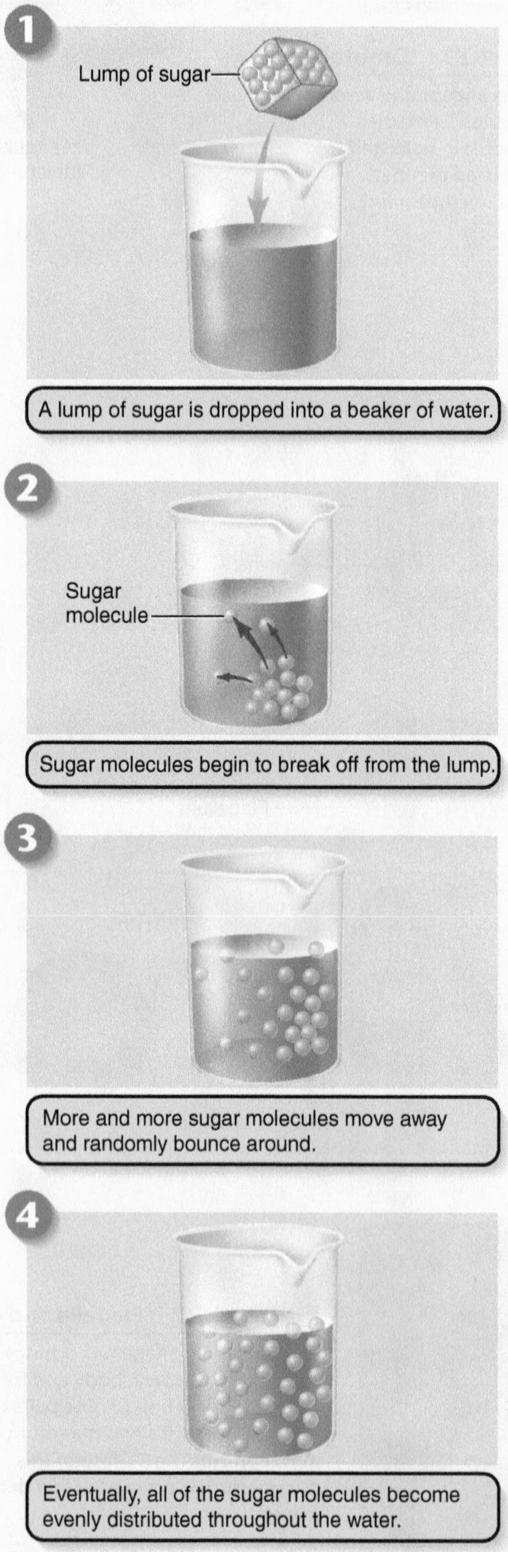

1

Lump of sugar

A lump of sugar is dropped into a beaker of water.

2

Sugar molecule

Sugar molecules begin to break off from the lump.

3

More and more sugar molecules move away and randomly bounce around.

4

Eventually, all of the sugar molecules become evenly distributed throughout the water.

4.9 Diffusion and Osmosis

CONCEPT PREVIEW: Random movements of molecules cause them to move to areas of lower concentration, a process called diffusion. Water associated with polar solutes is not free to diffuse, and there is a net movement of water across a membrane toward the side with less "free" water, a process called osmosis.

For cells to survive, nutrients, water, and other materials must pass into the cell, and waste materials must be eliminated. All of this moving back and forth across the cell's plasma membrane occurs in one of three ways: (1) water and other substances diffuse through the membrane, (2) food particles and sometimes liquids are engulfed by the membrane folding around them, or (3) proteins in the membrane act as doors that admit certain molecules only. First we will examine diffusion.

Diffusion

How a molecule moves—just where it goes—is totally random, like shaking marbles in a cup, so if two kinds of molecules are added together, they soon mix. The random motion of molecules always tends to produce uniform mixtures because a substance moves from regions where its concentration is high to regions where its concentration is lower (that is, *down* the **concentration gradient**). How does a molecule "know" in what direction to move? It doesn't—molecules don't "know" anything. A molecule is equally likely to move in any direction and is constantly changing course in random ways. There are simply more molecules able to move from where they are common than from where they are scarce. This mixing process is called **diffusion.** Diffusion (*Essential Biological Process 4A*) is the net movement of molecules down a concentration gradient toward regions of lower concentration (that is, where there are relatively fewer of them) as a result of random motion. For example, a lump of sugar dropped into a beaker of water will break apart into individual sugar molecules that will move about randomly. However, they will tend to travel away from the area of high concentration (the sugar cube) to an area of lower concentration (the rest of the beaker). Eventually, the substance will achieve a state of *equilibrium,* where there is no net movement toward any particular direction (as shown in panel 4). The individual molecules of the substance are still in motion, but there is no net change in direction.

Osmosis

Diffusion allows molecules like oxygen, carbon dioxide, and nonpolar lipids to cross the plasma membrane. Ions and polar molecules, by contrast, cannot cross the very nonpolar environment found in the lipid core of the membrane bilayer. However, the movement of water molecules, which are very polar, is not blocked—water diffuses freely across the plasma membrane. How is this possible? Water molecules pass through small channels, called **aquaporins,** that traverse the membrane. These water channels are very selective, even blocking the passage of protons (hydrogen ions), which are smaller than water molecules. This selectivity is due to a cluster of positively charged amino acids that line the pore and repel protons, which are also positively charged.

As in diffusion, water passes into and out of a cell down its concentration gradient, a process called **osmosis** (*Essential Biological Process 4B*). However, the movement of water into and out of a cell is dependent upon the concentration of other substances in solution. To understand how water moves into and out of a cell, let's focus on the water molecules already present inside a cell. What are they doing? Many of them are interacting with the sugars, proteins, and other polar molecules inside. Remember, water is very polar itself and readily interacts with other polar molecules. These social water molecules are not randomly moving about as they were outside; instead, they remain clustered around the polar molecules inside the cell. As a result, while water molecules keep coming into the cell by random motion, they don't randomly come out again. The simple experiment shown in *Essential Biological Process 4B* illustrates what happens. Think of the right side of the beaker as the inside of a cell, and the left side is a watery environment. Like the plasma membrane, a semipermeable membrane that allows some substances to pass but not all substances separates the two areas. When the polar molecule urea is present in the cell, water molecules cluster around each urea molecule and are no longer able to pass through the membrane to the "outside." In effect, the polar solute has reduced the number of free water molecules. Because the "outside" of the cell (on the left) has more unbound water molecules, water moves by diffusion into the cell (to the right).

The concentration of *all* molecules dissolved in a solution (the **solutes**) is called the osmotic concentration of the solution. If the osmotic concentrations of two solutions are equal, the solutions are **isotonic** (Greek *iso,* the same). If two solutions have unequal osmotic concentrations, the solution with the higher solute concentration is said to be **hypertonic** (Greek *hyper,* more than), and the solution with the lower one is **hypotonic** (Greek *hypo,* less than).

Movement of water into a cell by osmosis creates pressure, called osmotic pressure, which can cause a cell to swell and burst (figure 4.23). Most animal cells cannot withstand osmotic pressure unless their plasma membranes are braced to resist the swelling. If placed in pure water, they soon burst like overinflated balloons. That is why the cells of so many kinds of organisms have cell walls to stiffen their exteriors. In fact, this osmotic pressure, called turgor pressure in plants, is important for plant cells to maintain their shape. Without adequate water inside the cells, the plants wilt. In animals, the fluids bathing the cells have as many polar molecules dissolved in them as the cells do, making them isotonic, so the problem doesn't arise.

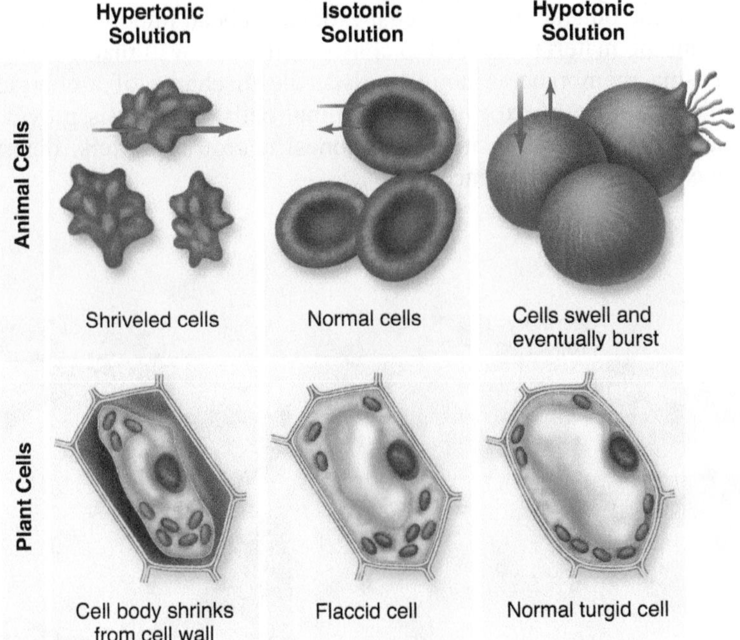

Figure 4.23 Osmotic pressure in animal and plant cells.

Essential Biological Process 4B

Osmosis

1

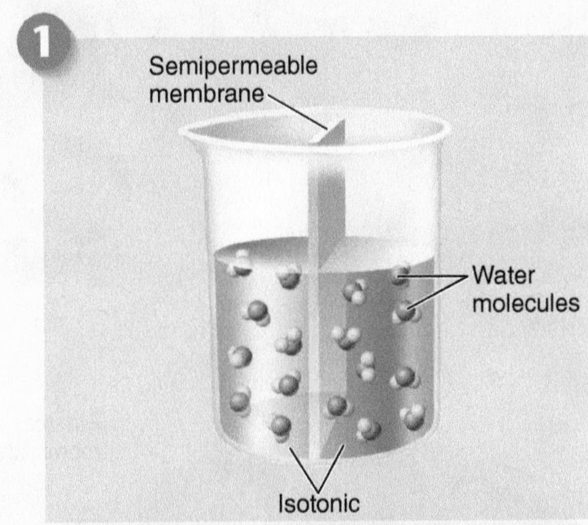

Diffusion causes water molecules to distribute themselves equally on both sides of a semipermeable membrane.

2

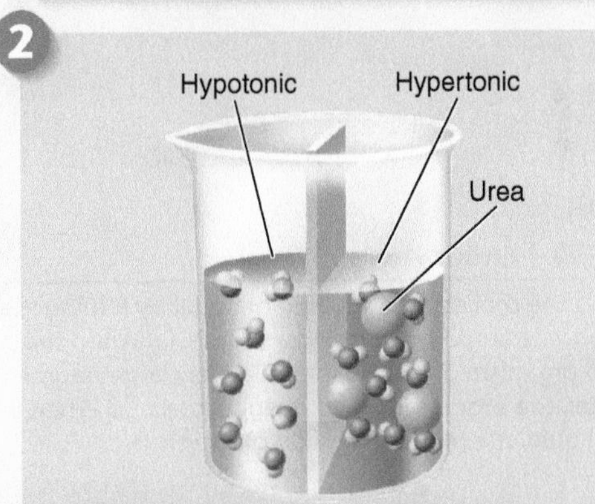

Addition of solute molecules that cannot cross the membrane reduces the number of free water molecules on that side, as they bind to the solute.

3

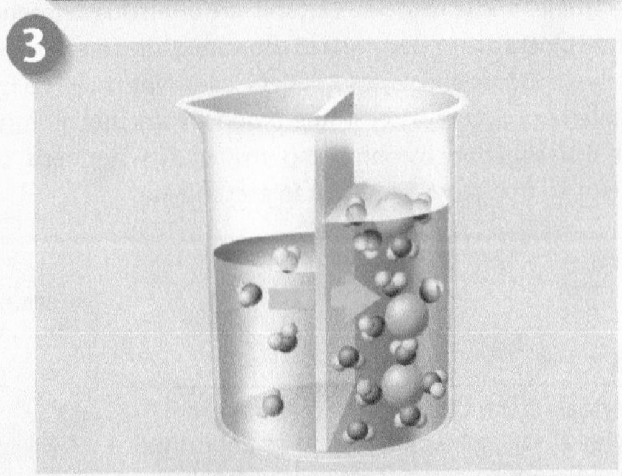

Diffusion then causes free water molecules to move from the side where their concentration is higher to the solute side, where their concentration is lower.

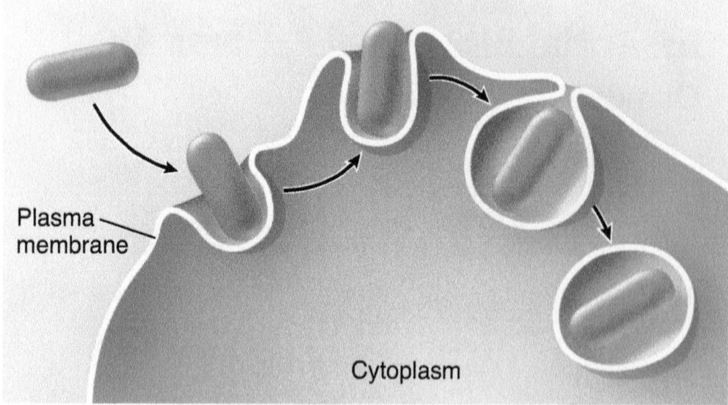

(a) Phagocytosis

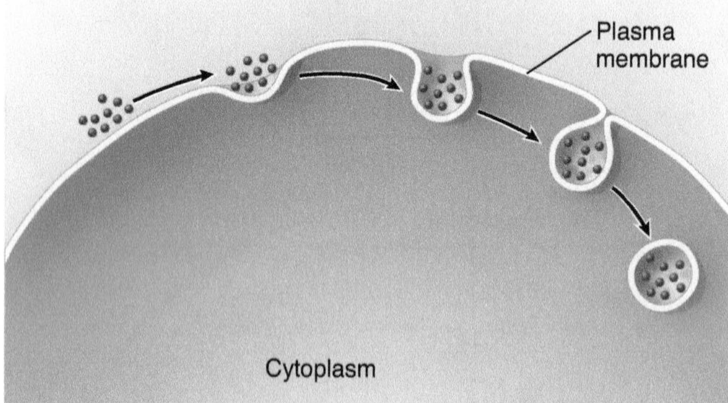

(b) Pinocytosis

Figure 4.24 Endocytosis.

Endocytosis is the process of engulfing material by folding the plasma membrane around it, forming a vesicle. (a) When the material is an organism or some other relatively large fragment of organic matter, the process is called phagocytosis. (b) When the material is a liquid, the process is called pinocytosis.

BIOLOGY & YOU

Statins. High levels of cholesterol, which can coat the arteries and lead to heart attacks, are often due to a gene defect that blocks the endocytosis of cholesterol (the membrane protein that triggers endocytosis is defective). Not taken up by cells, cholesterol accumulates in the bloodstream. Statin drugs combat this situation by inhibiting the body's synthesis of cholesterol, so that there is less of it to accumulate.

4.10 Bulk Passage into and out of Cells

CONCEPT PREVIEW: The plasma membrane can engulf materials by endocytosis, folding the membrane around the material to encase it within a vesicle. Exocytosis is essentially this process in reverse, using vesicles to expel substances.

Endocytosis

The cells of many eukaryotes take in food and liquids by extending their plasma membranes outward toward food particles. The membrane engulfs the particle and forms a vesicle—a membrane-bounded sac—around it. This process is called **endocytosis** (figure 4.24).

If the material the cell takes in is particulate (made up of discrete particles), such as an organism, like the red bacterium in figure 4.24*a*, or some other fragment of organic matter, the process is called **phagocytosis** (Greek *phagein,* to eat, and *cytos,* cell). If the material the cell takes in is liquid or substances dissolved in a liquid, like the small particles in figure 4.24*b*, it is called **pinocytosis** (Greek *pinein,* to drink). Pinocytosis is common among animal cells. Mammalian egg cells, for example, "nurse" from surrounding cells; the nearby cells secrete nutrients that the maturing egg cell takes up by pinocytosis. Virtually all eukaryotic cells constantly carry out these kinds of endocytosis, trapping particles and extracellular fluid in vesicles and ingesting them. Endocytosis rates vary from one cell type to another. They can be surprisingly high: Some types of white blood cells ingest 25% of their cell volume each hour!

Exocytosis

The reverse of endocytosis is **exocytosis,** the discharge of material from vesicles at the cell surface. The vesicle in figure 4.25 contains a substance to be discharged, or released, from the cell. The purple particles remain suspended in the vesicle as it fuses with the plasma membrane. The membrane that forms the vesicle is made of phospholipids, and as it comes in contact with the plasma membrane, the phospholipids of both membranes interact, forming a pore through which the contents leave the vesicle to the outside. In plant cells, exocytosis is an important means of exporting the materials needed to construct the cell wall that lies outside the plasma membrane. Among protists, the discharge of a contractile vacuole is a form of exocytosis. In animal cells, exocytosis provides a mechanism for secreting many hormones, neurotransmitters, digestive enzymes, and other substances.

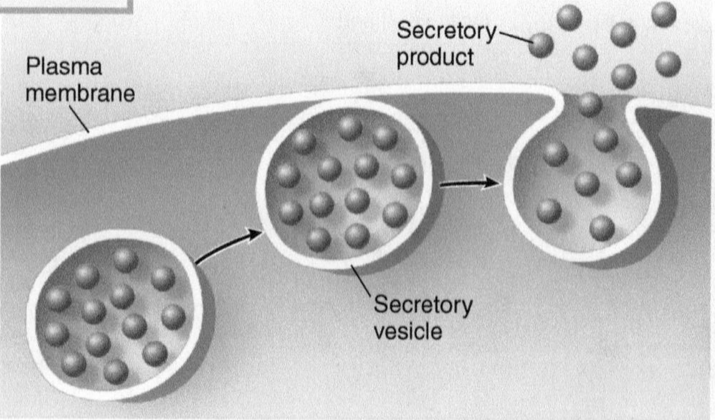

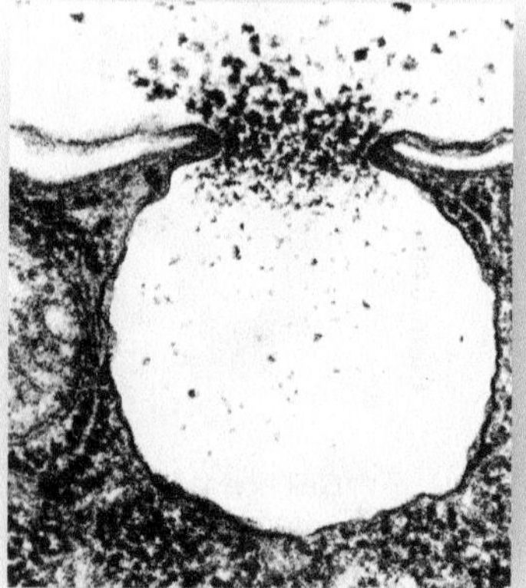

Figure 4.25 Exocytosis.

Exocytosis is the discharge of material from vesicles at the cell surface. Proteins and other molecules are secreted from cells in small pockets called secretory vesicles, whose membranes fuse with the plasma membrane, thereby allowing the secretory vesicles to release their contents to the cell surface. In the photomicrograph, you can see exocytosis taking place somewhat explosively.

4.11 Selective Permeability

CONCEPT PREVIEW: Cells are selectively permeable, admitting only certain molecules. Facilitated diffusion is selective transport across a membrane in the direction of lower concentration. Active transport is energy-driven transport across a membrane toward a region of higher concentration.

From the point of view of efficiency, the problem with endocytosis is that it is expensive to carry out—the cell must make and move a lot of membrane. Also, endocytosis is not picky—in pinocytosis particularly, engulfing liquid does not allow the cell to choose which molecules come in. Cells solve this problem by using proteins in the plasma membrane as channels to pass molecules into and out of the cell. Because each kind of channel allows passage of only a certain kind of molecule, the cell can control what enters and leaves, an ability called **selective permeability.**

Selective Diffusion

Some channels act like open doors. As long as a molecule fits the channel, it is free to pass through in either direction. Diffusion tends to equalize the concentration of such molecules on both sides of the membrane, with the molecules moving toward the side where they are scarcest. This mechanism of transport is called **selective diffusion.** One class of selectively open channels consists of ion channels, which are pores that span the membrane. Ions that fit the pore can diffuse through it in either direction. Such ion channels play an essential role in signaling by the nervous system.

Facilitated Diffusion

Most diffusion occurs through use of a special carrier protein. This protein binds only certain kinds of molecules, such as a particular sugar, amino acid, or ion. The molecule physically binds to the carrier on one side of the membrane and is released to the other side. The direction of the molecule's net movement depends on its concentration gradient across the membrane. If the concentration is greater outside the cell, the molecule is more likely to bind to the carrier on the extracellular side of the membrane, as shown in panel 1 of the *Essential Biological Process 4C*, and be released on the cytoplasmic side, as in panel 3. If the concentration of the molecule is greater inside the cell, the net movement will be from inside to outside. Thus the net movement always occurs from high concentration to low, just as it does in simple diffusion, but the process is facilitated by the carriers. For this reason, this mechanism of transport is given a special name, **facilitated diffusion.**

A characteristic feature of transport by carrier proteins is that its rate can be saturated. If the concentration of a substance is progressively increased, the rate of transport of the substance increases up to a certain point and then levels off. There are a limited number of carrier proteins in the membrane, and when the concentration of the transported substance is raised high enough, all the carriers will be in use. The transport system is then said to be "saturated." When an investigator wishes to know if a particular substance is being transported across a membrane by a carrier system, or is diffusing across, he or she conducts experiments to see if the transport system can be saturated. If it can be saturated, it is carrier-mediated; if it cannot be saturated, it is not.

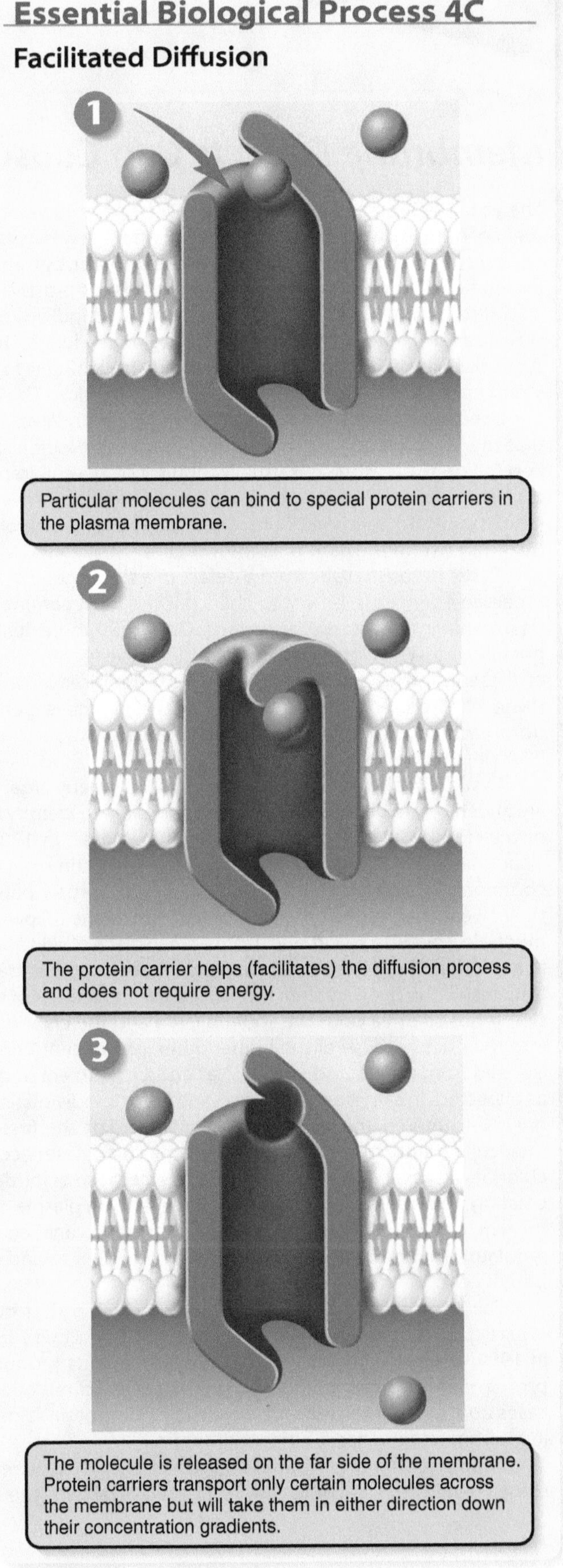

Essential Biological Process 4C
Facilitated Diffusion
1
Particular molecules can bind to special protein carriers in the plasma membrane.
2
The protein carrier helps (facilitates) the diffusion process and does not require energy.
3
The molecule is released on the far side of the membrane. Protein carriers transport only certain molecules across the membrane but will take them in either direction down their concentration gradients.

Membrane Defects Can Cause Disease

The year 1993 marked an important milestone in the treatment of human disease. That year the first attempt was made to cure **cystic fibrosis (CF)**, a deadly genetic disorder, by transferring healthy genes into sick individuals. Cystic fibrosis is a fatal disease in which the body cells of affected individuals secrete a thick mucus that clogs the airways of the lungs. The cystic fibrosis patient in the photograph is breathing into a Vitalograph, a device that measures lung function. These same secretions block the ducts of the pancreas and liver so that the few patients who do not die of lung disease die of liver failure. Cystic fibrosis is usually thought of as a children's disease because until recently few affected individuals lived long enough to become adults. Even today half die before their mid-twenties. There is no known cure.

Cystic fibrosis results from a defect in a single gene that is passed down from parent to child. It is the most common fatal genetic disease of Caucasians. One in 20 individuals possesses at least one copy of the defective gene. Most of these individuals are not afflicted with the disease; only those children who inherit a copy of the defective gene from each parent succumb to cystic fibrosis—about 1 in 2,500 infants.

Cystic fibrosis has proven difficult to study. Many organs are affected, and until recently it was impossible to identify the nature of the defective gene responsible for the disease. In 1985 the first clear clue was obtained. An investigator, Paul Quinton, seized on a commonly observed characteristic of cystic fibrosis patients, that their sweat is abnormally salty, and performed the following experiment. He isolated a sweat duct from a small piece of skin and placed it in a solution of salt (NaCl) that was three times as concentrated as the NaCl inside the duct. He then monitored the movement of ions. Diffusion tends to drive both the sodium (Na^+) and the chloride (Cl^-) ions into the duct because of the higher outer ion concentrations. In skin isolated from normal individuals, Na^+ and Cl^- both entered the duct, as expected. In skin isolated from cystic fibrosis individuals, however, only Na^+ entered the duct—no Cl^- entered. For the first time, the molecular nature of cystic fibrosis became clear. Water accompanies chloride, and was not entering the ducts because chloride was not, creating thick mucus. Cystic fibrosis is a defect in a plasma membrane protein called CFTR (*c*ystic *f*ibrosis *t*ransmembrane conductance *r*egulator) that normally regulates passage of Cl^- into and out of the body's cells.

The defective *cf* gene was isolated in 1987, and its position on a particular human chromosome (chromosome 7) was pinpointed in 1989. Interestingly, many cystic fibrosis patients produce a CFTR protein with a normal amino acid sequence. The *cf* mutation in these cases appears to interfere with how the CFTR protein folds, preventing it from folding into a functional shape.

Soon after the *cf* gene was isolated, experiments were begun to see if it would be possible to cure cystic fibrosis by gene therapy—that is, by transferring healthy *cf* genes into the cells with defective ones. In 1990 a working *cf* gene was successfully transferred into human lung cells growing in tissue culture, using adenovirus, a cold virus, to carry the gene into the cells. The CFTR-defective cells were "cured," becoming able to transport chloride ions across their plasma membranes. Then in 1991 a team of researchers successfully transferred a normal human *cf* gene into the lung cells of a living animal—a rat. The *cf* gene was first inserted into the adenovirus genome because adenovirus is a cold virus and easily infects lung cells. The treated virus was then inhaled by the rat. Carried piggyback, the *cf* gene entered the rat lung cells and began producing the normal human CFTR protein within these cells!

These results were very encouraging, and at first the future for all cystic fibrosis patients seemed bright. Clinical tests using adenovirus to introduce healthy *cf* genes into cystic fibrosis patients were begun with much fanfare in 1993.

They were not successful. As described in detail in chapter 13, there were insurmountable problems with the adenovirus being used to transport the *cf* gene into cystic fibrosis patients. The difficult and frustrating challenge that cystic fibrosis researchers had faced was not over. Research into clinical problems is often a time-consuming and frustrating enterprise, never more so than in this case. Recently, new ways of introducing the healthy *cf* gene have been tried with better results. The long, slow journey toward a cure has taught us not to leap to the assumption that a cure is now at hand, but the steady persistence of researchers has taken us a long way, and again the future for cystic fibrosis patients seems bright.

Active Transport

Other channels through the plasma membrane are closed doors. These channels open only when energy is provided. They are designed to enable the cell to maintain high or low concentrations of certain molecules, much more or less than exists outside the cell. Like motor-driven turnstiles, the channels operate to move a certain substance *up* its concentration gradient. The operation of these one-way, energy-requiring channels results in **active transport,** the movement of molecules across a membrane to a region of higher concentration by the expenditure of energy.

You might think that the plasma membrane possesses all sorts of active transport channels for the transport of sugars, amino acids, and other molecules, but in fact, most of the active transport in cells is carried out by one kind of channel, the sodium-potassium pump.

The Sodium-Potassium Pump. The most important active transport channel is the *sodium-potassium (Na^+-K^+) pump,* which expends metabolic energy to actively pump sodium ions (Na^+) out of cells, and potassium ions (K^+) into cells (*Essential Biological Process 4D*). More than one-third of all the energy expended by your body's cells is spent driving Na^+-K^+ pump channels. This energy is derived from *adenosine triphosphate (ATP),* a molecule we will learn more about in chapter 5. The transportation of two different ions in opposite directions happens because energy causes a change in the shape of the membrane protein carrier. The panels to the right walk you through one cycle of the pump. Each channel can move over 300 sodium ions per second when working full tilt. As a result of all this pumping, there are far fewer sodium ions in the cell. This concentration gradient, paid for by the expenditure of considerable metabolic energy in the form of ATP molecules, is exploited by your cells in many ways. Two of the most important are (1) the conduction of signals along nerve cells (discussed in detail in chapter 29) and (2) the pulling of valuable molecules such as sugars and amino acids into the cell *against* their concentration gradient!

Cells of the nervous system, called neurons, have an electrical charge difference across their plasma membranes that allows them to function properly, as discussed on page 553. This charge difference, called the resting membrane potential, is maintained through the actions of Na^+/K^+ pumps.

We will focus for a moment on this second process. The plasma membranes of many cells are studded with facilitated diffusion channels, which offer a path for sodium ions that have been pumped out by the Na^+-K^+ pump to diffuse back in. There is a catch, however; these channels require that the sodium ions have a partner in order to pass through—like a dancing party where only couples are admitted through the door—which is why these are called coupled channels. Coupled channels won't let sodium ions across unless another molecule tags along, crossing hand in hand with the sodium ion. In some cases the partner molecule is a sugar, in others an amino acid or other molecule. Because the concentration gradient for sodium is so large, many sodium ions are trying to get back in, this diffusion pressure drags in the partner molecules as well, even if they are already in high concentration within the cell. In this way, sugars and other actively transported molecules enter the cell—via special coupled channels.

Concept Check

1. How does water diffuse across the plasma membrane?
2. What happens when a red blood cell is placed in a: hyper-, hypo-, and isotonic solution?
3. Distinguish between selective diffusion and facilitated diffusion.

Essential Biological Process 4D

The Sodium-Potassium Pump

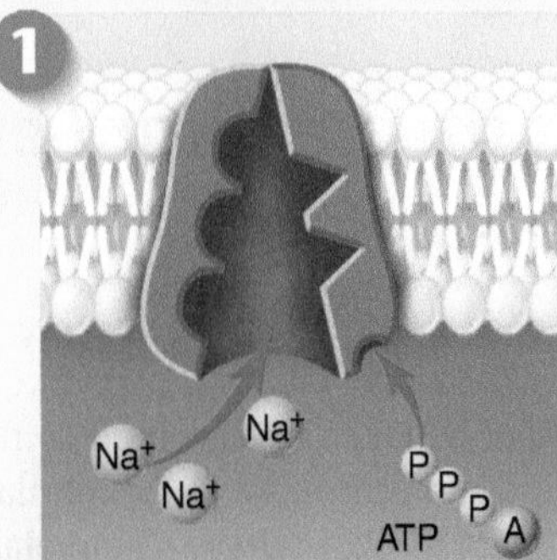

The sodium-potassium pump binds three sodium ions and a molecule of ATP.

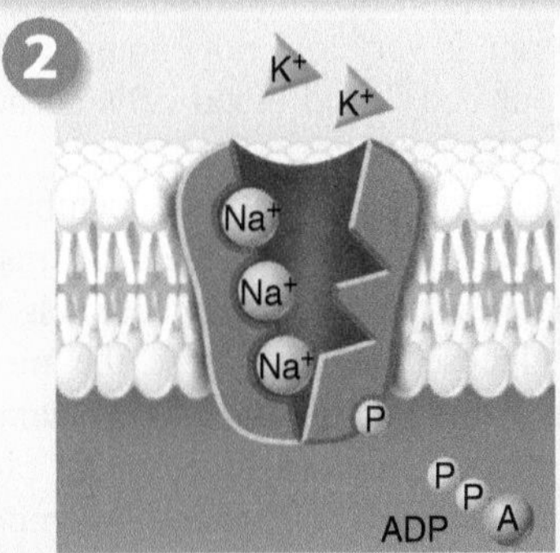

The splitting of ATP provides energy to change the shape of the channel. The sodium ions are driven through the channel.

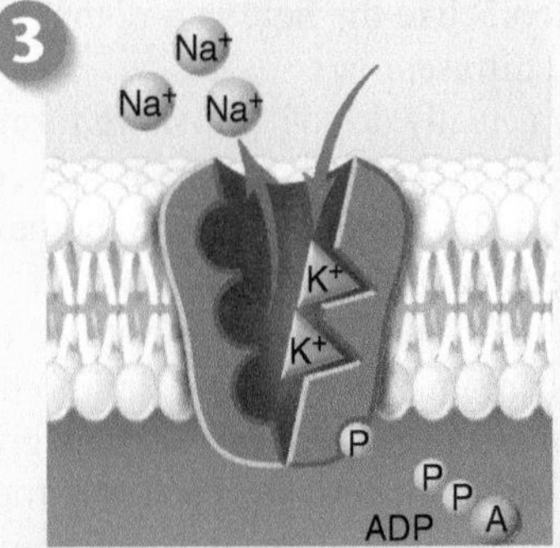

The sodium ions are released to the outside of the membrane, and the new shape of the channel allows two potassium ions to bind.

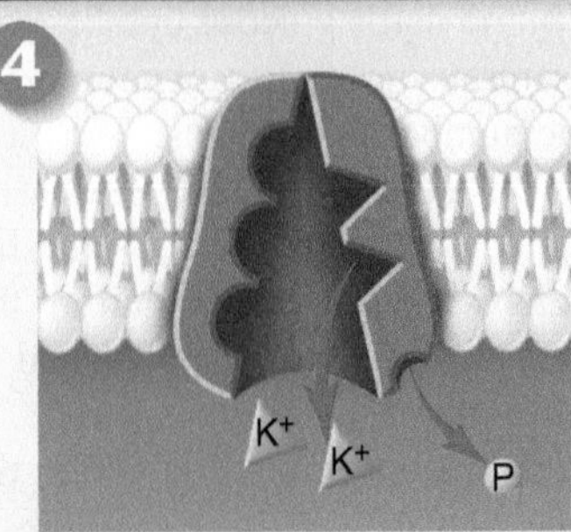

Release of the phosphate allows the channel to revert to its original form, releasing the potassium ions on the inside of the membrane.

Inquiry & Analysis

Eating at the Cellular Level: What Limits How Fast a Cell Can Take Up Glucose?

All animal cells need food molecules to power their lives. The food molecules you eat (proteins, fats, and carbohydrates) are broken into simpler bits that can be taken up and used as fuel by your cells. But many of these food molecules are polar (partially charged), and the lipid bilayer that surrounds all cells is a nonpolar barrier across which polar molecules cannot readily diffuse. The blue line on the graph to the right is the calculated curve for the rate of glucose uptake if it enters a cell solely by simple diffusion across a lipid bilayer membrane. As you can see, the rate is very low, not enough to keep a red blood cell alive. And yet your body's red blood cells do not starve. So how do these polar molecules get in?

When scientists learned that the membranes of human cells contain many proteins inserted into them, an answer suggested itself: Perhaps some of these proteins form channels which let polar food molecules like glucose pass in across the membrane. When they looked, they found that glucose-associated channels account for some 2% of the total protein in a red blood cell's plasma membrane! As you can see in the diagram, a channel is composed of a long rope-like protein consisting of alternating segments of polar and nonpolar amino acids, looping back and forth to create a passage spanning the membrane. In the glucose channels, 12 such polar-nonpolar segments form a polar "door," like the hole in a donut, through which glucose molecules could diffuse.

But do they actually do so? Said more formally, is the hypothesis that cells take up glucose using these "glucose channels" valid? To evaluate this hypothesis, researchers tested one of its key predictions: If glucose molecules enter a cell through special protein channels, then there must be an upper limit to how many glucose molecules can enter at any given time. When all the channels are occupied transporting glucose molecules, there is no other way for glucose molecules to enter the cell, no matter how much glucose is available. In technical terms, the rate of a red blood cell's glucose uptake would be expected to "saturate" at some maximum value, determined by the number of channels.

The red line on the graph above presents an experiment designed to investigate this question. Isolated blood cells were placed in a culture fluid containing glucose. Cells were removed and the amount of glucose they contain measured. The researchers plot the amount of glucose versus time and determine the rate of glucose entry into the cell (the **rate** of a molecular process is simply the speed at which it occurs, in this case, measured as the number of molecules diffused per unit volume [ml] per unit time [hour]). The rate is then plotted as a single red dot on the graph above. Repeating the experiment using increasing amounts of glucose in the culture fluid (measured as m*M* [m*M* is a **measure of concentration** which means millimolar, or one-thousandth of a mole per liter]), the researchers obtained the red curve seen above, in which the rate of glucose uptake is plotted against the extracellular concentration of glucose.

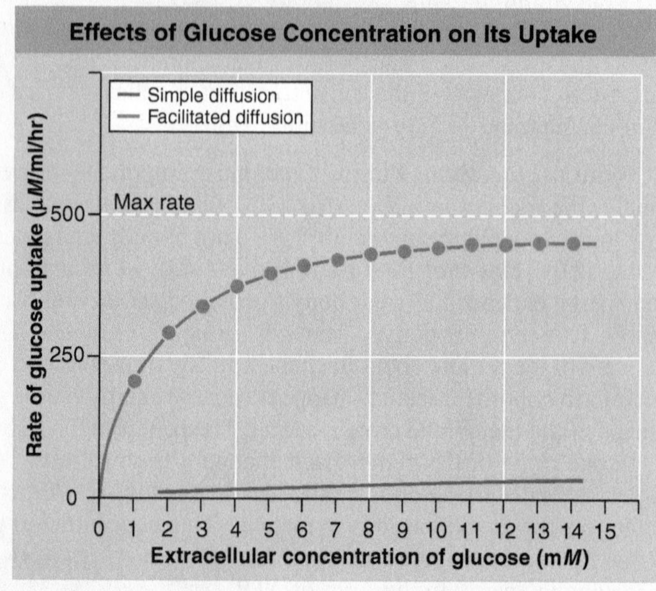

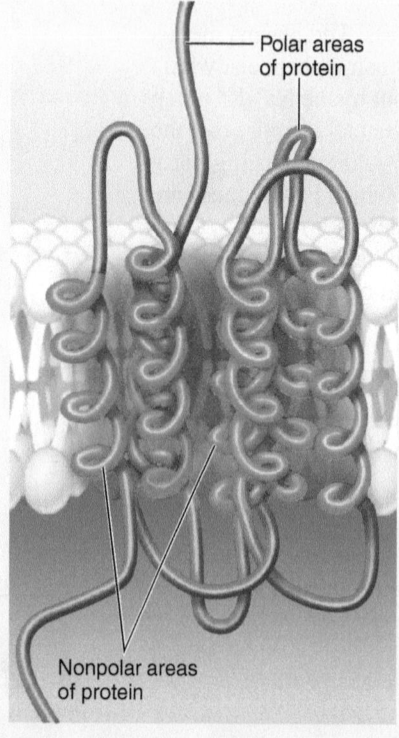

Analysis

1. **Applying Concepts** Is the rate of glucose uptake affected by the extracellular glucose concentration? How?
2. **Interpreting Data** What is the difference in the uptake rate between 1 m*M* and 4 m*M*? between 10 m*M* and 14 m*M*?
3. **Making Inferences** If the external glucose concentration was increased to 30 m*M*, what would you predict would be the rate of glucose uptake? to 100 m*M*? Why?
4. **Drawing Conclusions** Why do you think the rate of glucose uptake by red blood cells in this experiment never exceeds 500 μM/ml/hr? Cells in other tissues of the human body take up glucose more rapidly. How would you predict the plasma membranes of these cells to be different from those of red blood cells?

Concept Summary

The World of Cells

4.1 Cells

- Cells are the smallest living structure. They consist of cytoplasm enclosed in a plasma membrane. Organisms may be composed of a single cell or multiple cells (**figure 4.1**).
- A smaller cell can function more efficiently, from transporting materials throughout the cell to transporting materials across the plasma membrane. A smaller cell has a larger surface-to-volume ratio, which increases the area through which materials may pass. Because cells are so small, a microscope is needed to view and study them (**figure 4.3**).
- There are many different types of microscopes, each providing a slightly different view. Light microscopes magnify and enhance resolution. Transmission and scanning electron microscopes increase resolution.

Kinds of Cells

4.2 Prokaryotic Cells

- Prokaryotic cells are simple unicellular organisms that lack nuclei or other internal organelles and are usually encased in a rigid cell wall. They vary in shape (**figure 4.4**), and some contain external structures, as shown here from **figure 4.5.**

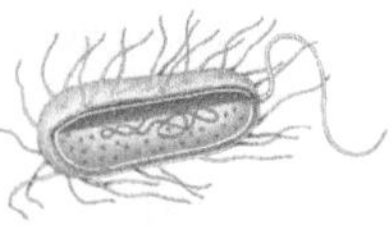

4.3 Eukaryotic Cells

- Eukaryotic cells are larger and more structurally complex compared with prokaryotic cells. They contain nuclei and have internal membrane systems (**figures 4.6** and **4.7**).

Tour of a Eukaryotic Cell

4.4 The Plasma Membrane

- The plasma membrane that encloses all cells consists of a double layer of lipids, called the lipid bilayer, in which proteins are embedded. The structure of the plasma membrane is called the fluid mosaic model.
- The lipid bilayer is made up of special lipid molecules called phospholipids (**figure 4.8**), which have a polar (water-soluble) end and a nonpolar (water-insoluble) end. The bilayer forms because the nonpolar ends move away from the watery surroundings, forming the two layers (**figure 4.9**). Membrane proteins are either attached to the surface of the cell or are embedded within the membrane, as shown here from **figure 4.10.** Transmembrane proteins are held in place by the interaction of nonpolar sections of amino acids with the interior lipid portion of the bilayer (**figure 4.11**).

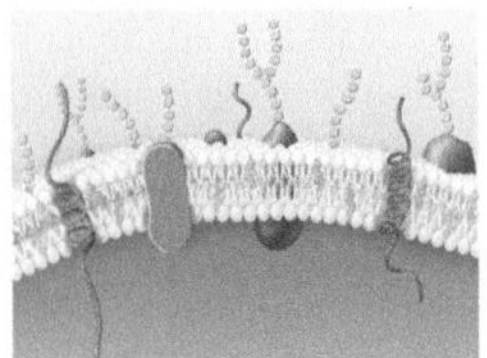

4.5 The Nucleus: The Cell's Control Center

- The nucleus is the command and control center of the cell. It contains the cell's DNA, which encodes the hereditary information that runs the cell (**figure 4.12**).

4.6 The Endomembrane System

- The endomembrane system is a collection of interior membranes that organize and divide the cell's interior into functional areas. The endoplasmic reticulum (**figure 4.13**) is a transport system that modifies and moves proteins and other molecules produced in the ER to the Golgi complex. The Golgi complex is a delivery system that carries molecules to the surface of the cell where they are released to the outside (**figures 4.14** and **4.15**).
- Lysosomes and vacuoles are other compartments in the cell. Lysosomes contain enzymes that digest worn out organelles. Vacuoles are storage compartments (**figure 4.16**).

4.7 Organelles That Harvest Energy

- The mitochondrion, shown here from **figure 4.17,** is called the powerhouse of the cell because it is the site of oxidative metabolism, an energy-extracting process. Chloroplasts are the site of photosynthesis and are present in plant and algal cells (**figure 4.18**). Mitochondria and chloroplasts are cell-like organelles that appear to be ancient bacteria that formed endosymbiotic relationships with early eukaryotic cells (**figure 4.19**).

4.8 The Cytoskeleton: Interior Framework of the Cell

- The interior of the cell contains a network of protein fibers, called the cytoskeleton, that supports the shape of the cell and anchors organelles in place (**figure 4.20**). Centrioles are paired structures that assemble microtubules in the cell (**figure 4.21**).
- Cells are dynamic structures. Cilia and flagella propel the cell through its environment (**figure 4.22**).

Transport Across Plasma Membranes

4.9 Diffusion and Osmosis

- Materials pass into and out of the cell passively through diffusion and osmosis. Diffusion is the movement of molecules from an area of high concentration to an area of low concentration, down their concentration gradients (***Essential Biological Process 4A***). Osmosis is the movement of water into and out of the cell, driven by differing concentrations of solute. Water molecules move to areas of higher solute concentrations (***Essential Biological Process 4B*** and **figure 4.23**).

4.10 Bulk Passage into and out of Cells

- Larger structures or larger quantities of material move into and out of the cell through endocytosis and exocytosis, respectively (**figures 4.24** and **4.25**). Endocytosis can involve bringing in larger particles, which is called phagocytosis, or bringing in liquids, which is called pinocytosis.

4.11 Selective Permeability

- Selective transport of materials across the membrane is accomplished by facilitated diffusion and active transport.
- Facilitated diffusion is driven by the concentration gradient, transporting substances down their concentration gradient, but substances must bind to a membrane transporter, called a carrier, in order to pass across the membrane (***Essential Biological Process 4C***).
- Active transport involves the input of energy to transport substances against (or up) their concentration gradients. Examples include the sodium-potassium pump (***Essential Biological Process 4D***), which pumps sodium ions out of the cell and potassium ions into the cell. Coupled channels are powered by the large sodium concentration gradient created by the actions of the sodium-potassium pump.

Self-Test

1. Cell theory includes the principle that
   a. cells are the smallest living things. Nothing smaller than a cell is considered alive.
   b. all cells are surrounded by cell walls that protect them.
   c. all organisms are made up of many cells arranged in specialized, functional groups.
   d. all cells contain membrane-bounded structures called organelles.
2. Organisms that have cells with a relatively uniform cytoplasm and no nucleus are called _____, and organisms whose cells have organelles and a nucleus are called _____.
   a. cellulose, nuclear c. flagellated, streptococcal
   b. eukaryotes, prokaryotes d. prokaryotes, eukaryotes
3. The plasma membrane is
   a. a carbohydrate layer that surrounds groups of cells to protect them.
   b. a double lipid layer with proteins inserted in it, which surrounds every cell individually.
   c. a thin sheet of structural proteins that encloses cytoplasm.
   d. composed of proteins that form a protective barrier.
4. Within the nucleus of a cell you can find
   a. a nucleolus. c. mitochondria.
   b. a cytoskeleton. d. All of these.
5. The endomembrane system within a cell includes the
   a. cytoskeleton and the ribosomes.
   b. prokaryotes and the eukaryotes.
   c. endoplasmic reticulum and the Golgi complex.
   d. mitochondria and the chloroplasts.
6. It was once thought that only the nucleus of each cell contained DNA. We now know that DNA is also found in the
   a. cytoskeleton and the ribosomes.
   b. prokaryotes and the eukaryotes.
   c. endoplasmic reticulum and the Golgi bodies.
   d. mitochondria and the chloroplasts.
7. Which of the following structures is not a component of the cytoskeleton?
   a. microtubules c. intermediate filaments
   b. cristae d. actin
8. If you put a drop of food coloring into a glass of water, the drop of color will
   a. fall to the bottom of the glass and sit there unless you stir the water; this is because of hydrogen bonding.
   b. float on the top of the water, like oil, unless you stir the water; this is because of surface tension.
   c. instantly disperse throughout the water; this is because of osmosis.
   d. slowly disperse throughout the water; this is because of diffusion.
9. When large molecules, such as food particles, need to get into a cell, they cannot easily pass through the plasma membrane, and so they move across the membrane through the processes of
   a. diffusion and osmosis.
   b. endocytosis and phagocytosis.
   c. exocytosis and pinocytosis.
   d. facilitated diffusion and active transport.
10. Active transport of specific molecules involves
    a. facilitated diffusion.
    b. endocytosis and pinocytosis.
    c. energy and specialized pumps or channels.
    d. permeability and a concentration gradient.

Visual Understanding

1. **Figure 4.3** The first microscope was used in about 1590. Electron microscopes came into common use about 70 years ago. Just over 100 years ago most physicians did not wash up between patients, even when someone had just died, or was very sick. Explain why early physicians didn't think it important to wash their hands.

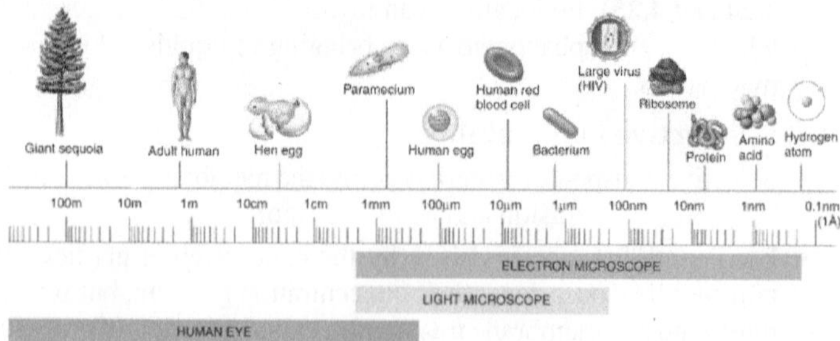

2. *Essential Biological Process 4C* In the lungs, there are steep concentration gradients for oxygen and carbon dioxide molecules such that large numbers of these molecules move across the plasma membrane of the cells that line the lungs. These molecules pass through the plasma membranes by simple diffusion. This process is fast and efficient. Would this process be just as efficient if the oxygen and carbon dioxide molecules passed through the membranes by facilitated diffusion? Why or why not?

Challenge Questions

1. You are using a computer program to design a new single-celled organism. Discuss why a smaller cell will be more efficient in transporting materials than a larger cell.
2. Antibiotics are medicines that target bacterial infections in vertebrates. How can an antibiotic kill all the bacterial cells and not harm vertebrate cells? Hint: what part of the bacterial cell must antibiotics be targeting?
3. Compare the cellular organelles and other structures to the parts of a city—for example, the nucleus is city hall and the DNA is all the city's laws and instructions.
4. A ribosome contains two subunits. The ribosome subunits are assembled within the nucleus, but ribosomes act in the cytoplasm. How do you imagine the subunits get out of the nucleus and into the cytoplasm?

Chapter 5

Energy and Life

CHAPTER AT A GLANCE

Cells and Energy

(a) Potential energy

(b) Potential energy

(c) Kinetic energy

Figure 5.1 Potential and kinetic energy.

Objects that have the capacity to move but are not moving have potential energy, while objects that are in motion have kinetic energy. (a) The kinetic energy of this skateboarder becomes potential energy at the peak of this slope. (b) The energy required to move the ball up the hill is stored as potential energy. (c) This stored energy is released as kinetic energy as the ball rolls down the hill.

5.1 The Flow of Energy in Living Things

CONCEPT PREVIEW: Energy is the capacity to do work, either actively (kinetic energy) or stored for later use (potential energy). Chemical reactions occur when the covalent bonds linking atoms together are formed or broken.

We are about to begin our discussion of energy and cellular chemistry. Although these subjects may seem difficult at first, remember that all life is driven by energy. The concepts and processes discussed in the next three chapters are key to life. We are chemical machines, powered by chemical energy, and for the same reason that a successful race car driver must learn how the engine of a car works, we must look at cell chemistry. Indeed, if we are to understand ourselves, we must "look under the hood" at the chemical machinery of our cells and see how it operates.

As described in chapter 2, **energy** is defined as the ability to do work. It can be considered to exist in two states: kinetic energy and potential energy. **Kinetic energy** is the energy of motion. Objects that are not in the process of moving but have the capacity to do so are said to possess **potential energy,** or stored energy (figure 5.1*a*). A boulder perched on a hilltop (figure 5.1*b*) has potential energy; after the man pushes the boulder and it begins to roll downhill (figure 5.1*c*), some of the boulder's potential energy is converted into kinetic energy. All of the work carried out by living organisms also involves the transformation of potential energy to kinetic energy.

Energy exists in many forms: mechanical energy, heat, sound, electric current, light, or radiation. Because it can exist in so many forms, there are many ways to measure energy. The most convenient is in terms of heat, because all other forms of energy can be converted to heat. Thus the study of energy is called *thermodynamics,* meaning "heat changes."

Energy flows into the biological world from the sun, which shines a constant beam of light on the earth. It is estimated that the sun provides the earth with more than 13×10^{23} calories per year, or 40 million billion calories per second! Plants, algae, and certain kinds of bacteria capture a fraction of this energy through photosynthesis. In photosynthesis, energy garnered from sunlight is used to combine small molecules (water and carbon dioxide) into more complex molecules (sugars). These complex sugar molecules have potential energy due to the arrangement of their atoms. This potential energy, in the form of chemical energy, will eventually be used by the cell to do its work. Recall from chapter 2 that an atom consists of a central nucleus surrounded by one or more orbiting electrons, and a covalent bond forms when two atomic nuclei share electrons. Breaking such a bond requires energy to pull the nuclei apart. Indeed, the strength of a covalent bond is measured by the amount of energy required to break it. For example, it takes 98.8 kcal to break 1 mole (6.023×10^{23}) of carbon–hydrogen (C—H) bonds.

You will see in chapter 6 how plants use the sun's energy to build carbohydrates, storing this energy as potential energy. Chapter 7 explains how this potential energy is used by the plants and other organisms to fuel the functions of living.

All the chemical activities within cells can be viewed as a series of chemical reactions between molecules. A **chemical reaction** is the making or breaking of chemical bonds—gluing atoms together to form new molecules, or tearing molecules apart and sometimes sticking the pieces onto other molecules.

5.2 The Laws of Thermodynamics

CONCEPT PREVIEW: The first law of thermodynamics states that energy cannot be created or destroyed; it can only undergo conversion from one form to another. The second law states that disorder (entropy) in the universe tends to increase.

Running, thinking, singing, reading these words—all activities of living organisms involve changes in energy. A set of universal laws we call the laws of thermodynamics govern these and all other energy changes in the universe.

The First Law of Thermodynamics

The first of these universal laws, the **first law of thermodynamics,** concerns the amount of energy in the universe. It states that energy can change from one state to another (from potential to kinetic, for example) but it can never be destroyed, nor can new energy be made. The total amount of energy in the universe remains constant.

The lion eating a giraffe in figure 5.2 is in the process of acquiring energy. The lion isn't creating new energy, rather it is merely transferring some of the potential energy stored in the giraffe's tissues to its own body. Within any living organism, this chemical potential energy can be shifted to other molecules and stored in chemical bonds, or it can be converted into kinetic energy, or into other forms of energy. During each conversion, some of the energy dissipates into the environment as heat energy, a measure of the random motions of molecules (and, hence, a measure of one form of kinetic energy). Energy continuously flows through the biological world in one direction, with new energy from the sun constantly entering the system to replace the energy dissipated as heat.

Figure 5.2 Giraffe for dinner.

EVOLUTION

Creationists and the Law. One objection often made by creationists to the theory of evolution is that it violates the second law of thermodynamics. If disorder is continually increasing in the universe, making disorder more likely than order, then they assert that a more ordered system (cells) could not arise spontaneously without direction. Evolutionary biologists respond to this criticism by pointing out that this creationist objection misstates the second law of thermodynamics by omitting a key provision: *"in a closed system."* The living world is by no means a closed system, as energy is continually being supplied to it by the sun. It is this energy, captured in photosynthesis, that powers the organized system we call life. In no sense does this in any way violate the second law.

The Second Law of Thermodynamics

The **second law of thermodynamics** concerns this transformation of potential energy into heat, or random molecular motion. It states that the disorder in a closed system like the universe is continuously increasing. Put simply, disorder is more likely than order. For example, it is much more likely that a column of bricks will tumble over than that a pile of bricks will arrange themselves spontaneously to form a column. In general, energy transformations proceed spontaneously to convert matter from a more ordered, less stable form, to a less ordered, more stable form. Without an input of energy from the teenager (or a parent), the ordered room in figure 5.3 falls into disorder. When the input of energy is localized, one area can become far more organized than its disordered surroundings, like cleaning one room of a messy house. It is in just this way that a cell uses energy to keep more organized than its surroundings.

Entropy is a measure of the degree of disorder of a system, so the second law of thermodynamics can also be stated simply as "entropy increases." When the universe formed 10 to 20 billion years ago, it held all the potential energy it will ever have. It has become progressively more disordered ever since, with every energy exchange increasing the entropy of the universe.

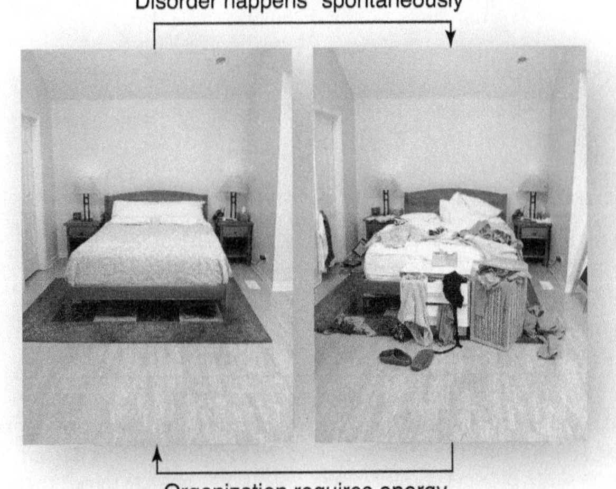
Disorder happens "spontaneously"
Organization requires energy

Figure 5.3 Entropy in action.

As time elapses, a teenager's room becomes more disorganized. It takes energy to clean it up.

Concept Check

1. Is the energy in a "high energy" food bar kinetic or potential? Explain.
2. When Tiger Woods strikes a golf ball, is what happens to the golf ball a chemical reaction?
3. When an organism dies, what happens to its entropy?

Cell Chemistry

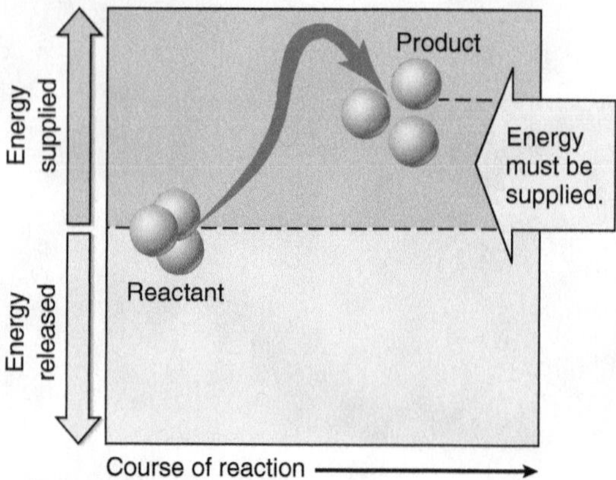

(a) Endergonic reaction

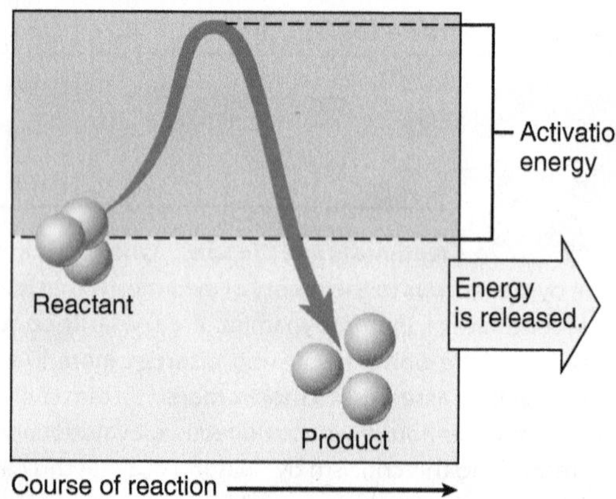

(b) Exergonic reaction

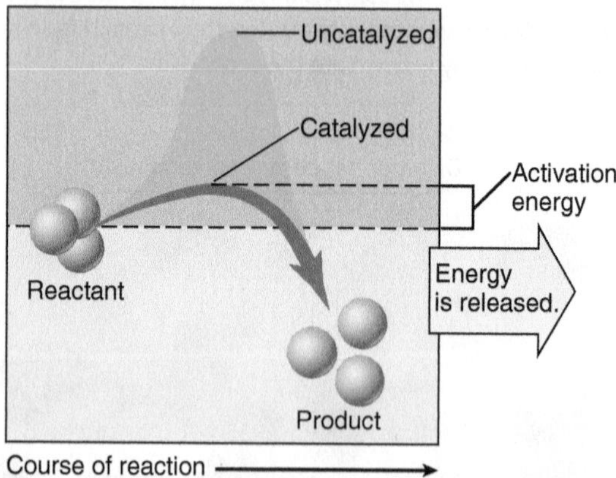

(c) Catalyzed reaction

Figure 5.4 Chemical reactions and catalysis.

(a) The products of endergonic reactions contain more energy than the reactants. (b) The products of exergonic reactions contain less energy than the reactants, but exergonic reactions do not necessarily proceed rapidly because it takes energy to get them going. The "hill" in this energy diagram represents energy that must be supplied to destabilize existing chemical bonds. (c) Catalyzed reactions occur faster because the amount of activation energy required to initiate the reaction—the height of the energy hill that must be overcome—is lowered.

5.3 Chemical Reactions

CONCEPT PREVIEW: The products of endergonic reactions contain more energy than the reactants, while the products of exergonic reactions contain less energy than the reactants. Catalysis can lower the activation energy needed to initiate a reaction.

In a chemical reaction, the original molecules before the chemical reaction occurs are called **reactants,** or sometimes **substrates,** whereas the molecules that result after the reaction has taken place are called the **products** of the reaction. Not all chemical reactions are equally likely to occur. Just as a boulder is more likely to roll downhill than uphill, so a reaction is more likely to occur if it releases energy than if it needs to have energy supplied. Consider how the chemical reaction proceeds in figure 5.4*a*. Like rolling a boulder uphill, energy needs to be supplied. This is because the product of the reaction contains more energy than the reactant. This type of chemical reaction, called **endergonic,** does not occur spontaneously. By contrast, an **exergonic** reaction, shown in figure 5.4*b*, tends to occur spontaneously because the product has less energy than the reactant, like a boulder that has rolled downhill.

Covalent bonds form when two or more atoms share electrons, as discussed on page 35. Many important chemical reactions involve the formation or breaking of these bonds.

Activation Energy

If all chemical reactions that release energy tend to occur spontaneously, it is fair to ask, "Why haven't all exergonic reactions occurred already?" Why doesn't all the gasoline in all the automobiles in the world just burn up right now? It doesn't because the burning of gasoline, and almost all other chemical reactions, requires an input of energy to get it started—it is first necessary to break existing chemical bonds in the reactants, and this takes energy. The extra energy required to destabilize existing chemical bonds and so initiate a chemical reaction is called **activation energy,** indicated by brackets in figure 5.4*b* and *c*. You must first nudge a boulder out of the hole it sits in before it can roll downhill. Activation energy is simply a chemical nudge.

Catalysis

One way to make a reaction more likely to happen is to lower the necessary activation energy. Like digging away the ground below your boulder, lowering activation energy reduces the nudge needed to get things started. The process of lowering the activation energy of a reaction is called **catalysis.** Catalysis cannot make an endergonic reaction occur spontaneously—you cannot avoid the need to supply energy—but it can make a reaction, endergonic or exergonic, proceed much faster. Compare the activation energy levels (the red arched arrows) in the second and third panels to the left: The catalyzed reaction in figure 5.4*c* has a lower barrier to overcome.

Concept Check

1. If exergonic reactions tend to occur spontaneously, why haven't they all done so? What stops the world's gasoline from burning?
2. Can catalysis make endergonic reactions occur spontaneously?
3. Why is the speed of a chemical reaction affected by the amount of activation energy required to initiate it?

Enzymes

5.4 How Enzymes Work

CONCEPT PREVIEW: Enzymes catalyze chemical reactions within cells. Sometimes enzymes are organized into biochemical pathways. Enzymes are sensitive to temperature and pH, because both of these variables influence enzyme shape.

Macromolecules called **enzymes** are the catalysts used by cells to touch off particular chemical reactions. By controlling which enzymes are present, and when they are active, cells are able to control what happens within themselves, just as a conductor controls the music an orchestra produces by dictating which instruments play when.

An enzyme works by binding to a specific molecule in such a way as to make a particular reaction more likely (*Essential Biological Process 5A*). The key to this activity is the shape of the enzyme. An enzyme is specific for a particular reactant, or substrate, because the enzyme surface provides a mold that very closely fits the shape of the desired reactant. For example, the blue-colored lysozyme enzyme in figure 5.5 is contoured to fit a specific sugar molecule (the yellow reactant). Other molecules that fit less perfectly simply don't adhere to the enzyme's surface. The site on the enzyme surface where the reactant fits is called the **active site.** The site on the reactant that binds to an enzyme is called its **binding site.** In figure 5.5*b*, the edges of the lysozyme hug the sugar molecule, leading to an "induced fit" between the enzyme and its reactant, like a hand wrapping around a baseball.

An enzyme lowers the activation energy of a particular reaction. In the case of lysozyme, an enzyme found in human tears, the enzyme has an antibacterial function, encouraging the breaking of a particular chemical bond in molecules that make up the cell wall of

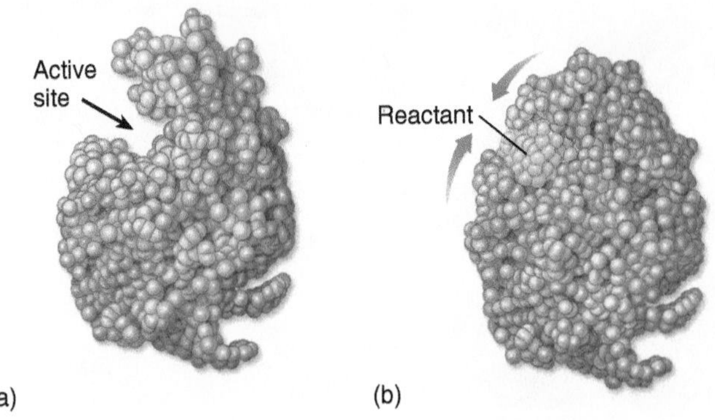

Figure 5.5 An enzyme's shape determines its activity.

(a) A groove runs through the lysozyme enzyme that fits the shape of the reactant (in this case, a chain of sugars). (b) When such a chain of sugars slides into the groove, it induces the protein to change its shape slightly and embrace the substrate more intimately. This induced fit causes a chemical bond between two sugar molecules within the chain to break.

IMPLICATION University of Chicago researchers have found the activity levels of protein kinase C (an enzyme linked to depression) to be much lower in the brains of teenage suicides. What sort of investigations would you propose to look into the link between this enzyme and teen suicide?

Essential Biological Process 5A

How Enzymes Work

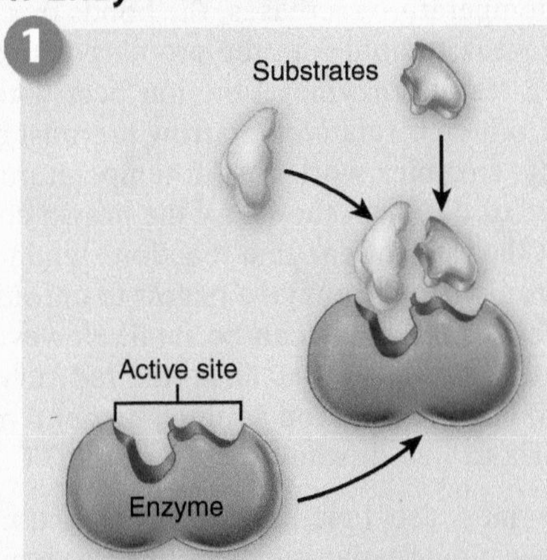

Enzymes have a complex three-dimensional surface to which particular reactants (called substrates of that enzyme) fit, like a hand in a glove.

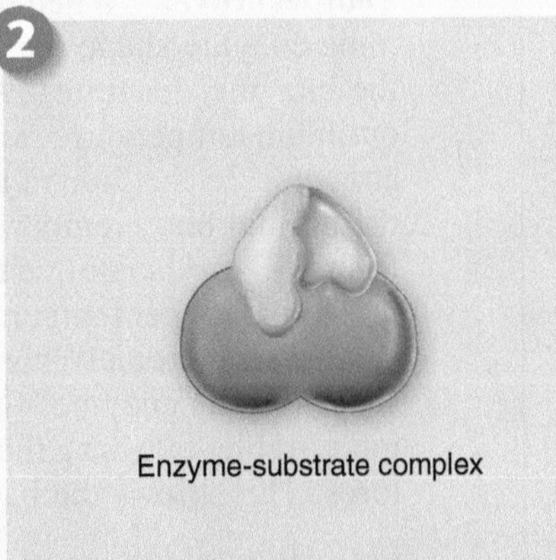

An enzyme and its substrate(s) bind tightly together, forming an enzyme-substrate complex. The binding brings key atoms near each other and stresses key covalent bonds.

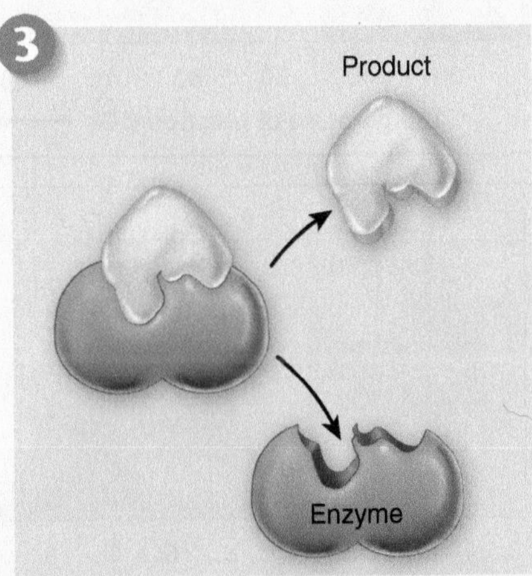

As a result, a chemical reaction occurs within the active site, forming the product. The product then diffuses away, freeing the enzyme to work again.

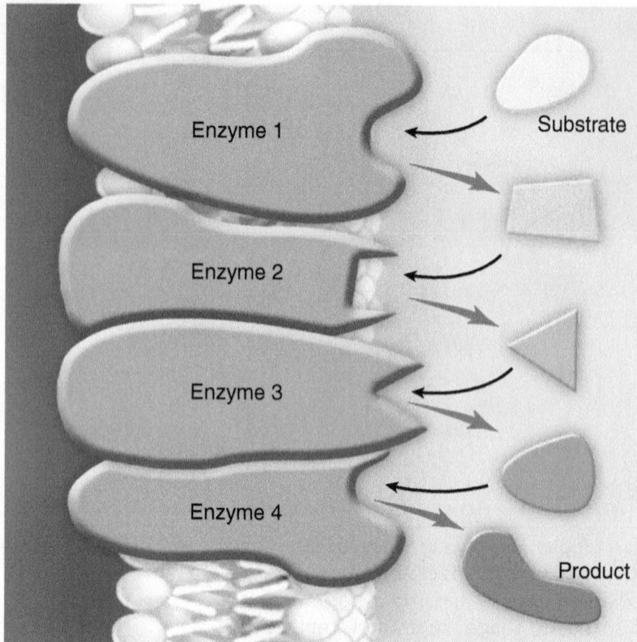

Figure 5.6 A biochemical pathway.

The original substrate is acted on by enzyme 1, changing the substrate to a new form recognized by enzyme 2. Each enzyme in the pathway acts on the product of the previous stage.

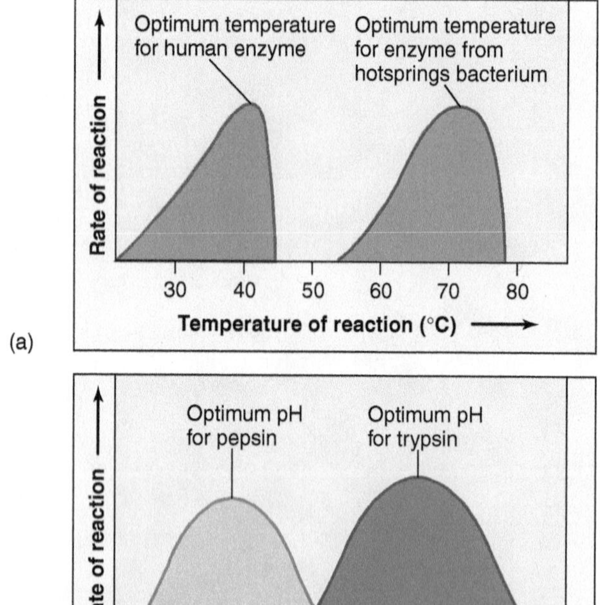

Figure 5.7 Enzymes are sensitive to their environment.

The activity of an enzyme is influenced by both (a) temperature and (b) pH. Most human enzymes work best at temperatures near 37°C and within a pH range of 6 to 8.

bacteria. The enzyme weakens the bond by drawing away some of its electrons. Alternatively, an enzyme may encourage the formation of a link between two reactants, like in *Essential Biological Process 5A,* by holding them near each other. Regardless of the type of reaction, the enzyme is not affected by the chemical reaction and is available to be used again.

Biochemical Pathways

Every organism contains thousands of different kinds of enzymes that together catalyze a bewildering variety of reactions. Often several of these reactions occur in a fixed sequence called a **biochemical pathway,** the product of one reaction becoming the substrate for the next. You can see in figure 5.6 how the initial substrate is altered by enzyme 1 so that it now fits into the active site of another enzyme, becoming the substrate for enzyme 2, and so on until the final product is produced. Because these reactions occur in sequence, the enzymes involved are often positioned near each other in the cell. For example, the enzymes involved in this biochemical pathway are all embedded in a membrane near each other. Many biochemical pathways occur in membranes, although enzyme assemblies also occur in organelles and within the cytoplasm. The close proximity of the enzymes allows the reactions of a biochemical pathway to proceed faster. Biochemical pathways are the organizational units of metabolism. We will explore them in chapters 6 and 7.

The Calvin cycle on page 108 is a biochemical pathway in photosynthesis where the product of one reaction is the substrate for the next reaction. Similarly, glycolysis on page 116 and the Krebs cycle on page 118 are biochemical pathways.

Factors Affecting Enzyme Activity

Enzyme activity is affected by any change in condition that alters the enzyme's three-dimensional shape. For this reason, temperature and pH can have a major influence on the action of enzymes.

Temperature. When the temperature increases, the bonds that determine enzyme shape are too weak to hold it in the proper position, and the enzyme denatures. As a result, enzymes function best within an optimum temperature range, which is relatively narrow for most human enzymes. In the human body, enzymes work best at temperatures near the normal body temperature of 37°C, as shown by the brown curve in figure 5.7*a*. Also notice that the rates of enzyme reactions tend to drop quickly at higher temperatures, when the enzyme begins to unfold. This is why an extremely high fever in humans can be fatal. However, the shapes of the enzymes found in hotsprings bacteria (the red curve) are more stable, allowing the enzymes to function at much higher temperatures. This allows the bacteria to live in water that is near 70°C.

pH. In addition, most enzymes also function within an optimal pH range, because the shape-determining polar interactions of enzymes are quite sensitive to hydrogen ion (H^+) concentration. Most human enzymes, such as the protein-degrading enzyme trypsin (the dark blue curve in figure 5.7*b*) work best within the range of pH 6 to 8. Blood has a pH of 7.4. However, some enzymes, such as the digestive enzyme pepsin (the light blue curve) are able to function in very acidic environments such as the stomach, but can't function at higher pHs, such as those where trypsin works best.

Essential Biological Process 5B

Regulating Enzyme Activity

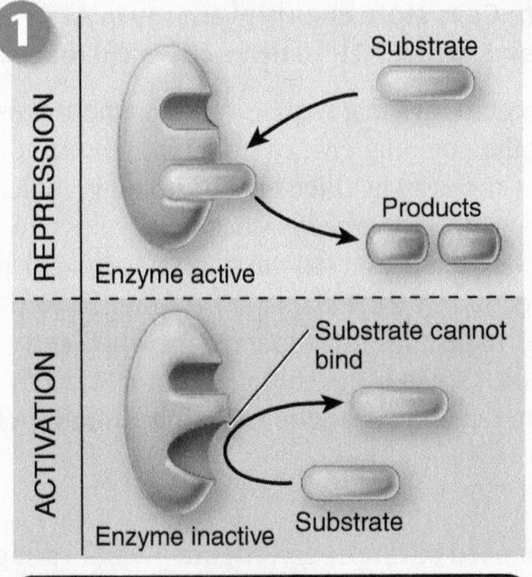

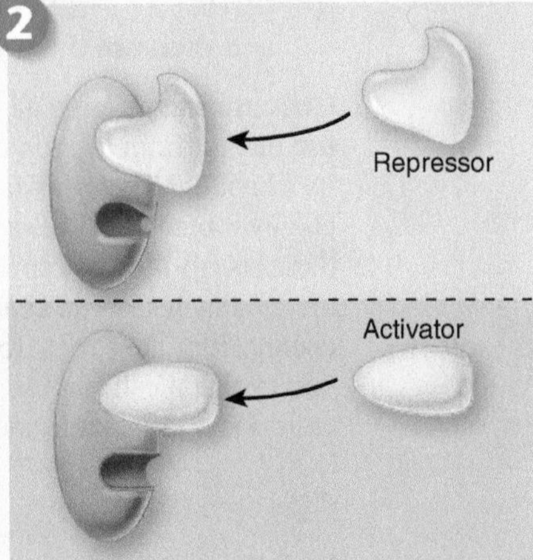

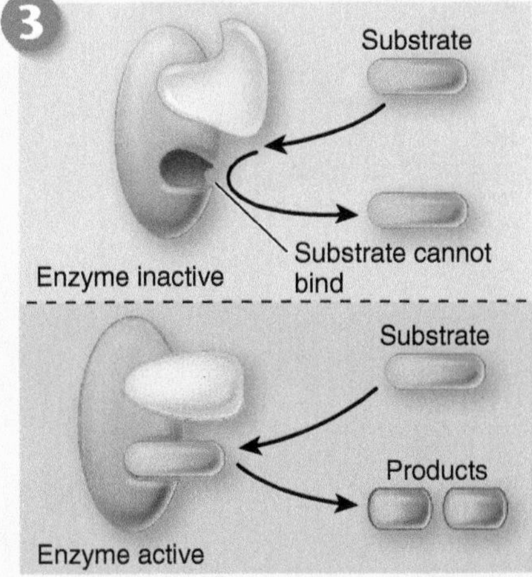

Allosteric enzymes subject to repression are active in the absence of signal molecules, while allosteric enzymes that rely on activation are not active in the absence of signal molecules.

When signal molecules bind allosteric enzymes, they change the shape of the active site. Repressors disrupt the active site, while activators restore it.

Allosteric enzymes subject to repression are not active in the presence of signal molecules, while allosteric enzymes that rely on activation require signal molecules to be active.

5.5 How Cells Regulate Enzymes

CONCEPT PREVIEW: An enzyme's activity can be affected by signal molecules that bind to it, changing its shape.

Because an enzyme must have a precise shape to work correctly, it is possible for the cell to control when an enzyme is active by altering its shape. Many enzymes have shapes that can be altered by the binding of "signal" molecules to their surfaces, making them work better (activation) or worse (inhibition). These are called *allosteric enzymes.* For example, the upper panels of *Essential Biological Process 5B* show an enzyme that is inhibited. The binding of a signal molecule called a **repressor** (the yellow molecule in panel 2) alters the shape of the enzyme's active site such that it cannot bind the substrate (the red molecule). In other cases, the enzyme may not be able to bind the reactants *unless* the signal molecule is bound to the enzyme. The lower set of panels shows a signal molecule serving as an **activator.** The red substrate cannot bind to the enzyme's active site unless the activator (the yellow molecule) is first in place.

Enzymes are often regulated by a mechanism called **feedback inhibition,** where the product of the reaction acts as a repressor. Feedback inhibition can occur in two ways: *competitive* and, much more commonly, *noncompetitive.* The blue molecule in figure 5.8*a* functions as a competitive inhibitor, blocking the active site so that the substrate cannot bind. The yellow molecule in figure 5.8*b* functions as a noncompetitive inhibitor. It binds to an allosteric site, changing the shape of the enzyme such that it is unable to bind to the substrate.

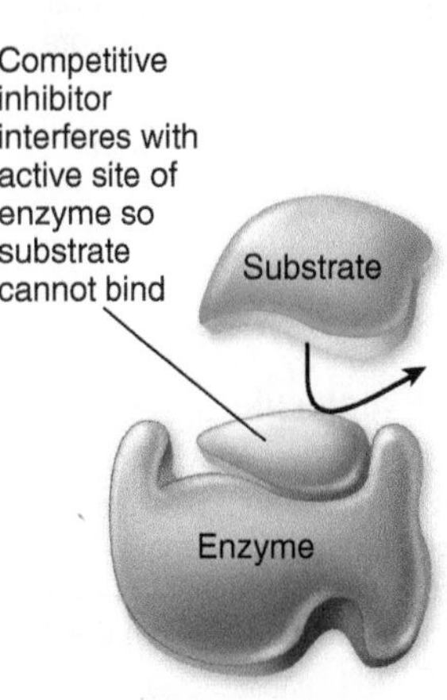

(a) Competitive inhibition

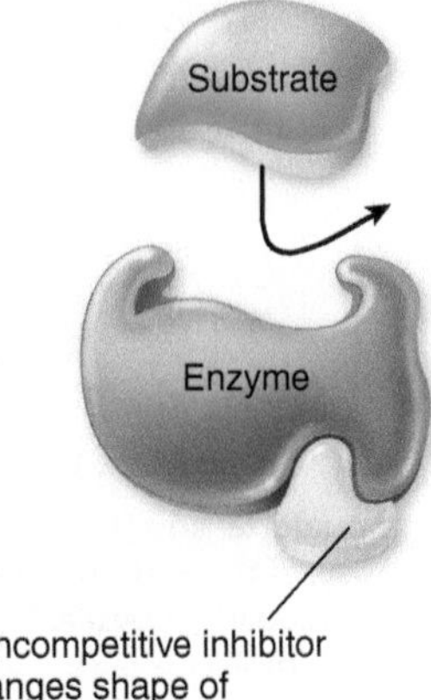

(b) Noncompetitive inhibition

Figure 5.8 How enzymes can be inhibited.

(a) In competitive inhibition, the inhibitor interferes with the active site of the enzyme. (b) In noncompetitive inhibition, the inhibitor binds to the enzyme at a place away from the active site, effecting a conformational change in the enzyme so that it can no longer bind to its substrate.

IMPLICATION Many antibiotics work by inhibiting enzymes. The antibiotic penicillin inhibits an enzyme bacteria use in making cell walls. Imagine a confused patient mistakenly took two to three times the number of prescribed penicillin pills at one time. Is it likely the patient would be seriously harmed? Explain.

Concept Check

1. What is the difference between an active site and a binding site?
2. Explain how hotsprings bacteria can live in near-boiling water (70° C = 158° F) that would kill a human bather.
3. Can a signal molecule activate one enzyme and repress another?

How Cells Use Energy

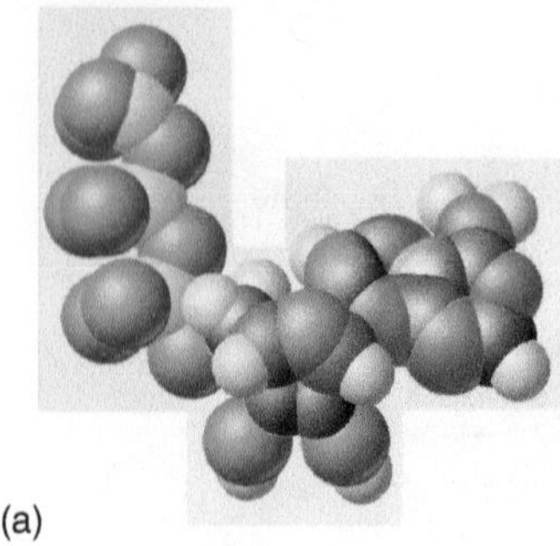

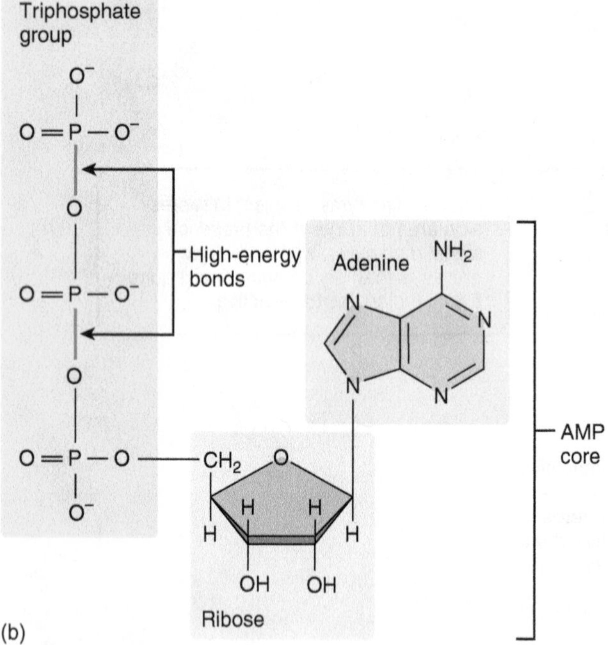

Figure 5.9 The parts of an ATP molecule.

The model (a) and structural diagram (b) both show that ATP consists of three phosphate groups attached to a ribose (five-carbon sugar) molecule. The ribose molecule is also attached to an adenine molecule (also one of the nitrogenous bases of DNA and RNA). When the endmost phosphate group is split off from the ATP molecule, considerable energy is released.

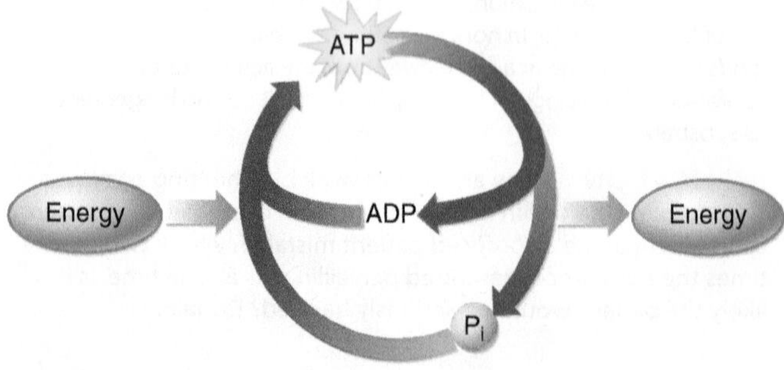

Figure 5.10 The ATP-ADP cycle.

5.6 ATP: The Energy Currency of the Cell

CONCEPT PREVIEW: Cells store chemical energy in ATP molecules and then use the breakdown of ATP to drive chemical reactions.

Cells use energy to do all those things that require work, but how does the cell use energy from the sun or the potential energy stored in molecules to power its activities? The sun's radiant energy and the energy stored in molecules are energy sources, but like money that is invested in stocks and bonds or real estate, these energy sources cannot be used directly to run a cell, any more than money invested in stocks can be used to buy a candy bar at the store. To be useful, the energy from the sun or food molecules must first be converted to a source of energy that a cell can use, like someone converting stocks and bonds to ready cash. The "cash" molecule in the body is **adenosine triphosphate (ATP).**

Structure of the ATP Molecule

Each ATP molecule is composed of three parts (figure 5.9): (1) a sugar (colored blue) serves as the backbone to which the other two parts are attached, (2) adenine (colored peach), which is also one of the four nitrogenous bases in DNA and RNA, and (3) a chain of three phosphates (colored yellow) contain high-energy bonds. As you can see in the figure, the phosphates carry negative electrical charges, and so it takes considerable chemical energy to hold the line of three phosphates next to one another at the end of ATP. Like a compressed spring, the phosphates are poised to push apart. It is for this reason that the chemical bonds linking the phosphates are such chemically reactive bonds. When the endmost phosphate is broken off an ATP molecule, a sizable packet of energy is released. The reaction converts ATP to adenosine diphosphate, ADP, and P_i, inorganic phosphate:

$$\text{ATP} \longleftrightarrow \text{ADP} + \text{P}_i + \text{energy}$$

Chemical reactions require activation energy, and endergonic reactions require the input of even more energy, and so these reactions in the cell are usually coupled with the breaking of the phosphate bond in ATP, called *coupled reactions*. Because almost all chemical reactions in cells require less energy than is released by this reaction, ATP is able to power many of the cell's activities. Table 5.1 introduces you to some of the key cell activities powered by the breakdown of ATP. ATP is continually recycled from ADP and P_i via the ATP-ADP cycle (figure 5.10).

Cells use two different but complementary processes to convert energy from the sun and food molecules into potential energy stored in the chemical bonds of ATP. Some cells convert energy from the sun into molecules of ATP through the process of **photosynthesis,** the subject of chapter 6. This ATP is then used to manufacture sugar molecules, converting the energy from ATP into potential energy stored in the bonds that hold the atoms in the sugar molecule together. All cells convert the potential energy found in food molecules like sugar into ATP through **cellular respiration,** the subject of chapter 7.

Concept Check

1. Compare and contrast ATP with the nucleotides found in DNA and RNA. [Hint: see figure 3.11.]
2. Why are the chemical bonds linking the phosphates in ATP so reactive?
3. How do the roots of a plant, far from light, get the ATP they need?

TABLE 5.1 How Cells Use ATP Energy to Power Cellular Work

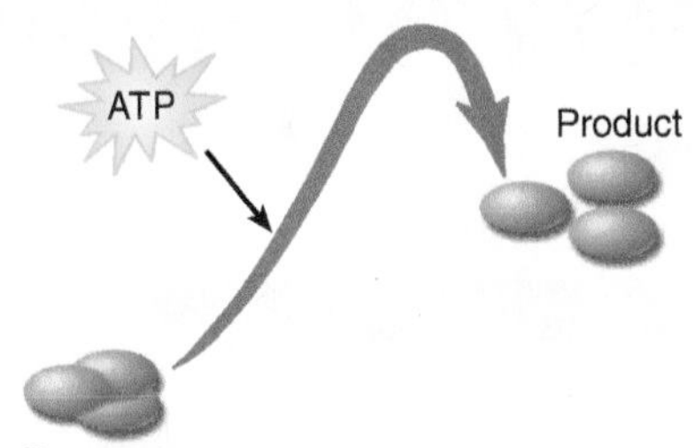

Biosynthesis

Cells use the energy released from the exergonic hydrolysis of ATP to drive endergonic reactions like those of protein synthesis, an approach called energy coupling.

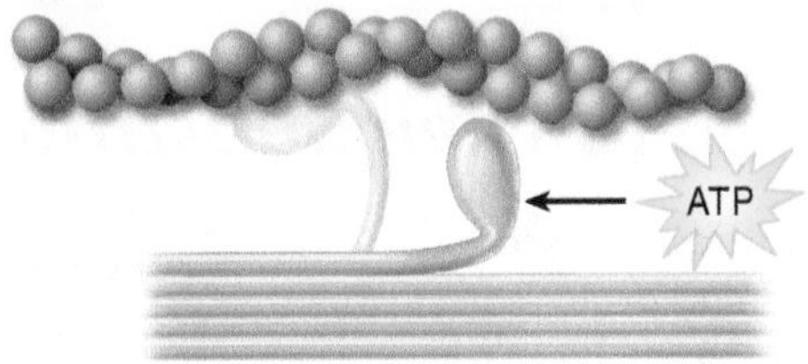

Contraction

In muscle cells, filaments of protein repeatedly slide past each other to achieve contraction of the cell. An input of ATP is required for the filaments to reset and slide again.

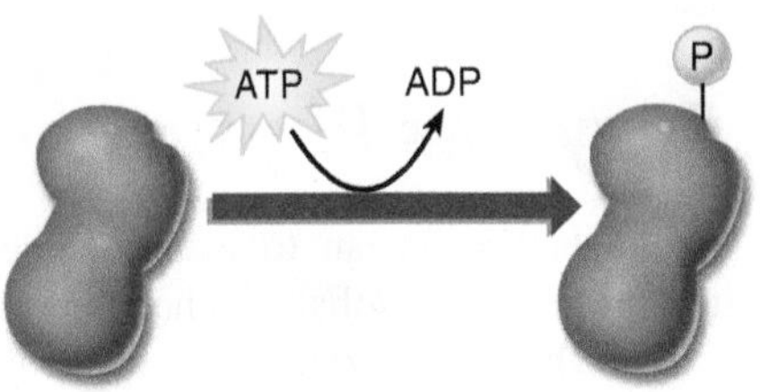

Chemical Activation

Proteins can become activated when a high-energy phosphate from ATP attaches to the protein, activating it. Other types of molecules can also become phosphorylated by transfer of a phosphate from ATP.

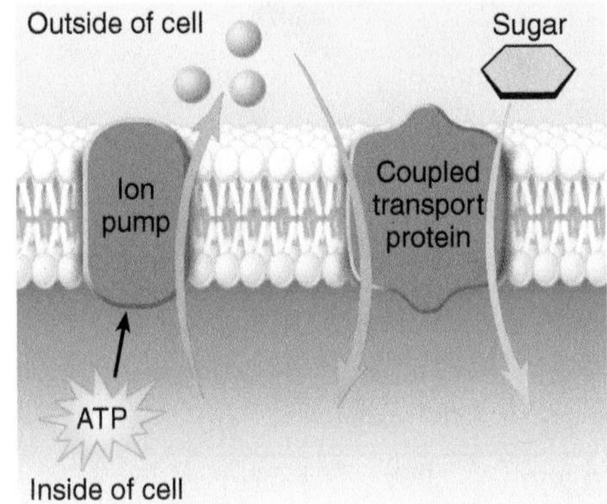

Importing Metabolites

Metabolite molecules such as amino acids and sugars can be transported into cells against their concentration gradients by coupling the intake of the metabolite to the inward movement of an ion moving down its concentration gradient, this ion gradient being established using ATP.

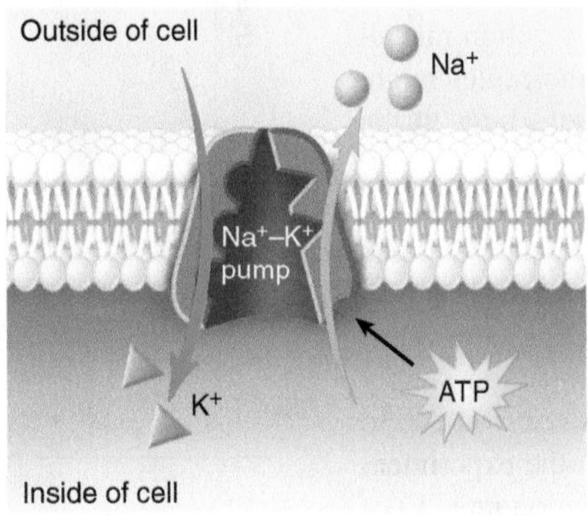

Active Transport: Na^+–K^+ Pump

Most animal cells maintain a low internal concentration of Na^+ relative to their surroundings, and a high internal concentration of K^+. This is achieved using a protein called the sodium-potassium pump, which actively pumps Na^+ out of the cell and K^+ in, using energy from ATP.

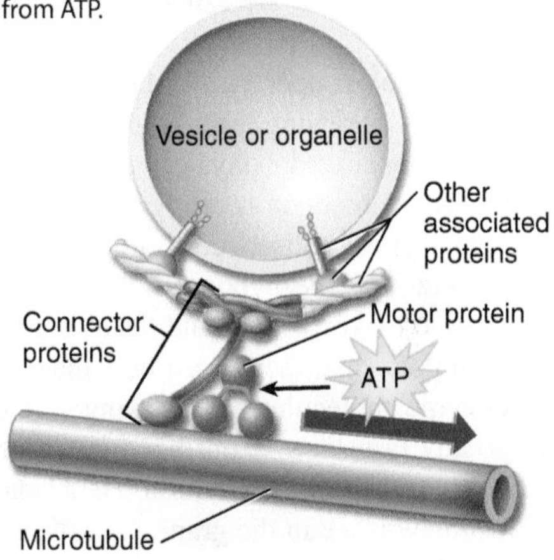

Cytoplasmic Transport

Within a cell's cytoplasm, vesicles or organelles can be dragged along microtubular tracks using molecular motor proteins, which are attached to the vesicle or organelle with connector proteins. The motor proteins use ATP to power their movement.

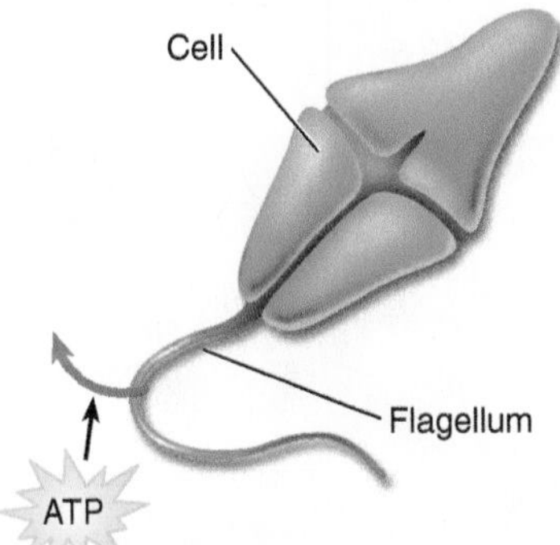

Flagellar Movements

Microtubules within flagella slide past each other to produce flagellar movements. ATP powers the sliding of the microtubules.

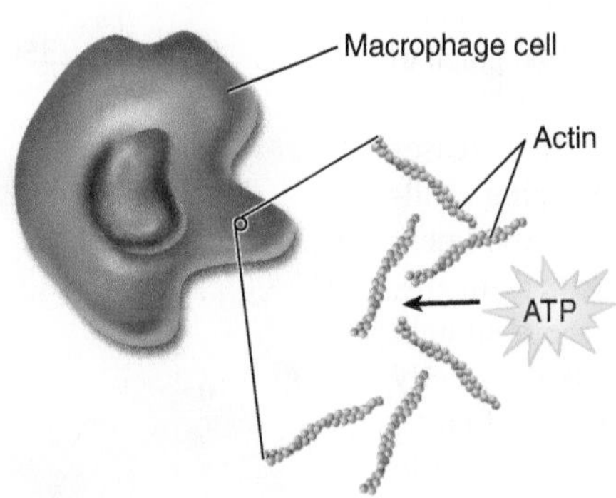

Cell Crawling

Actin filaments in a cell's cytoskeleton continually assemble and disassemble to achieve changes in cell shape and to allow cells to crawl over substrates or engulf materials. The dynamic character of actin is controlled by ATP molecules bound to actin filaments.

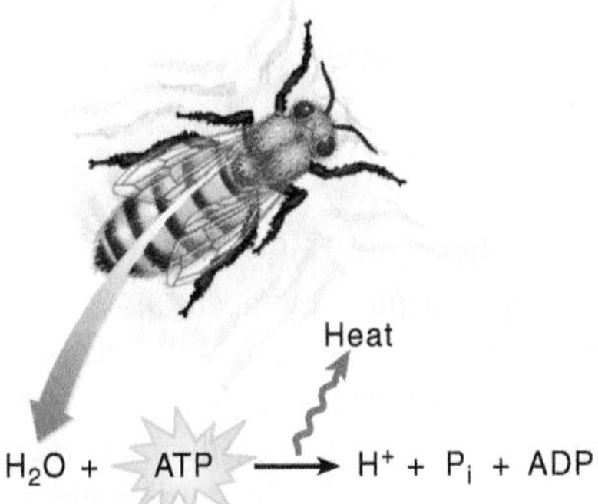

Heat Production

The hydrolysis of the ATP molecule releases heat. Reactions that hydrolyze ATP often take place in mitochondria or in contracting muscle cells and may be coupled to other reactions. The heat generated by these reactions can be used to maintain an organism's temperature.

Inquiry & Analysis

Do Enzymes Physically Attach to Their Substrates?

When scientists first began to examine the chemical activities of organisms, no one knew that biochemical reactions were catalyzed by enzymes. The first enzyme was discovered in 1833 by French chemist Anselme Payen. He was studying how beer is made from barley: First barley is pressed and gently heated so its starches break down into simple two-sugar units; then yeasts convert these units into ethanol. Payen found that the initial breakdown requires a chemical factor that is not alive, and which does not seem to be used up during the process—a catalyst. He called this first enzyme *diastase* (we call it amylase today).

Did this catalyst operate at a distance, increasing reaction rate all around it, much as raising the temperature of nearby molecules might do? Or did it operate in physical contact, actually attaching to the molecules whose reaction it catalyzed (its "substrate")?

The answer was discovered in 1903 by French chemist Victor Henri. He saw that the hypothesis that an enzyme physically binds to its substrate makes a clear and testable prediction: In a solution of substrate and enzyme, there must be a maximum reaction rate. When all the enzyme molecules are working full tilt, the reaction simply cannot go any faster, no matter how much more substrate you add to the solution. To test this prediction, Henri carried out the experiment whose results you see in the graph, measuring the reaction rate (V) of diastase at different substrate concentrations (S).

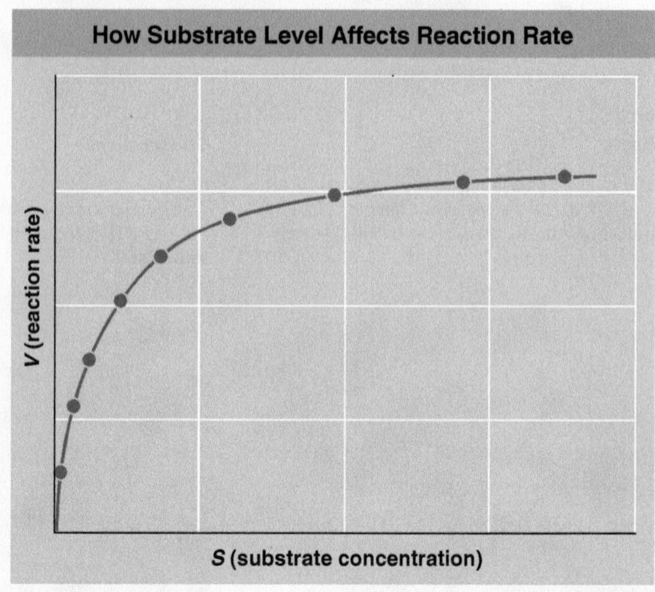

Trial	S	1/S	V	1/V
1	5	0.200	7.7	0.130
2	10	____	15.4	____
3	25	____	23.1	____
4	50	____	30.8	____
5	75	____	38.5	____
6	125	____	40.7	____
7	200	____	46.2	____
8	275	____	47.7	____
9	350	____	48.5	____

Analysis

1. **Making Inferences** As S increases, does V increase? If so, in what manner—steadily, or by smaller and smaller amounts? Is there a maximum reaction rate?
2. **Drawing Conclusions** Does this result provide support for the hypothesis that an enzyme binds physically to its substrate? Explain. If the hypothesis were incorrect, what would you expect the graph to look like?
3. **Further Analysis** If the smaller amounts by which V increases are strictly the result of fewer unoccupied enzymes being available at higher values of S, then the curve in Henri's experiment should show a pure exponential decline in V—mathematically, meaning a reciprocal plot ($1/V$ versus $1/S$) should be a straight line. If some other factor is also at work that reacts differently to substrate concentration, then the reciprocal plot would curve upward or downward. Fill in the reciprocal values in the table to the right, and then plot the values on the lower graph ($1/S$ on the x axis and $1/V$ on the y axis). Is a reciprocal plot of Henri's data a straight line?

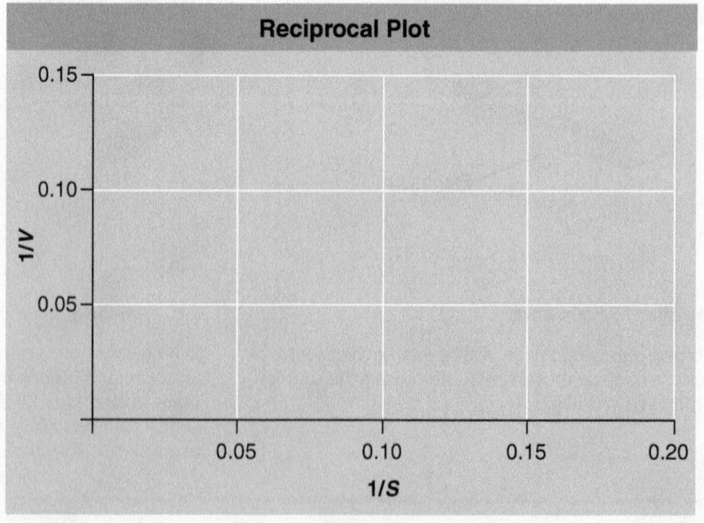

Concept Summary

Cells and Energy

5.1 The Flow of Energy in Living Things

- Energy is the ability to do work. Energy exists in two states: kinetic energy and potential energy.
- Kinetic energy is the energy of motion. Potential energy is stored energy, which exists in objects that aren't in motion but have the capacity to move, like a ball poised at the top of a hill shown here from **figure 5.1.** Work carried out by living organisms involves the transformation of potential energy into kinetic energy. Energy also exists in different forms in the universe, such as light, electrical, or heat energy.

- Energy flows from the sun to the earth, where it is trapped by photosynthetic organisms and stored in carbohydrates as potential energy. This energy is transferred during chemical reactions.

5.2 The Laws of Thermodynamics

- The laws of thermodynamics describe changes in energy in our universe. The first law of thermodynamics explains that energy can not be created or destroyed, only changed from one state to another. The total amount of energy in the universe remains constant.
- The second law of thermodynamics explains that the conversion of potential energy into random molecular motion is constantly increasing. This conversion of energy progresses from an ordered but less stable form to a disordered but stable form. Entropy, which is a measure of disorder in a system, is constantly increasing such that disorder is more likely than order. Energy must be used to maintain order (**figure 5.3**).

Cell Chemistry

5.3 Chemical Reactions

- Chemical reactions involve the breaking or formation of covalent bonds. The starting molecules are called the reactants, and the molecules produced by the reaction are called the products. Chemical reactions in which the products contain more potential energy than the reactants are called endergonic reactions (**figure 5.4*a***). Chemical reactions that release energy are called exergonic reactions (**figure 5.4*b***) and are more likely to occur.
- All chemical reactions require an input of energy. The energy required to start a reaction is called activation energy and is indicated by the red arrow in the chemical reaction shown here from **figure 5.4.** A chemical reaction proceeds faster when its activation energy is lowered, and this occurs through a process called catalysis (**figure 5.4*c***).

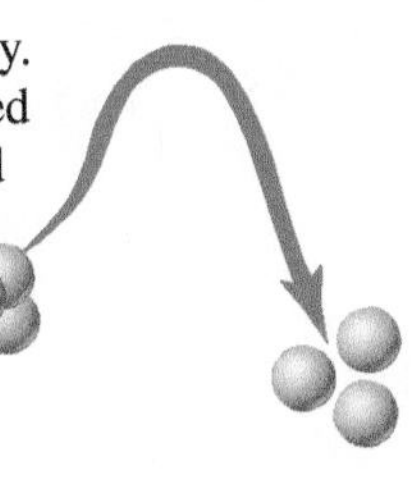

Enzymes

5.4 How Enzymes Work

- Enzymes are molecules that lower the activation energy of chemical reactions in the cell. Enzymes are cellular catalysts.
- An enzyme, like the lysozyme shown here from **figure 5.5,** binds the reactant, or substrate. The substrate binds to the enzyme's active site. The enzyme forms around the reactant and acts to stress covalent bonds or bring atoms into closer proximity (***Essential Biological Process 5A***). The actions of the enzyme increase the likelihood that chemical bonds will break or form. An enzyme lowers the activation energy of the reaction. The enzyme is not affected by the reaction and can be used over and over again.
- Sometimes enzymes work in a series of reactions called a biochemical pathway. The product of one reaction becomes the substrate for the next reaction. The enzymes that are involved are usually located near each other in the cell (**figure 5.6**).
- In the cell, chemical reactions are regulated by controlling which enzymes are active. Other factors, such as temperature and pH, can also affect enzyme function, and so most enzymes have an optimal temperature and pH range (**figure 5.7**).
- Higher temperatures can disrupt the bonds that hold the enzyme in its proper shape, decreasing its ability to catalyze a chemical reaction. The bonds that hold the enzyme's shape are also affected by hydrogen ion concentrations, and so increasing or decreasing the pH can disrupt the enzyme's function.

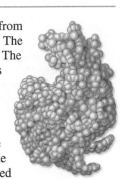

5.5 How Cells Regulate Enzymes

- An enzyme can be inhibited or activated in the cell as a means of regulation by temporarily altering the enzyme's shape (***Essential Biological Process 5B***). An enzyme can be inhibited when a molecule, called a repressor, binds to the enzyme, altering the shape of the active site so that it cannot bind the substrate. Some enzymes need to be activated, or turned on, in order to bind to their substrate. A molecule called an activator binds to the enzyme, changing the shape of the active site so that it is able to bind the substrate. Enzymes that are controlled in this way are allosteric enzymes.
- A repressor molecule can bind to the active site of the enzyme, blocking it. This is called a competitive inhibition. In noncompetitive inhibition, the repressor binds to a different site on the enzyme, altering the shape of the active site so it cannot bind its substrate (**figure 5.8**).

How Cells Use Energy

5.6 ATP: The Energy Currency of the Cell

- Cells require energy to do work in the form of ATP (**table 5.1**). ATP contains a sugar, an adenine, and a chain of three phosphates, as shown here from **figure 5.9.** The three phosphates are held together with high-energy bonds. When the endmost phosphate bond breaks, considerable energy is released. A cell uses this energy to drive reactions in the cell by coupling the breakdown of ATP with other chemical reactions in the cell.

Self-Test

1. The ability to do work is the definition for
   a. thermodynamics.
   b. radiation.
   c. energy.
   d. entropy.
2. The first law of thermodynamics
   a. says that energy recycles constantly, as organisms use and reuse it.
   b. says that entropy, or disorder, continually increases in a closed system.
   c. is a formula for measuring entropy.
   d. says that energy can change forms, but cannot be created or destroyed.
3. The second law of thermodynamics
   a. says that energy recycles constantly, as organisms use and reuse it.
   b. says that entropy, or disorder, continually increases in a closed system.
   c. is a formula for measuring entropy.
   d. says that energy can change forms, but cannot be made nor destroyed.
4. Chemical reactions that occur spontaneously are called
   a. exergonic and release energy.
   b. exergonic and their products contain more energy.
   c. endergonic and release energy.
   d. endergonic and their products contain more energy.
5. The catalysts that help an organism carry out needed chemical reactions are called
   a. hormones.
   b. enzymes.
   c. reactants.
   d. substrates.
6. Factors that affect the activity of an enzyme molecule include
   a. peptides and energy.
   b. activation energy.
   c. temperature and pH.
   d. entropy and thermodynamics.
7. In order for an enzyme to work properly
   a. it must have a particular shape.
   b. the temperature must be within certain limits.
   c. the pH must be within certain limits.
   d. All of the above.
8. In competitive inhibition
   a. an enzyme molecule has to compete with other enzyme molecules for the necessary substrate.
   b. an enzyme molecule has to compete with other enzyme molecules for the necessary energy.
   c. an inhibitor molecule competes with the substrate for the active site on the enzyme.
   d. two different products compete for the same active site on the enzyme.
9. Which of the following is not a component of ATP?
   a. active site
   b. ribose
   c. adenine
   d. phosphate groups
10. Endergonic reactions can occur in the cell because they are coupled with
    a. the breaking of phosphate bonds in ATP.
    b. uncatalyzed reactions.
    c. activators.
    d. all of the above.

Visual Understanding

1. **Figure 5.7** Examine the graphs shown here. Describe what happens to a human enzyme at a temperature of 50°C. Looking at part (b), what happens to trypsin's ability to function as the surrounding concentration of H^+ ions increases? How would the enzyme pepsin respond to a change in pH from 4 to 3?

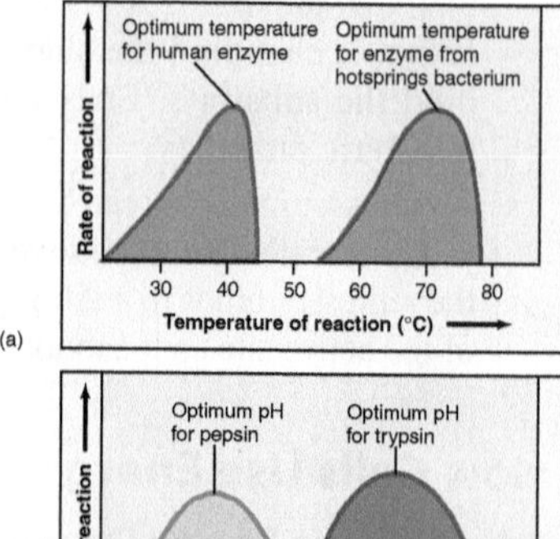

2. **Table 5.1** ATP forms primarily from the breakdown of glucose. If your blood glucose level drops, what sorts of problems can that cause in your body?

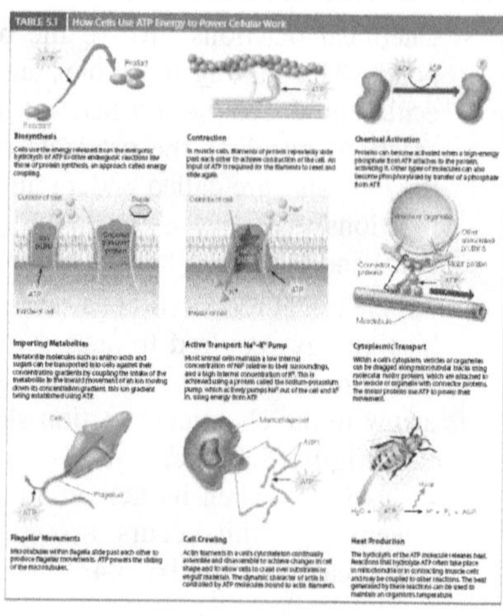

Challenge Questions

1. Photosynthetic organisms, such as plants, algae, and bacteria, capture the sun's energy and use it to build sugar molecules that other organisms can use. The formation of these molecules involves endergonic reactions. Explain what this means and where the sun's energy is stored in these sugar molecules.
2. What sorts of things can keep an enzyme from doing its job?
3. When a baseball thrown by a pitcher encounters the swinging bat of a slugger, what happens to the ball's kinetic energy? What happens to the bat's kinetic energy?

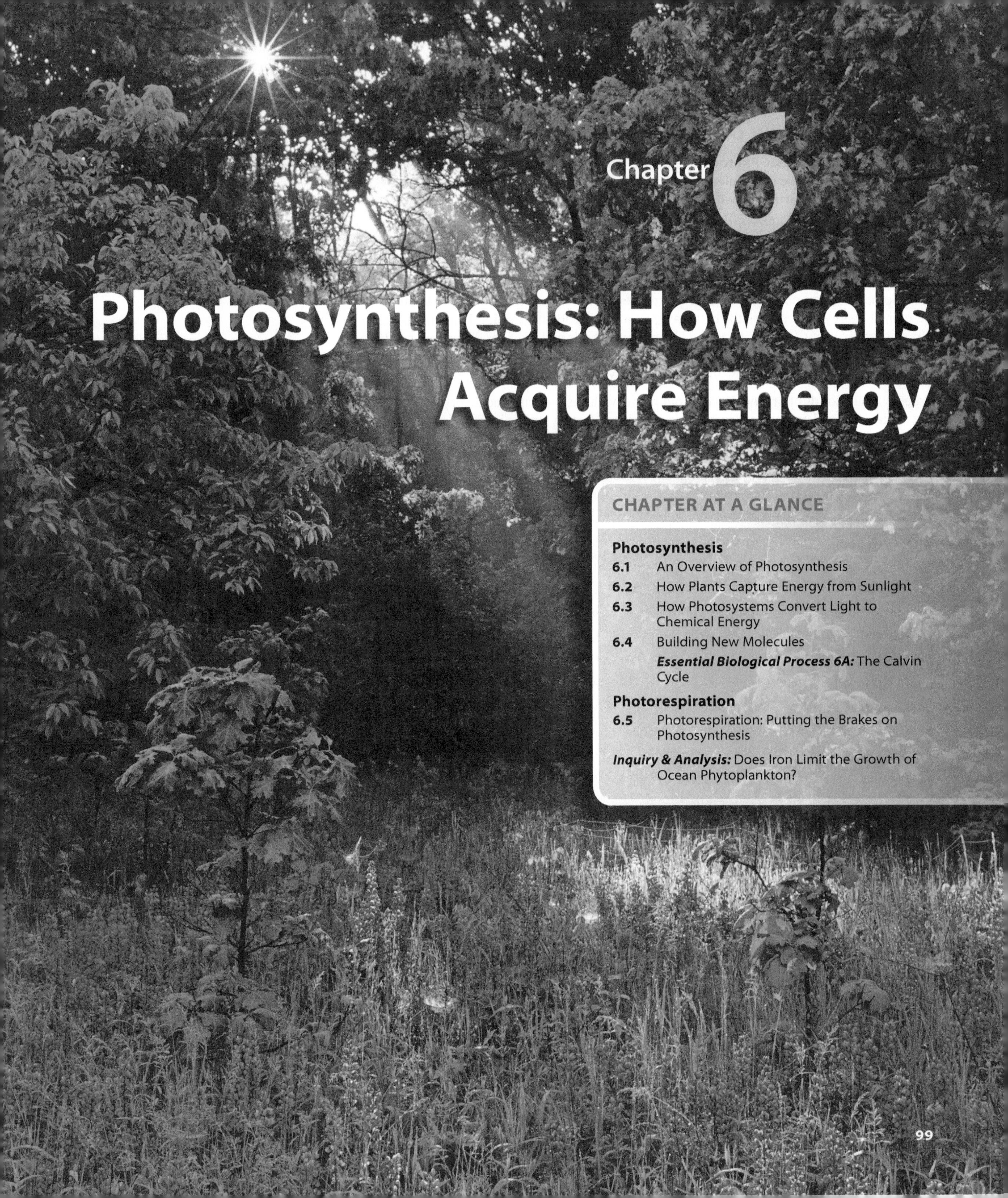

Chapter 6

Photosynthesis: How Cells Acquire Energy

CHAPTER AT A GLANCE

Photosynthesis

6.1 An Overview of Photosynthesis

CONCEPT PREVIEW: Photosynthesis uses energy from sunlight to power the synthesis of organic molecules from CO_2 in the air. In plants this takes place in specialized compartments within chloroplasts.

Life is powered by sunshine. All of the energy used by almost all living cells comes ultimately from the sun, captured by plants, algae, and some bacteria through the process of **photosynthesis.** Every oxygen atom in the air we breathe was once part of a water molecule, liberated by photosynthesis as you will discover in this chapter. Life as we know it is only possible because our earth is awash in energy streaming inward from the sun. Each day, the radiant energy that reaches the earth is equal to that of about 1 million Hiroshima-sized atomic bombs. About 1% of it is captured by photosynthesis and provides the energy needed to synthesize carbohydrates that drives almost all life on earth. Use the arrows on this page and the next three pages to follow the path of energy from the sun through photosynthesis.

Trees. Many kinds of organisms carry out photosynthesis, not only the diversity of plants that make our world green, but also bacteria and algae. Photosynthesis is somewhat different in bacteria, but we will focus our attention on photosynthesis in plants, starting with this maple tree crowned with green leaves. Later we will look at the grass growing beneath the maple tree—it turns out that grasses and other related plants sometimes take a different approach to photosynthesis depending on the conditions.

Leaves. To learn how this maple tree captures energy from sunlight, follow the light. It comes beaming in from the sun, down through earth's atmosphere, bathing the top of the tree in light. What part of the maple tree is actually being struck by this light? Its green leaves. Each branch at the top of the tree ends in a spread of these leaves, each leaf flat and thin like the page of a book. Within these green leaves is where photosynthesis occurs. No photosynthesis occurs within this tree's stem, covered with bark, and none in the roots, buried within the soil—no light reaches these parts of the plant. The tree has a very efficient internal plumbing system that transports the products of photosynthesis to the stem, roots, and other parts of the plant so that they too may benefit from the capture of the sun's energy.

The Leaf Surface. Now follow the light as it passes into a leaf. The beam of light first encounters a waxy protective layer called the cuticle. The cuticle acts a bit like a layer of clear fingernail polish, providing a thin, watertight and surprisingly strong layer of protection. Light passes right through this transparent wax, and then proceeds to pass right on through a layer of cells immediately beneath the cuticle called the epidermis. Only one cell layer thick, this epidermis acts as the "skin" of the leaf, providing more protection from damage and, very importantly, controlling how gases and water enter and leave the leaf. Very little of the light is absorbed by the cuticle or the epidermis.

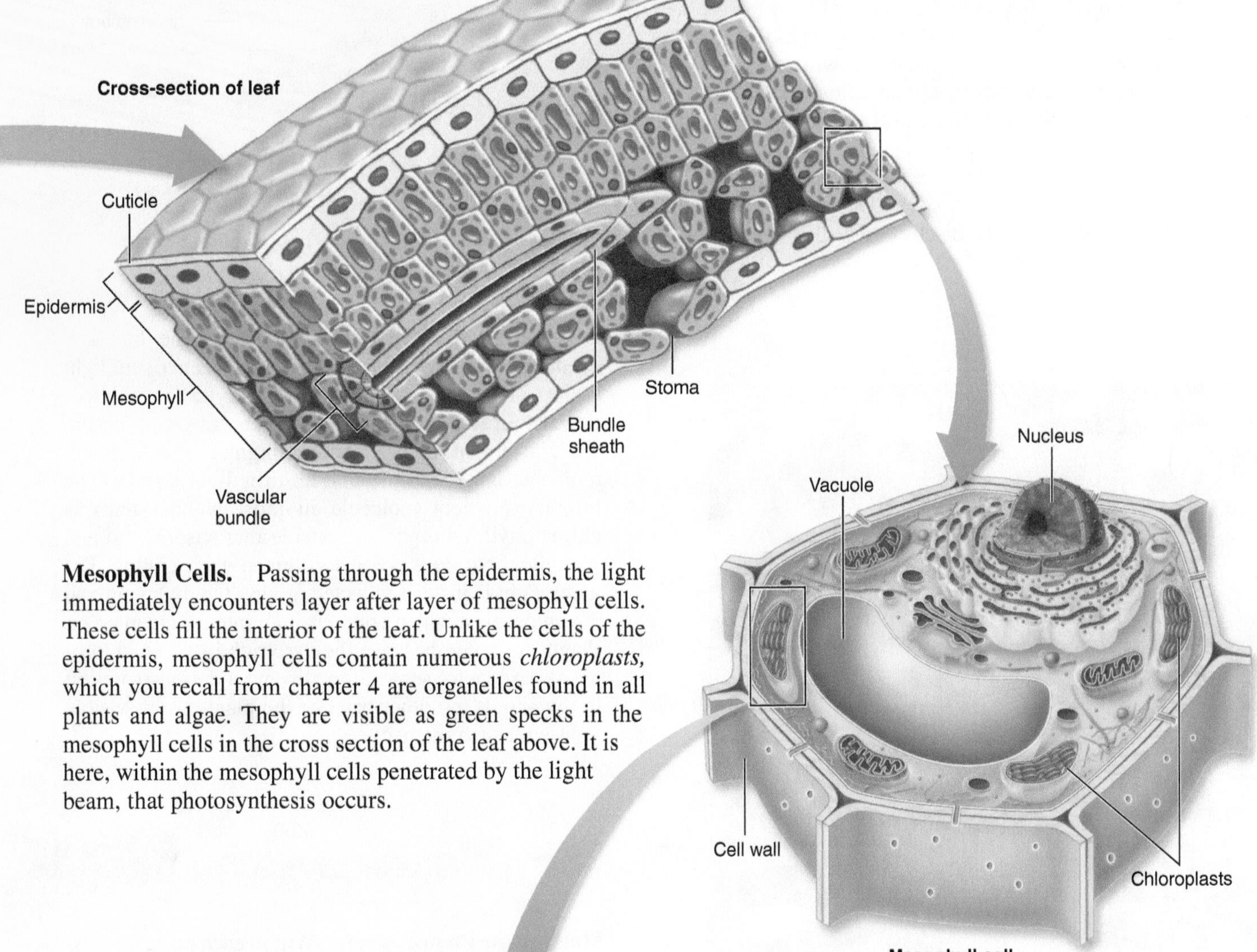

Mesophyll Cells. Passing through the epidermis, the light immediately encounters layer after layer of mesophyll cells. These cells fill the interior of the leaf. Unlike the cells of the epidermis, mesophyll cells contain numerous *chloroplasts,* which you recall from chapter 4 are organelles found in all plants and algae. They are visible as green specks in the mesophyll cells in the cross section of the leaf above. It is here, within the mesophyll cells penetrated by the light beam, that photosynthesis occurs.

Thylakoid
Inner membrane
Outer membrane
Granum
Stroma
Chloroplast

Chloroplasts. Light penetrates into mesophyll cells. The cell walls of the mesophyll cells don't absorb it, nor does the plasma membrane or nucleus or mitochondria. Why not? Because these elements of the mesophyll cell contain few if any molecules that absorb visible light. If chloroplasts were not also present in these cells, most of this light would pass right through, just as it passed through the epidermis. But chloroplasts are present, lots of them. One chloroplast is highlighted by a box in the mesophyll cell above. Light passes into the cell and when it reaches the chloroplast, it passes through the outer and inner membranes to reach the thylakoid structures within the chloroplast, clearly seen as the green disks in the cutaway chloroplast shown here.

Inside the Chloroplast

All the important events of photosynthesis happen inside the chloroplast. The journey of light into the chloroplasts ends when the light beam encounters a series of internal membranes within the chloroplast organized into flattened sacs called *thylakoids.* Often, numerous thylakoids are stacked on top of one another in columns called *grana.* In the drawing below, the grana look not unlike piles of dishes. While each thylakoid is a separate compartment that functions more-or-less independently, the membranes of the individual thylakoids are all connected, part of a single continuous membrane system. Occupying much of the interior of the chloroplast, this thylakoid membrane system is submerged within a semi-liquid substance called *stroma,* which fills the interior of the chloroplast in much the same way that cytoplasm fills the interior of a cell. Suspended within the stroma are many enzymes and other proteins, including the enzymes that act later in photosynthesis to assemble organic molecules from carbon dioxide (CO_2) in reactions that do not require light and which are discussed later.

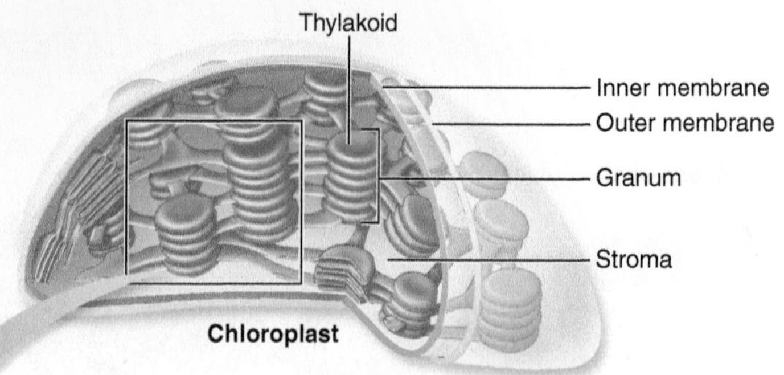

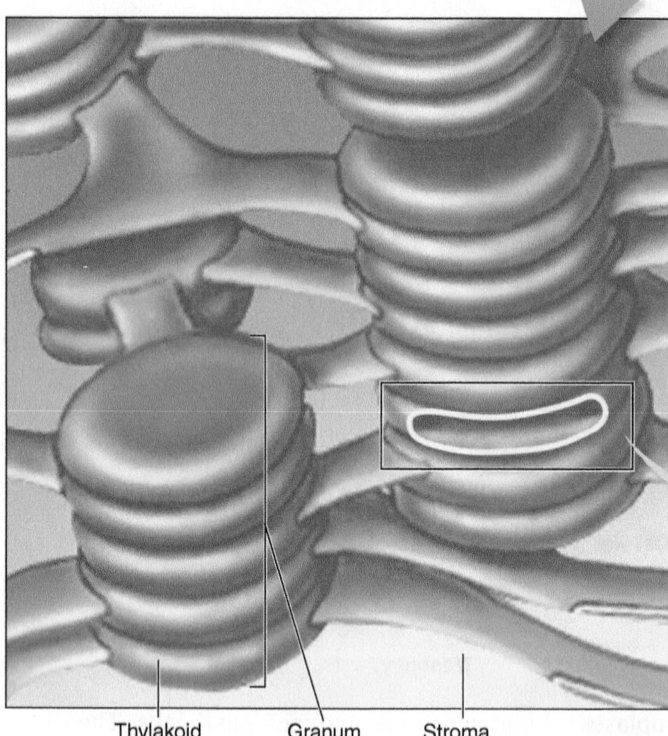

Penetrating the Thylakoid Surface. The first key event of photosynthesis occurs when a beam of sunlight strikes the surface membrane of a thylakoid. Embedded within this membrane, like icebergs on an ocean, are clusters of light-absorbing pigments. A pigment molecule is a molecule that absorbs light energy. The primary pigment molecule in most photosystems is **chlorophyll,** an organic molecule that absorbs red and blue light, but does not absorb green wavelengths. The green light is instead reflected, giving the thylakoid and the chloroplast which contains it an intense green color. Plants are green because they are rich in green chloroplasts. Except for some alternative pigments also present in thylakoids, no other parts of the plant absorb visible light with such intensity.

Striking the Photosystem. Within each pigment cluster, the chlorophyll molecules are arranged in a network called a *photosystem.* The light-absorbing chlorophyll molecules of a photosystem act together as an antenna to capture photons (units of light energy). A lattice of structural proteins, indicated by the purple structure inserted into the thylakoid membrane in the diagram on the facing page, anchors each of the chlorophyll molecules of a photosystem into a precise position, such that every chlorophyll molecule is touching several others. Wherever light strikes the photosystem, some chlorophyll molecule will be in position to receive it.

Energy Absorption. When sunlight strikes any chlorophyll molecule in the photosystem, the chlorophyll molecule absorbs energy. The energy becomes part of the chlorophyll molecule, boosting some of its electrons to higher energy levels. Possessing these more energetic electrons, the chlorophyll molecule is said to now be "excited." With this key event, the biological world has captured energy from the sun.

Excitation of the Photosystem. The excitation that the absorption of light creates is then passed from the chlorophyll molecule which was hit to another, and then to another, like a hot potato being passed down a line of people. This shuttling of excitation is not a chemical reaction, in which an electron physically passes between atoms. Rather, it is energy that passes from one chlorophyll molecule to its neighbor. A crude analogy to this form of energy transfer is the initial "break" in a game of pool. If the cue ball squarely hits the point of the triangular array of 15 billiard balls, the two balls at the far corners of the triangle fly off, and none of the central balls move at all. The kinetic energy is transferred through the central balls to the most distant ones. In much the same way, the sun's excitation energy moves through the photosystem from one chlorophyll to the next.

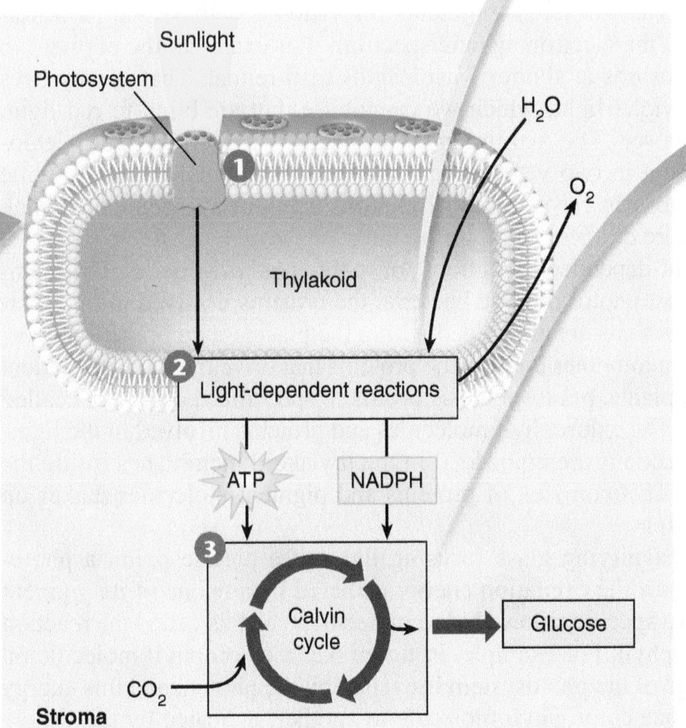

Energy Capture. As the energy shuttles from one chlorophyll molecule to another within the photosystem network, it eventually arrives at a key chlorophyll molecule, the only one that is touching a membrane-bound protein. Like shaking a marble in a box with a walnut-sized hole in it, the excitation energy will find its way to this special chlorophyll just as sure as the marble will eventually find its way to and through the hole in the box. The special chlorophyll then transfers an excited (high-energy) electron to the acceptor molecule it is touching.

The Light-Dependent Reactions. Like a baton being passed from one runner to another in a relay race, the electron is then passed from that acceptor protein to a series of other proteins in the membrane that put the energy of the electron to work making ATP and NADPH. In a way you will explore later in this chapter, the energy is used to power the movement of protons across the thylakoid membrane to make ATP and another key molecule, NADPH. So far, photosynthesis has consisted of two stages, indicated by numbers in the diagram to the lower left: ❶ capturing energy from sunlight—accomplished by the photosystem; and ❷ using the energy to make ATP and NADPH. These first two stages of photosynthesis take place only in the presence of light, and together are traditionally called the **light-dependent reactions.** ATP and NADPH are important energy-rich chemicals, and after this, the rest of photosynthesis becomes a chemical process.

The Light-Independent Reactions. The ATP and NADPH molecules generated by the light-dependent reactions are then used to power a series of chemical reactions in the stroma of the chloroplast, each catalyzed by an enzyme present there. Acting together like the many stages of a manufacturing assembly line, these reactions accomplish the synthesis of carbohydrates from CO_2 in the air ❸. This third stage of photosynthesis, the formation of organic molecules like glucose from atmospheric CO_2, is called the **Calvin cycle,** but is also referred to as the **light-independent reactions** because it doesn't require light directly. We will examine the Calvin cycle in detail later in this chapter.

This completes our brief overview of photosynthesis. In the rest of the chapter we will revisit each stage and consider its elements in more detail. For now, the overall process may be summarized by the following simple equation:

$$6\,CO_2 + 12\,H_2O + \text{light} \longrightarrow C_6H_{12}O_6 + 6\,H_2O + 6\,O_2$$

carbon dioxide · water · energy · glucose · water · oxygen

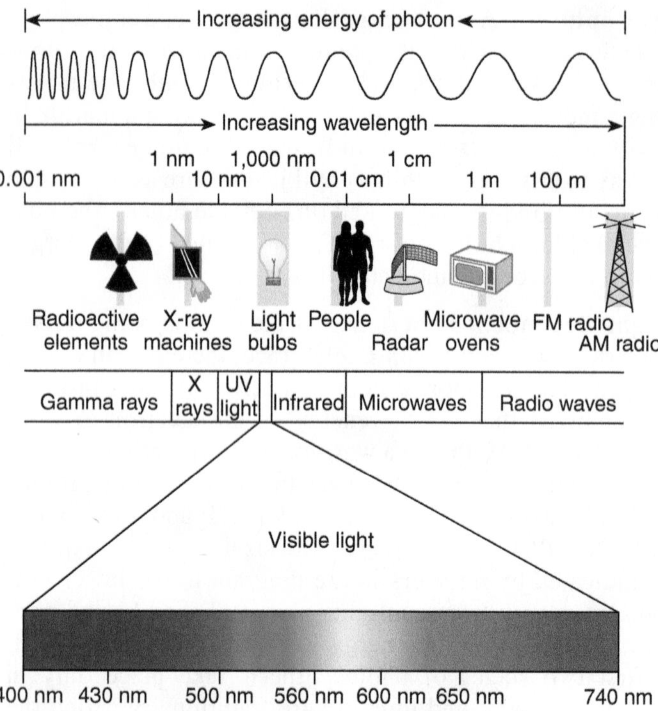

Figure 6.1 Photons of different energy: the electromagnetic spectrum.

Light is composed of packets of energy called photons. Some of the photons in light carry more energy than others. The shorter the wavelength of light, the greater the energy of its photons. Visible light represents only a small part of the electromagnetic spectrum, that with wavelengths between about 400 and 740 nanometers.

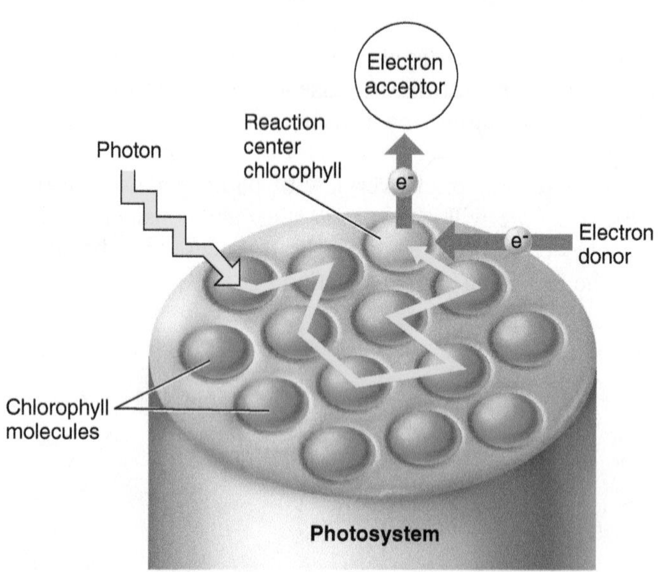

Figure 6.2 How a photosystem works.

When light of the proper wavelength strikes any pigment molecule within a photosystem, the light is absorbed and its excitation energy is then transferred from one molecule to another within the cluster of pigment molecules until it encounters the reaction center, which exports the energy as high-energy electrons to an acceptor molecule.

6.2 How Plants Capture Energy from Sunlight

CONCEPT PREVIEW: Photons from red and blue light are captured by chlorophyll pigments and used to excite electrons in the reaction center. The excited electrons are used to do the chemical work of producing ATP and NADPH.

Where is the energy in light? What is there about sunlight that a plant can use to create chemical bonds? The revolution in physics in the twentieth century taught us that light actually consists of tiny packets of energy called **photons,** which have properties both of particles and of waves. When light shines on your hand, your skin is being bombarded by a stream of these photons.

Sunlight contains photons of many energy levels, only some of which we "see." We call the full range of these photons the **electromagnetic spectrum.** As you can see in figure 6.1, some of the photons in sunlight have shorter wavelengths (toward the left side of the spectrum) and carry a great deal of energy—for example, gamma rays and ultraviolet (UV) light. Others such as radio waves carry very little energy and have longer wavelengths (hundreds to thousands of meters long). Molecules that absorb light energy are called **pigments.** When we speak of visible light, we refer to those wavelengths that the pigment within human eyes, called *retinal,* can absorb—roughly with wavelengths from 400 nanometers (violet) to 740 nanometers (red). Plants are even more picky, absorbing mainly blue and red light and reflecting back what is left of the visible light. Plants are perceived by our eyes as green simply because only the green wavelengths of light are reflected off the plant leaves.

Pigments and Photosystems

Other animals use different pigments for vision and thus "see" a different portion of the electromagnetic spectrum. For example, the pigment in insect eyes absorbs at shorter wavelengths than retinal. That is why bees can see ultraviolet light, which we cannot see, but are blind to red light, which we can see. The main pigment in plants that absorbs light is chlorophyll, present in two versions: chlorophyll *a* and chlorophyll *b*. While chlorophyll absorbs fewer kinds of photons than our eye pigment retinal, it is much more efficient at capturing them.

The light-dependent reactions of photosynthesis occur on membranes. In most photosynthetic bacteria, the proteins involved in the light-dependent reactions are embedded within the plasma membrane. In algae, intracellular membranes contain the proteins that drive the light-dependent reactions. In plants, photosynthesis occurs in specialized organelles called chloroplasts. The chlorophyll molecules and proteins involved in the light-dependent reactions are embedded in the thylakoid membranes inside the chloroplasts. This complex of proteins and pigment molecules makes up the **photosystem.**

Like a magnifying glass focusing light on a precise point, a photosystem channels the excitation energy gathered by any one of its pigment molecules to a specific chlorophyll *a* molecule, which is called the reaction center chlorophyll. For example, in figure 6.2, a chlorophyll molecule on the outer edge of the photosystem is excited by the photon, and this energy passes from one chlorophyll molecule to another, indicated by the yellow zigzag arrow, until it reaches the reaction center molecule. This molecule then passes the energy, in the form of an excited electron, out of the photosystem to drive the synthesis of ATP and organic molecules.

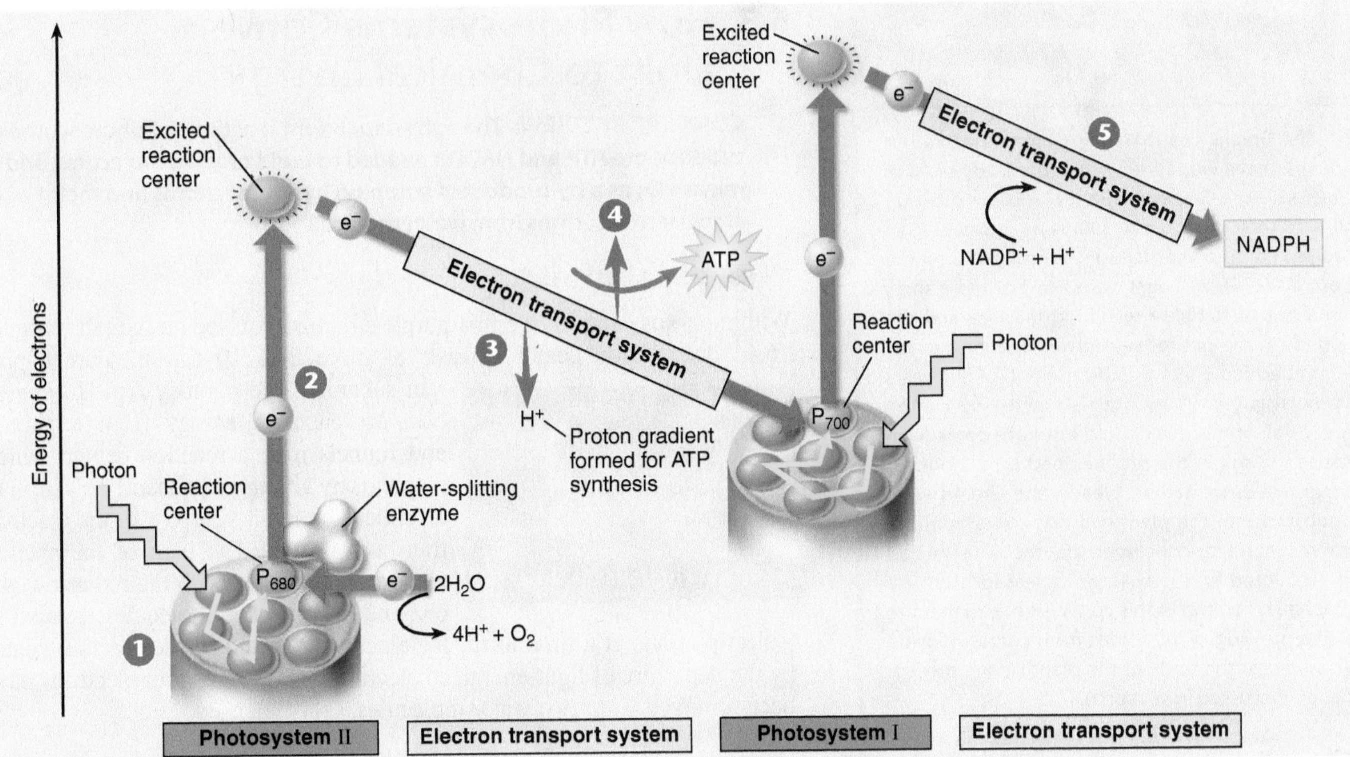

Figure 6.3 Plants use two photosystems.

In stage ❶, a photon excites pigment molecules in photosystem II. In stage ❷, a high-energy electron from photosystem II is transferred to the electron transport system. In stage ❸, the excited electron is used to pump a proton across the membrane. In stage ❹, the concentration gradient of protons is used to produce a molecule of ATP. In stage ❺, the ejected electron then passes to photosystem I, which uses it with a photon of light energy, to drive the formation of NADPH.

IMPLICATION: Photosystem I consists entirely of chlorophyll *a* pigment molecules, while photosystem II is made up of half chlorophyll *a* and half chlorophyll *b* molecules. Both chlorophyll *a* and *b* absorb blue and red light but reflect green light. What color would plant leaves be if they absorbed all wavelengths of visible light?

Using Two Photosystems

Plants and algae use two photosystems, photosystems I and II, indicated by the two purple cylinders in figure 6.3. Photosystem II captures the energy that is used to produce the ATP needed to build sugar molecules. The light energy that it captures is used in stages ❶ and ❷ to transfer the energy of a photon of light to an excited electron; the energy of this electron is then used by the electron transport system ❸ to produce ATP ❹.

Photosystem I powers the production of the hydrogen atoms needed to build sugars and other organic molecules from CO_2 (which has no hydrogen atoms). Photosystem I uses an energized electron, carried by a hydrogen ion (a proton), to form NADPH from $NADP^+$ in stage ❺. NADPH shuttles hydrogens to the Calvin cycle where sugars are made.

The photosystems are not numbered in the order in which they are used. Photosystem II actually acts first in the series, and photosystem I acts second. The confusion arises because the photosystems were named in the order in which they were discovered, and photosystem I was discovered before photosystem II.

IN THE NEWS

Nanotubes and Artificial Photosynthesis. Chemists have long tried in vain to reproduce photosynthesis in the test tube. Artificial photosynthesis could efficiently mop up CO_2 from the atmosphere, as well as produce clean hydrogen fuel for vehicles. The key problem blocking progress has been properly channeling the sun's energy. Visible photons can only contribute a limited amount of energy to a chemical reaction, the amount absorbed by an energized electron. Because the synthesis of carbohydrates requires more energy than that, photosynthesis can only proceed when two energized electrons are contributed, a class of reaction the chemists call a "multiple electron system." The problem is that existing artificial systems are all "single electron systems" that can donate and receive only one electron at a time. A team of Chinese researchers has recently found that a single-walled carbon nanotube can act as the chemical heart of a multiple electron system. To a short nanotube just 1 micrometer long they attach over a hundred molecules of a chemical that releases electrons when it absorbs light. The nanotube in turn absorbs the electrons, which are now available for the carbon-fixing reactions of photosynthesis. Much more remains to be done before artificial photosynthesis becomes a reality, but the key roadblock has now been overcome.

BIOLOGY & YOU

The Greeks Get It Wrong. From the time of the Greeks, people have wondered where the body mass of a plant comes from—the Greeks thought plants sucked it up from the soil with their roots. Over 300 years ago a Belgian doctor named Jan Baptista van Helmont thought of a simple way to find out if the Greeks were right. He planted a small willow tree in a pot of soil after weighing the tree and the soil. The tree grew in the pot for several years, during which time van Helmont added only water. At the end of five years the tree was much larger: its weight had increased by 164 pounds. However, all of this mass could not have come from the soil, because the soil in the pot weighed only 2 ounces less than it had five years earlier! Clearly, the Greeks were wrong—the substance of the plant had not come from the soil. van Helmont incorrectly concluded that the water he had been adding accounted for the willow's increased mass. We now know that he was wrong in this conclusion, and that the added mass of a growing plant comes from carbon dioxide gas in the air, added to the body of the plant by the process of carbon fixation discussed in section 6.4.

6.3 How Photosystems Convert Light to Chemical Energy

CONCEPT PREVIEW: The light-dependent reactions of photosynthesis produce the ATP and NADPH needed to build organic molecules, and release O_2 as a by-product of stripping hydrogen atoms and their associated electrons from water molecules.

Photosystem II

Within photosystem II, the first purple structure you see on the left in figure 6.4, the reaction center consists of more than 10 transmembrane protein subunits. The photosystem II *antenna complex* captures energy from a photon and funnels it to a reaction center, which responds by giving up an excited electron to a primary electron acceptor in the electron transport system. The path of the excited electron is indicated with the red arrow. An enzyme splits water molecules, removing electrons one at a time to fill the electron hole left in the reaction center by the departure of light-energized electrons. As soon as four electrons have been removed from two water molecules, O_2 is released.

To better understand how energy from the sun is captured by the plant, look back to figure 2.3 on page 33. An electron in the reaction center absorbs energy from the sun and is moved to a higher energy level. This energized electron is now carrying energy from the sun.

Electron Transport System

The light-energized electrons leaving photosystem II are passed to a series of electron-carrier molecules called the *electron transport system*. These proteins are embedded within the thylakoid membrane. Importantly, one of them is a "proton pump" protein. The energy of the electron is used by this protein to pump a proton from the stroma into the thylakoid space (indicated by the blue arrow through the electron transport system). A nearby protein in the membrane then carries the now energy-depleted electron on to photosystem I.

The transfer of electrons from one carrier protein to another along the electron transport system is a type of chemical reaction called oxidation-reduction, or redox. Redox reactions involve the transfer of energy along with electrons and are discussed in chapter 7 on page 114.

Figure 6.4 The photosynthetic electrons are used to produce ATP and NADPH.

The energy of the electron absorbed by photosystem II powers the pumping of protons into the thylakoid space. These protons then pass back out through ATP synthase channels, their movement powering the production of ATP. The energy of the electron absorbed by photosystem I powers the attachment of a proton to $NADP^+$, forming NADPH.

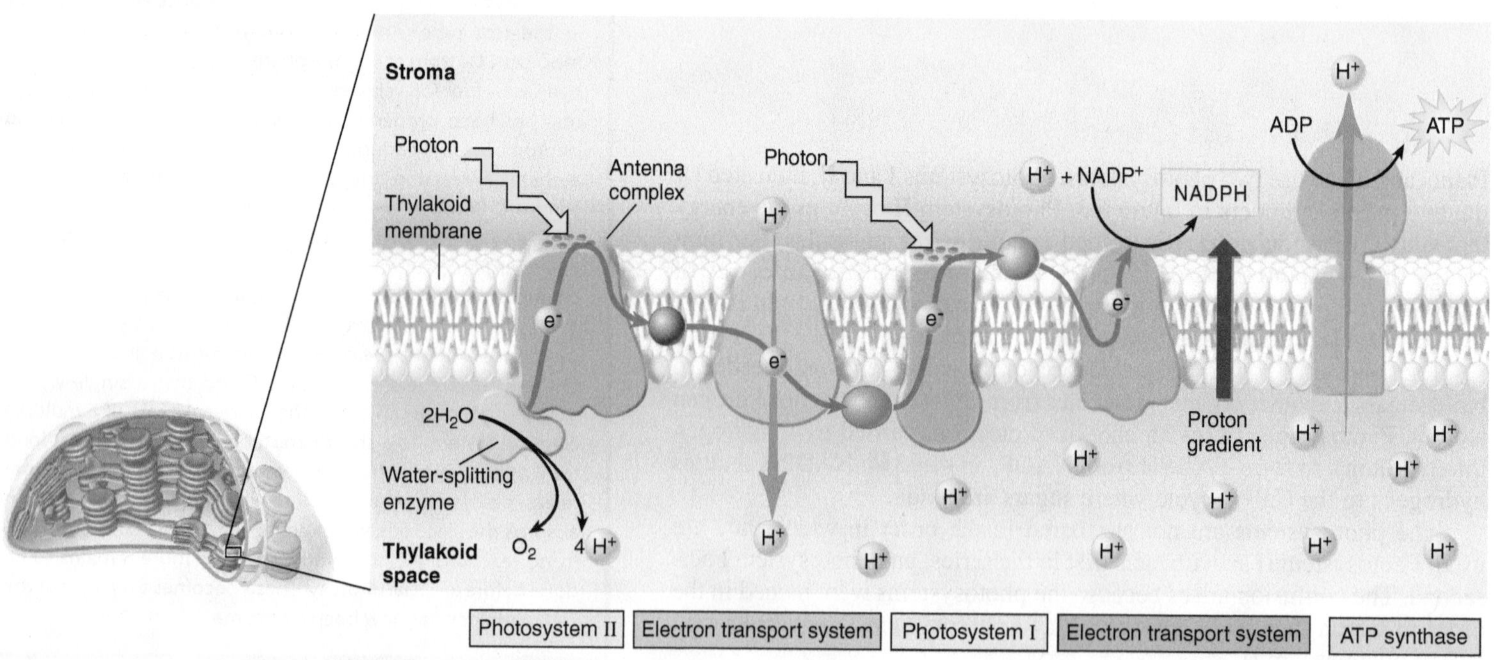

Making ATP: Chemiosmosis

Before progressing onto photosystem I, let's see what happens with the protons that were pumped into the thylakoid by the electron transport system. The process of ATP formation is called **chemiosmosis,** and involves three elements: photosystem II, the first electron transport system, and a protein channel called ATP synthase. The thylakoid membrane you see in figure 6.4 is impermeable to protons, so protons that have been pumped across the membrane by the first electron transport system build up inside the thylakoid space, creating a very large concentration gradient. These protons now diffuse back out of the thylakoid space, down their concentration gradient, passing through a special channel protein called *ATP synthase.*

As you may recall from the discussion of diffusion on page 78, molecules in solution diffuse from areas of higher concentration to areas of lower concentration, down their concentration gradient.

The ATP synthase is the membrane protein on the far right side of figure 6.4, protruding like a knob out of the external surface of the thylakoid membrane. As protons pass out of the thylakoid through the ATP synthase channels, a phosphate group is added onto ADP to form ATP in a process called phosphorylation. ATP is released into the stroma (the fluid matrix inside the chloroplast). The stroma contains the enzymes that catalyze the light-independent reactions, where ATP is used to build carbohydrate molecules.

The ATP molecule, as described on page 94, contains high-energy phosphate bonds. The chemical reaction that forms the outermost high-energy bond from ADP and a phosphate group uses energy from the sun harvested by exciting electrons.

Photosystem I

Now, with ATP formed, let's return to the middle of figure 6.4 where photosystem I accepts an electron from the electron transport system. Energy is fed to photosystem I by an antenna complex of chlorophyll molecules. The electron arriving from the first electron transport system has by no means lost all of its light-excited energy; almost half remains. Thus, the absorption of another photon of light energy by photosystem I boosts the electron leaving its reaction center to a very high energy level.

Making NADPH

Like photosystem II, photosystem I passes electrons to an electron transport system. When two of these electrons reach the end of this electron transport system, they are then donated to a molecule of $NADP^+$ along with a proton (a hydrogen ion) to form NADPH. Because the reaction occurs on the stromal side of the membrane and involves the uptake of a proton in forming NADPH, it contributes further to the proton concentration gradient established during photosynthetic electron transport.

Although photosynthetic bacteria carry out the light-dependent reactions in a slightly different way, photosynthesis in algae, such as those shown in figure 6.5, functions in the same way as in plants.

Products of the Light-Dependent Reactions

The ATP and NADPH produced in the light-dependent reactions end up being passed on to the Calvin cycle in the stroma of the chloroplast. There, ATP is used to power chemical reactions that build carbohydrates. NADPH provides the hydrogens and electrons used in building carbohydrates. In the next section we examine how the Calvin cycle of photosynthesis puts these two molecules to work.

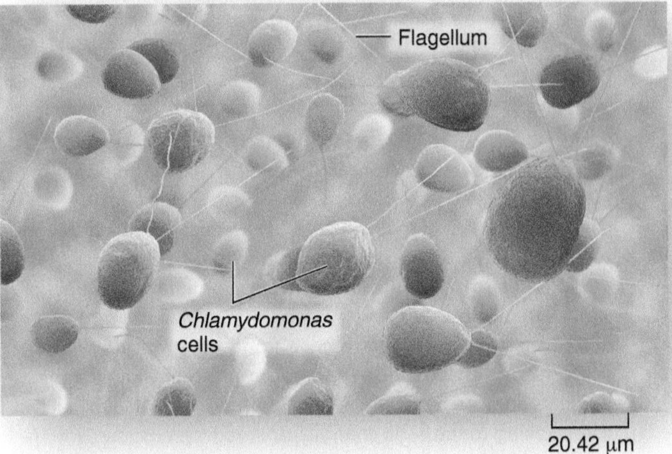

Figure 6.5 Plants aren't the only ones that carry out photosynthesis.

Each of these green balls is a single-celled photosynthetic organism, a green alga called *Chlamydomonas* that is common in pond water.

IMPLICATION Photosynthetic algae and bacteria in the oceans, called phytoplankton, carry out much of the earth's photosynthesis, removing far more CO_2 from the atmosphere than their cellular respiration adds to it. However, increases in ocean temperatures speed up cellular respiration much faster than photosynthesis. What would you expect the effect of global warming to be on the ocean's influence on atmospheric CO_2? Why is this consequence important?

IN THE NEWS

Using Algae to Fix Global Warming. Engineers at Ohio University have come up with a novel solution to the problem of what to do with the massive amounts of CO_2 that will be generated by burning coal. They have created a photo bioreactor that passes streams of CO_2 over sheets of a woven material made of living algae. The algae use photosynthesis to remove CO_2 from the air stream! When an algal sheet has grown substantially, it is removed and the algae dried and used as feed for farm animals. Test facilities are already up and running. A full-scale reactor that produces 1.25 million square meters of algae sheets may be operational by 2010.

EVOLUTION

Global Warming and the Calvin Cycle. Photosynthesis removes CO_2 from air by binding it to the compound RuBP in the first step of the Calvin cycle. The enzyme that catalyzes this reaction, with a long chemical name usually shortened to RuBisCO, is the most abundant enzyme in the world, and also one of the least efficient. It is a thousand times slower than most other enzymes. Its inefficiency limits the amount of CO_2 plants can remove from the atmosphere. For years scientists have tried to engineer a speedier variant of the RuBisCO enzyme by altering specific sites on the enzyme and then looking to see if the change improved the enzyme. Nothing they tried has worked—there are just too many possible changes to test. However, scientists at Emory University have found a way through the thicket of possibilities. With a nod to Darwin, they have used a process called "directed evolution." They added the gene for RuBisCO to a bacterium in such a way that the bacterium could not survive unless the enzyme functioned; then they randomly altered the gene. The fastest growing bacteria were those with the most efficient RuBisCO! The best experimental results exhibited a 500% increase in enzyme speed. The next step . . . to get this engineered enzyme into plants.

6.4 Building New Molecules

CONCEPT PREVIEW: In a series of reactions, called the Calvin cycle, CO_2, ATP, and NADPH are used to assemble new organic molecules.

The Calvin Cycle

Stated very simply, photosynthesis is a way of making organic molecules from carbon dioxide (CO_2). The actual assembly of new molecules employs a complex battery of enzymes in what is called the **Calvin cycle,** or **C_3 photosynthesis** (C_3 because the first molecule produced in the process is a three-carbon molecule). The process takes place in three stages, indicated by the three panels in *Essential Biological Process 6A*. Three turns of the cycle are needed to produce one molecule of glyceraldehyde 3-phosphate. In any *one* turn of the cycle, a carbon atom from a carbon dioxide molecule is first added to a five-carbon sugar, producing two three-carbon sugars. This process is called **carbon fixation** because it attaches a carbon atom that was in a gas to an organic molecule. The cycle has to "turn" six times in order to form a new glucose molecule. The cycle is driven by energy from ATP and hydrogen atoms are supplied by NADPH, both produced in the light-dependent reactions.

Concept Check

1. In what cells of a leaf does photosynthesis occur?
2. Which photosystem powers the production of ATP, I or II?
3. What three substances are needed by the Calvin cycle to produce a molecule of glucose?

Essential Biological Process 6A

The Calvin Cycle

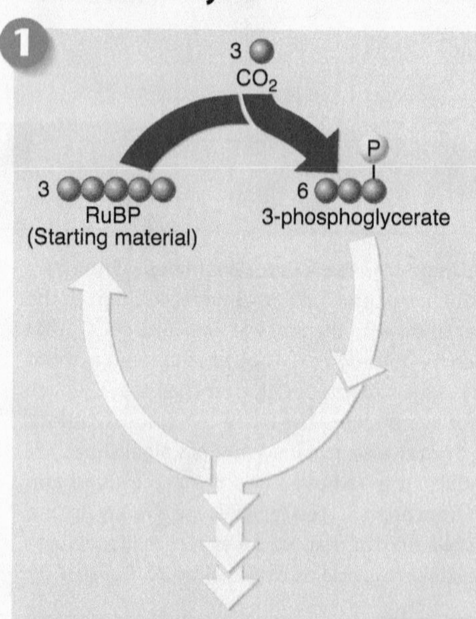

The Calvin cycle begins when a carbon atom from a CO_2 molecule is added to a five-carbon molecule (the starting material). The resulting six-carbon molecule is unstable and immediately splits into three-carbon molecules. (Three "turns" of the cycle are indicated here with three molecules of CO_2 entering the cycle.)

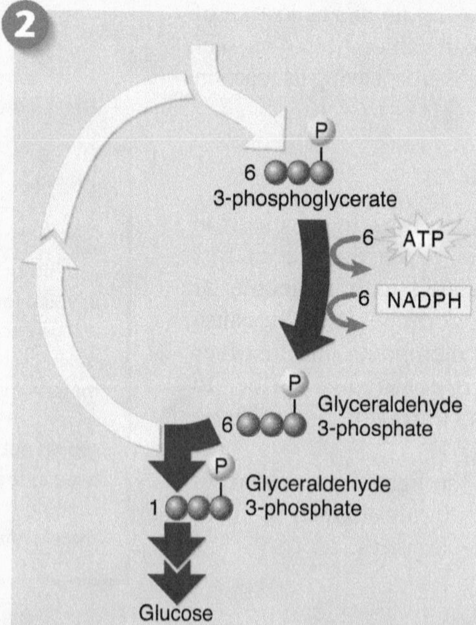

Then, through a series of reactions, energy from ATP and hydrogens from NADPH (the products of the light-dependent reactions) are added to the three-carbon molecules. The now-reduced three-carbon molecules either combine to make glucose or are used to make other molecules.

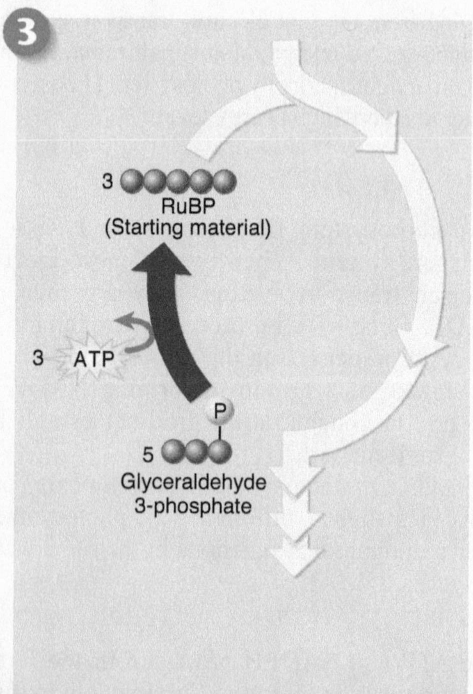

Most of the reduced three-carbon molecules are used to regenerate the five-carbon starting material, thus completing the cycle.

Photorespiration

6.5 Photorespiration: Putting the Brakes on Photosynthesis

CONCEPT PREVIEW: Photorespiration occurs due to a buildup of oxygen within photosynthetic cells. C_4 plants get around photorespiration by synthesizing sugars in bundle-sheath cells, and CAM plants delay the light-independent reactions until night, when stomata are open.

Many plants have trouble carrying out C_3 photosynthesis when the weather is hot. As temperatures increase in hot, arid weather, plants partially close their **stomata** (singular, **stoma**) to conserve water. The stomata are openings in the epidermis through which water vapor and O_2 pass out of the leaf and CO_2 passes in. As a result, when stomata close, CO_2 and O_2 are not able to enter and exit the leaves (figure 6.6). The concentration of CO_2 in the leaves falls, while the concentration of O_2 in the leaves rises. Under these conditions the active site of the enzyme that carries out the first step of the Calvin cycle (called rubisco) binds O_2 instead of CO_2. When this occurs, CO_2 is ultimately released as a by-product of an alternate reaction, effectively short-circuiting the Calvin cycle. This failure of photosynthesis is called **photorespiration.**

Oxygen and carbon dioxide both bind to rubisco at the same active site. In this way, oxygen is a competitive inhibitor of the enzyme, a topic discussed on page 93.

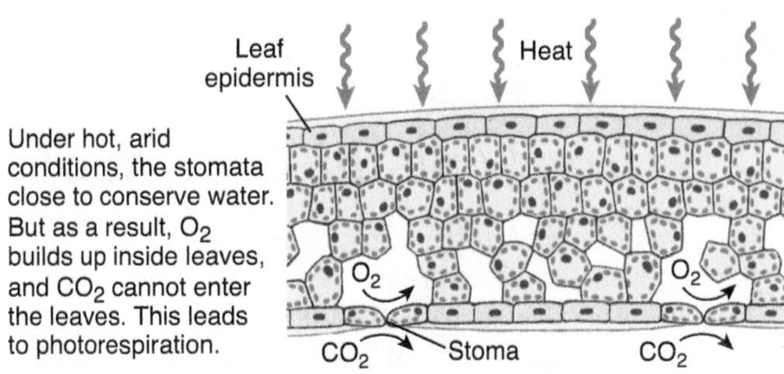

Figure 6.6 Plant response in hot weather.

C_4 Photosynthesis

Some plants are able to adapt to climates with higher temperatures by performing **C_4 photosynthesis.** In this process, plants such as sugarcane, corn, and many grasses are able to fix carbon using different types of cells and chemical reactions within their leaves, thereby avoiding this reduction in photosynthesis due to higher temperatures.

A cross section of a leaf from a C_4 plant is shown in figure 6.7. Examining it, you can see how these plants solve the problem of photorespiration. In the enlargement, you see two cell types: The green cell is a mesophyll cell and the tan cell is a bundle-sheath cell. In the mesophyll cell, CO_2 combines with a three-carbon molecule instead of RuBP (the five-carbon starting molecule in the Calvin cycle). This reaction produces a four-carbon molecule, oxaloacetate (hence the name, C_4 photosynthesis), rather than the three-carbon molecule, phosphoglycerate, shown in panel 1 of *Essential Biological Process 6A*. C_4 plants carry out this process using a different enzyme. The oxaloacetate is then converted to malate, which is transferred to the bundle-sheath cells of the leaf. In the tan bundle-sheath cell, malate is broken down to regenerate CO_2, which enters the Calvin cycle and sugars are synthesized. Why go to all this trouble? Because the bundle-sheath cells are impermeable to CO_2 and so the concentration of CO_2 increases within them, which substantially lowers the rate of photorespiration.

A second strategy to decrease photorespiration is used by many succulent (water-storing) plants such as cacti and pineapples. Called **crassulacean acid metabolism (CAM)** plants after the plant family Crassulaceae in which it was first discovered, these plants open their stomata and fix CO_2 into organic compounds during the night when it's cooler, and then close the stomata during the day.

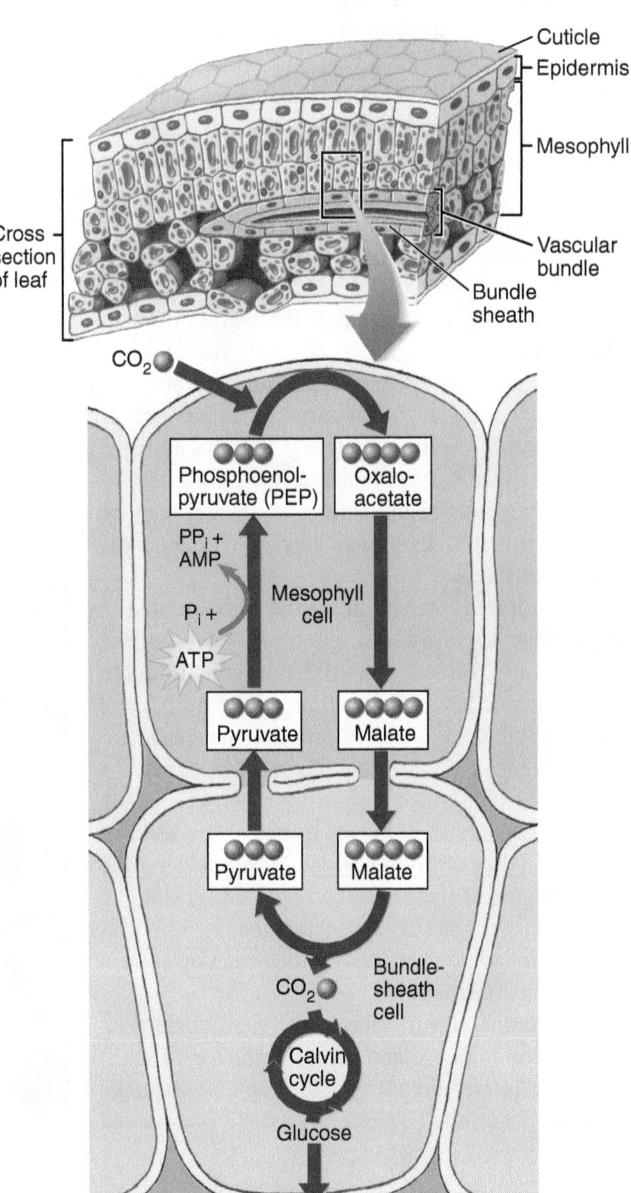

Figure 6.7 Carbon fixation in C_4 plants.

In mesophyll cells, oxaloacetate is converted into malate that is transported into bundle-sheath cells. Once there, malate undergoes a chemical reaction producing carbon dioxide. The carbon dioxide is trapped in the bundle-sheath cell, where it enters the Calvin cycle.

Concept Check

1. Are C_4 plants more likely to be common in Arizona or Maine? Why?
2. In what phase of photosynthesis does photorespiration occur?
3. In what two types of cells does C_4 photosynthesis occur? Why these?

Inquiry & Analysis

Does Iron Limit the Growth of Ocean Phytoplankton?

Phytoplankton are microscopic organisms that live in the oceans, carrying out much of the earth's photosynthesis. The photo below is of *Chaetoceros,* a phytoplankton. Decades ago, scientists noticed "dead zones" in the ocean where little photosynthesis occurred. Looking more closely, they found that phytoplankton collected from these waters are not able to efficiently fix CO_2 into carbohydrates. In an attempt to understand why not, the scientists hypothesized that lack of iron was the problem (an electron carrier in the electron transport system requires iron to function properly), and they predicted that fertilizing these ocean waters with iron could trigger an explosively rapid growth of phytoplankton.

To test this idea, they carried out a field experiment, seeding large areas of phytoplankton-poor ocean waters with iron crystals to see if this triggered phytoplankton growth. Other similarly phytoplankton-poor areas of ocean were not seeded with iron and served as controls.

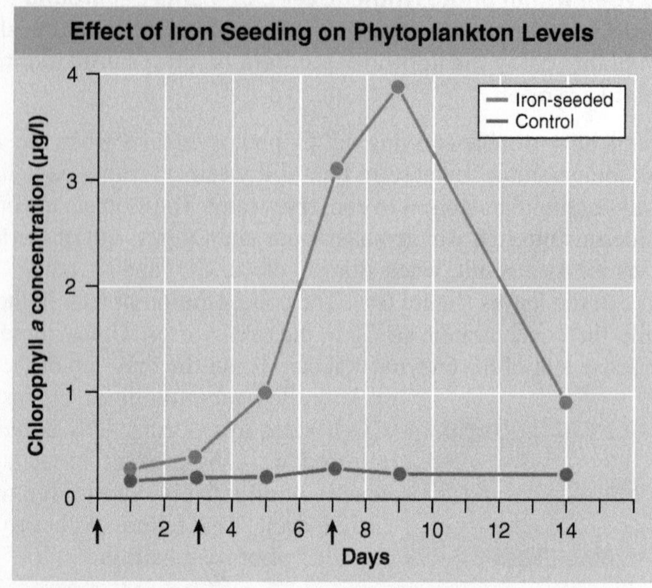

In one such experiment, the results of which are presented in the graph to the right, a 72-km^2 grid of phytoplankton-deficient ocean water was seeded with iron crystals and a tracer substance in three successive treatments, indicated with arrows on the *x* axis of the graph (on days 0, 3, and 7). The multiple seedings were carried out to reduce the effect of the iron crystals dissipating over time. A smaller control grid, 24 km^2, was seeded with just the tracer substance.

To assess the numbers of phytoplankton organisms carrying out photosynthesis in the ocean water, investigators did not actually count organisms. Instead, they estimated the amount of chlorophyll *a* in water samples as an easier-to-measure index. An **index** is a parameter that accurately reflects the quantity of another less easily measured parameter. In this instance, the level of chlorophyll *a*, easily measured by monitoring the wavelengths of light absorbed by a liquid sample, is a suitable index of phytoplankton, as this pigment is found nowhere else in the ocean other than within phytoplankton.

Chlorophyll *a* measurements were made periodically on both test and control grids for 14 days. The results are plotted on the graph. Red points indicate chlorophyll *a* concentrations in iron-seeded waters; blue points indicate chlorophyll *a* levels in the control grid waters that were not seeded.

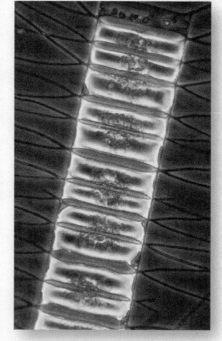

Analysis

1. **Applying Concepts** What substance is lacking in the waters sampled in the blue-dot plots ?
2. **Interpreting Data** Comparing the red line to the blue line, about how many times more numerous are phytoplankton in iron-seeded waters on each of the three days of seeding?
3. **Making Inferences**
   a. What general statement can be made regarding the effect of seeding phytoplankton-poor regions of the ocean with iron?
   b. Why did chlorophyll *a* levels drop by day 14?
4. **Drawing Conclusions** Do these results support the claim that lack of iron is limiting the growth of phytoplankton, and thus of photosynthesis, in certain areas of the oceans?

Concept Summary

Photosynthesis

6.1 An Overview of Photosynthesis

- Photosynthesis is a biochemical process whereby, energy from the sun is captured and used to build carbohydrates from CO_2 gas and water.
- Photosynthesis consists of a series of chemical reactions that occurs in two stages (overview figure from **page 103**): the light-dependent reactions that produce ATP and NADPH occur on the thylakoid membranes of chloroplasts in plants, while the light-independent reactions (the Calvin cycle) that synthesize carbohydrates occur in the stroma.

6.2 How Plants Capture Energy from Sunlight

- Sunlight contains packets of energy called photons that contain varying amounts of energy. Photons of shorter wavelengths, such as gamma rays and UV light, have a lot of energy. As the wavelengths increase in size, the amount of energy in the photons decrease (**figure 6.1**). Visible light are wavelengths absorbed by pigments in the human eye (between 400 and 740 nanometers). Pigments are molecules that capture light energy. Plants use the pigment chlorophyll to absorb light energy.
- Plants appear green because of their chlorophyll pigments. Chlorophyll absorbs wavelengths in the far ends of the visual spectrum (the blue and red wavelengths) and reflect the green wavelengths, which is why leaves appear green.
- The light-dependent reactions occur on the thylakoid membranes of chloroplasts in plants. The chlorophyll molecules and other pigments involved in photosynthesis are embedded in a complex of proteins within the membrane called a photosystem.
- The energy from a photon of light is absorbed by a chlorophyll molecule and is transferred between chlorophyll molecules in the photosystem, as shown here from **figure 6.2.** Once the energy is passed to the reaction center it excites an electron which is transferred to the electron transport system.
- The energized electron is used to generate ATP and NADPH. ATP powers the Calvin cycle and NADPH donates hydrogen atoms toward the building of carbohydrate molecules. Plants utilize two photosystems that occur in series (**figure 6.3**). Photosystem II leads to the formation of ATP, and photosystem I leads to the formation of NADPH.

6.3 How Photosystems Convert Light to Chemical Energy

- The excited electron that leaves the reaction center of photosystem II is replenished with an electron from the breakdown of a water molecule. Oxygen gas is a by-product of this reaction.
- The excited electron is passed from one protein to another in the electron transport system, where energy from the electron is used to operate a proton pump that pumps hydrogen ions across the membrane against a concentration gradient (**figure 6.4**).
- The hydrogen ion concentration gradient is used as a source of energy to generate molecules of ATP. This energy is used to drive H^+ back across the membrane through a specialized channel protein called ATP synthase, which catalyzes the formation of ATP, as shown here from **figure 6.4.**

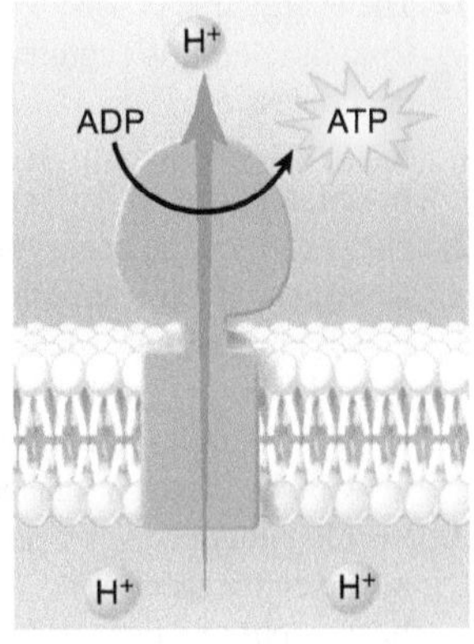

- After the electron passes along the first electron transport system, it is then transferred to a second photosystem, photosystem I, where it gets an energy boost from the capture of another photon of light (**figure 6.4**). This reenergized electron is passed along another electron transport system to an ultimate electron acceptor, $NADP^+$. $NADP^+$ binds electrons and a H^+ to produce NADPH, which is shuttled to the Calvin cycle.

6.4 Building New Molecules

- ATP and NADPH, from the light-dependent reactions, are shuttled to the stroma where they are used in the Calvin cycle.
- The Calvin cycle is carried out by a series of enzymes that use the energy from ATP and electrons and hydrogen ions from NADPH to build molecules of carbohydrates by reducing CO_2 from the air (***Essential Biological Process 6A***).

Photorespiration

6.5 Photorespiration: Putting the Brakes on Photosynthesis

- In hot dry weather, plants will close the stomata in their leaves to conserve water. As a result, the levels of O_2 increase in the leaves, and CO_2 levels drop, as shown here from **figure 6.6.** Under these conditions, the Calvin cycle, also called C_3 photosynthesis, is disrupted. When there is a higher internal concentration of oxygen, O_2 rather than CO_2 enters the Calvin cycle in a process called photorespiration. In this case, the first enzyme in the Calvin cycle, rubisco, binds oxygen instead of carbon dioxide.

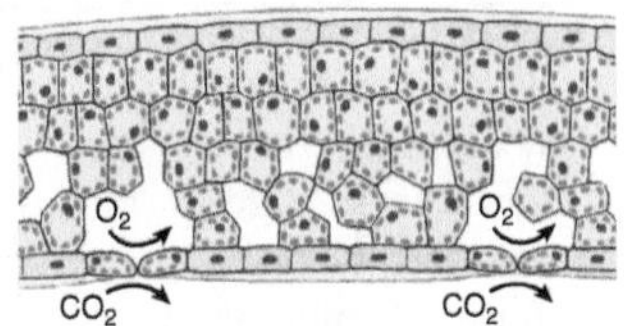

- C_4 plants reduce the effects of photorespiration by modifying the carbon-fixation step, splitting it into two steps that take place in different cells. The C_4 pathway produces malate in mesophyll cells. Malate is then transferred to bundle-sheath cells, where it breaks down to produce carbon dioxide. This CO_2 then enters the Calvin cycle in the bundle-sheath cells (**figure 6.7**).
- In CAM plants, carbon dioxide is processed into organic molecules through the C_4 pathway during the night when stomata are open.

Self-Test

1. The energy that is used by almost all living things on our planet comes from the sun. It is captured by plants, algae, and some bacteria through the process of
   a. thylakoid.
   b. chloroplasts.
   c. photosynthesis.
   d. the Calvin cycle.
2. Plants capture the energy from sunlight
   a. through photorespiration.
   b. with molecules called pigments that absorb photons and use their energy.
   c. with the light-independent reactions.
   d. with the electron transport system.
3. Visible light occupies what part of the electromagnetic spectrum?
   a. the entire spectrum
   b. the upper half of the spectrum (with longer wavelengths)
   c. a small portion in the middle of the spectrum
   d. the lower half of the spectrum (with shorter wavelengths)
4. The colors of light that are absorbed by chlorophyll are
   a. red and blue.
   b. green and yellow.
   c. infrared and ultraviolet.
   d. All colors are equally absorbed.
5. Once a plant has initially captured the energy of a photon,
   a. a series of reactions occurs in thylakoid membranes of the cell.
   b. the energy is transferred through several steps into a molecule of ATP.
   c. a water molecule is broken down, releasing oxygen.
   d. All of the above.
6. Plants use two photosystems to capture energy used to produce ATP and NADPH. The electrons used in these photosystems
   a. recycle through the system, with energy added from the photons.
   b. recycle through the system several times and then are lost due to entropy.
   c. only go through the system once; they are obtained by splitting a water molecule.
   d. only go through the system once; they are obtained from the photon.
7. During photosynthesis, ATP molecules are generated by
   a. the Calvin cycle.
   b. chemiosmosis.
   c. the splitting of a water molecule.
   d. photons of light being absorbed by chlorophyll molecules.
8. NADPH is recycled during photosynthesis. It is produced during the ________ and used in the__________.
   a. electron transport system of photosystem I, Calvin cycle
   b. process of chemiosmosis, Calvin cycle
   c. electron transport system of photosystem II, electron transport system of photosystem I
   d. light-independent reactions, light-dependent reactions
9. The overall purpose of the Calvin cycle is to
   a. generate molecules of ATP.
   b. generate NADPH.
   c. build sugar molecules.
   d. produce oxygen.
10. Many plants cannot carry out the typical C_3 photosynthesis in hot weather, so some plants
    a. use the ATP cycle.
    b. use C_4 photosynthesis or CAM.
    c. shut down photosynthesis completely.
    d. All of these are true for different plants.

Visual Understanding

1. This figure shows the areas of the visible spectrum that are absorbed by two forms of chlorophyll. The green and yellow wavelengths are reflected back and so plants appear green. The red skin of an apple contains different pigments. What areas of the spectrum do you think are absorbed and reflected by these pigments?

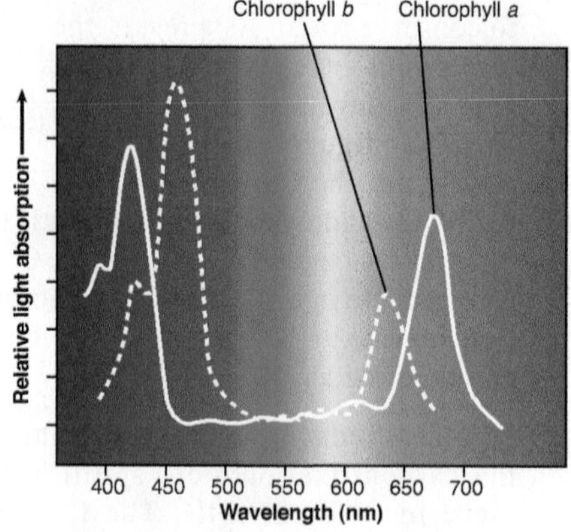

2. **Figure 6.4** Could a plant cell produce ATP through chemiosmosis if the thylakoid membrane was "leaky" with regards to protons? Explain.

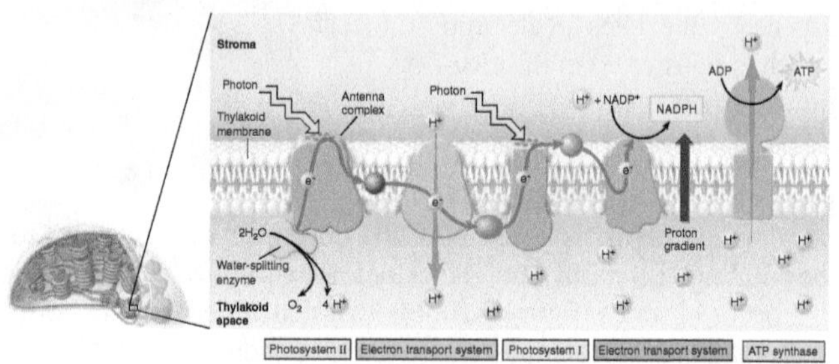

Challenge Questions

1. To reduce six molecules of carbon dioxide to glucose via photosynthesis, how many molecules of NADPH and ATP are required?
2. In theory, a plant kept in total darkness could still manufacture glucose if it were supplied with which molecules?
3. If you were going to design a plant that would survive in the deserts of Arizona and New Mexico, how would you balance its need for CO_2 with its need to avoid water loss in the hot summer temperatures?

Chapter 7

How Cells Harvest Energy from Food

CHAPTER AT A GLANCE

An Overview of Cellular Respiration

Figure 7.1 A human acquiring energy.

Energy that this teen extracts from the hamburger he is eating will be used to power his singing, fuel his running, and build a bigger teenager.

7.1 Where Is the Energy in Food?

CONCEPT PREVIEW: Cellular respiration is the dismantling of food molecules to obtain energy. In aerobic respiration, the cell harvests energy from glucose molecules in two stages, glycolysis and oxidation.

In plants and animals, and in fact in almost all organisms, the energy for living is obtained by breaking down the organic molecules originally produced by photosynthetic organisms, such as plants, algae, and certain bacteria. The energy invested in building the organic molecules is retrieved by stripping away the energetic electrons and using them to make ATP, a process called **cellular respiration.** Do not confuse the term cellular respiration with the breathing of oxygen gas that your lungs carry out, which is called simply respiration.

All cells use ATP to power biological functions. The depth and breadth of some of these functions were illustrated in table 5.1, page 95.

The cells of plants fuel their activities with sugars and other molecules that they produce through photosynthesis which they break down in cellular respiration. Nonphotosynthetic organisms eat plants, extracting energy from plant tissue in cellular respiration. Other animals, like the teenager gobbling up the hamburger in figure 7.1, eat these animals.

Eukaryotes produce the majority of their ATP by harvesting electrons from chemical bonds of the food molecule glucose. The electrons are transferred along an electron transport chain (similar to the electron transport system in photosynthesis), and eventually donated to oxygen gas. Chemically, there is little difference between this process in a cell and the burning of wood in a fireplace. In both instances, the reactants are carbohydrates and oxygen, and the products are carbon dioxide, water, and energy:

$$C_6H_{12}O_6 + 6\ O_2 \longrightarrow 6\ CO_2 + 6\ H_2O + \text{energy (heat or ATP)}$$

In a chemical reaction, when an atom or molecule loses an electron, it is said to be *oxidized,* and the process by which this occurs is called **oxidation.** The name reflects the fact that in biological systems, oxygen, which attracts electrons strongly, is the most common electron acceptor. This is certainly the case in cellular respiration, where oxygen is the final electron acceptor. Conversely, when an atom or molecule gains an electron, it is said to be *reduced,* and the process is called **reduction.** Oxidation and reduction always take place together, because every electron that is lost by an atom through oxidation is gained by some other atom through reduction. Therefore, chemical reactions of this sort are called **oxidation-reduction (redox) reactions.** In redox reactions, energy follows the electron, as shown in figure 7.2.

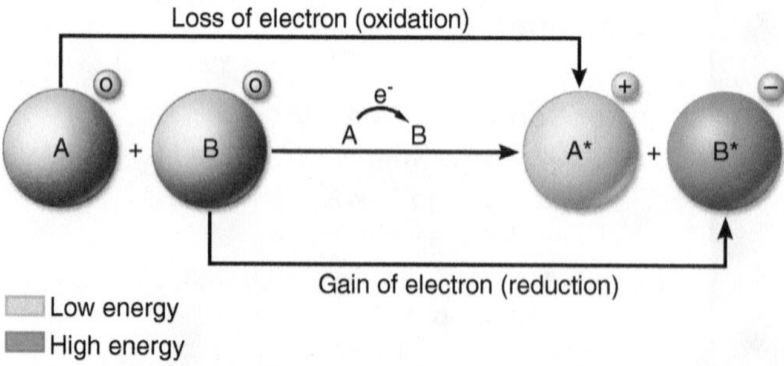

Figure 7.2 Redox reactions.

Oxidation is the loss of an electron; reduction is the gain of an electron. Here the charges of molecules A and B are shown in small circles to the upper right of each molecule. Molecule A loses energy as it loses an electron, while molecule B gains energy as it gains an electron.

Cellular respiration is carried out in two stages, illustrated in figure 7.3. The first stage uses coupled reactions to make ATP. This stage, *glycolysis,* takes place in the cell's cytoplasm (the blue area in figure 7.3). Importantly, it is anaerobic (that is, it does not require oxygen). This ancient energy-extracting process is thought to have evolved over 2 billion years ago, when there was no oxygen in the earth's atmosphere.

The second stage is aerobic (requires oxygen) and takes place within the mitochondrion (the tan sausage-shaped structure in figure 7.3). The focal point of this stage is the *Krebs cycle,* a cycle of chemical reactions that harvests electrons from C—H chemical bonds and passes the energy-rich electrons to carrier molecules, NADH and $FADH_2$. These molecules deliver the electrons to the electron transport chain, which uses their energy to power the production of ATP. The harvesting of electrons, a form of *oxidation,* is far more powerful than glycolysis at recovering energy from food molecules, and is how the bulk of the energy used by eukaryotic cells is extracted from food molecules.

Concept Check

1. When an atom is oxidized, does it gain or lose an electron?
2. The Krebs cycle harvests electrons from what kind of chemical bond?
3. Which stage of cellular respiration occurs in the cytoplasm?

Figure 7.3 An overview of cellular respiration.

Electrons harvested from C—H chemical bonds are first transferred to NADH and $FADH_2$; these then carry the electrons to the electron transport chain, as indicated by the long red arrow on the left. The energy-depleted electron is finally donated with a proton to oxygen, forming a molecule of water.

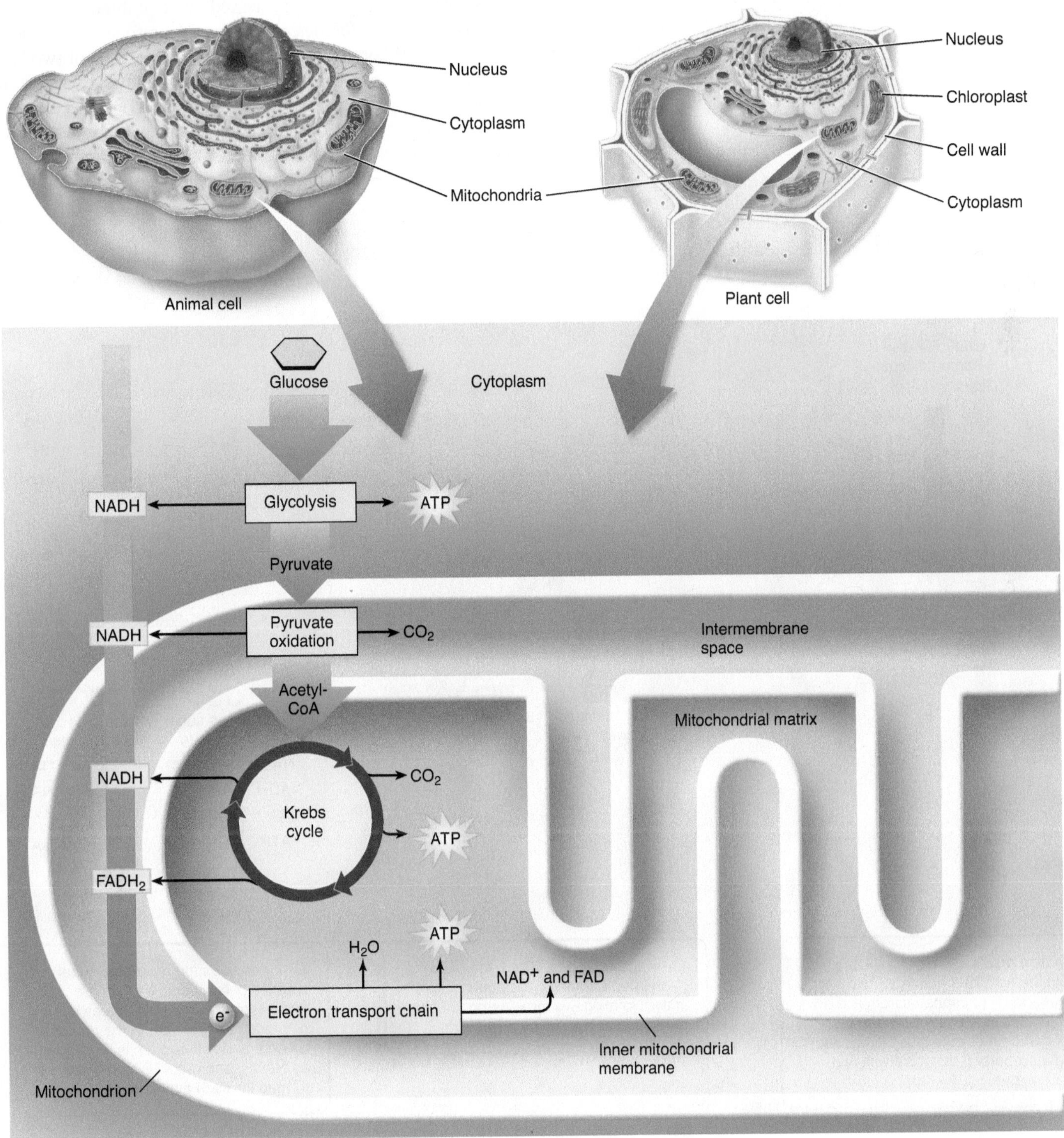

Cellular Respiration

7.2 Respiration Without Oxygen: Glycolysis

CONCEPT PREVIEW: In glycolysis, cells shuffle around chemical bonds in glucose to produce ATP by substrate-level phosphorylation.

The first stage in cellular respiration, called **glycolysis,** is a series of sequential biochemical reactions, a *biochemical pathway.* In 10 enzyme-catalyzed reactions, the six-carbon sugar glucose is cleaved into two three-carbon molecules called pyruvate. *Essential Biological Process 7A* presents a conceptual overview of the process. Where is the energy extracted? In each of two "coupled" reactions (panel 3), the breaking of a chemical bond in an exergonic reaction releases enough energy to drive the formation of an ATP molecule from ADP (an endergonic reaction). This transfer of a high-energy phosphate group from a substrate to ADP is called **substrate-level phosphorylation.** In the absence of oxygen, this is the only way organisms can get energy from food.

Essential Biological Process 7A

Glycolysis

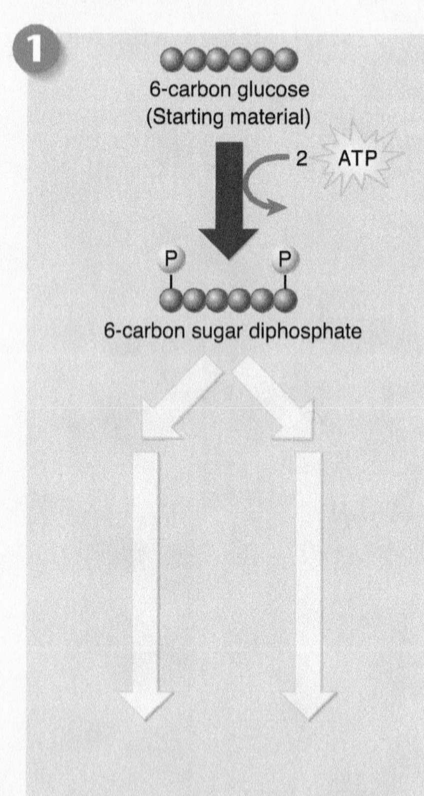

Priming reactions. Glycolysis begins with the addition of energy. Two high-energy phosphates from two molecules of ATP are added to the six-carbon molecule glucose, producing a six-carbon molecule with two phosphates.

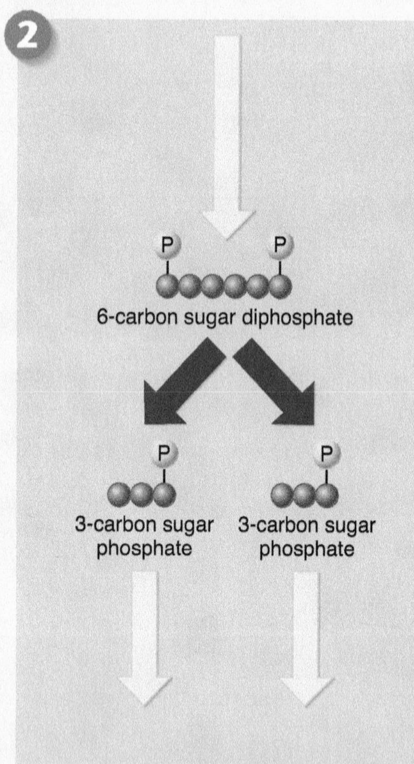

Cleavage reactions. Then, the phosphorylated six-carbon molecule is split in two, forming two three-carbon sugar phosphates.

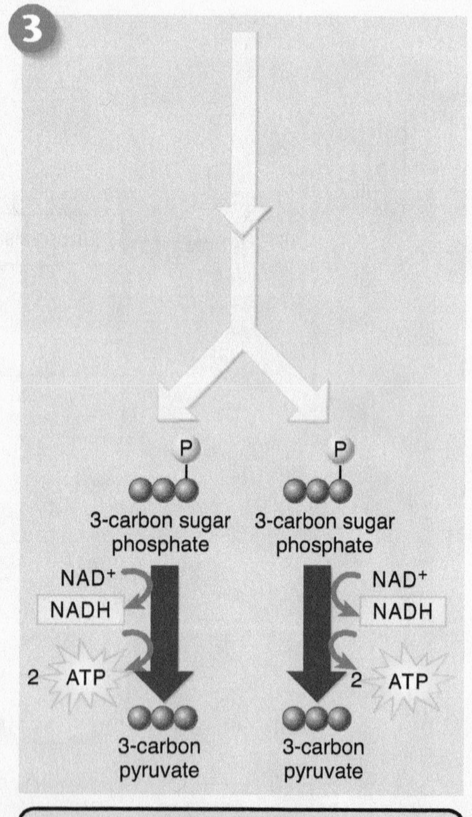

Energy-harvesting reactions. Finally, in a series of reactions, each of the two three-carbon sugar phosphates is converted to pyruvate. In the process, an energy-rich hydrogen is harvested as NADH, and two ATP molecules are formed for each pyruvate.

7.3 Respiration With Oxygen: the Krebs Cycle

CONCEPT PREVIEW: Pyruvate, the end product of glycolysis, is oxidized in the Krebs cycle yielding ATP and many energized electrons.

The first step of oxidative respiration in the mitochondrion is the oxidation of the three-carbon molecule called pyruvate, which is the end product of glycolysis. The cell harvests electrons from pyruvate in two steps: first, by oxidizing pyruvate to form acetyl-CoA, and then by oxidizing acetyl-CoA in the Krebs cycle.

Step One: Producing Acetyl-CoA

Pyruvate is oxidized in a single reaction that cleaves off one of pyruvate's three carbons. This carbon then departs as part of the CO_2 molecule shown coming off the pathway in figure 7.4. Pyruvate dehydrogenase, the complex of enzymes that removes CO_2 from pyruvate, is one of the largest enzymes known. It contains 60 subunits! In the course of the reaction, a hydrogen and electrons are removed from pyruvate and donated to NAD^+ to form NADH. *Essential Biological Process 7B* shows how an enzyme catalyzes this redox reaction, bringing the substrate (pyruvate) into proximity with NAD^+. As with all redox reactions, the oxidation and reduction reactions are coupled—pyruvate is oxidized when an electron and its energy, along with a hydrogen atom, is transferred to NAD^+, reducing it to NADH. Now focus again on figure 7.4. The two-carbon fragment (called an acetyl group) that remains after removing CO_2 from pyruvate is joined to a cofactor called coenzyme A (CoA) by pyruvate dehydrogenase, forming a compound known as **acetyl-CoA.** If the cell has a plentiful supply of ATP, acetyl-CoA is funneled into fat synthesis, with its energetic electrons preserved for later needs. If the cell needs ATP, the fragment is directed instead into ATP production through the Krebs cycle.

Carbon dioxide, a by-product of cellular respiration, is released from organisms as waste. As you will see on page 496, vertebrates expel this waste as carbon dioxide gas from the lungs.

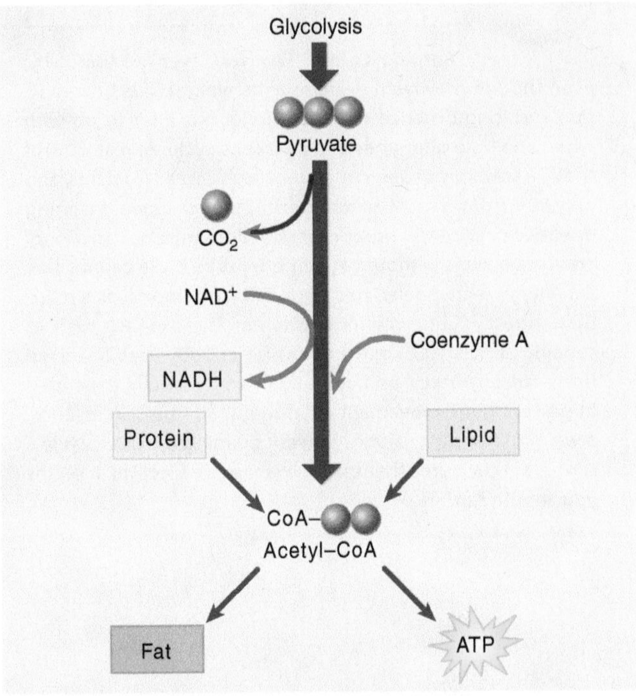

Figure 7.4 Producing acetyl-CoA.

Pyruvate, the three-carbon product of glycolysis, is oxidized to the two-carbon molecule acetyl-CoA, and in the process loses one carbon atom as CO_2 and an electron (donated to NAD^+ to form NADH). Almost all the molecules you use as foodstuffs are converted to acetyl-CoA; the acetyl-CoA is then channeled into fat synthesis or into ATP production, depending on your body's needs.

IMPLICATION What do you think might determine how much of your acetyl-CoA is channeled into fat?

Essential Biological Process 7B

Transferring Hydrogen Atoms

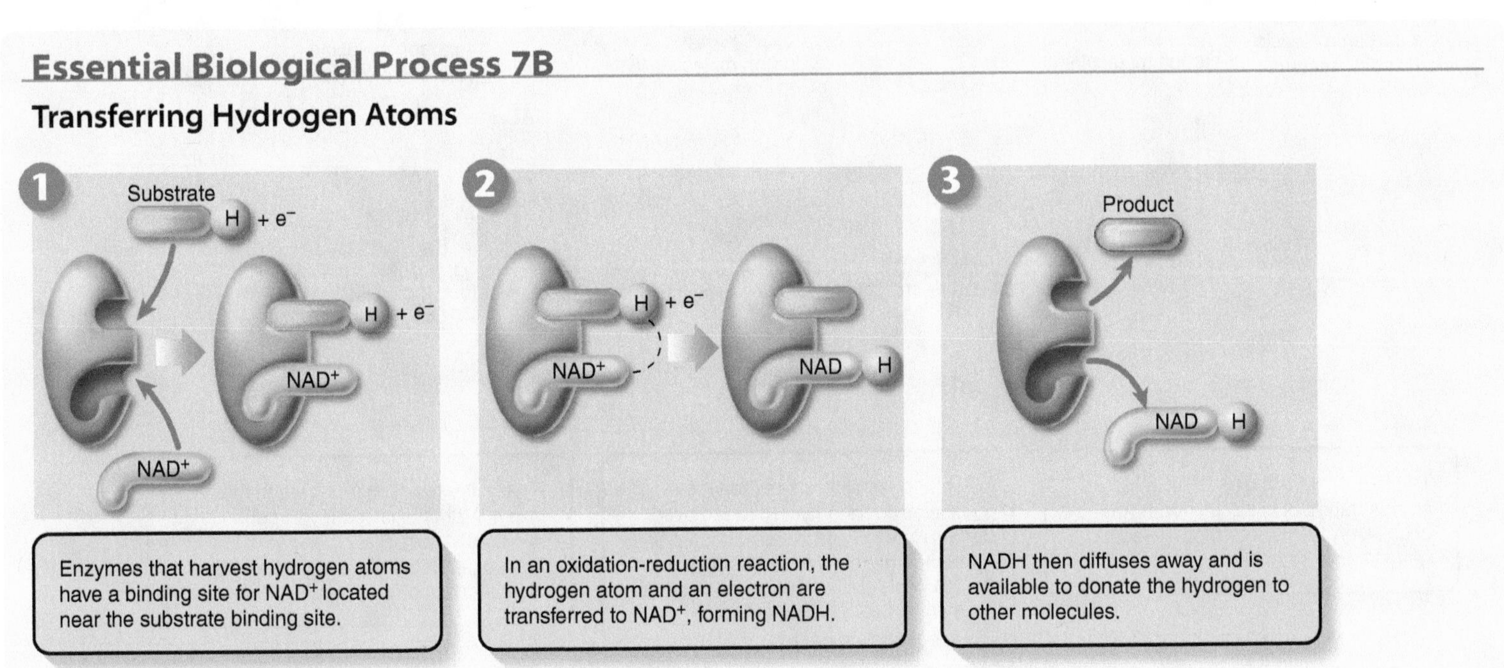

BIOLOGY & YOU

Burning Carbs. Did you ever wonder why, even though they both exercise a lot, weight lifters are massive and long distance runners thin? It has a lot to do with when and how often they use the Krebs cycle. At rest, 70% of the ATP your body uses to maintain itself comes from fats, and only 30% from carbs. Anaerobic exercise such as weight lifting does not change this proportion, but does miss out on a lot of energy because without oxygen the Krebs cycle cannot run. Fat energy is channeled to the job of increasing muscle mass. By contrast, during high-intensity aerobic exercise such as running almost 100% of the energy your body uses is derived from carbohydrates, and all of this energy is fully expended in powering the movement of your muscle fibers. In essence, a weight lifter puts calories to work building muscles, while a runner simply burns them. If you want to lose weight, it seems you should run.

Step Two: The Krebs Cycle

The next stage in oxidative respiration is called the **Krebs cycle,** named after the man who discovered it. The Krebs cycle (not to be confused with the Calvin cycle in photosynthesis) takes place within the mitochondrion. While a complex process, its nine reactions can be broken down into three stages, as indicated by the overview presented in *Essential Biological Process 7C*:

Stage 1. The cycle starts when the two-carbon acetyl-CoA fragment produced from pyruvate is stuck onto a four-carbon sugar, producing a six-carbon molecule.

Stage 2. Then, in rapid-fire order, two carbons are removed as CO_2, their electrons donated to NAD^+, and a four-carbon molecule is left. A molecule of ATP is also produced.

Stage 3. When it is all over, two carbon atoms have been expelled as CO_2, more energetic electrons are extracted and taken away as NADH or on other carriers such as $FADH_2$ (which serves the same function as NADH), and we are left with the same four-carbon sugar we started with.

The process is a cycle—that is, a circle of reactions. In each turn of the cycle, a new acetyl group replaces the two CO_2 molecules lost, and more electrons are extracted. The Krebs cycle makes two turns for every molecule of glucose broken down during respiration.

In the process of cellular respiration, glucose is entirely consumed. All that is left to mark the passing of the glucose molecule into six CO_2 molecules is its energy, preserved in four ATP molecules (two from glycolysis and two from the Krebs cycle) and electrons carried by 10 NADH and two $FADH_2$ carriers.

Essential Biological Process 7C

The Krebs Cycle

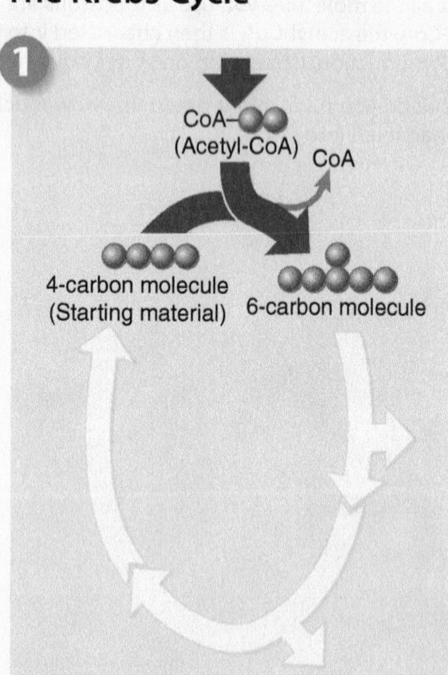

The Krebs cycle begins when a two-carbon fragment is transferred from acetyl-CoA to a four-carbon molecule (the starting material).

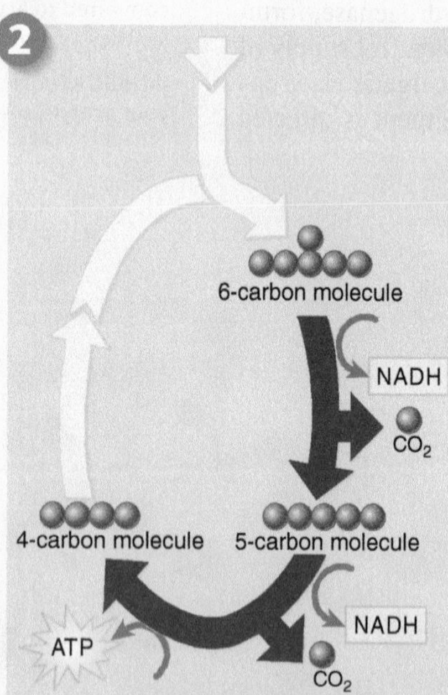

Then, the resulting six-carbon molecule is oxidized (a hydrogen removed to form NADH) and decarboxylated (a carbon removed to form CO_2). Next, the five-carbon molecule is oxidized and decarboxylated again, and a coupled reaction generates ATP.

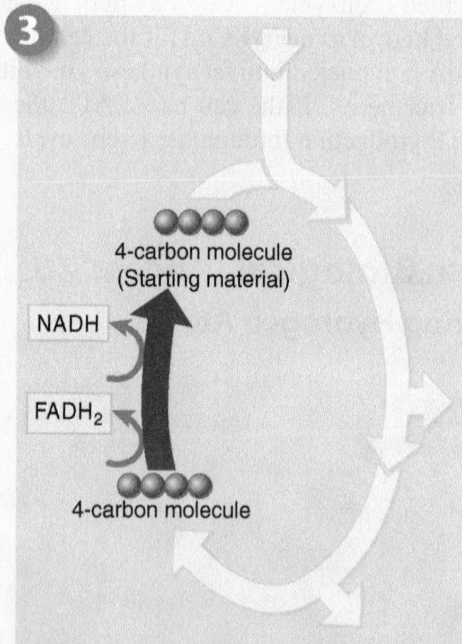

Finally, the resulting four-carbon molecule is further oxidized (hydrogens removed to form $FADH_2$ and NADH). This regenerates the four-carbon starting material, completing the cycle.

A Closer Look

Metabolic Efficiency and the Length of Food Chains

In the earth's ecosystems, the organisms that carry out photosynthesis are often consumed as food by other organisms. We call these "organism-eaters" *heterotrophs.* Humans are heterotrophs, as no human photosynthesizes.

It is thought that the first heterotrophs were ancient bacteria living in a world where photosynthesis had not yet introduced much oxygen into the oceans or atmosphere. The only mechanism they possessed to harvest chemical energy from their food was glycolysis. Neither oxygen-generating photosynthesis nor the oxidative stage of cellular respiration had evolved yet. It has been estimated that a heterotroph limited to glycolysis, as these ancient bacteria were, captures only 3.5% of the energy in the food it consumes. Hence, if such a heterotroph preserves 3.5% of the energy in the photosynthesizers it consumes, then any other heterotrophs that consume the first heterotroph will capture through glycolysis 3.5% of the energy in it, or 0.12% of the energy available in the original photosynthetic organisms. A very large base of photosynthesizers would thus be needed to support a small number of heterotrophs.

When organisms became able to extract energy from organic molecules by oxidative cellular respiration, which we discuss on the next page, this constraint became far less severe, because the efficiency of oxidative respiration is estimated to be about 32%. This increased efficiency results in the transmission of much more energy from one trophic level to another than does glycolysis. (A *trophic level* is a step in the movement of energy through an ecosystem.) The efficiency of oxidative cellular respiration has made possible the evolution of food chains, in which photosynthesizers are consumed by heterotrophs, which are consumed by other heterotrophs, and so on. You will read more about food chains in chapter 20.

Even with this very efficient oxidative metabolism, approximately two-thirds of the available energy is lost at each trophic level, and that puts a limit on how long a food chain can be. Most food chains, like the East African grassland ecosystem illustrated here, involve only three or rarely four trophic levels. Too much energy is lost at each transfer to allow chains to be much longer than that. For example, it would be impossible for a large human population to subsist by eating lions captured from the grasslands of East Africa; the amount of grass available there would not support enough zebras and other herbivores to maintain the number of lions needed to feed the human population. Thus, the ecological complexity of our world is fixed in a fundamental way by the chemistry of oxidative cellular respiration.

Photosynthesizers. The grass under this yellow fever tree grows actively during the hot, rainy season, capturing the energy of the sun and storing it in molecules of glucose, which are then converted into starch and stored in the grass.

Herbivores. These zebras consume the grass and transfer some of its stored energy into their own bodies.

Carnivores. The lion feeds on zebras and other animals, capturing part of their stored energy and storing it in its own body.

Scavengers. This hyena and the vultures occupy the same stage in the food chain as the lion. They also consume the body of the dead zebra, after it has been abandoned by the lion.

Refuse utilizers. These butterflies, mostly *Precis octavia,* are feeding on the material left in the hyena's dung after the food the hyena consumed had passed through its digestive tract.

A food chain in the savannas, or open grasslands, of East Africa.

At each of these levels in the food chain, only about a third or less of the energy present is used by the recipient.

7.4 Using the Electrons to Make ATP

CONCEPT PREVIEW: The electrons harvested by oxidizing food molecules are used to power proton pumps that chemiosmotically drive the production of ATP.

Mitochondria use chemiosmosis to make ATP in much the same way that chloroplasts do, although a mitochondrion's proton pumps transport protons *out of* an enclosed space (the matrix) while the electron transport system in chloroplasts transport protons *into* an enclosed space (the thylakoid). Mitochondria use energetic electrons extracted from food molecules to power proton pumps that drive protons across the inner mitochondrial membrane. As protons become far more scarce inside than outside, the concentration gradient drives protons back in through special ATP synthase channels. Their passage powers the production of ATP from ADP. The ATP then passes out of the mitochondrion through ATP-transport channels.

A similar electron carrier is used in photosynthesis as described on page 107. In the light-dependent reactions, two electrons and a hydrogen ion are transferred to $NADP^+$ producing NADPH, which carries these to the Calvin cycle.

Moving Electrons Through the Electron Transport Chain

The NADH and $FADH_2$ molecules formed during the first stages of aerobic respiration each contain electrons and hydrogens

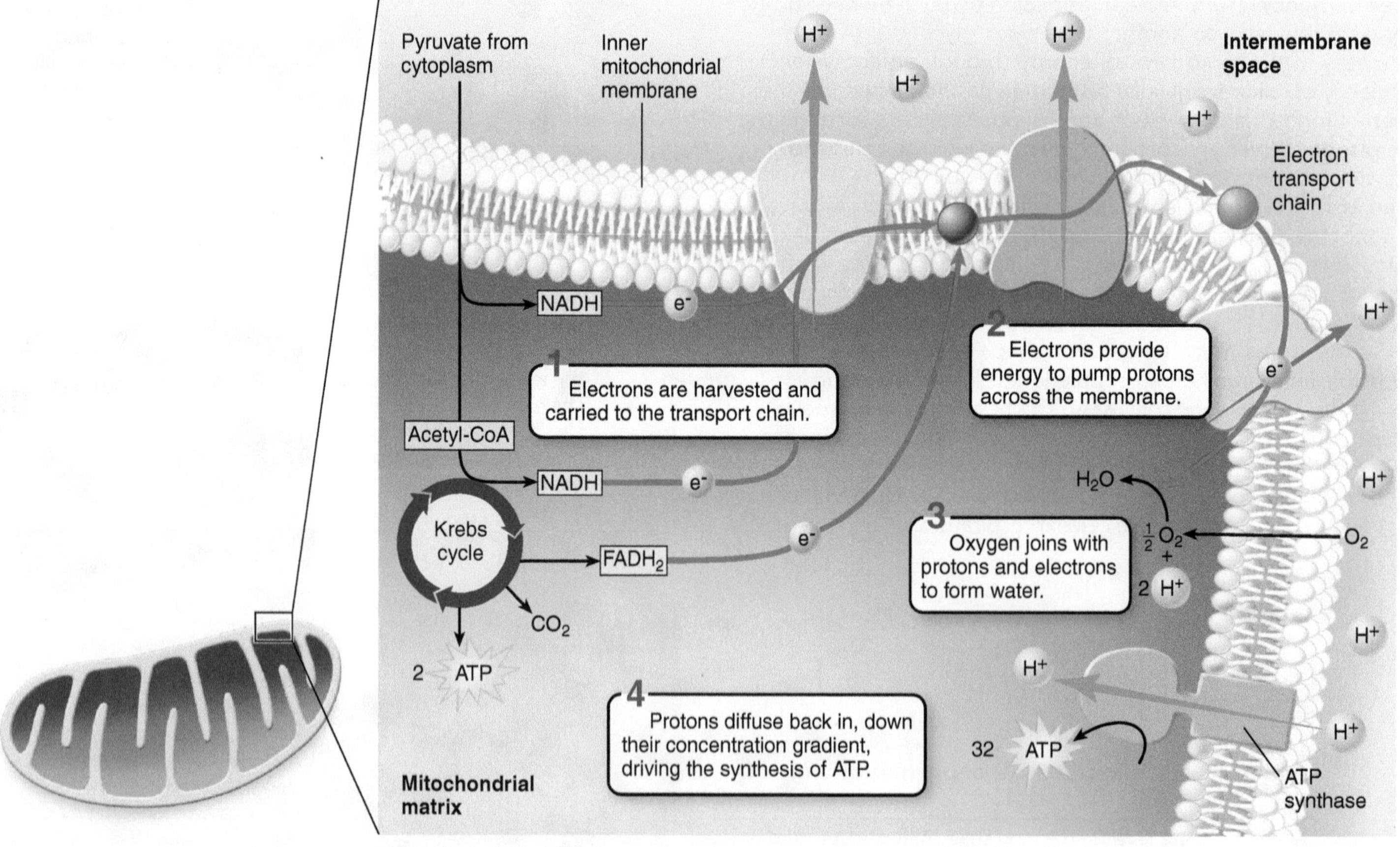

Figure 7.5 The electron transport chain.

High-energy electrons are transported (*red arrows*) along a chain of electron-carrier molecules. Three of these molecules are protein complexes that use portions of the electrons' energy to pump protons (*blue arrows*) out of the matrix and into the intermembrane space. The electrons are finally donated to oxygen to form water.

IMPLICATION In harvesting the energy contained within the chemical bonds of a molecule of glucose, a cell gains a net of four ATP molecules from glycolysis and the Krebs cycle. Assuming that each proton pumped out of the mitochondrial matrix reenters via ATP synthase to produce an ATP molecule, how many ATP molecules in total are obtained by metabolizing the glucose molecule?

that were gained when NAD^+ and FAD were reduced (refer back to figure 7.2). The NADH and $FADH_2$ molecules carry their electrons to the inner mitochondrial membrane (an enlarged area of the membrane is shown in figure 7.5), where they transfer the electrons to a series of membrane-associated molecules collectively called the **electron transport chain.** The electron transport chain works much as does the electron transport system you encountered in studying photosynthesis.

There are two electron transport systems in photosynthesis, one produces ATP and the other produces NADPH, as described on page 106. In both cases, an energized electron is passed along a series of membrane proteins, and the energy drives proton gradient formation.

A protein complex (the pink structure in figure 7.5) receives the electrons and, using a mobile carrier, passes these electrons to a second protein complex (the purple structure). This protein complex, along with others in the chain, operates as a proton pump, using the energy of the electron to drive a proton out across the membrane into the **intermembrane space.** The arrows indicate the transport of the protons out of the matrix of the mitochondrion into the intermembrane space.

The electron is then carried by another carrier to a third protein complex (the light blue structure). This complex uses electrons such as this one to link oxygen atoms with hydrogen ions to form molecules of water.

Producing ATP: Chemiosmosis

In eukaryotes, aerobic respiration takes place within the mitochondria present in virtually all cells. The internal compartment, or **matrix,** of a mitochondrion contains the enzymes that carry out the reactions of the Krebs cycle. As described earlier, the electrons harvested by oxidative respiration are passed along the electron transport chain, and the energy they release transports protons out of the matrix and into the intermembrane space. Proton pumps in the inner mitochondrial membrane accomplish the transport. The electrons contributed by NADH activate three of these proton pumps, and those contributed by $FADH_2$ activate two, as indicated in figure 7.5. As the proton concentration in the intermembrane space rises above that in the matrix, the concentration gradient induces the protons to reenter the matrix by diffusion through a special proton channel called **ATP synthase.** This channel is embedded in the inner mitochondrial membrane, as shown in figures 7.5 and 7.6. As the protons pass through, the channel synthesizes ATP from ADP and P_i within the matrix. The ATP is then transported by facilitated diffusion out of the mitochondrion into the cell's cytoplasm. This ATP synthesizing process is the same **chemiosmosis** process that you encountered in studying photosynthesis in chapter 6.

This pumping of protons is an example of active transport, discussed on page 83, where energy drives the transport of a substance against a concentration gradient. In active transport, energy can come from ATP, or as in this case, from energized electrons.

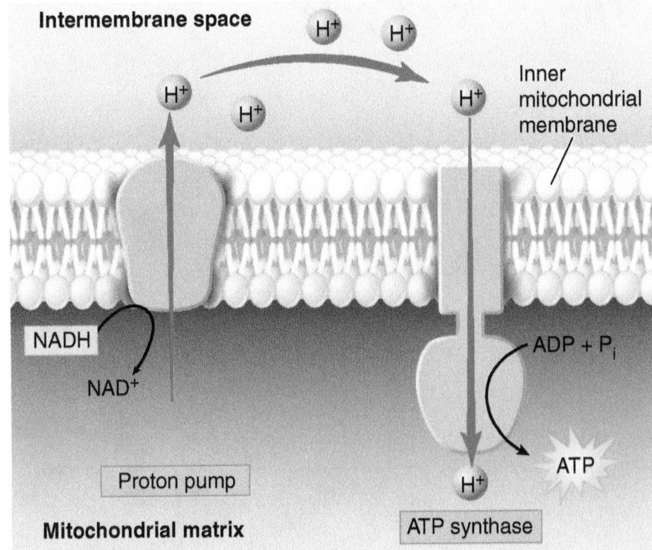

Figure 7.6 Chemiosmosis.

NADH transports high-energy electrons harvested from macromolecules to "proton pumps" that use the energy to pump protons out of the mitochondrial matrix. As a result, the concentration of protons outside the inner mitochondrial membrane rises, inducing protons to diffuse back into the matrix. Many of the protons pass through ATP synthase channels that couple the reentry of protons to the production of ATP.

EVOLUTION

Evolution of ATP Synthase. ATP synthase is an example of "molecular evolution," where two proteins with their own functions have become associated to form a new two-subunit protein with an entirely new function. In this instance, the gene for one subunit of ATP synthase has a very similar DNA sequence to a DNA-binding enzyme called helicase, allowing ATP synthase to bind the adenine of ADP. The gene for the other subunit of ATP synthase is very similar to that of the proton-driven motor that bacteria use to power the rotation of their flagella, allowing ATP synthase to join P_i to ADP by running the motor in reverse.

Concept Check

1. In glycolysis, by what process is ATP produced?
2. What molecule is the starting material for the Krebs cycle?
3. If the electron transport chain uses the energy harvested from C—H bonds to drive protons out of the matrix, how is it that the ATP molecules formed as a consequence are *within* the matrix?

A Closer Look

The Redox Cycle

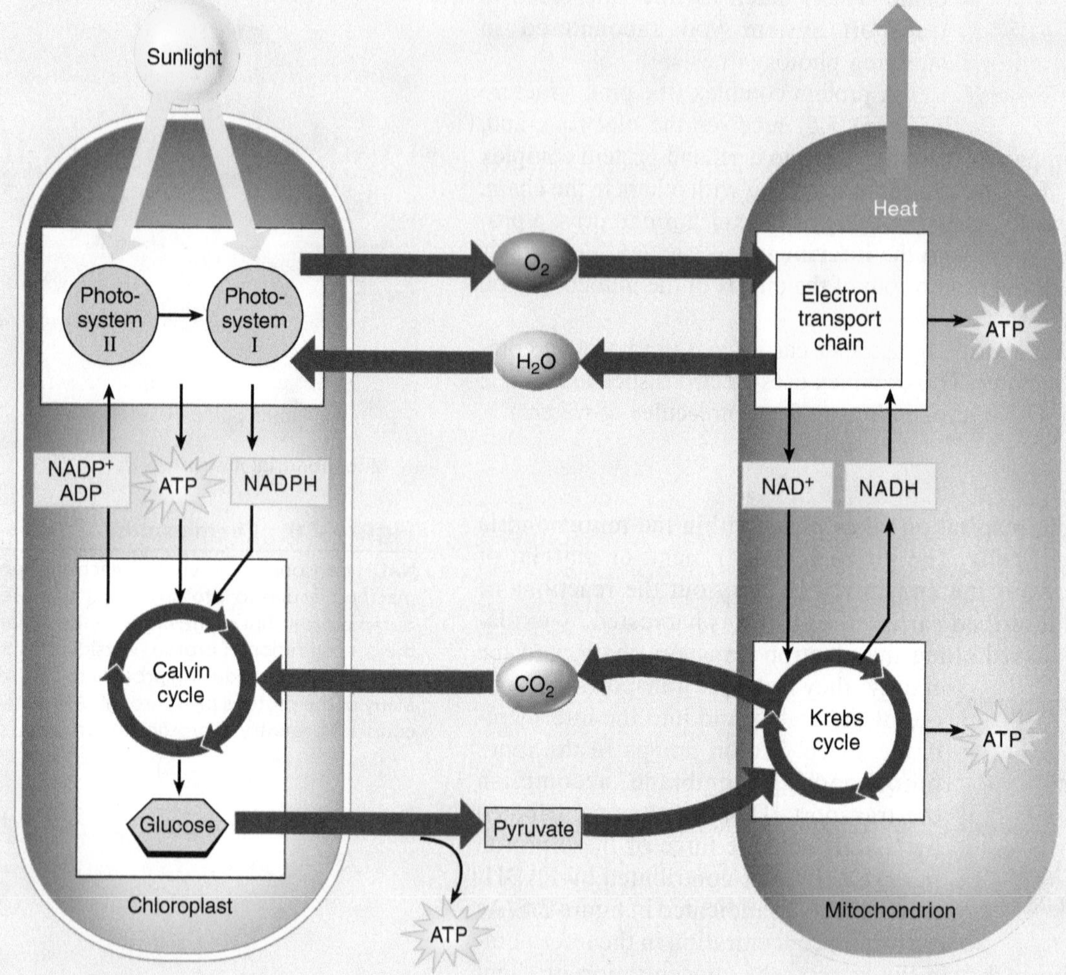

The energy-capturing metabolism of the chloroplasts studied in the previous chapter and the energy-utilizing metabolism of the mitochondria studied in this chapter are intimately related. Photosynthesis carried out by chloroplasts uses the products of cellular respiration as starting substrates and reduces carbon by adding hydrogen atoms. Cellular respiration carried out by mitochondria uses the products of photosynthesis as its starting substrates and oxidizes carbon by removing hydrogen atoms. Together, photosynthesis and cellular respiration form an oxidation-reduction cycle, as diagrammed here. Note that it is electrons that cycle between chloroplasts and mitochondria. Energy passes through the redox cycle, flowing into the cycle from the sun, passing through newly assembled molecules, and eventually flowing out of the cycle as heat.

The evolutionary history of the redox cycle can be seen in its elements. The Calvin cycle of photosynthesis uses part of the glycolytic pathway of cellular respiration, run in reverse, to produce glucose. The principal proteins involved in electron transport in chloroplasts are related to those in mitochondria, and in many cases are actually the same. Biologists believe the glycolysis stage of cellular respiration, which takes place in the cytoplasm, converting glucose to pyruvate and requiring no oxygen, to be the most ancient process in the redox cycle. The chloroplast's oxygen-generating photosynthesis is thought to have evolved next, followed later by the oxidative reactions of the mitochondria's cellular respiration.

Harvesting Electrons Without Oxygen: Fermentation

7.5 Cells Can Metabolize Food Without Oxygen

CONCEPT PREVIEW: In fermentation, which occurs in the absence of oxygen, the electrons that result from the glycolytic breakdown of glucose are donated as hydrogen atoms to an organic molecule, regenerating NAD⁺ from NADH.

Fermentation

In the absence of oxygen, aerobic metabolism (the Krebs cycle and electron transport chain) cannot occur, and cells must rely exclusively on glycolysis to produce ATP. Under these conditions, the hydrogen atoms and electrons that were involved in the oxidation of NAD^+ to NADH in glycolysis are donated to organic molecules instead of the electron transport chain, in a process called **fermentation.** Fermentation recycles NAD^+ so that glycolysis can continue.

Ethanol Fermentation. Bacteria carry out more than a dozen kinds of fermentations, all using some form of organic molecule to accept the hydrogen atom from NADH. By contrast, eukaryotic cells are capable of only a few types of fermentation. In one type, which occurs in single-celled fungi called yeast, the molecule that accepts hydrogen from NADH is pyruvate, the end product of glycolysis itself. Yeast enzymes remove a CO_2 group from pyruvate through decarboxylation, producing a two-carbon molecule called acetaldehyde. The CO_2 released causes bread made with yeast to rise, while bread made without yeast (unleavened bread) does not. The acetaldehyde accepts a hydrogen atom from NADH, producing NAD^+ and ethanol (figure 7.7, *upper panel*). This particular type of fermentation is of great interest to humans, because it is the source of the ethanol in wine and beer. Ethanol is a by-product of fermentation that is actually toxic to yeast; as it approaches a concentration of about 12%, it begins to kill the yeast. That is why naturally fermented wine contains only about 12% ethanol.

Humans have been using yeast for thousands of years to produce bread and alcohol, but yeast has many other commercial uses. The manufacturing potential of yeast will be discussed in more detail on page 309.

Lactic Acid Fermentation. Most animal cells regenerate NAD^+ by a second type of fermentation, using an enzyme called lactate dehydrogenase to transfer a hydrogen atom from NADH back to the pyruvate that is produced by glycolysis. This reaction converts pyruvate into lactic acid and regenerates NAD^+ from NADH (figure 7.7, *lower panel*). It therefore closes the metabolic circle, allowing glycolysis to continue as long as glucose is available. Circulating blood removes excess lactate (the ionized form of lactic acid) from muscles. It was once thought that during strenuous exercise, when the removal of lactic acid cannot keep pace with its production, the accumulation induces muscle fatigue. However, scientists now believe that lactic acid is actually used by muscles as another source of fuel.

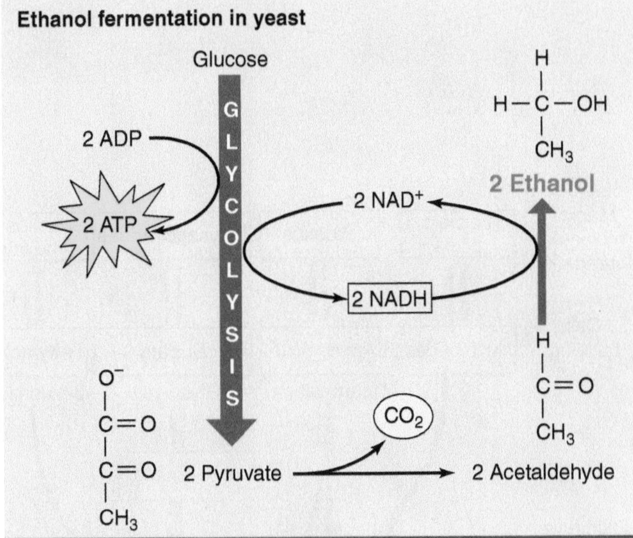

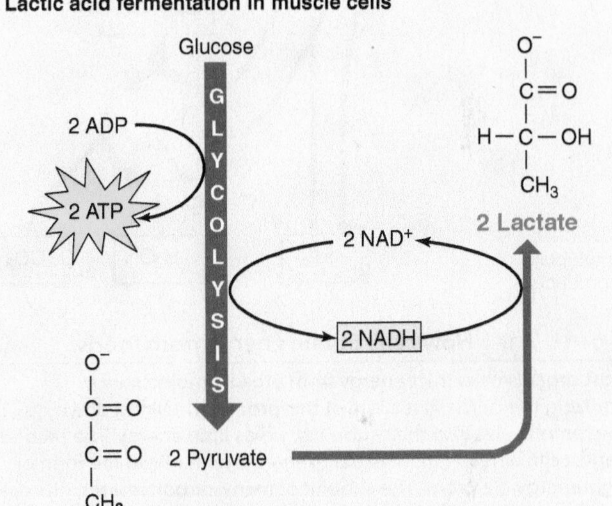

Figure 7.7 Fermentation.

Yeasts carry out the conversion of pyruvate to ethanol. Muscle cells convert pyruvate into lactate, which is less toxic than ethanol. In both cases, NAD^+ is regenerated to allow glycolysis to continue.

IMPLICATION Despite our best intentions, once in a while most of us consume a little more alcohol than we should and wake up the next morning with a "hangover"—a pounding headache, nausea, shakiness, and often a very dry mouth. Many of these symptoms are those of dehydration. What sort of hangover prevention does this hypothesis suggest?

Concept Check

1. Why can't the Krebs cycle function in the absence of oxygen?
2. In eukaryotic fermentations, the hydrogen and electron from NADH are donated to what molecules?
3. What would happen to glycolysis if NAD^+ wasn't recycled?

Other Sources of Energy

7.6 Glucose Is Not the Only Food Molecule

CONCEPT PREVIEW: Cells also garner energy from proteins and fats, which are broken down into products that feed into cellular respiration.

We have considered in detail the fate of a molecule of glucose, a simple sugar, in cellular respiration. But how much of what you eat is sugar? As a more realistic example of the food you eat, consider the fate of a fast-food hamburger. The hamburger is composed primarily of carbohydrates, fats, and proteins. This diverse collection of complex molecules is broken down by the process of digestion in your stomach and intestines into simpler molecules. Carbohydrates are broken down into simple sugars, fats into fatty acids, and proteins into amino acids. Nucleic acids are also present in the food you eat, but these macromolecules store little energy that the body actually uses.

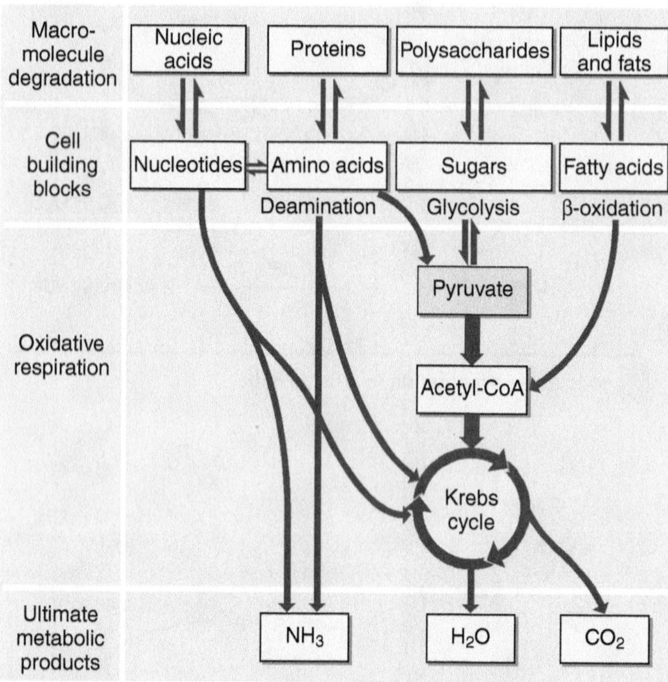

Figure 7.8 How cells obtain energy from foods.

Most organisms extract energy from organic molecules by oxidizing them. The first stage of this process, breaking down macromolecules into their subunits, yields little energy. The second stage, cellular respiration, extracts energy, primarily in the form of high-energy electrons. The subunit of many carbohydrates, glucose, readily enters glycolysis and passes through the biochemical pathways of oxidative respiration. However, the subunits of other macromolecules must be converted into products that can enter the biochemical pathways found in oxidative respiration.

IMPLICATION Many fad diets assert that weight loss will result from a high protein–low carb diet such as the ones discussed on the facing page. Have you ever tried this sort of diet? Did you lose weight? For how long?

Cellular Respiration of Protein

Proteins (the second category in figure 7.8) are first broken down into their individual amino acids. A series of *deamination* reactions removes the nitrogen side groups (called amino groups) and converts the rest of the amino acid into a molecule that takes part in the Krebs cycle. For example, alanine is converted into pyruvate, glutamate into α-ketoglutarate, and aspartate into oxaloacetate. The reactions of the Krebs cycle then extract the high-energy electrons from these molecules and put them to work making ATP.

Cellular Respiration of Fat

Lipids and fats (the fourth category in figure 7.8) are first broken down into fatty acids. A fatty acid typically has a long tail of sixteen or more —CH_2 links, and the many C—H bonds in these long tails provide a rich harvest of energy. Enzymes in the matrix of the mitochondrion first remove one two-carbon acetyl group from the end of a fatty acid tail, and then another, and then another, in effect chewing down the length of the tail in two-carbon bites. Eventually the entire fatty acid tail is converted into acetyl groups. Each acetyl group then combines with coenzyme A to form acetyl-CoA, which feeds into the Krebs cycle. This process is known as *β-oxidation.*

Recall from the discussion of lipids on page 56 that fats are composed of a three-carbon glycerol backbone attached to three fatty acid tails. The breakdown of fats, as described here, occurs with the removal of two carbons at a time from the fatty acid tails.

Concept Check

1. How can your body obtain energy from proteins or fats when they don't go through glycolysis?
2. Proteins and fatty acids have to undergo chemical reactions before they can enter into oxidative respiration. What are the names of these two types of reactions?
3. What part of a hamburger would yield energy in the absence of oxygen?

Fad Diets and Impossible Dreams

Most Americans put on weight in middle age, slowly adding 30 or more pounds. They did not ask for that weight, do not want it, and are constantly looking for a way to get rid of it. It is not a lonely search—it seems like everyone past the flush of youth is trying to lose weight. Many have been seduced by fad diets, investing hope only to harvest frustration. The much discussed Atkins' diet is the fad diet most have tried—*Dr. Atkins' Diet Revolution* is one of the 10 best-selling books in history, prominently displayed in bookstores. The reason this diet doesn't deliver on its promise of pain-free weight loss is well understood by science, but not by the general public. Only hope and hype make it a perpetual best seller.

The secret of the Atkins' diet, stated simply, is to avoid carbohydrates. Atkins' basic proposition is that your body, if it does not detect blood glucose (from metabolizing carbohydrates), will think it is starving and start to burn body fat, even if there is lots of fat already circulating in your bloodstream. You may eat all the fat and protein you want, all the steak and eggs and butter and cheese, and you will still burn fat and lose weight—just don't eat any carbohydrates, any bread or pasta or potatoes or fruit or candy. Despite the title of Atkins' book, this diet is hardly revolutionary. A basic low-carbohydrate diet was first promoted over a century ago in the 1860s by William Banting, an English casket maker, in his best-selling book *Letter on Corpulence*. Books promoting low-carbohydrate diets have continued to be best sellers ever since.

Those who try the Atkins' diet often lose 10 pounds in two to three weeks. In three months it is all back, and then some. So what happened? Where did the pounds go, and why did they come back? The temporary weight loss turns out to have a simple explanation. Carbohydrates act as water sponges in your body, and so forcing your body to become depleted of carbohydrates causes your body to lose water. The 10 pounds lost on this diet was not fat weight but water weight, quickly regained with the first starchy foods eaten.

The Atkins' diet is the sort of diet the American Heart Association tells us to avoid (all those saturated fats and cholesterol), and it is difficult to stay on. If you do hang in there, you will lose weight, simply because you eat less. Other popular diets these days, *The Zone* diet of Dr. Barry Sears and *The South Beach Diet* of Dr. Arthur Agatston, are also low-carbohydrate diets, although not as extreme as the Atkins' diet. Like the Atkins' diet, they work not for the bizarre reasons claimed by their promoters, but simply because they are low-calorie diets.

There are two basic laws that no diet can successfully violate:

1. All calories are equal.
2. (calories in) – (calories out) = fat.

The fundamental fallacy of the Atkins' diet, the Zone diet, the South Beach diet, and indeed of all fad diets, is the idea that somehow carbohydrate calories are different from fat and protein calories. This is scientific foolishness. Every calorie you eat contributes equally to your eventual weight, whether it comes from carbohydrate, fat, or protein.

To the extent these diets work at all, they do so because they obey the second law. By reducing calories in, they reduce fat. If that were all there was to it, we should all go out and buy a diet book. Unfortunately, losing weight isn't that simple, as anyone who has seriously tried already knows. The problem is that your body will not cooperate.

If you try to lose weight by exercising and eating less, your body will attempt to compensate by metabolizing more efficiently. It has a fixed weight, what obesity researchers call a "set point," a weight to which it will keep trying to return. A few years ago, a group of researchers at Rockefeller University in New York, in a landmark study, found that if you lose weight, your metabolism slows down and becomes more efficient, burning fewer calories to do the same work—your body will do everything it can to gain the weight back! Similarly, if you gain weight, your metabolism speeds up. In this way your body uses its own natural weight control system to keep your weight at its set point. No wonder it's so hard to lose weight!

Clearly our bodies don't keep us at one weight all our adult lives. It turns out your body adjusts its fat thermostat—its set point—depending on your age, food intake and amount of physical activity. Adjustments are slow, however, and it seems to be a great deal easier to move the body's set point up than to move it down. Apparently higher levels of fat reduce the body's sensitivity to the leptin hormone that governs how efficiently we burn fat. That is why you can gain weight, despite your set point resisting the gain—your body still issues leptin alarm calls to speed metabolism, but your brain doesn't respond with as much sensitivity as it used to. Thus the fatter you get, the less effective your weight control system becomes.

This doesn't mean that we should give up and learn to love our fat. Rather, now that we are beginning to understand the biology of weight gain, we must accept the hard fact that we cannot beat the requirements of the two diet laws. The real trick is not to give up. Eat less and exercise more, and keep at it. In one year, or two, or three, your body will readjust its set point to reflect the new reality you have imposed by constant struggle. There simply isn't any easy way to lose weight.

How Do Swimming Fish Avoid Low Blood pH?

Animals that live in oxygen-poor environments, like worms living in the oxygen-free mud at the bottom of lakes, are not able to obtain the energy required for muscle movement from the Krebs cycle. Their cells lack the oxygen needed to accept the electrons stripped from food molecules. Instead, these animals rely on glycolysis to obtain ATP, donating the electron to pyruvate, forming lactic acid. While much less efficient than the Krebs cycle, glycolysis does not require oxygen. Even when oxygen is plentiful, the muscles of an active animal may use up oxygen more quickly than it can be supplied by the bloodstream and so be forced to temporarily rely on glycolysis to generate the ATP for continued contraction.

This presents a particular problem for fish. Fish blood is much lower in carbon dioxide than yours is, and as a consequence, the amount of sodium bicarbonate acting as a buffer in fish blood is also quite low. Now imagine you are a trout, and need to suddenly swim very fast to catch a mayfly for dinner. The vigorous swimming will cause your muscles to release large amounts of lactic acid into your poorly buffered blood; this could severely disturb the blood's acid-base balance and so impede contraction of your swimming muscles before the prey is captured.

The graph to the right presents the results of an experiment designed to explore how a trout solves this dilemma. In the experiment, the trout was made to swim vigorously for 15 minutes in a laboratory tank, and then allowed a day's recovery. The lactic acid concentration in its blood was monitored periodically during swimming and recovery phases.

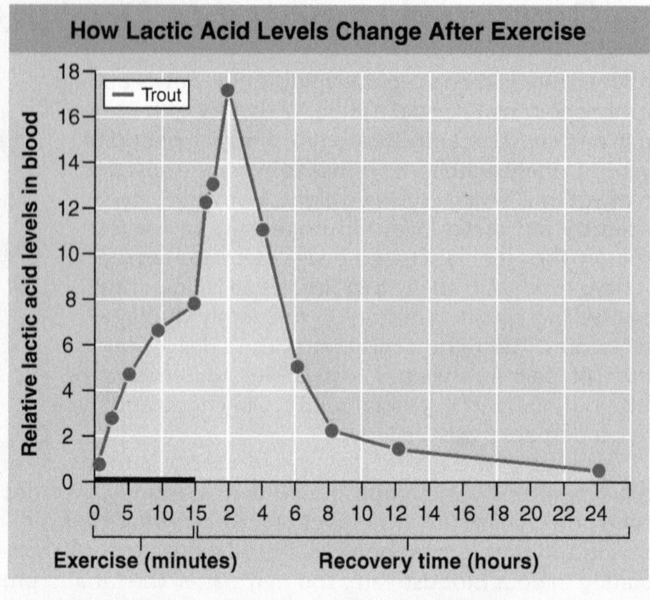

Analysis

1. **Applying Concepts** Lactic acid levels are presented for both swimming and recovery periods. In what time units are the swimming data presented? The recovery data?
2. **Interpreting Data** What is the effect of exercise on the level of lactic acid in the trout's blood? How does the level of lactic acid change after exercise stops?
3. **Making Inferences** About how much of the total lactic acid created by vigorous swimming is released after this exercise stops? [Hint: Notice the *x* axis scale changes from minutes to hours.]
4. **Drawing Conclusions** Is this result consistent with the hypothesis that fish maintain blood pH levels by delaying the release of lactic acid from muscles? Why might this be beneficial to the fish?

Concept Summary

An Overview of Cellular Respiration

7.1 Where Is the Energy in Food?

- Nonphotosynthetic organisms acquire energy from the breakdown of food, either by eating plants that store the food or by eating animals that have eaten plants. Energy stored in carbohydrate molecules is extracted through the process of cellular respiration and is stored in the cell as ATP.
- Coupled reactions, called oxidation-reduction or redox reactions, involve the transfer of electrons from one atom or molecule to another. The atom or molecule that loses an electron is said to be oxidized and loses energy. The atom or molecule that gains the electron is said to be reduced and gains energy (**figure 7.2**).
- Cellular respiration is carried out in two stages: glycolysis occurring in the cytoplasm and oxidation occurring in the mitochondria (**figure 7.3**).

Cellular Respiration

7.2 Respiration Without Oxygen: Glycolysis

- Glycolysis is an energy-extracting process. It is a series of 10 chemical reactions in which glucose is broken down into two three-carbon pyruvate molecules. The energy is extracted from glucose by two exergonic reactions that are coupled with an endergonic reaction that leads to the formation of ATP. This is called substrate-level phosphorylation and is shown in ***Essential Biological Process 7A.***

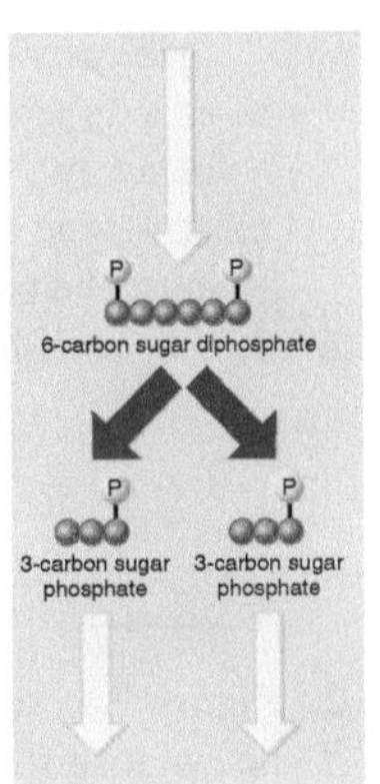

- Electrons extracted from glucose are donated to a carrier molecule, NAD^+, which becomes NADH. NADH carries electrons and hydrogen atoms to be used in a later stage of oxidative respiration.

7.3 Respiration With Oxygen: The Krebs Cycle

- The two molecules of pyruvate formed in glycolysis are passed into the mitochondrion, where they are converted into two molecules of acetyl-coenzyme A (**figure 7.4**). What the cell does with acetyl-CoA depends on the needs of the cell. If the cell has enough ATP, acetyl-CoA is used in synthesizing fat molecules. If the cell needs energy, acetyl-CoA is directed to the Krebs cycle.
- The formation of NADH is an enzyme catalyzed reaction, as shown here from ***Essential Biological Process 7B.*** The enzyme brings the substrate and NAD^+ into close proximity. Through a redox reaction, a hydrogen atom and an electron are transferred to NAD^+, reducing it to NADH. NADH then carries the electrons and hydrogen to a later step in oxidative respiration.

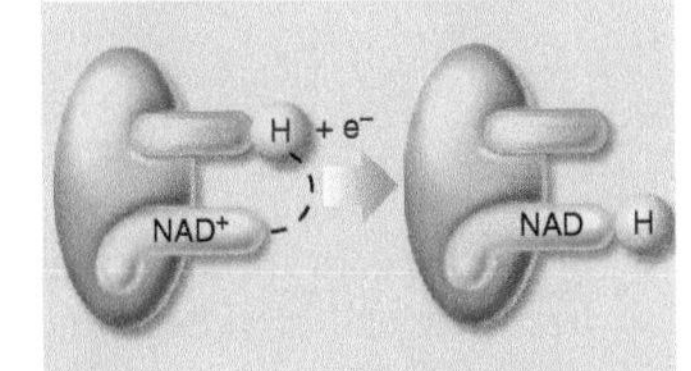

- Acetyl-CoA enters a series of chemical reactions called the Krebs cycle, where one molecule of ATP is produced in a coupled reaction. Energy is also harvested in the form of electrons that are transferred to molecules of NAD^+ and FAD to produce NADH and $FADH_2$, respectively (***Essential Biological Process 7C***).
- The Krebs cycle makes two turns for every molecule of glucose that is oxidized.

7.4 Using the Electrons to Make ATP

- The molecules of NADH and $FADH_2$ that were produced during glycolysis and the Krebs cycle carry electrons to the inner mitochondrial membrane. Here they give up electrons to the electron transport chain. The electrons, along with their energy, are passed along the electron transport chain. The energy from the electrons drives proton pumps that pump H^+ across the inner membrane from the matrix to the intermembrane space, creating an H^+ concentration gradient (**figure 7.5**).
- When the electrons reach the end of the electron transport chain, they bind with oxygen and hydrogen to form water molecules.
- ATP is produced in the mitochondrion through chemiosmosis. The H^+ concentration gradient in the intermembrane space drives H^+ back across the membrane through ATP synthase channels, as shown here from **figure 7.6.** The energy from the movement of H^+ through the channel is transferred to the chemical bonds in ATP. Thus, the energy stored in the glucose molecule is harvested through glycolysis and the Krebs cycle with the formation of NADH and $FADH_2$ and ultimately the formation of ATP. The energy carried by NADH and $FADH_2$ is transferred to the electron transport chain and is stored in ATP.

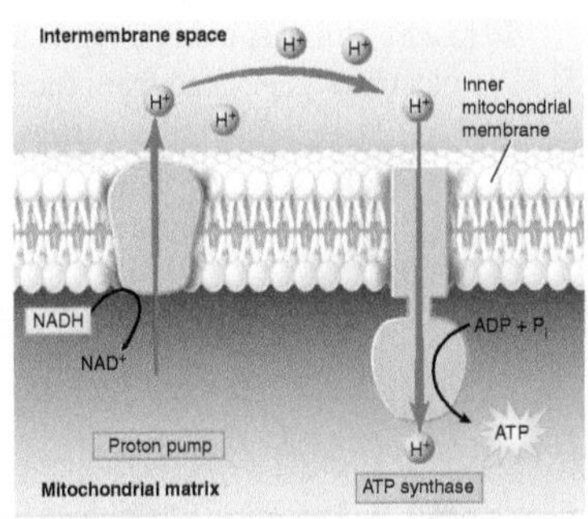

Harvesting Electrons Without Oxygen: Fermentation

7.5 Cells Can Metabolize Food Without Oxygen

- In the absence of oxygen, other molecules can be used as electron acceptors. When the electron acceptor is an organic molecule, the process is called fermentation. Depending on what type of organic molecule accepts the electrons, either ethanol or lactic acid, in the form of lactate is formed (**figure 7.7**).

Other Sources of Energy

7.6 Glucose Is Not the Only Food Molecule

- Food sources other than glucose are also used in oxidative respiration. Macromolecules, such as proteins, lipids, and nucleic acids, are broken down into intermediate products that enter cellular respiration in different reaction steps, as shown here from **figure 7.8.**

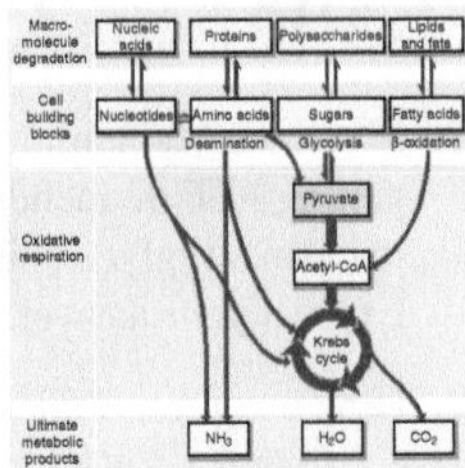

Self-Test

1. In animals, the energy for life is obtained by cellular respiration. This involves
   a. breaking down the organic molecules that were consumed.
   b. capturing photons from plants.
   c. obtaining ATP from plants.
   d. breaking down CO_2 that was produced by plants.
2. During glycolysis, ATP forms by
   a. the breakdown of pyruvate.
   b. chemiosmosis.
   c. substrate-level phosphorylation.
   d. NAD^+.
3. Which of the following processes can occur in the absence of oxygen?
   a. the Krebs cycle **c.** chemiosmosis
   b. glycolysis **d.** All of the above
4. Every living creature on this planet is capable of carrying out the rather inefficient biochemical process of glycolysis, which
   a. makes glucose, using the energy from ATP.
   b. makes ATP by splitting a molecule of glucose in half and capturing the energy.
   c. phosphorylates ATP to make ADP.
   d. makes glucose, using oxygen and carbon dioxide and water.
5. The electrons generated from the Krebs cycle are transferred to ____________ which then carries them to ______________.
   a. NAD^+, oxygen
   b. NAD^+, the electron transport chain
   c. NADH, oxygen
   d. NADH, the electron transport chain
6. After glycolysis, the pyruvate molecules go to the
   a. nucleus of the cell and provide energy.
   b. membranes of the cell and are broken down in the presence of CO_2 to make more ATP.
   c. mitochondria of the cell and are broken down in the presence of O_2 to make more ATP.
   d. Golgi bodies and are packaged and stored until needed.
7. The vast majority of the ATP molecules produced within a cell are produced
   a. during pyruvate oxidation.
   b. during glycolysis.
   c. during the Krebs cycle.
   d. during the electron transport chain.
8. NAD^+ is recycled during
   a. glycolysis. **c.** the Krebs cycle.
   b. fermentation. **d.** the formation of acetyl-CoA.
9. The final electron acceptor in lactic acid fermentation is
   a. pyruvate. **c.** lactic acid.
   b. NAD^+. **d.** O_2.
10. Cells can extract energy from foodstuffs other than glucose because
    a. proteins, fatty acids, and nucleic acids get converted to glucose and then enter oxidative respiration.
    b. each type of macromolecule has its own oxidative respiration pathway.
    c. each type of macromolecule is broken down into its subunits, which enter the oxidative respiration pathway.
    d. they can all enter the glycolytic pathway.

Visual Understanding

1. Consider the structure of a mitochondrion, as shown here in a cutaway view. If you poke a hole in a mitochondrion, can it still perform oxidative respiration? Explain. Can fragments of a mitochondrion perform oxidative respiration? Explain.

2. **Figure 7.8** Your friend wants to go on a low-carbohydrate diet so that he can lose some of the "baby fat" he's still carrying. He asks your advice; what do you tell him?

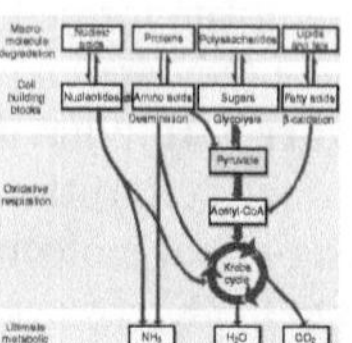

Challenge Questions

1. If cellular respiration were the stock market (you're investing ATPs and getting ATP dividends), where would you get the most return on your investment: glycolysis, the Krebs cycle, or the electron transport chain? Explain your answer.
2. How much less ATP would be generated in the cells of a person who consumed a diet of pyruvate instead of glucose (use one molecule of each for your calculation)?
3. Soft drinks are artificially carbonated, which is what causes them to fizz. Beer and sparkling wines are naturally carbonated. How does this natural carbonation occur?
4. Which of the following food molecules would generate the most ATP molecules, assuming that glycolysis, the Krebs cycle, and the electron transport chain were all functioning and that the foods were consumed in equal amounts; carbohydrates, proteins, or fats? Explain your answer.

Chapter 8

Mitosis

CHAPTER AT A GLANCE

Cell Division

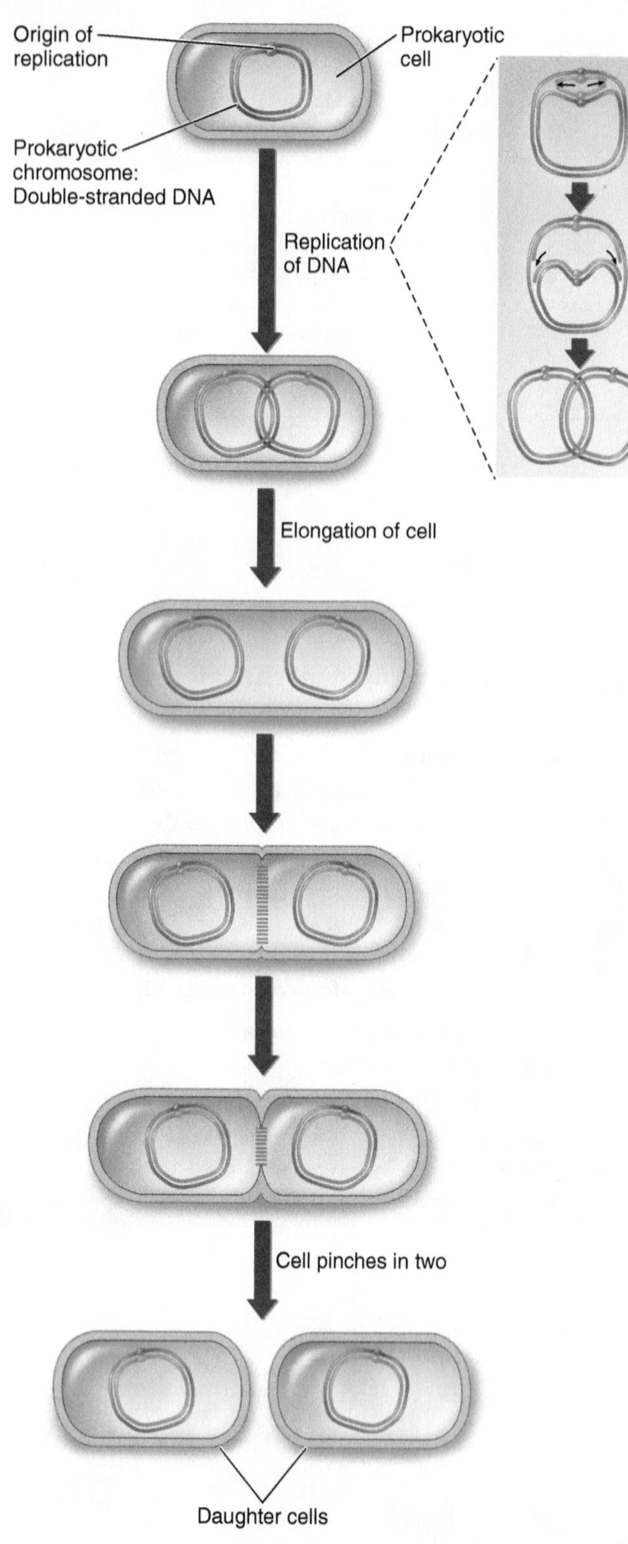

8.1 Prokaryotes Have a Simple Cell Cycle

CONCEPT PREVIEW: Prokaryotes divide by binary fission after the DNA has replicated.

All species reproduce, passing their hereditary information on to their offspring. In this chapter, we begin our consideration of heredity with a look at how cells reproduce. Cell division in prokaryotes takes place in two stages, which together make up a simple cell cycle. First the DNA is copied, and then the cell splits in half by a process called **binary fission.** The cell in figure 8.1 is undergoing binary fission.

In prokaryotes, the hereditary information—that is, the genes that specify the prokaryote—is encoded in a single circle of DNA, called a prokaryotic chromosome. Before the cell itself divides, the DNA circle makes a copy of itself, a process called *replication.* Starting at one point, the origin of replication (indicated at the top of figure 8.1*a*), the double helix of DNA begins to unzip, exposing the two strands. The enlargement on the right of figure 8.1*a* shows how the DNA replicates. The purple strand is from the original DNA and the red strand is the newly formed DNA. The new double helix is formed from each naked strand by placing on each exposed nucleotide its complementary nucleotide (that is, A with T, G with C, as discussed in chapter 3). DNA replication is discussed in more detail in chapter 11. When the unzipping has gone all the way around the circle, the cell possesses two copies of its hereditary information.

As described on pages 52 and 53, DNA is a type of nucleic acid. The hereditary information is encoded in the DNA molecule through the order of the nucleotides that make up the long double-stranded DNA molecule.

When the DNA has been copied, the cell grows, resulting in elongation. The newly replicated DNA molecules are partitioned toward each end of the cell. This partitioning process involves DNA sequences near the origin of replication, and results in these sequences being attached to the membrane. When the cell reaches an appropriate size, the prokaryotic cell begins to split into two equal halves. New plasma membrane and cell wall are added at a point between where the two DNA copies are partitioned, indicated by the green divider in figure 8.1*a*. As the growing plasma membrane pushes inward, the cell is constricted in two, eventually forming two *daughter cells.* Each contains one prokaryotic chromosome that is genetically identical to the parent cell's and each is a complete living cell in its own right.

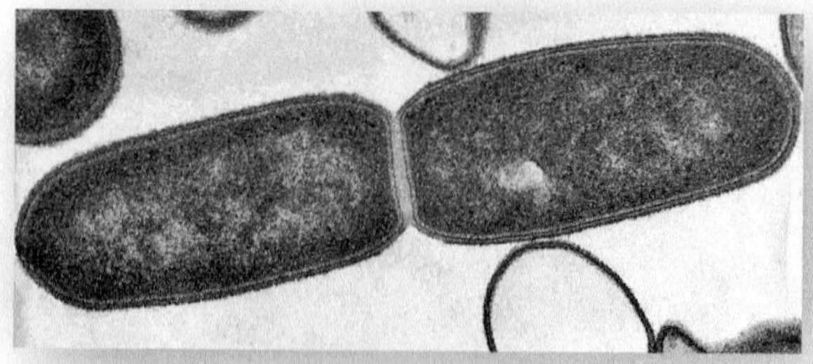
(b)

Figure 8.1 Cell division in prokaryotes.

Prokaryotic cells divide by a process of binary fission. (a) Before the cell splits, the circular DNA molecule of a prokaryote initiates replication at a single site, called the origin of replication, moving out in both directions. When the two moving replication points meet on the far side of the molecule its replication is complete. The cell then undergoes binary fission, where the cell divides into two daughter cells. (b) Here, a prokaryotic cell has divided in two and is about to be pinched apart by the growing plasma membrane.

8.2 Eukaryotes Have a Complex Cell Cycle

CONCEPT PREVIEW: Eukaryotic cells divide by separating copies of their chromosomes into daughter cells.

Cell division in eukaryotes is more complex than in prokaryotes, both because eukaryotes contain far more DNA and because the DNA is packaged in chromosomes that reside in the nucleus. A eukaryotic **chromosome** is a single, long DNA molecule wound tightly around proteins that condense into a compact shape. The cells of eukaryotic organisms either undergo mitosis or meiosis to divide up the DNA. **Mitosis** is the mechanism of cell division that occurs in an organism's nonreproductive cells, or *somatic cells*. **Meiosis,** divides the DNA in cells that participate in sexual reproduction, or *germ cells*.

The events that prepare the eukaryotic cell for division and the division process itself constitute a **complex cell cycle.** *Essential Biological Process 8A* walks you through the phases of the cell cycle:

Interphase. Interphase is composed of three phases:

G_1 phase. This "first gap" phase is the cell's primary growth phase. For most organisms, this phase occupies much of the cell's life span.

S phase. In this "synthesis" phase, the DNA replicates, producing two copies of each chromosome.

G_2 phase. Cell division preparation continues in the "second gap" phase with the replication of mitochondria, chromosome condensation, and the synthesis of microtubules.

M phase. In mitosis, a microtubular apparatus binds to the chromosomes and moves them apart.

C phase. In cytokinesis, the cytoplasm divides, creating two daughter cells.

IN THE NEWS

Alzheimer's Disease Linked to Cell Cycle. Alzheimer's disease, common among the elderly, involves the degeneration of brain nerve cells. The dying cells become clogged with masses of protein called amyloid plaques, but why the plaques appear is not known. Recently several research laboratories have reported findings that shed light on this critical point. What they report is that the nerve cell degeneration of Alzheimer's appears to be a disease of inappropriate cell cycle control. Six months or more before the first amyloid deposits appear, proteins associated with the cell cycle, such as proteins called cyclins, are seen within affected nerve cells in the frontal cortex of the brain. What is important to note is that normally adult brain cells don't divide; after development they go into a resting state. Apparently, this initiation of the cell cycle leads to amyloid deposits and cell death because nerve cells that reenter the cell cycle die rather than divide. These findings suggest that therapies targeted toward preventing mitotic changes may have a profound and positive impact on Alzheimer's disease progression.

Essential Biological Process 8A

The Cell Cycle

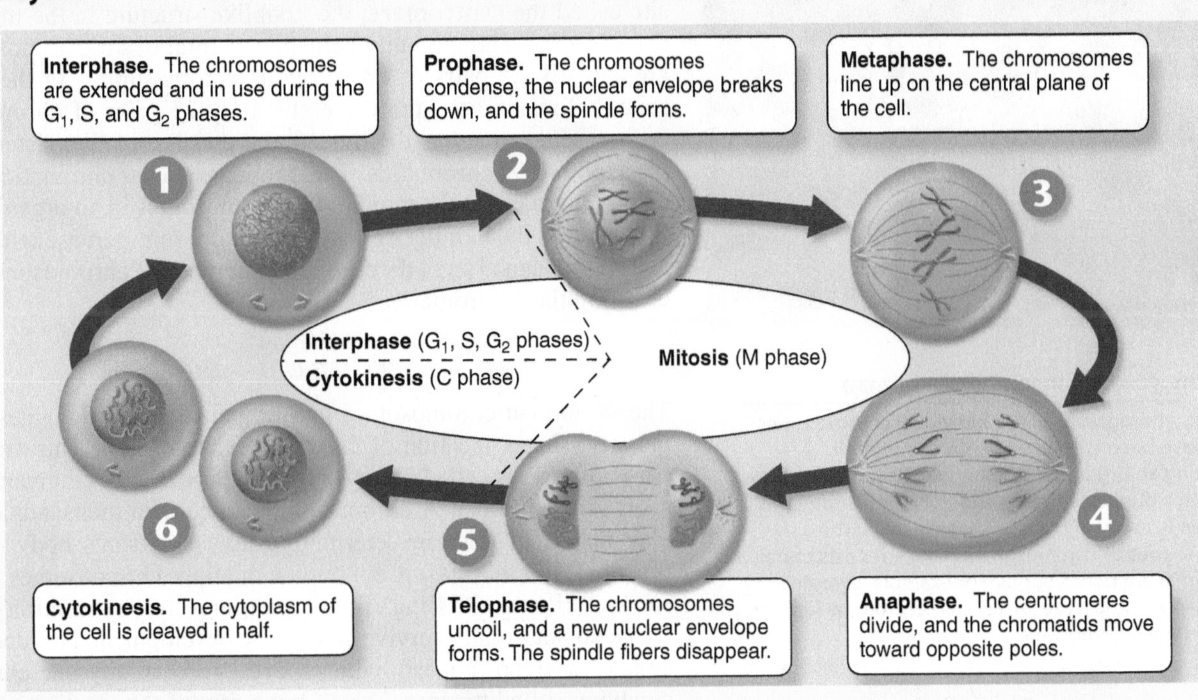
Interphase. The chromosomes are extended and in use during the G_1, S, and G_2 phases.
Prophase. The chromosomes condense, the nuclear envelope breaks down, and the spindle forms.
Metaphase. The chromosomes line up on the central plane of the cell.
1
2
3
Interphase (G_1, S, G_2 phases)
Cytokinesis (C phase)
Mitosis (M phase)
6
5
4
Cytokinesis. The cytoplasm of the cell is cleaved in half.
Telophase. The chromosomes uncoil, and a new nuclear envelope forms. The spindle fibers disappear.
Anaphase. The centromeres divide, and the chromatids move toward opposite poles.

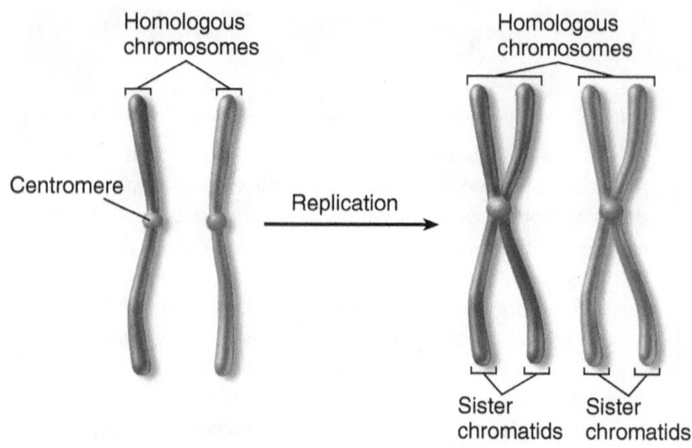

Figure 8.2 The difference between homologous chromosomes and sister chromatids.

Homologous chromosomes are a pair of the same chromosome—say, chromosome number 16. Sister chromatids are the two replicas of a single chromosome held together by the centromere after DNA replication. A duplicated chromosome looks somewhat like an X.

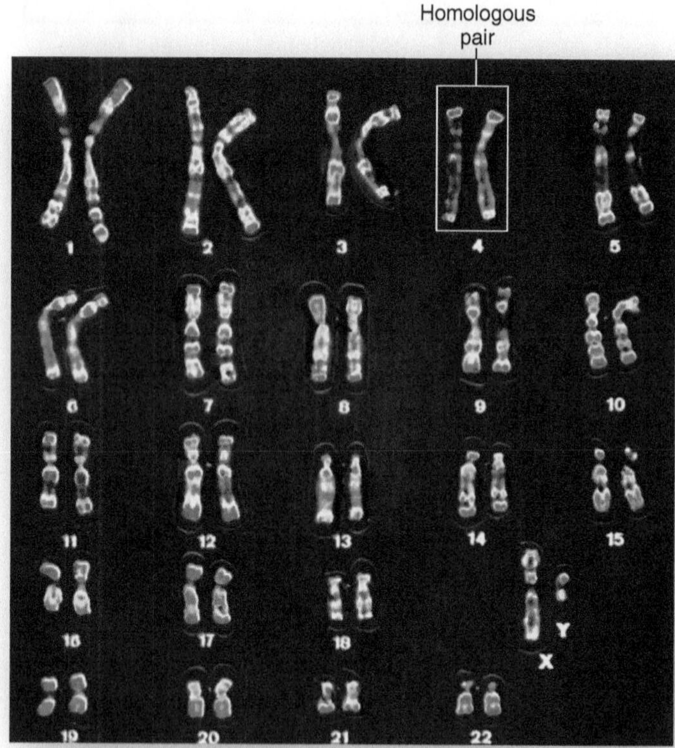

Figure 8.3 The 46 chromosomes of a human.

In this presentation, photographs of the individual chromosomes of a human male have been cut out and paired with their homologues, creating an organized display called a karyotype. The chromosomes are in a duplicated state, and the sister chromatids can actually be seen in many of the homologous pairs. The different sizes and shapes of chromosomes allow scientists to pair together the ones that are homologous. For example, chromosome 1 is much larger than chromosome 14, and its centromere is more centrally located on the chromosome.

8.3 Chromosomes

CONCEPT PREVIEW: All eukaryotic cells store their hereditary information in chromosomes. Coiling of the DNA into chromosomes allows it to fit in the nucleus.

Chromosomes were first observed by the German embryologist Walther Fleming in 1882, while he was examining the rapidly dividing cells of salamander larvae. When Fleming looked at the cells through what would now be a rather primitive light microscope, he saw minute threads within their nuclei that appeared to be dividing lengthwise. Fleming called their division *mitosis,* based on the Greek word *mitos,* meaning "thread."

Chromosome Number

Since their initial discovery, chromosomes have been found in the cells of all eukaryotes examined. Their number may vary enormously from one species to another. A few kinds of organisms—such as the Australian ant *Myrmecia* spp.; the plant *Haplopappus gracilis,* a relative of the sunflower that grows in North American deserts; and the fungus *Penicillium*—have only 1 pair of chromosomes, while some ferns have more than 500 pairs. Most eukaryotes have between 10 and 50 chromosomes in their body cells.

Homologous Chromosomes

Chromosomes exist in somatic cells as pairs, called **homologous chromosomes,** or **homologues.** Homologues carry information about the same traits at the same locations on each chromosome but the information can vary between homologues, which will be discussed in chapter 10. Cells that have two of each type of chromosome are called **diploid cells.** One chromosome of each pair is inherited from the mother (colored green in figure 8.2) and the other from the father (colored purple). Before cell division, each homologous chromosome replicates, resulting in two identical copies, called **sister chromatids.** You see in figure 8.2 that the sister chromatids remain joined together after replication at a special linkage site called the **centromere,** the knoblike structure in the middle of each chromosome. Human body cells have a total of 46 chromosomes, which are actually 23 pairs of homologous chromosomes. In their duplicated state, before mitosis, there are still only 23 pairs of chromosomes, but each chromosome has duplicated and consists of two sister chromatids, for a total of 92 chromatids. The duplicated sister chromatids can make it confusing to count the number of chromosomes in an organism, but keep in mind that the number of centromeres doesn't increase with replication, and so you can always determine the number of chromosomes simply by counting the centromeres.

The Human Karyotype

The 46 human chromosomes can be paired as homologues by comparing size, shape, location of centromeres, and so on. This arrangement of chromosomes is called a **karyotype.** An example of a human karyotype is shown in figure 8.3. A chromosome can contain thousands of genes that play important roles in determining how a person's body develops and functions. For this reason, possession of all the chromosomes is essential to survival. Humans missing even one chromosome, a condition called monosomy, do not usually survive embryonic development. Nor does the human embryo develop properly with an extra copy of any one chromosome, a condition called trisomy. For all but a few of the smallest chromosomes, trisomy is fatal; even in those cases, serious problems result. We will revisit this issue of differences in chromosome number in chapter 10.

Chromosome Structure

Chromosomes are composed of **chromatin,** a complex of DNA and protein; most are about 40% DNA and 60% protein. A significant amount of RNA is also associated with chromosomes because chromosomes are the sites of RNA synthesis. The DNA of a chromosome is one very long, double-stranded fiber that extends unbroken through the entire length of the chromosome. A typical human chromosome contains about 140 million (1.4×10^8) nucleotides in its DNA. Furthermore, if the strand of DNA from a single chromosome were laid out in a straight line, it would be about 5 centimeters (2 inches) long. The amount of information in one human chromosome would fill about 2,000 printed books of 1,000 pages each! Fitting such a strand into a nucleus is like cramming a string the length of a football field into a baseball—and that's only 1 of 46 chromosomes! In the cell, however, the DNA is coiled, allowing it to fit into a much smaller space than would otherwise be possible.

Chromosome Coiling

The DNA of eukaryotes is divided into several chromosomes, although the chromosomes you see in figure 8.3 hardly look like long double-stranded molecules of DNA. These chromosomes, duplicated as sister chromatids, are formed into the shape we see here by winding and twisting the long DNA strands into a much more compact form. Winding up DNA presents an interesting challenge. Because the phosphate groups of DNA molecules have negative charges, it is impossible to just tightly wind up DNA because all the negative charges would simply repel one another. As you can see in figure 8.4, the DNA helix wraps around proteins with positive charges called **histones.** The positive charges of the histones counteract the negative charges of the DNA, so that the complex has no net charge. Every 200 nucleotides, the DNA duplex is coiled around a core of eight histone proteins, forming a complex known as a **nucleosome.** The nucleosomes are further coiled into a solenoid. This solenoid is then organized into looped domains. The final organization of the chromosome is not known, but it appears to involve further radial looping into rosettes around a preexisting scaffolding of protein. This complex of DNA and histone proteins, coiled tightly, forms a compact chromosome.

Figure 8.4 Levels of eukaryotic chromosomal organization.

Compact, rod-shaped chromosomes are in fact highly wound-up molecules of DNA. The arrangement illustrated here is one of many possibilities.

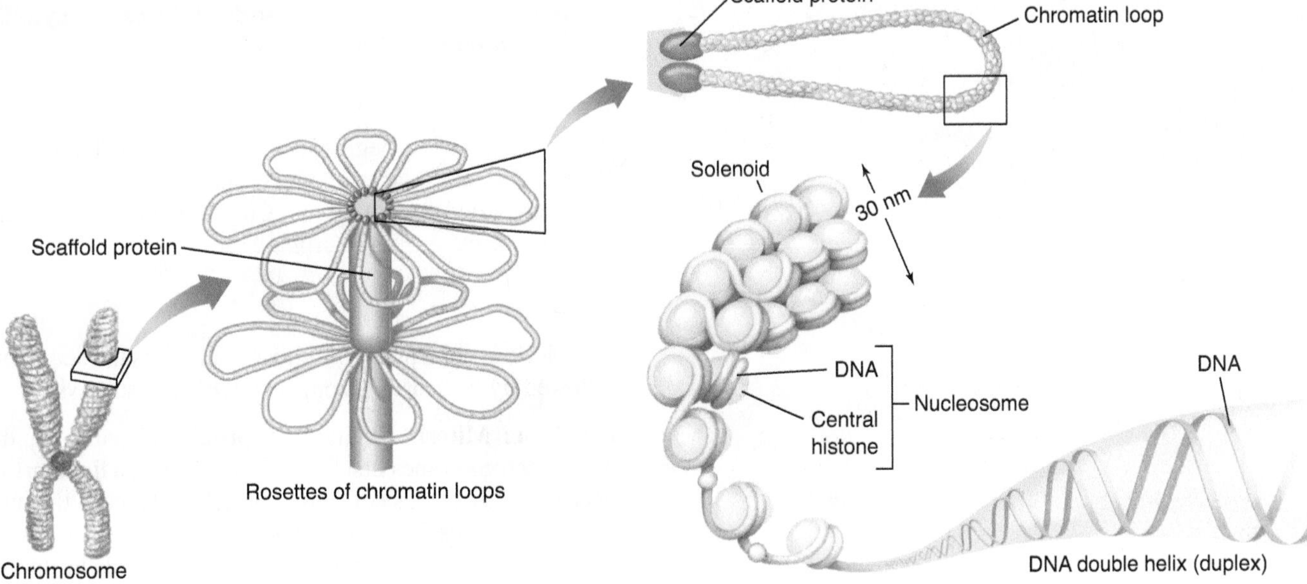

Essential Biological Process 8B

Cell Division

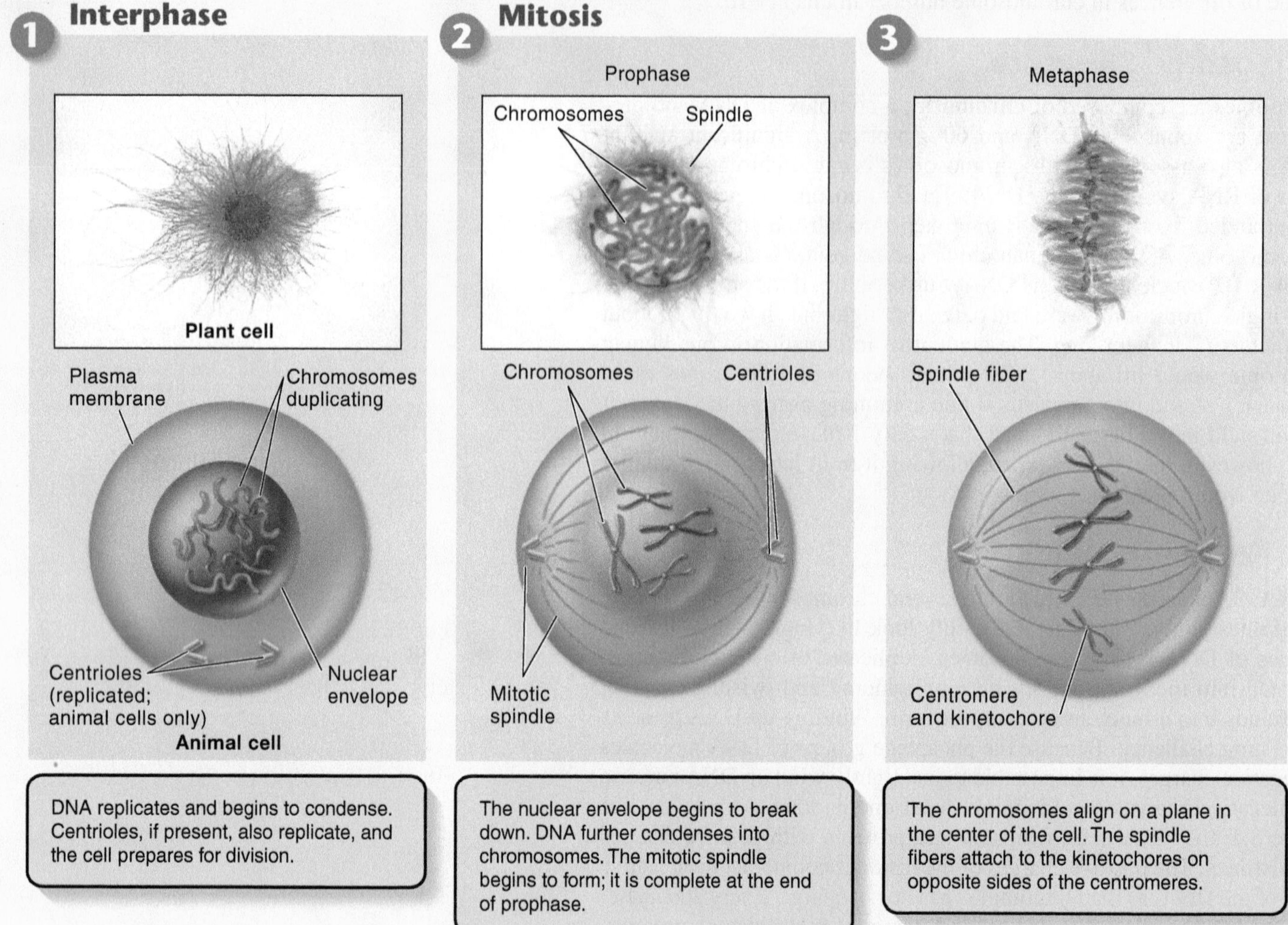
1
Interphase
Plant cell
Plasma membrane
Chromosomes duplicating
Centrioles (replicated; animal cells only)
Nuclear envelope
Animal cell
2
Mitosis
Prophase
Chromosomes
Spindle
Chromosomes
Centrioles
Mitotic spindle
3
Metaphase
Spindle fiber
Centromere and kinetochore
DNA replicates and begins to condense. Centrioles, if present, also replicate, and the cell prepares for division.
The nuclear envelope begins to break down. DNA further condenses into chromosomes. The mitotic spindle begins to form; it is complete at the end of prophase.
The chromosomes align on a plane in the center of the cell. The spindle fibers attach to the kinetochores on opposite sides of the centromeres.

8.4 Cell Division

CONCEPT PREVIEW: In interphase, the replicated chromosomes begin to condense. In mitosis, these chromosomes are drawn by microtubules to opposite ends of the cell; in cytokinesis, the cell is split into two daughter cells.

Interphase

When cell division begins in interphase (panel 1 of *Essential Biological Process 8B*), chromosomes first replicate, and then begin to wind up tightly, a process called **condensation.** Chromosomes are not usually visible under the microscope during interphase.

Mitosis

Interphase is not a phase of mitosis, but it sets the stage for cell division. It is followed by nuclear division, called *mitosis,* subdivided into four stages:

Prophase: Mitosis Begins. In **prophase** (panel 2), the individual condensed chromosomes first become visible with a light microscope. As the replicated chromosomes condense, the cell dismantles the nuclear envelope and two centrosomes (centrioles in animal cells) begin to assemble the apparatus it will use to pull the replicated sister chromatids to opposite ends ("poles")

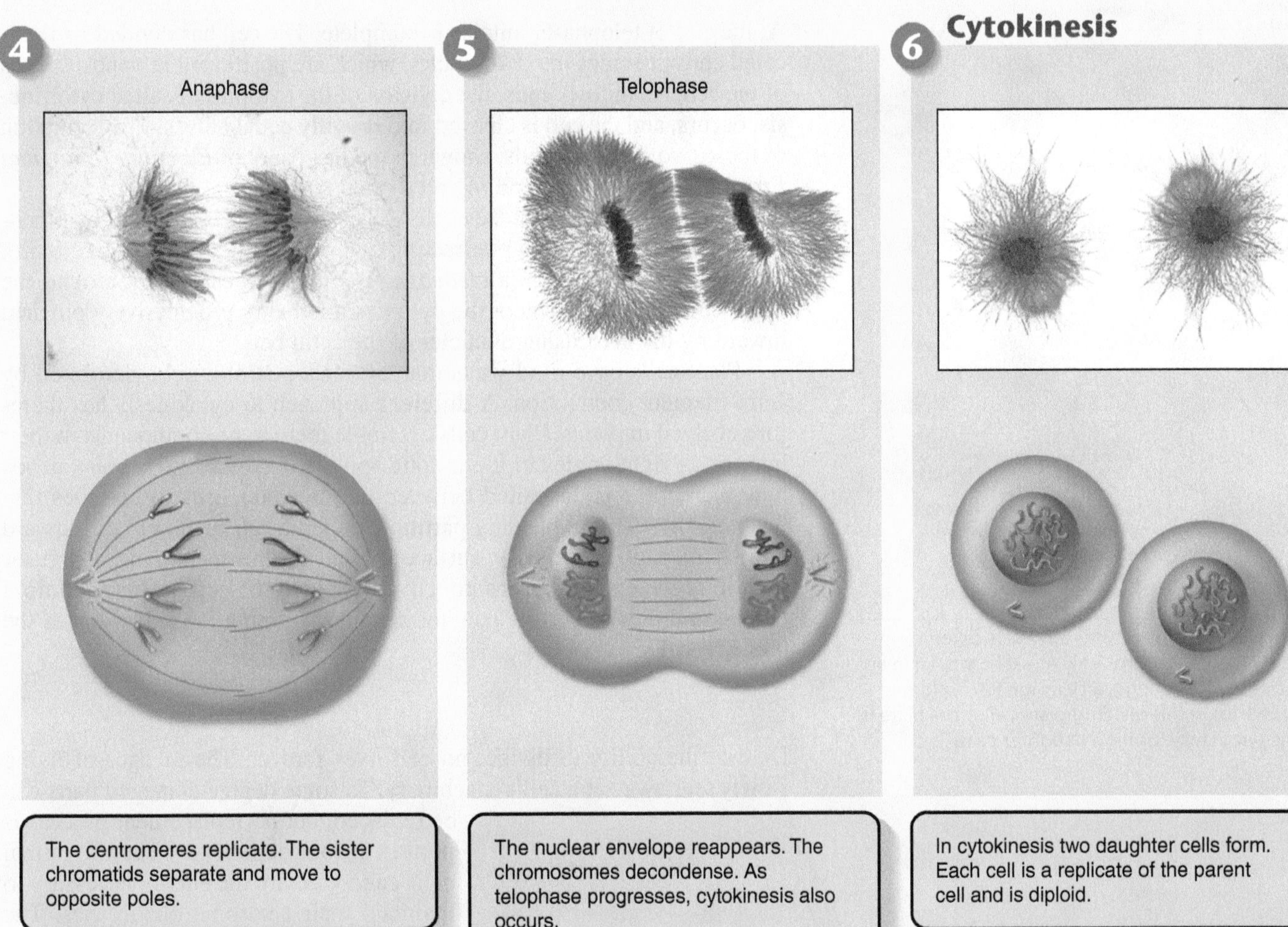

4
Anaphase
5
Telophase
6
Cytokinesis
The centromeres replicate. The sister chromatids separate and move to opposite poles.
The nuclear envelope reappears. The chromosomes decondense. As telophase progresses, cytokinesis also occurs.
In cytokinesis two daughter cells form. Each cell is a replicate of the parent cell and is diploid.

of the cell. In the center of an animal cell, the pairs of centrioles separate and move apart toward opposite poles of the cell, forming between them as they move apart a network of protein cables called the **spindle.** Each cable is called a *spindle fiber* and is made of microtubules, which are long, hollow tubes of protein. Plant cells lack centrioles and instead brace the ends of the spindle toward the poles. The spindle fibers attach to the chromosomes, and when the process is complete, one sister chromatid of each pair is attached by microtubules to one pole and the other sister chromatid to the other pole.

Metaphase: Alignment of the Chromosomes. The second phase of mitosis, **metaphase,** begins when the chromosomes, each consisting of a pair of sister chromatids, align in the center of the cell along an imaginary plane that divides the cell in half, referred to as the equatorial plane. Microtubules attached to the centromeres extend back toward the opposite poles of the cell.

Anaphase: Separation of the Chromatids. In **anaphase,** the centromeres split, and the sister chromatids are freed from each other. Cell division is now simply a matter of reeling in the microtubules, dragging the sister chromatids (now referred to as daughter chromosomes) to the poles.

Telophase: Re-formation of the Nuclei. In **telophase,** the mitotic spindle disassembles, and a nuclear envelope forms around each set of chromosomes while they begin to uncoil. The nucleolus also reappears.

EVOLUTION

Doing Mitosis More Efficiently. Fungi carry out mitosis in a strikingly different way than the process described here. Instead of completely disassembling the nuclear envelope before chromosome segregation, fungi and other lower eukaryotes carry out a more primitive form of mitosis in which the nuclear membrane remains intact, and all of mitosis occurs within the nucleus. Why the difference? In fungi and other lower eukaryotes, the bodies from which the spindle microtubules emanate are embedded within the nuclear envelope, with the tubulin molecules used to build the spindle being imported from the cytoplasm through special channels in the nuclear envelope. Higher eukaryotes dispense with this complex arrangement. Their spindle microtubules emanate from centrioles or other structures outside the nucleus, not the nuclear envelope. Removal of the nuclear envelope allows chromosomes within the nucleus to have direct access to microtubules being made in the cytoplasm without passing the microtubule subunits across a membrane.

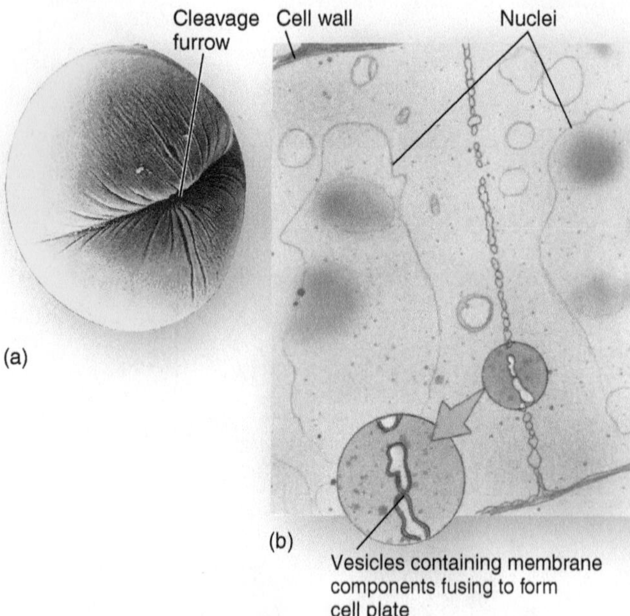

Figure 8.5 Cytokinesis.

The division of cytoplasm that occurs after mitosis is called cytokinesis and cleaves the cell into roughly equal halves. (a) In an animal cell, such as this sea urchin egg, a cleavage furrow forms around the dividing cell. (b) In this dividing plant cell, a cell plate is forming between the two newly forming daughter cells.

Cytokinesis

At the end of telophase, mitosis is complete. The cell has divided its replicated chromosomes into two nuclei, which are positioned at opposite ends of the cell. As mitosis ends, the division of the cytoplasm, called **cytokinesis,** occurs, and the cell is cleaved into roughly equal halves. The formation of these two daughter cells, shown in the last panel of *Essential Biological Process 8B,* signals the end of cell division.

In animal cells, which lack cell walls, cytokinesis is achieved by pinching the cell in two with a contracting belt of actin filaments (figure 8.5*a*). As contraction proceeds, a *cleavage furrow* becomes evident around the cell's circumference, where the cytoplasm is being progressively pinched inward by the decreasing diameter of the actin belt.

Plant cells have rigid walls that are far too strong to be deformed by actin filament contraction. A different approach to cytokinesis has therefore evolved in plants. Plant cells assemble membrane components in their interior, at right angles to the mitotic spindle. In figure 8.5*b,* you can see how membrane is deposited between the daughter cells by vesicles that fuse together. This expanding partition, called a *cell plate*, grows outward until it reaches the interior surface of the plasma membrane and fuses with it, at which point it has effectively divided the cell in two. Cellulose is then laid down over the new membranes, forming the cell walls of the two new cells.

Cell Death

Despite the ability to divide, no cell lives forever. The ravages of living slowly tear away at a cell's machinery. To some degree damaged parts can be replaced, but no replacement process is perfect. If food supplies are cut off, animal cells cannot obtain the energy necessary to maintain their lysosome membranes. The cells die, digested from within by their own enzymes.

Lysosomes are vesicles within the cell described on page 73. They are filled with digestive enzymes that break down cellular debris, and if the lysosome's membrane becomes leaky, the enzymes spill out into the cell, killing it.

During fetal development, many cells are programmed to die. In human embryos, hands and feet appear first as "paddles" (figure 8.6), but the skin cells between bones die as programmed to form the separated toes and fingers. The cells in the tissue between the bones will later die, leaving behind a set of fingers. In ducks, this cell death is not part of the developmental program, which is why ducks have webbed feet.

Human cells appear to be programmed to undergo only so many cell divisions and then die, following a plan written into the genes. In tissue culture, cell lines divide about 50 times, and then the entire population of cells dies off. Even if some of the cells are frozen for years, when they are thawed they simply resume where they left off and die on schedule. Only cancer cells appear to thwart these instructions, dividing endlessly. All other cells in your body contain a hidden clock that keeps time by counting cell divisions, and when the alarm goes off the cells die.

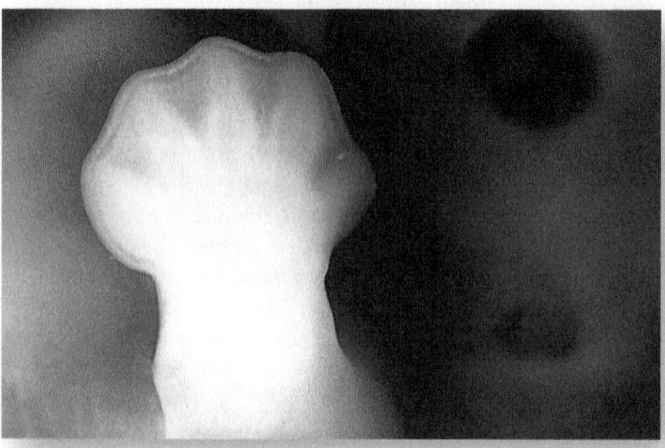

Figure 8.6 Programmed cell death.

In the human embryo, programmed cell death results in the formation of fingers and toes from paddlelike hands and feet.

Concept Check

1. What are the three phases of interphase, and what happens in each?
2. At the end of interphase, how many chromatids does a human cell contain?
3. What are the four stages of mitosis, and what happens in each?

Cancer and the Cell Cycle

8.5 What Is Cancer?

CONCEPT PREVIEW: Cancer is unrestrained cell growth and division caused by damage to genes regulating the cell division cycle.

Cancer is a growth disorder of cells. It starts when an apparently normal cell begins to divide in an uncontrolled way. The result is a cluster of cells, called a **tumor,** that constantly expands in size. The cluster of pink lung cells in the photo in figure 8.7 have begun to form a malignant tumor called a *carcinoma*. Malignant tumors are invasive, their cells able to break away from the tumor, enter the bloodstream, and spread to other areas of the body (figure 8.8), forming new tumors at distant sites called **metastases.**

Cancer is perhaps the most devastating and deadly disease. Most of us have had family or friends affected by the disease. In 2007, 1,444,920 American men and women were diagnosed with cancer; in that same year, 559,650 Americans died of cancer. One in every two Americans born in 2009 will be diagnosed with some form of cancer during their lifetime. In the U.S., the three deadliest human cancers are lung cancer, cancer of the colon and rectum, and breast cancer. Lung cancer, responsible for the most cancer deaths, is largely preventable; most cases result from smoking cigarettes. Colorectal cancers appear to be fostered by the high-meat diets so favored in the United States. The cause of breast cancer is still a mystery.

Not surprisingly, researchers are expending a great deal of effort to learn the cause of cancer. Scientists have made considerable progress in the last 30 years using molecular biological techniques, and the rough outlines of understanding are now emerging. We now know that cancer is a gene disorder of somatic tissue, in which damaged genes fail to properly control cell growth and division. The cell division cycle is regulated by a sophisticated group of proteins called growth factors. Cancer results from damage to the genes encoding these proteins. Damage to DNA, such as damage to these genes, is called **mutation.** Cancer can be caused by chemicals that alter DNA like the tars in cigarette smoke, by environmental factors such as UV rays that damage DNA, or in some instances by viruses that circumvent the cell's normal growth and division controls.

Mutations are errors in DNA and are discussed in detail in chapter 11, pages 192–193. Damage to DNA often involves an incorrect nucleotide being inserted during DNA replication, which changes the information encoded in the DNA.

There are two general classes of growth factor genes that are usually involved in cancer: proto-oncogenes and tumor-suppressor genes. Genes known as **proto-oncogenes** encode proteins that stimulate cell division. Mutations to these genes can cause cells to divide excessively. Mutated proto-oncogenes become cancer-causing genes called **oncogenes.**

The second class of cancer-causing genes are called **tumor-suppressor genes.** Cell division is normally turned off in healthy cells by proteins encoded by tumor-suppressor genes. Mutations to these genes essentially "release the brakes," allowing the cell containing the mutated gene to divide uncontrolled.The cell cycle never stops in a cancerous line of cells.

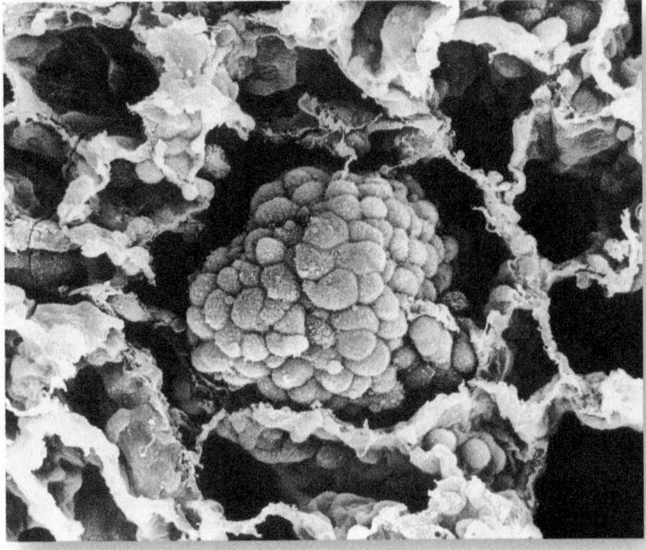

Figure 8.7 Lung cancer cells (300×).

These cells are from a tumor located in the alveolus (air sac) of a human lung.

IMPLICATION 160,390 people died of lung cancer in the United States in 2007, almost all of them cigarette smokers. Fully 7 1/2 % of pack-a-day smokers will die of lung cancer within 30 years of their first cigarette. That's 1 in 13. Do you smoke? Do any of your friends? Can you think of a reason that would justify the risk?

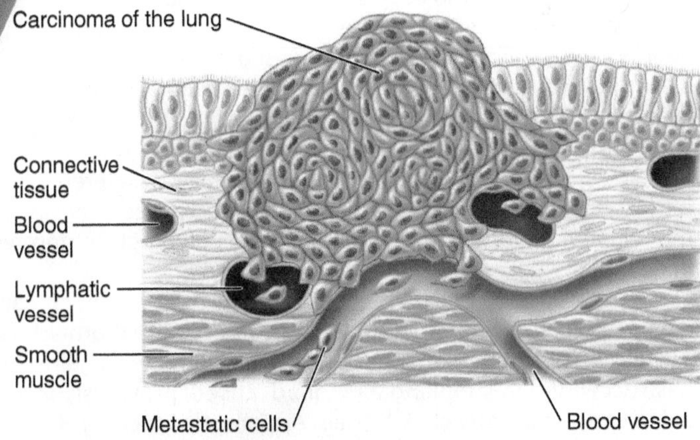

Figure 8.8 Portrait of a tumor.

This ball of cells is a carcinoma (cancer tumor) developing from epithelial cells that line the interior surface of a human lung. As the mass of cells grows, it invades surrounding tissues, eventually penetrating lymphatic and blood vessels, both of which are plentiful within the lung. These vessels carry metastatic cancer cells throughout the body, where they lodge and grow, forming new masses of cancerous tissue.

Concept Check

1. What are the three deadliest human cancers?
2. Cancer results from damage to which two general classes of genes?
3. Name three sorts of things that cause cancer.

Curing Cancer

Half of all Americans will face cancer at some point in their lives. Potential cancer therapies are being developed on many fronts. Some act to prevent the start of cancer within cells. Others act outside cancer cells, preventing tumors from growing and spreading. The figure on the right indicates targeted areas for the development of cancer treatments. The following discussion will examine each of these areas.

Preventing the Start of Cancer

Many promising cancer therapies act within potential cancer cells, focusing on different stages of the cell's "Shall I divide?" decision-making process.

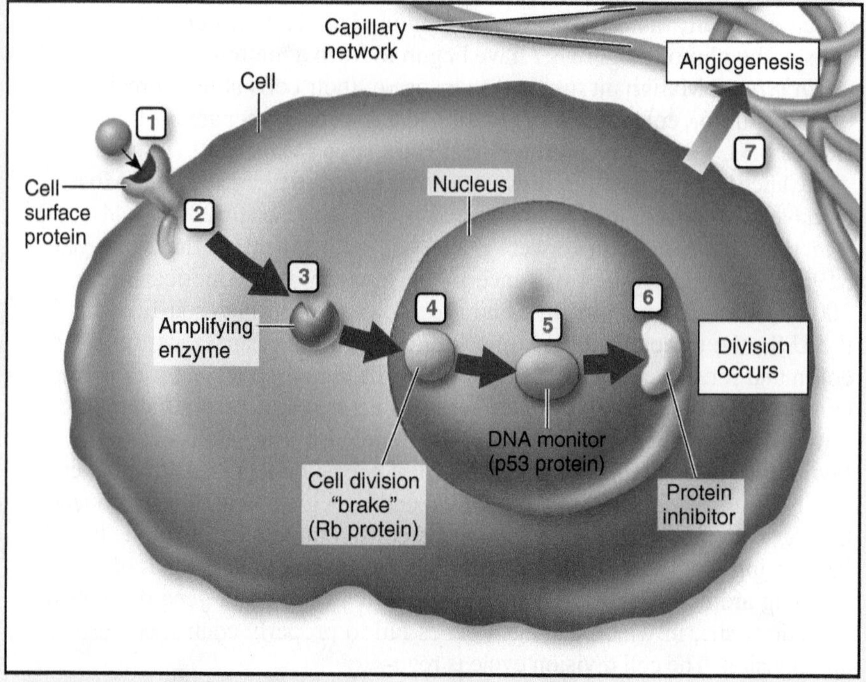

Seven different stages in the cancer process.

(1) On the cell surface, a growth factor's signal to divide is increased. (2) Just inside the cell, a protein relay switch that passes on the divide signal gets stuck in the "ON" position. (3) In the cytoplasm, enzymes that amplify the signal are amplified even more. In the nucleus, (4) a "brake" preventing DNA replication is inoperable, (5) proteins that check for damage in the DNA are inactivated, and (6) other proteins that inhibit the elongation of chromosome tips are destroyed. (7) The new tumor promotes angiogenesis, the formation of new blood vessels that promote growth.

1 Receiving the Signal to Divide. The first step in the decision process is receiving a "divide" signal, usually a small protein called a growth factor released from a neighboring cell. The growth factor, the red ball at #1 in the figure, is received by a protein receptor on the cell surface. Like banging on a door, its arrival signals that it's time to divide. Mutations that increase the number of receptors on the cell surface amplify the division signal and so lead to cancer. Over 20% of breast cancer tumors prove to overproduce a protein called HER2 associated with the receptor for epidermal growth factor (EGF).

Therapies directed at this stage of the decision process utilize the human immune system to attack cancer cells. Special protein molecules called *monoclonal antibodies,* created by genetic engineering, are the therapeutic agents. These monoclonal antibodies are designed to seek out and stick to HER2. Like waving a red flag, the presence of the monoclonal antibody calls down attack by the immune system on the HER2 cell. Because breast cancer cells overproduce HER2, they are killed preferentially. The biotechnology research company Genentech's recently approved monoclonal antibody, called herceptin, has given promising results in clinical tests.

Up to 70% of colon, prostate, lung, and head/neck cancers have excess copies of a related receptor, epidermal growth factor 1 (HER1). The monoclonal antibody C225, directed against HER1, has succeeded in shrinking 22% of advanced, previously incurable colon cancers in early clinical trials. Apparently blocking HER1 interferes with the ability of tumor cells to recover from chemotherapy or radiation.

2 Passing the Signal via a Relay Switch. The second step in the decision process is the passage of the signal into the cell's interior, the cytoplasm. This is carried out in normal cells by a protein called Ras that acts as a relay switch, #2 in the figure. When growth factor binds to a receptor like EGF, the adjacent Ras protein acts like it has been "goosed," contorting into a new shape. This new shape is chemically active, and initiates a chain of reactions that passes the "divide" signal inward toward the nucleus. Mutated forms of the Ras protein behave like a relay switch stuck in the "ON" position, continually instructing the cell to divide when it should not. Thirty percent of all cancers have a mutant form of Ras. So far, no effective therapies have been developed targeting this step.

3 Amplifying the Signal. The third step in the decision process is the amplification of the signal within the cytoplasm. Just as a TV signal needs to be amplified in order to be received at a distance, so a "divide" signal must be amplified if it is to reach the nucleus at the interior of the cell, a very long journey at a molecular scale. To get a signal all the way into the nucleus, the cell employs a sort of pony express. The "ponies" in this case are enzymes called *tyrosine kinases,* #3 in the figure. These enzymes add phosphate groups to proteins, but only at a particular amino acid, tyrosine. No other enzymes in the cell do this, so the tyrosine kinases form an elite corps of signal carriers not confused by the myriad of other molecular activities going on around them.

Cells use an ingenious trick to amplify the signal as it moves toward the nucleus. Ras, when "ON," activates the initial protein kinase. This protein kinase activates other protein kinases that in their turn activate still others. The trick is that once a protein kinase enzyme is activated, it goes to work like a demon, activating hoards of others every second! And each and every one it activates behaves the same way too, activating still more, in a cascade of ever-widening effect. At each stage of the relay, the signal is amplified a thousandfold.

Mutations stimulating any of the protein kinases can dangerously increase the already amplified signal and lead to cancer. Some 15 of the cell's 32 internal tyrosine kinases have been implicated in cancer. Five percent of all cancers, for example, have a mutant hyperactive form of the protein kinase Src. The trouble begins when a mutation causes one of the tyrosine kinases to become locked into the "ON" position, sort of like a stuck doorbell that keeps ringing and ringing.

To cure the cancer, you have to find a way to shut the bell off. Each of the signal carriers presents a different problem, as you must quiet it without knocking out all the other signal pathways the cell needs. The cancer therapy drug Gleevec, a monoclonal antibody, has just the right shape to fit into a groove on the surface of the tyrosine kinase called "abl." Mutations locking abl "ON" are responsible for chronic myelogenous leukemia, a lethal form of white blood cell cancer. Gleevec totally disables abl. In clinical trials, blood counts revert to normal in more than 90% of cases.

4 Releasing the Brake. The fourth step in the decision process is the removal of the "brake" the cell uses to restrain cell division. In healthy cells this brake, a tumor-suppressor protein called Rb, blocks the activity of a protein called E2F, #4 in the figure. When free, E2F enables the cell to copy its DNA. Normal cell division is triggered to begin when Rb is inhibited, unleashing E2F. Mutations that destroy Rb release E2F from its control completely, leading to ceaseless cell division. Forty percent of all cancers have a defective form of Rb.

Therapies directed at this stage of the decision process are only now being attempted. They focus on drugs able to inhibit E2F, which should halt the growth of tumors arising from inactive Rb. Experiments in mice in which the *E2F* genes have been destroyed provide a model system to study such drugs, which are being actively investigated.

5 Checking That Everything Is Ready. The fifth step in the decision process is the mechanism used by the cell to ensure that its DNA is undamaged and ready to divide. This job is carried out in healthy cells by the tumor-suppressor protein p53, which inspects the integrity of the DNA, #5 in the figure. When it detects damaged or foreign DNA, p53 stops cell division and activates the cell's DNA repair systems. If the damage doesn't get repaired in a reasonable time, p53 pulls the plug, triggering events that kill the cell. In this way, mutations such as those that cause cancer are either repaired or the cells containing them eliminated. If p53 is itself destroyed by mutation, future damage accumulates unrepaired. Among this damage are mutations that lead to cancer. Fifty percent of all cancers have a disabled p53. Fully 70% to 80% of lung cancers have a mutant inactive p53—the chemical benzo[*a*]pyrene in cigarette smoke is a potent mutagen of p53.

6 Stepping on the Gas. Cell division starts with replication of the DNA. In healthy cells, another tumor suppressor "keeps the gas tank nearly empty" for the DNA replication process by inhibiting production of an enzyme called *telomerase.* Without this enzyme, a cell's chromosomes lose material from their tips, called *telomeres.* Every time a chromosome is copied, more tip material is lost. After some 30 divisions, so much is lost that copying is no longer possible. Cells in the tissues of an adult human have typically undergone 25 or more divisions. Cancer can't get very far with only the five remaining cell divisions, so inhibiting telomerase is a very effective natural brake on the cancer process, #6 in the figure. It is thought that almost all cancers involve a mutation that destroys the telomerase inhibitor, releasing this brake and making cancer possible. It should be possible to block cancer by reapplying this inhibition. Cancer therapies that inhibit telomerase are just beginning clinical trials.

Preventing the Spread of Cancer

7 Stopping Tumor Growth. Once a cell begins cancerous growth, it forms an expanding tumor. As the tumor grows ever-larger, it requires an increasing supply of food and nutrients, obtained from the body's blood supply. To facilitate this necessary grocery shopping, tumors leak out substances into the surrounding tissues that encourage the formation of small blood vessels, a process called angiogenesis, #7 in the figure. Chemicals that inhibit this process are called *angiogenesis inhibitors.* Two such natural angiogenesis inhibitors, angiostatin and endostatin, caused tumors to regress to microscopic size in mice, but initial human trials were disappointing.

Laboratory drugs are more promising. A monoclonal antibody drug called Avastin, targeted against a blood vessel growth promoting substance called vascular endothelial growth factor (VEGF), destroys the ability of VEGF to carry out its blood-vessel-forming job. Given to hundreds of advanced colon cancer patients as part of a large clinical trial, Avastin improved colon cancer patients' chance of survival by 50% over chemotherapy.

Inquiry & Analysis

Why Do Human Cells Age?

Human cells appear to have built-in life spans. In 1961 cell biologist Leonard Hayflick reported the startling result that skin cells growing in tissue culture, such as those growing in culture flasks in the photo below, will divide only a certain number of times. After about 50 population doublings cell division stops (a **doubling** is a round of cell division producing two daughter cells for each dividing cell, for example going from a population of 30 cells to 60 cells). If a cell sample is taken after 20 doublings and frozen, when thawed it resumes growth for 30 more doublings, and then stops. An explanation of the "Hayflick limit" was suggested in 1986 when researchers first glimpsed an extra length of DNA at the end of chromosomes. Dubbed *telomeres*, these lengths proved to be composed of the simple DNA sequence TTAGGG, repeated nearly a thousand times. Importantly, telomeres were found to be substantially shorter in the cells of older body tissues. This led to the hypothesis that a run of some 16 TTAGGGs was where the DNA replicating enzyme, called polymerase, first sat down on the DNA (16 TTAGGGs being the size of the enzyme's "footprint"), and because of being its docking spot, the polymerase was unable to copy that bit. Thus a 100-base portion of the telomere was lost by a chromosome during each doubling as DNA replicated. Eventually, after some 50 doubling cycles, each with a round of DNA replication, the telomere would be used up and there would be no place for the DNA replication enzyme to sit. The cell line would then enter senescence, no longer able to proliferate.

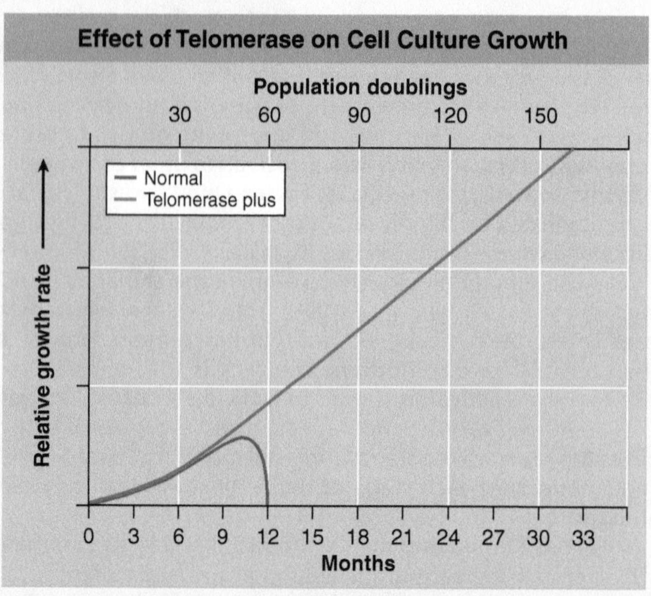

TTAGGG TTAGGG TTAGGG TTAGGG TTAGGG--------

This hypothesis was tested in 1998. Using genetic engineering, researchers transferred into newly established human cell cultures a gene that leads to expression of an enzyme called *telomerase* that all cells possess but no body cell uses. This enzyme adds TTAGGG sequences back to the end of telomeres, in effect rebuilding the lost portions of the telomere. Laboratory cultures of cell lines with (telomerase plus) and without (normal) this gene were then monitored for many generations. The graph above displays the results.

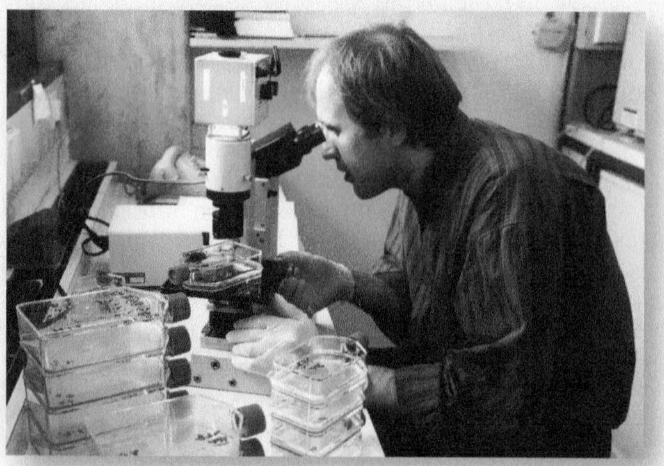

Analysis

1. **Applying Concepts** Comparing continuous processes, how do normal skin cells (blue line) differ in their growth history from telomerase plus cells with the telomerase gene (red line)?
2. **Interpreting Data** After how many doublings do the normal cells cease to divide? the telomerase plus cells?
3. **Making Inferences** After 9 population doublings, would the rate of cell division be different between the two cultures? after 15? Why?
4. **Drawing Conclusions** How does the addition of the telomerase gene affect the senescence (death by old age) of skin cells growing in culture? Does this result confirm the telomerase hypothesis this experiment had set out to test?

Concept Summary

Cell Division

8.1 Prokaryotes Have a Simple Cell Cycle

- Prokaryotic cells divide in a two-step process: DNA replication and binary fission. The genetic information in a prokaryotic cell is present as a single loop of DNA. The DNA begins replication at a site called the origin of replication. The DNA double strand unzips, and new strands form along the original strands, producing two circular prokaryotic chromosomes that separate to the ends of the cell. New plasma membrane and cell wall are added down the middle of the cell, as shown here from **figure 8.1,** splitting the cell in two. This cell division, called binary fission, produces two daughter cells that are genetically identical to the parent cell.

8.2 Eukaryotes Have a Complex Cell Cycle

- Cell division in eukaryotes is more complex than in prokaryotes because eukaryotic cells contain more DNA and their DNA is packaged into linear chromosomes.
- Eukaryotic cells divide by one of two methods, mitosis or meiosis. Mitosis occurs in nonreproductive cells, called somatic cells. Meiosis occurs in cells that are involved in sexual reproduction, forming germ cells, such as sperm and eggs.
- The complex cell cycle in eukaryotic cells occurs in several phases: interphase, M phase, and C phase. Interphase is the first portion of the cell cycle. Interphase is also broken down into phases. The G_1 phase is the growing phase and takes up the major portion of the cell's life cycle. The S phase is the synthesis phase and is when the DNA is replicated. The G_2 phase involves the final preparations for cell division with the replication of mitochondria, chromosome condensation, and synthesis of microtubules.
- During the M phase the chromosomes are distributed into opposite sides of the cell. During the C phase the cell divides its cytoplasm into two separate daughter cells (***Essential Biological Process 8A***).

8.3 Chromosomes

- Eukaryotic DNA is organized into chromosomes. Chromosomes are found in all eukaryotic cell, but the number of chromosomes varies greatly between species. Most eukaryotes have between 10 and 50 chromosomes.
- Chromosomes exist in cells as pairs called homologous chromosomes. Two chromosomes that carry copies of the same genes, like the two shown here from **figure 8.2,** are homologous chromosomes.
- Before cells divide, the DNA replicates forming two identical copies of each chromosome, called sister chromatids. Sister chromatids stay connected at an area called the centromere. Human somatic cells have 46 chromosomes but just before cell division, their DNA replicates forming 92 sister chromatids.
- Chromosomes are not uniform; they vary in size, shape, and placement of centromeres. These variations allow researchers to match up homologues making an array, called a karyotype, where homologues are positioned next to each other (**figure 8.3**).
- The DNA in a chromosome is one long double-stranded fiber. After the DNA is replicated, it associates with proteins, forming chromatin. Chromatin begins to coil up in a process called condensation. The negatively charged DNA can coil up tightly because it wraps around positively charged histone proteins. There are several levels of chromosomal organization. The DNA wraps around a histone complex forming a nucleosome and then further folds and loops on itself forming a compact chromosome (**figure 8.4**).

8.4 Cell Division

- Interphase begins the cell cycle followed by mitosis, which consists of four phases: prophase, metaphase, anaphase, and telophase (***Essential Biological Process 8B***).
- Prophase signals the beginning of mitosis. The DNA that was replicated during interphase condenses into chromosomes. The sister chromatids stay attached at the centromeres. The nuclear envelope disappears. Centrioles, when present, migrate to opposite sides of the cell, called the poles, and begin forming the spindle. Microtubules that form the spindle extend from the poles and attach to the chromosomes at the centromeres, anchoring sister chromatids to opposite poles.
- Metaphase involves the alignment of sister chromatids along the equatorial plane.
- During anaphase, the centromeres split, freeing the sister chromatids. The microtubules shorten, pulling the sister chromatids apart and toward opposite poles.
- Telophase signals the completion of nuclear division. The microtubule spindle is dismantled, the chromosomes begin to uncoil; nuclear envelopes form.
- Following mitosis, the cell separates into two daughter cells in a process called cytokinesis (**figure 8.5**). Cytokinesis in animal cells involves a pinching in of the cell around its equatorial plane until the cell eventually splits into two cells. Cytokinesis in plant cells involves the assembly of plasma membranes and cell walls between the two poles, eventually, forming two separate cells.
- Many cells are programmed to die, either as part of development or after a set number of cell divisions (usually about 50 divisions). Only cancer cells appear to divide endlessly.

Cancer and the Cell Cycle

8.5 What Is Cancer?

- Cancer is a growth disorder of cells, where there is a loss of control over cell division. Cells begin to divide in an uncontrolled way, forming a mass of cells called a tumor (**figure 8.7**). A tumor in which cells break away from the mass and spread to other tissues is called metastasis (**figure 8.8**). Cancer results when genes that encode proteins that control the cell cycle, such as proto-oncogenes and tumor-suppressor genes, are damaged.

Self-Test

1. Prokaryotes reproduce by
   a. copying DNA then undergoing binary fission.
   b. splitting in half.
   c. undergoing mitosis.
   d. copying DNA then undergoing the M phase.
2. The eukaryotic cell cycle is different from prokaryotic cell division in all the following ways *except*
   a. the amount of DNA present in the cells.
   b. how the DNA is packaged.
   c. in the production of genetically identical daughter cells.
   d. the involvement of microtubules.
3. In eukaryotes, the genetic material is found in chromosomes
   a. and the more complex the organism, the more pairs of chromosomes it has.
   b. and many organisms have only one chromosome.
   c. and most eukaryotes have between 10 and 50 pairs of chromosomes.
   d. and most eukaryotes have between 2 and 10 pairs of chromosomes.
4. Homologous chromosomes
   a. are also referred to as sister chromatids.
   b. are genetically identical.
   c. carry information about the same traits located in the same places on the chromosomes.
   d. are connected to each other at their centromeres.
5. Chromosomes are composed of
   a. DNA.
   b. proteins.
   c. chromatin.
   d. all of the above.
6. In mitosis, when the duplicated chromosomes line up in the center of the cell, that stage is called
   a. prophase.
   b. metaphase.
   c. anaphase.
   d. telophase.
7. The division of the cytoplasm in the eukaryotic cell cycle is called
   a. interphase.
   b. mitosis.
   c. cytokinesis.
   d. binary fission.
8. Which of the following pairings is correct?
   a. interphase/DNA replication
   b. animal cells/cell plate
   c. plant cells/cleavage furrow
   d. cytokinesis/cell death
9. The cell cycle is controlled by
   a. growth factors.
   b. proto-oncogenes.
   c. tumor-suppressor genes.
   d. all of the above.
10. When cell division becomes unregulated, and a cluster of cells begins to grow without regard for the normal controls, that is called
    a. a mutation.
    b. cancer.
    c. metastases.
    d. oncogenes.

Visual Understanding

1. **Figure 8.3** This karyotype shows a complete set of human chromosomes of an individual. At what stage of the cell cycle are such photos taken? Explain.

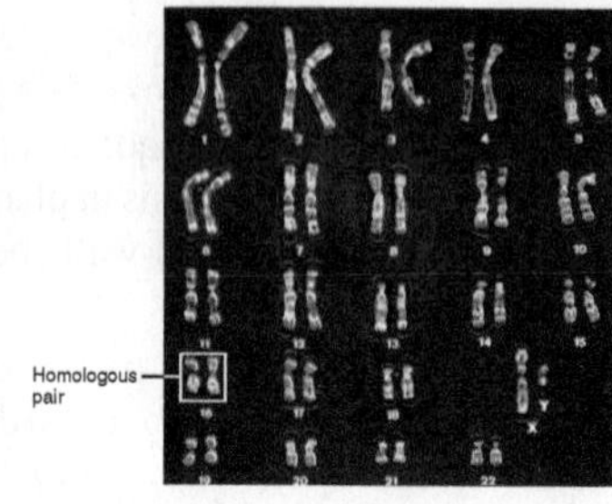

2. **Figure 8.4** During interphase the DNA is not visible through a microscope. Why isn't it visible, and why would you expect this to be the case?

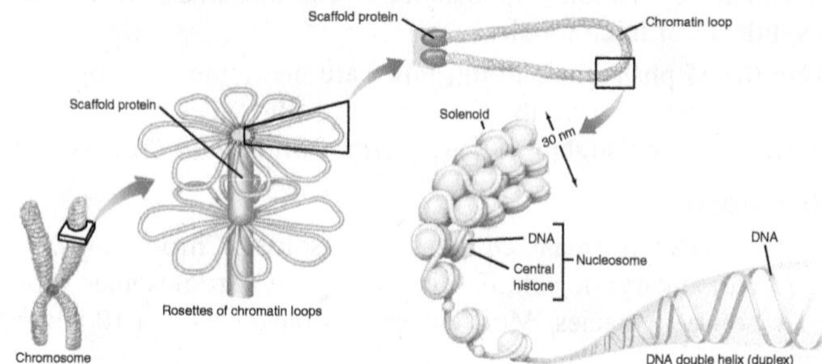

Challenge Questions

1. Why does the DNA in a cell need to change periodically from a long, double-helix chromatin molecule into a tightly wound-up chromosome? What does it do in one configuration that it cannot do in the other?
2. Despite all we know about cancer today, some types of cancers are still increasing in frequency. Lung cancer in women is one of those. What reason(s) might there be for this increasing problem? Can you suggest a solution?

2500×

Chapter 9

Meiosis

CHAPTER AT A GLANCE

Meiosis

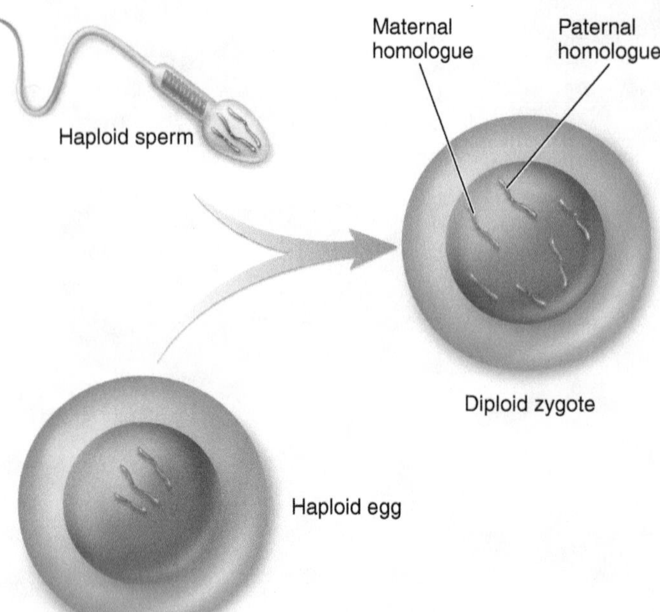

Figure 9.1 Diploid cells carry chromosomes from two parents.

A diploid cell contains two versions of each chromosome, a maternal homologue contributed by the haploid egg of the mother, and a paternal homologue contributed by the haploid sperm of the father.

IMPLICATION Many male veterans of the Vietnam War claim that their children born years later have birth defects caused by the herbicide Agent Orange used as a defoliant in the war. What types of cells would the chemical have to have affected in these men to cause the birth defects? How might these cells have become exposed to the chemical?

Figure 9.2 Sexual and asexual reproduction.

Reproduction in an organism is not always either sexual or asexual. The strawberry reproduces both asexually (runners) and sexually (flowers).

9.1 Discovery of Meiosis

CONCEPT PREVIEW: Meiosis is a process of cell division in which the number of chromosomes in certain cells is halved during gamete formation.

Only a few years after Walther Fleming's discovery of chromosomes in 1882, Belgian cytologist Pierre-Joseph van Beneden was surprised to find different numbers of chromosomes in different types of cells in the roundworm *Ascaris.* Specifically, he observed that the **gametes** (eggs and sperm) each contained two chromosomes, whereas the somatic (nonreproductive) cells of embryos and mature individuals each contained four. From his observations, van Beneden proposed in 1887 that an egg and a sperm, each containing half the complement of chromosomes found in other cells, fuse to produce a single cell called a **zygote.** The zygote, like all of the somatic cells ultimately derived from it, contains two copies of each chromosome. The fusion of gametes to form a new cell is called **fertilization,** or **syngamy.**

Meiosis

It was clear even to early investigators that gamete formation must involve some mechanism that reduces the number of chromosomes to half the number found in other cells. If it did not, the chromosome number would double with each fertilization, and after only a few generations, the number of chromosomes in each cell would become impossibly large. For example, after one generation the 46 chromosomes present in human cells would increase to 92 (46×2^1) chromosomes, after two generations it would increase to 184, and by 10 generations, the 46 chromosomes present in human cells would increase to over 47,000 (46×2^{10}) chromosomes.

The number of chromosomes does not explode in this way because of a special reduction division that occurs during gamete formation, producing cells with half the normal number of chromosomes. The subsequent fusion of two of these cells ensures a consistent chromosome number from one generation to the next. This reduction division process is known as **meiosis.**

The Sexual Life Cycle

Meiosis and fertilization together constitute a cycle of reproduction. Two sets of chromosomes are present in the somatic cells of adult individuals, making them **diploid** cells (Greek, *di,* two and often indicated by $2n$, where "n" is the number of sets of chromosomes), but only one set is present in the gametes, which are thus **haploid** (Greek, *haploos,* one and often indicated by $1n$). Figure 9.1 shows how two haploid cells, a sperm cell containing three chromosomes from the father and an egg cell containing three chromosomes from the mother, fuse to form a diploid zygote with six chromosomes. Reproduction that involves this alternation of meiosis and fertilization is called **sexual reproduction.** Some organisms however, reproduce by mitotic division and don't involve the fusion of gametes. Reproduction in these organisms is referred to as **asexual reproduction.** Some organisms are able to reproduce both asexually and sexually (figure 9.2).

9.2 The Sexual Life Cycle

CONCEPT PREVIEW: In the sexual life cycle, there is an alternation of diploid and haploid phases.

Alternation of Generations

The life cycles of all sexually reproducing organisms follow the same basic pattern of alternation between diploid chromosome numbers and haploid ones (figure 9.3). In unicellular eukaryotic organisms like the protist shown in figure 9.4*a*, individuals are haploid for most of their lives. When they encounter environmental stress, haploid cells sometimes fuse with other haploid cells to form a diploid cell. Later, this cell undergoes meiosis to reform the haploid phase.

In most animals like the frog you see in figure 9.4*b*, fertilization results in the formation of a diploid zygote. This single diploid cell divides by mitosis, eventually gives rise to the adult frog shown in the photo. All animals are diploid for the muticellular stage of their life cycle.

In plants like the fern you see in figure 9.4*c*, haploid and diploid individuals alternate. Certain cells of a diploid individual undergo meiosis making haploid gametes that divide repeatedly by mitosis to form a multicellular haploid individual. Some cells of this haploid individual eventually differentiate into eggs or sperm, which fuse to form a diploid zygote. Dividing by mitosis, the zygote forms a diploid individual.

Germ-Line Tissues

In animals, the cells that will eventually undergo meiosis to produce gametes are set aside from other cells early in the course of development. The cells of the body are called **somatic** cells, from the Latin word for "body," while gamete-forming cells, located in the reproductive organs of males and females, are referred to as **germ-line** cells. Both the somatic cells and the gamete-producing germ-line cells are diploid. Somatic cells undergo mitosis to form genetically identical, diploid daughter cells. The germ-line cells undergo meiosis, producing haploid gametes.

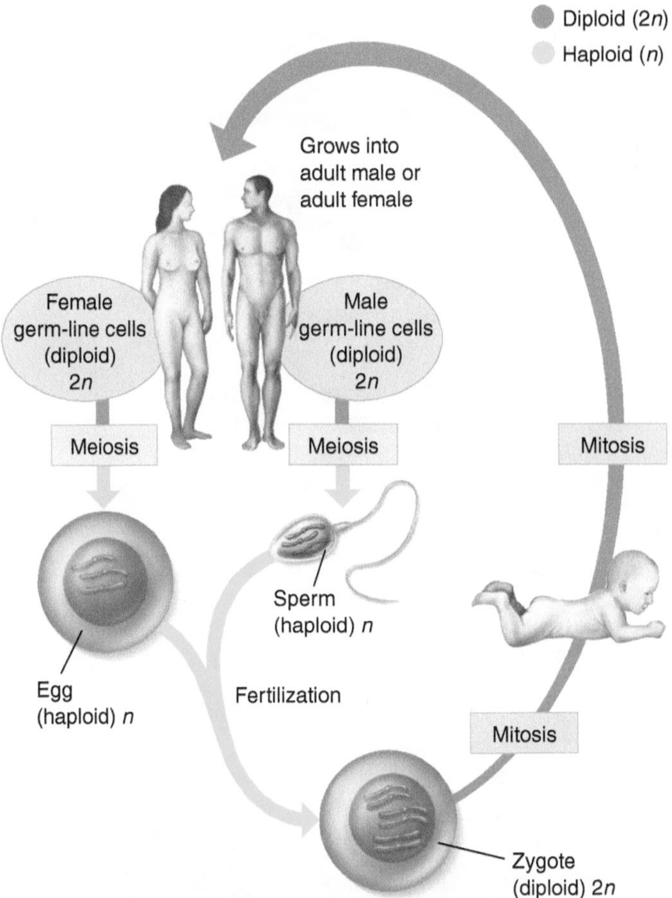

Figure 9.3 The sexual life cycle in animals.

In animals, the completion of meiosis is followed soon by fertilization. Thus, the vast majority of the life cycle is spent in the diploid stage. In this text, *n* stands for haploid and 2*n* stands for diploid. Germ-line cells are set aside early in development and undergo meiosis to form haploid gametes (eggs or sperm). The rest of the body cells are called somatic cells.

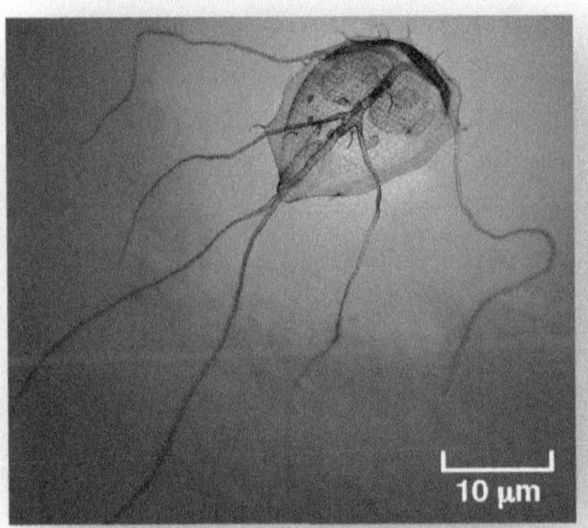

(a) Protist: spends most of its life cycle as a haploid individual

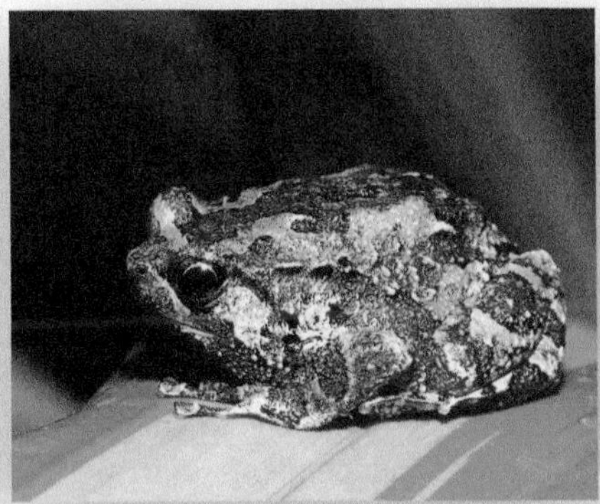

(b) Animal: spends most of its life cycle as a diploid individual

(c) Plant: spends significant portions of its life cycle as haploid and diploid individuals

Figure 9.4 Three types of sexual life cycles.

In sexual reproduction, haploid cells or organisms alternate with diploid cells or organisms.

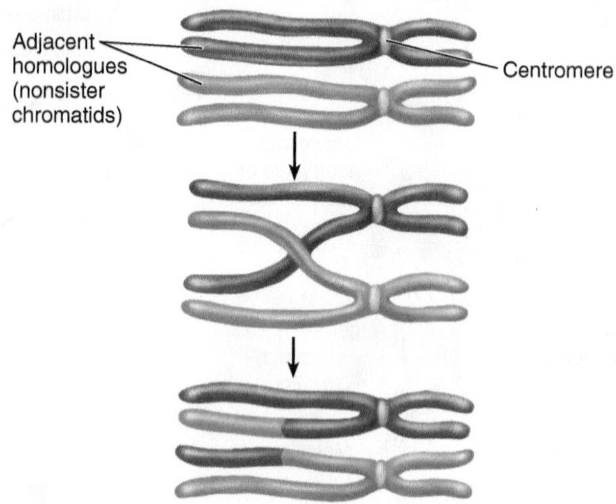

Figure 9.5 Crossing over.

In crossing over, the two homologues of a chromosome exchange portions. During the crossing over process, nonsister chromatids that are next to each other exchange chromosome arms or segments.

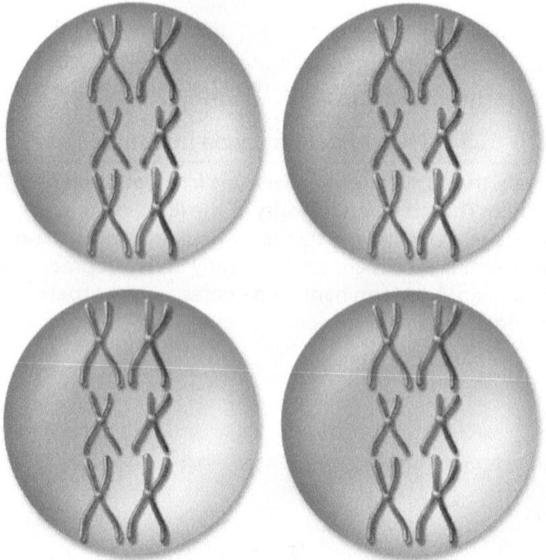

Figure 9.6 Independent assortment.

Independent assortment occurs because the orientation of chromosomes on the metaphase plate is random. Shown here are four possible orientations of chromosomes in a hypothetical cell. Each of the many possible orientations results in gametes with different combinations of parental chromosomes.

IMPLICATION The number of different combinations of gametes can be calculated using 2^n, where "n" is the number of pairs of chromosomes. A dog has 39 pairs of chromosomes. Considering only the independent assortment of homologous chromosomes to the gametes, how many genetically different gametes are possible?

9.3 The Stages of Meiosis

CONCEPT PREVIEW: During meiosis I, homologous chromosomes move to opposite poles of the cell. At the end of meiosis II, each of the four haploid cells contains one copy of every chromosome in the set, rather than two. Because of crossing over, no two cells are the same.

Now, let's look more closely at the process of meiosis. Just as in mitosis, the chromosomes have replicated before meiosis begins, during a period called interphase. The first of the two divisions of meiosis, called **meiosis I,** serves to separate the homologous chromosomes (or homologues); the second division, **meiosis II,** serves to separate the *sister chromatids.* Thus when meiosis is complete, what started out as one diploid cell ends up as four haploid cells. Because there was one replication of DNA but *two* cell divisions, the process reduces the number of chromosomes by half.

Meiosis I

Meiosis I is traditionally divided into four stages (see the left side of *Essential Biological Process 9A* on page 148):

1. **Prophase I.** The two versions of each chromosome (the two homologues) pair up and exchange segments.
2. **Metaphase I.** The chromosomes align on a central plane.
3. **Anaphase I.** One homologue with its two sister chromatids still attached moves to a pole of the cell, and the other homologue moves to the opposite pole.
4. **Telophase I.** Individual chromosomes gather together at the two poles.

In **prophase I,** individual chromosomes first become visible, when viewed with a light microscope, as their DNA coils more and more tightly. Because the DNA replicates before the onset of meiosis, each of the threadlike chromosomes actually consists of two sister chromatids associated along their lengths and joined at their centromeres, just as in mitosis. However, now meiosis begins to differ from mitosis. During prophase I, the two homologous chromosomes line up side by side, physically touching one another, as you see in figure 9.5 and in the photo opening this chapter. It is at this point that a process called **crossing over** is initiated, in which the chromosomes actually break in the same place on both nonsister chromatids and sections of chromosomes are swapped between the homologous chromosomes, producing a hybrid chromosome that is part maternal chromosome (the green sections) and part paternal chromosome (the purple sections).

Crossing over between homologous chromosomes can occur because, as discussed in chapter 8 on page 132, homologues carry information about the same traits at the same locations on the chromosomes, although details of the information may vary between the homologues.

In **metaphase I,** the spindle apparatus forms, but because homologues are held close together by crossovers, spindle fibers can attach to only the outward-facing portion of each centromere. For each pair of homologues, the orientation on the metaphase plate is random. Each orientation of homologues results in gametes with different combinations of parental chromosomes. This process is called **independent assortment** (figure 9.6).

In **anaphase I,** the spindle attachment is complete, and homologues are pulled apart and move toward opposite poles. At the end of anaphase I, each pole has half as many chromosomes as were present in the cell when meiosis began. Remember that the chromosomes replicated and thus contained two sister chromatids before the start of meiosis, but sister chromatids are not counted as separate chromosomes. As in mitosis, count the number of centromeres to determine the number of chromosomes.

Evolutionary Consequences of Sex

Meiosis is a lot more complicated than mitosis. Why has evolution gone to so much trouble? While our knowledge of how meiosis and sex evolved is sketchy, it is abundantly clear that meiosis and sexual reproduction have an enormous impact on how species continue to evolve today, because of their ability to rapidly generate new genetic combinations. Three mechanisms each make key contributions: independent assortment, crossing over, and random fertilization.

Independent Assortment

The reassortment of genetic material that takes place during meiosis is the principal factor that has made possible the evolution of eukaryotic organisms, in all their bewildering diversity, over the past 1.5 billion years. Sexual reproduction represents an enormous advance in the ability of organisms to generate genetic variability. To understand, recall that most organisms have more than one pair of chromosomes. For example, the organism represented in the figure below has three pairs of chromosomes, each offspring receiving three homologues from each parent, purple from the father and green from the mother. The offspring in turn produces gametes, but the distribution of homologues into the gametes is completely random. A gamete could receive all homologues that are paternal in origin, as on the far left; or it could receive all maternal homologues, as on the far right, or any combination. Independent assortment alone leads to eight possible gamete combinations in this example. In humans, each gamete receives one homologue of each of the 23 chromosomes, but which homologue of a particular chromosome it receives is determined randomly. Each of the 23 pairs of chromosomes migrates independently, so there are 2^{23} (more than 8 million) different possible kinds of gametes that can be produced.

To make this point to his class, one professor offers an "A" course grade to any student who can write down all the possible combinations of heads and tails (an "either/or" choice, like that of a chromosome migrating to one pole or the other) with flipping a coin 23 times (like 23 chromosomes moving independently). No student has ever won an "A;" there are over 8 million possibilities.

Crossing Over

The DNA exchange that occurs when the arms of nonsister chromatids cross over adds even more recombination to the independent assortment of chromosomes that occurs later in meiosis. Thus, the number of possible genetic combinations that can occur among gametes is virtually unlimited.

Random Fertilization

Also, the zygote that forms a new individual is created by the fusion of two gametes, each produced independently, so fertilization squares the number of possible outcomes ($2^{23} \times 2^{23}$ = 70 trillion).

Importance of Generating Diversity

Paradoxically, the evolutionary process is both revolutionary and conservative. It is revolutionary in that the pace of evolutionary change is quickened by genetic recombination, much of which results from sexual reproduction. It is conservative in that change is not always favored by selection, which may instead preserve existing combinations of genes. These conservative pressures appear to be greatest in some asexually reproducing organisms that do not move around freely and that live in especially demanding habitats. In vertebrates, on the other hand, the evolutionary premium appears to have been on versatility, and sexual reproduction is the predominant mode of reproduction.

Whatever the forces that led to sexual reproduction, its evolutionary consequences have been profound. No genetic process generates diversity more quickly; and as you will see in chapter 10, genetic diversity is the raw material of evolution, the fuel that drives it and determines its potential directions.

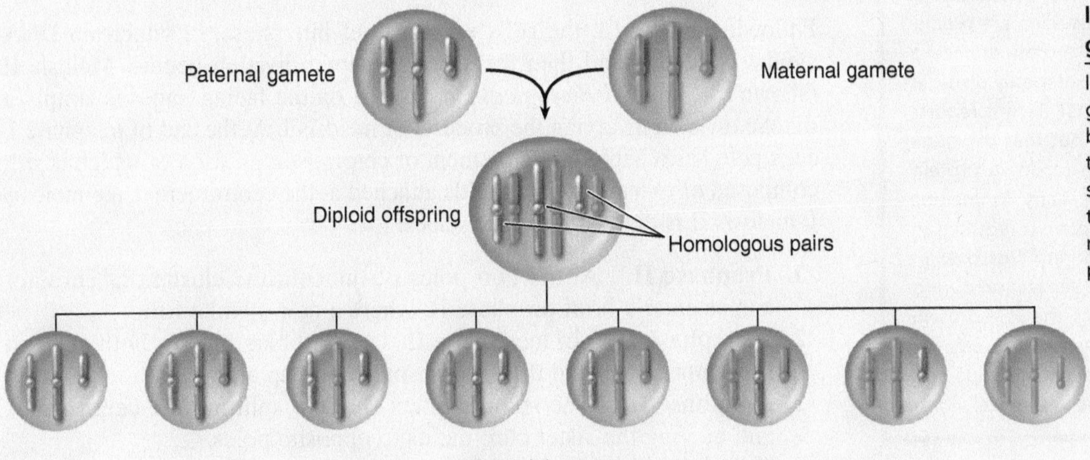

Independent assortment increases genetic variability.

Independent assortment contributes new gene combinations to the next generation because the orientation of chromosomes on the metaphase plate is random. In the cell shown here with three chromosome pairs, there are eight different gametes that can result, each with different combinations of parental chromosomes.

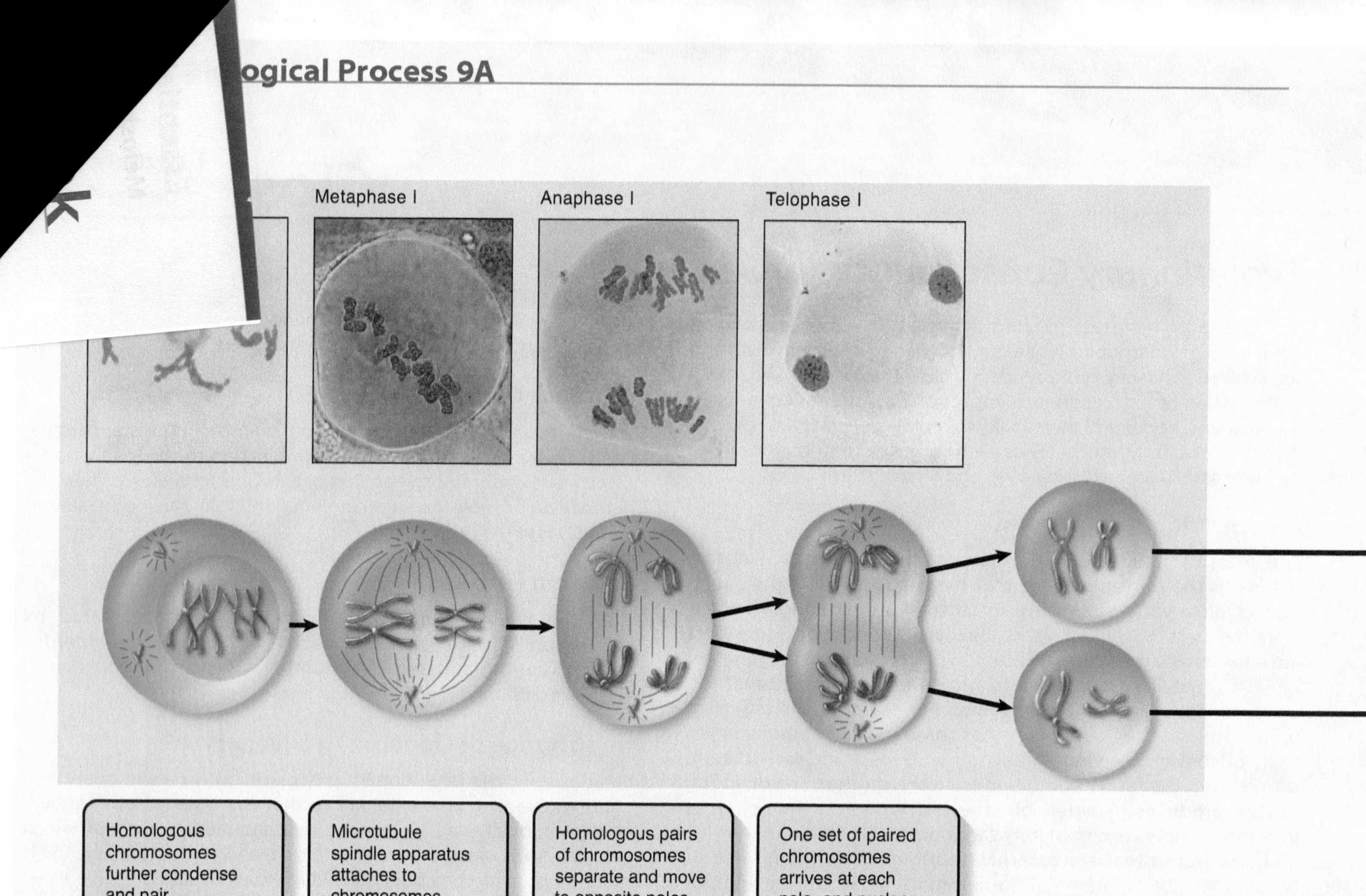

Metaphase I
Anaphase I
Telophase I
Homologous chromosomes further condense and pair. Crossing over occurs. Spindle fibers form.
Microtubule spindle apparatus attaches to chromosomes. Homologous pairs align along spindle equator.
Homologous pairs of chromosomes separate and move to opposite poles.
One set of paired chromosomes arrives at each pole, and nuclear division begins.

IN THE NEWS

Bloom's Syndrome. A rare inherited disorder called Bloom's syndrome has long puzzled investigators. Affected people have severe growth deficiencies, are predisposed to a wide variety of cancers, and are often sterile—a very unhappy state of affairs. What sort of gene disorder could lead to such a broad array of defects? Recent reports implicate events early in meiosis. It turns out that the gene defective in Bloom's syndrome patients encodes a protein dubbed BLM that binds to homologues early in meiotic prophase I. A properly functioning BLM protein is required to release homologues that are interlocked during crossover, in preparation for homologous chromosome separation during anaphase I. In Bloom's syndrome individuals, the BLM protein is defective and cannot remove cross-links that are created during crossover, resulting in a high incidence of gaps and breaks in homologous chromosomes as they separate.

In **telophase I,** the chromosomes gather at their respective poles to form two chromosome clusters. After an interval, meiosis II occurs, in which the sister chromatids are separated as in mitosis.

Meiosis II

Following meiosis I, the cells enter a brief interphase, in which no DNA synthesis occurs, and then the second meiotic division begins. Meiosis II (shown in *Essential Biological Process 9A* on the facing page) is simply a mitotic division involving the products of meiosis I. At the end of telophase I, each pole has a haploid complement of chromosomes, each of which is still composed of two sister chromatids attached at the centromere. Like meiosis I, meiosis II is divided into four stages:

1. **Prophase II.** At the two poles of the cell, the clusters of chromosomes enter a brief prophase II, where a new spindle forms.
2. **Metaphase II.** In metaphase II, spindle fibers bind to both sides of the centromeres and the chromosomes line up along a central plane.
3. **Anaphase II.** The spindle fibers shorten, splitting the centromeres and moving the sister chromatids to opposite poles.
4. **Telophase II.** Finally, the nuclear envelope re-forms around the four sets of daughter chromosomes.

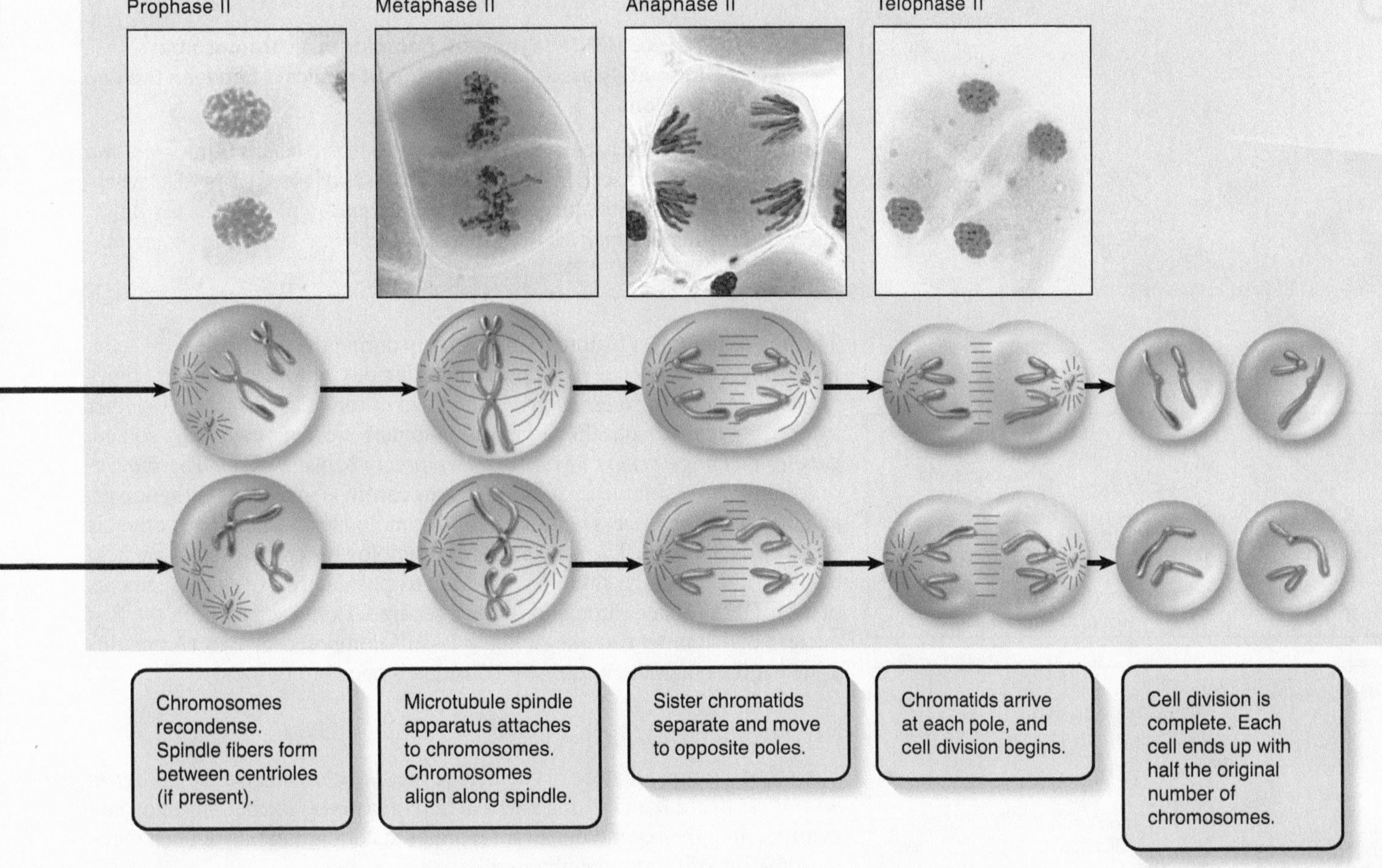
Meiosis II
Prophase II
Metaphase II
Anaphase II
Telophase II
Chromosomes recondense. Spindle fibers form between centrioles (if present).
Microtubule spindle apparatus attaches to chromosomes. Chromosomes align along spindle.
Sister chromatids separate and move to opposite poles.
Chromatids arrive at each pole, and cell division begins.
Cell division is complete. Each cell ends up with half the original number of chromosomes.

The main outcome of the four stages of meiosis II is to separate the sister chromatids. The final result of this division is four cells containing haploid sets of chromosomes. No two are alike because of the crossing over in prophase I.

If you think about it, the key to meiosis is that the sister chromatids of each chromosome do not separate from each other in the first division, prevented by the crossing over that occurred in prophase I. Imagine two people dancing closely—you can tie a rope to the back of each person's belt, but you cannot tie a second rope to their belt buckles in front because the two dancers are facing each other and are very close. In just the same way, microtubules cannot attach to the inner sides of the centromeres to pull the two sister chromatids apart because crossing over holds the homologous chromosomes together like dancing partners.

If you compare metaphase of mitosis in panel 3 of *Essential Biological Process 8B* on page 134 with metaphase of meiosis I, you will see how they differ. In meiosis I shown above, the homologous pairs align side by side so the spindle can't attach to the inside of the centromeres.

Concept Check

1. Are human gamete-producing germ line cells haploid? Explain.
2. How is the plant sexual life cycle different from the animal sexual life cycle?
3. Do sister chromatids separate in meiosis I or II?

g Meiosis and Mitosis

9.4 How Meiosis Differs from Mitosis

CONCEPT PREVIEW: In meiosis, homologous chromosomes become intimately associated and do not replicate between the two nuclear divisions.

While there are differences between eukaryotes in the details of meiosis, two consistent features are seen in the meiotic processes of every eukaryote: synapsis and reduction division. Indeed, these two unique features are the key differences that distinguish meiosis from mitosis, which you studied in chapter 8.

Synapsis

The first of these two features happens early during the first nuclear division. Following chromosome replication, homologous chromosomes or homologues *pair all along their lengths,* with sister chromatids being held together by proteins called cohesin. While homologues are thus physically joined, *genetic exchange occurs at one or more points between them.* The process of forming these complexes of homologous chromosomes is called **synapsis,** and the exchange process between paired homologues, as described earlier, is crossing over. Figure 9.7*a* shows how the homologous chromosomes are held together close enough that they are able to physically exchange segments of their DNA. Sister chromatids do not separate from each other in the first nuclear division, so each homologue is still composed of two chromatids joined at the centromere, and still considered one chromosome.

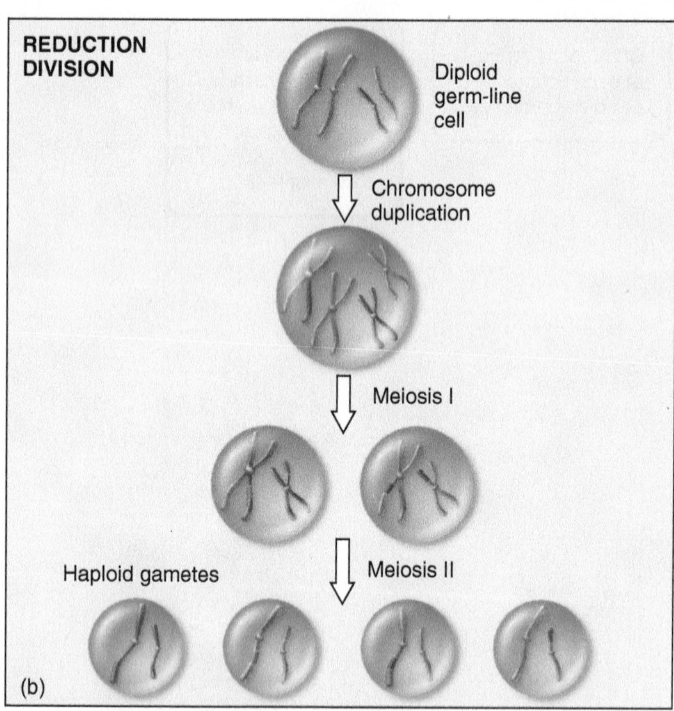

Figure 9.7 Unique features of meiosis.

(a) Synapsis draws homologous chromosomes together, all along their lengths, creating a situation (indicated by the circle) where two homologues can physically exchange portions of arms, a process called crossing over. (b) Reduction division, omitting a chromosome duplication before meiosis II, produces haploid gametes, thus ensuring that the chromosome number remains the same as that of the parents, following fertilization.

Reduction Division

The second unique feature of meiosis is that *the chromosome homologues do not replicate between the two nuclear divisions,* so that chromosome assortment in the second division separates sister chromatids of each chromosome into different daughter cells.

In most respects, the second meiotic division is identical to a normal mitotic division. However, because of the crossing over that occurred during the first division, the sister chromatids in meiosis II are not identical to each other. Also, there are only half the number of chromosomes in each cell at the beginning of meiosis II because only one of the homologues is present. Figure 9.7*b* shows how reduction division occurs. The diploid cell contains four chromosome (two homologous pairs). After meiosis I, the cells contain just two chromosomes (remember to count the number of *centromeres,* because sister chromatids are not considered separate chromosomes). During meiosis II, the sister chromatid separate, but each gamete still only contains two chromosomes, half as many of the germ-line cell.

Because mitosis and meiosis use similar terminology, it is easy to confuse the two processes. Figure 9.8 compares the two processes side-by-side. Both processes start with a diploid cell, but you can see that early during meiosis I crossing over occurs, and that as a consequence homologous *pairs,* not individual centromeres, line up along the meiosis I metaphase plate. These two differences result in haploid cells in meiosis and diploid cells in mitosis.

Concept Check

1. How many chromatids does each homologue contain after meiosis I?
2. How do two sister chromatids entering meiosis II differ?
3. Compare the arrangement of chromosomes at the metaphase plate of meiosis I with that of mitosis.

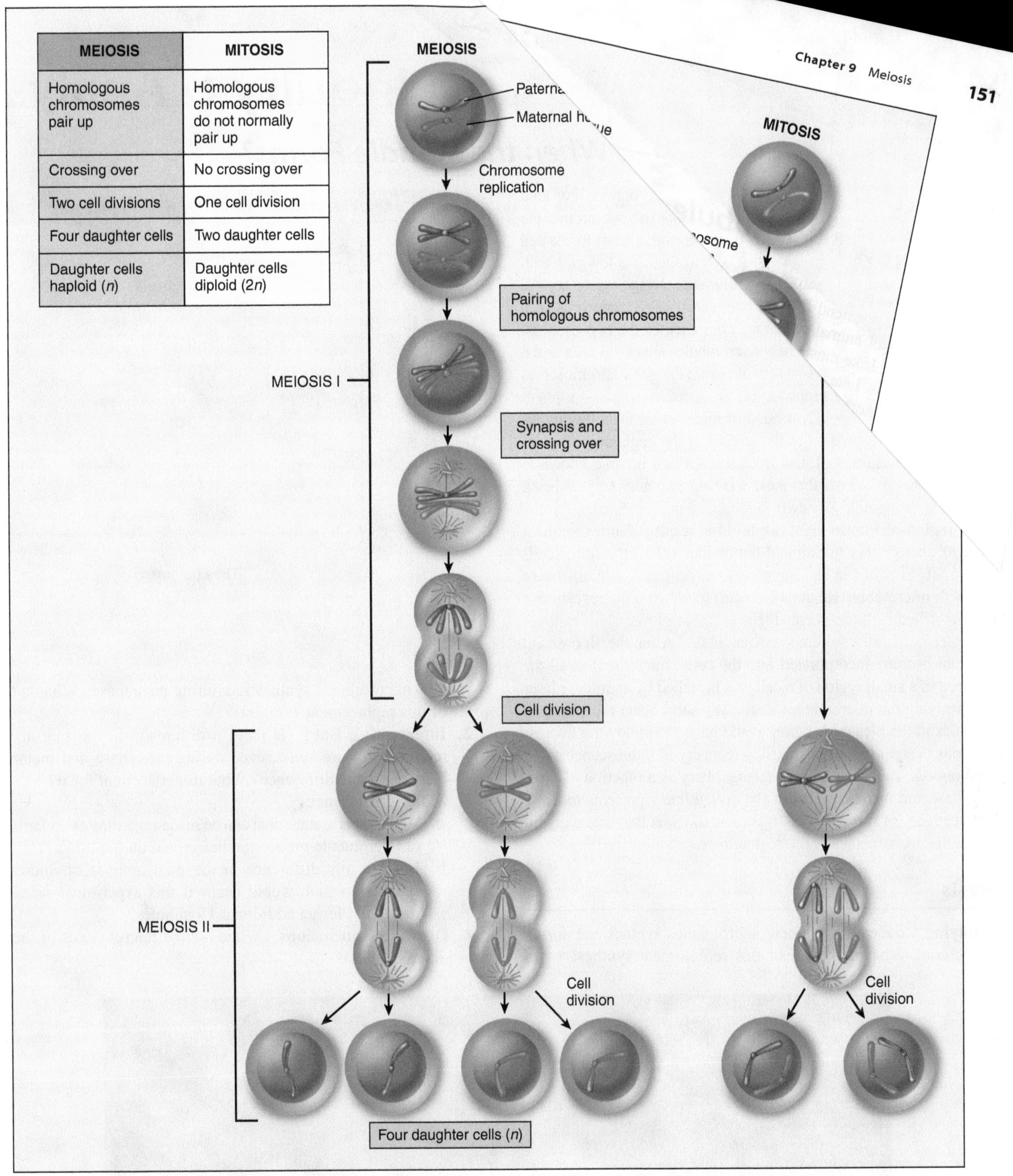

MEIOSIS	MITOSIS
Homologous chromosomes pair up	Homologous chromosomes do not normally pair up
Crossing over	No crossing over
Two cell divisions	One cell division
Four daughter cells	Two daughter cells
Daughter cells haploid (n)	Daughter cells diploid ($2n$)

Figure 9.8 A comparison of meiosis and mitosis.

Meiosis differs from mitosis in several key ways, highlighted by the orange boxes. Meiosis involves two nuclear divisions with no DNA replication between them. It thus produces four daughter cells, each with half the original number of chromosomes. Also, crossing over occurs in prophase I of meiosis. Mitosis involves a single nuclear division after DNA replication. Thus, it produces two daughter cells, each containing the original number of chromosomes, which are genetically identical to those in the parent cell.

Are New Microt... ...ude When the Spindle Forms?

... meiosis, only a few long ... *centrosome* (a zone around the ...otubules are organized) to the cell ..., they are refreshed at a low rate with ... During interphase, however, a dramatic change can be seen— microtubules ex... divide into two, and a large increase is seen ...tubules radiating from each of the two daughter centrioles. ... clusters of new microtubules are easily seen as the peri...hecting to the two sets of purple daughter chromosomes ...graph of early prophase below (a **micrograph** is a photo ...ough a microscope). This burst of microtubule assembly marks ...ginning of the formation of the spindle at the beginning of meta...ase. When these clusters of new microtubules first became known to cell biologists, they asked whether these were existing microtubules being repositioned in the spindle, or newly synthesized microtubules.

The graph to the upper right displays the results of an experiment designed to answer this question. Mammalian cells in culture (**cells in culture** are growing in the laboratory on artificial medium) were injected with microtubule subunits (tubulin) to which a fluorescent dye had been attached (a **fluorescent dye** is one that glows when exposed to ultraviolet or short-wavelength visual light). After the fluorescent subunits had become incorporated into the cells' microtubules, all the fluorescence in a small region of a cell was bleached by an intense laser beam, destroying the microtubules there. Any subsequent rebuilding of microtubules in the bleached region would have to employ the fluorescent subunits present in the cell, causing recovery of fluorescence in the bleached region. The graph reports this recovery as a function of time, for interphase and metaphase cells. The dotted line represents the time for 50% recovery of fluorescence ($t_{1/2}$) (that is, $t_{1/2}$ is the time required for half of the microtubules in the region to be resynthesized).

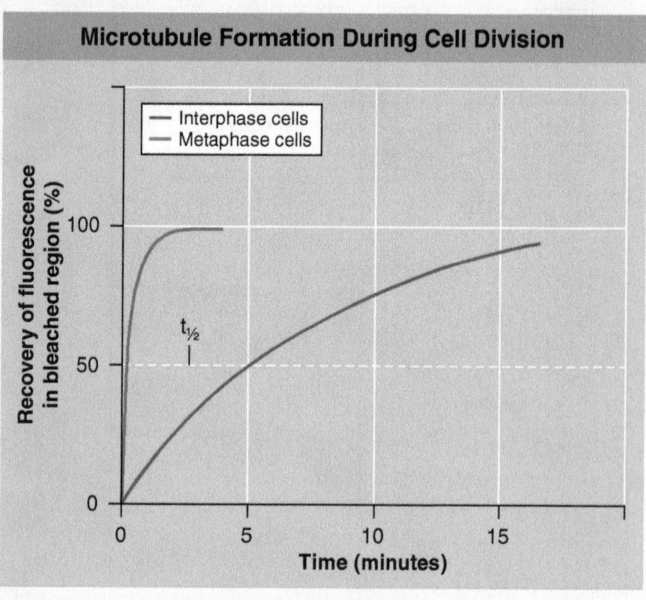

Analysis

1. **Applying Concepts** Are new microtubules synthesized during interphase? What is the $t_{1/2}$ of this replacement synthesis? Are new microtubules synthesized during metaphase? What is the $t_{1/2}$ of this replacement synthesis?
2. **Interpreting Data** Is there a difference in the rate at which microtubules are synthesized during interphase and metaphase? How big is the difference? What might account for it?
3. **Making Inferences**
   a. What general statement can be made regarding the relative rates of microtubule production before and during meiosis?
   b. Is there any difference in the final amount of microtubule synthesis which would occur if this experiment were to be continued for an additional 15 minutes?
4. **Drawing Conclusions** When are the microtubules of the spindle assembled?

Concept Summary

Meiosis

9.1 Discovery of Meiosis

- In sexually reproducing organisms, a gamete from the male fuses with a gamete from the female to form a cell called the zygote. This process is called fertilization or syngamy. The number of chromosomes in gametes must be halved to maintain the correct number of chromosomes in offspring (**figure 9.1**). Organisms accomplish this through a cell division process called meiosis.

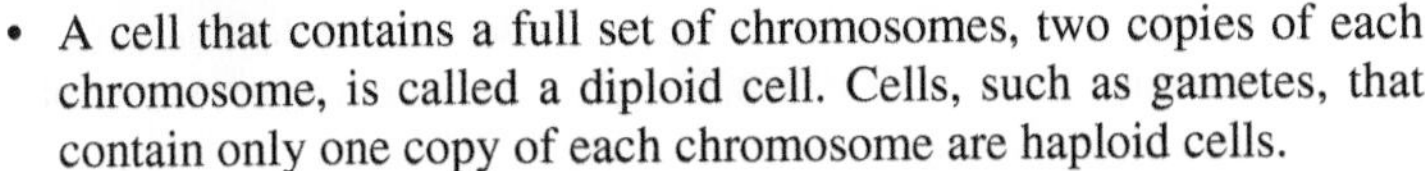

- A cell that contains a full set of chromosomes, two copies of each chromosome, is called a diploid cell. Cells, such as gametes, that contain only one copy of each chromosome are haploid cells.
- Sexual reproduction involves meiosis, but some organisms also undergo asexual reproduction, which is reproducing by mitosis or binary fission.

9.2 The Sexual Life Cycle

- Sexual life cycles alternate between diploid and haploid stages, with variation in the amount of time devoted to each stage. Three types of sexual life cycles exist: In many protists the majority of the life cycle is devoted to the haploid stage; in most animals the majority of the life cycle is devoted to the diploid stage (**figure 9.3**); and in plants the life cycle is split more equally between a haploid stage and a diploid stage.
- Germ-line cells of an organism are diploid but produce haploid gametes through meiosis.

9.3 The Stages of Meiosis

- Meiosis involves two nuclear divisions, meiosis I and meiosis II, each containing a prophase, metaphase, anaphase, and telophase. Like mitosis, the DNA replicates during interphase, before meiosis begins. Because there are two nuclear divisions but only one round of DNA replication, the four daughter cells contain half the number of chromosomes as the parent cell.
- Meiosis I is divided into four stages: prophase I, metaphase I, anaphase I, and telophase I. Prophase I is distinguished by the exchange of genetic material between homologous chromosomes, a process called crossing over. In this process, homologous chromosomes align with each other along their lengths, and sections of non-sister chromatids are physically exchanged, as shown here from **figure 9.5.** This recombines the genetic information contained in the chromosomes.

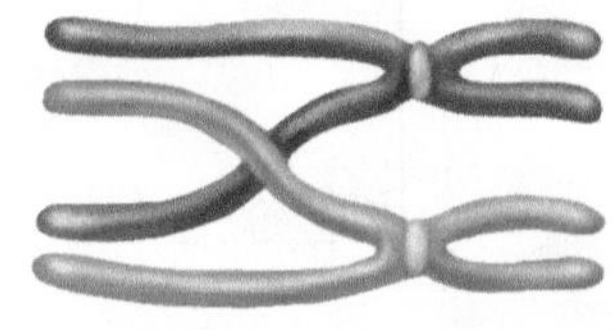

- During metaphase I, microtubules in the spindle apparatus attach to homologous chromosomes, and chromosome pairs align along the metaphase plate. The alignment of the chromosomes is random: there is shuffling in the arrangement of paternal and maternal chromosomes along the metaphase plate, leading to the independent assortment of chromosomes into the gametes (**figure 9.6**).
- The homologous chromosomes separate during anaphase I, being pulled apart by the spindle apparatus toward their respective poles. This differs from mitosis and later in meiosis II, where sister chromatids separate in anaphase.
- In telophase I, the chromosomes cluster at the poles. This leads to the next phase of meiosis, called meiosis II.
- Meiosis II mirrors mitosis in that it involves the separation of sister chromatids through the phases of prophase II, metaphase II, anaphase II, and telophase II. Meiosis II differs from mitosis in that there is no DNA replication before meiosis II. Because homologous pairs were separated during meiosis I, each daughter cell, shown forming here in telophase II from ***Essential Biological Process 9A,*** has only one-half the number of chromosomes. Also, the chromosomes in the daughter cells at the end of meiosis II are not genetically identical because of crossing over.

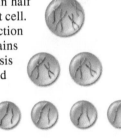

Comparing Meiosis and Mitosis

9.4 How Meiosis Differs from Mitosis

- Two processes that distinguish meiosis from mitosis are crossing over through synapsis and reduction division.
- When homologous chromosomes come together during prophase I, they associate with each other along their lengths, a process called synapsis (**figure 9.7*a***). Synapsis does not occur in mitosis. During synapsis, sections of homologous chromosomes are physically exchanged in crossing over. Crossing over results in daughter cells that are not genetically identical to the parent cell or to each other. In contrast, mitosis results in daughter cells that are genetically identical to the parent cell and to each other.
- Meiosis also differs from mitosis in reduction division, where the daughter cells contain half the number of chromosomes as the parent cell. As shown here from **figure 9.7*b*,** reduction division occurs because meiosis contains two nuclear divisions (the first in meiosis I where the parent cell divides in two and the second in meiosis II, where the cells produced in meiosis I divide producing four daughter cells) but only one round of DNA replication during interphase.
- The primary reasons for the differences in meiosis and mitosis stem from the synapsis of homologous chromosomes in prophase I. Because of synapsis, the arms of homologous chromosomes are close enough to undergo crossing over. Also, the close association of the homologous chromosomes in synapsis blocks the inner centromeres from attaching to the spindle. As a result, sister chromatids do not separate during meiosis I, resulting in reduction division (**figure 9.8**).

Self-Test

1. An egg and a sperm unite to form a new organism. To prevent the new organism from having twice as many chromosomes as its parents,
   a. half of the chromosomes in the new organism quickly disassemble, leaving the correct number.
   b. half of the chromosomes from the egg, and half from the sperm, are ejected from the new cell.
   c. the large egg contains all the chromosomes, the tiny sperm only contributes some DNA.
   d. the egg and sperm have only half the number of chromosomes found in the parents because of meiosis.
2. The diploid number of chromosomes in humans is 46. The haploid number is
   a. 138. **c.** 46.
   b. 92. **d.** 23.
3. In organisms that have sexual life cycles, there is a time when there are
   a. $1n$ gametes (haploid), followed by $2n$ zygotes (diploid).
   b. $2n$ gametes (haploid), followed by $1n$ zygotes (diploid).
   c. $2n$ gametes (diploid), followed by $1n$ zygotes (haploid).
   d. $1n$ gametes (diploid), followed by $2n$ zygotes (haploid).
4. Crossing over occurs during prophase I and is when
   a. homologous chromosomes exchange sections of chromosomes.
   b. homologous chromosomes cross over to opposite sides of the cell.
   c. sister chromatids exchange genetic information.
   d. the DNA replicates forming two sister chromatids that are attached at the centromere.
5. Which of the following occurs in meiosis I?
   a. All chromosomes duplicate.
   b. Homologous chromosomes randomly orient themselves on the metaphase plate, called independent assortment.
   c. The duplicated sister chromatids separate.
   d. The original cell divides into four diploid cells.
6. Which of the following occurs in meiosis II?
   a. All chromosomes duplicate.
   b. Homologous chromosomes randomly separate, called independent assortment.
   c. The duplicated sister chromatids separate.
   d. Genetically identical daughter cells are produced.
7. During which stage of meiosis does synapsis occur?
   a. prophase I **c.** metaphase II
   b. anaphase I **d.** interphase
8. Synapsis is the process whereby
   a. homologous pairs of chromosomes separate and migrate toward a pole.
   b. homologous chromosomes exchange chromosomal material.
   c. homologous chromosomes become closely associated.
   d. the daughter cells contain half of the number of chromosomes of the parent cell.
9. Mitosis results in ____, while meiosis results in _____.
   a. cells that are genetically identical to the parent cell/haploid cells
   b. haploid cells/diploid cells
   c. four daughter cells/two daughter cells
   d. cells with half the number of chromosomes as the parent cell/cells which vary in chromosome number
10. Sister chromatids don't separate during meiosis I because
    a. they are held together through synapsis.
    b. of crossing over.
    c. the spindle fibers can only attach to the outward-facing side of the centromeres.
    d. All of the above.

Visual Understanding

1. **Figure 9.5** How is it that, in meiosis, you can end up with four "daughter cells" that are all genetically different from one another?

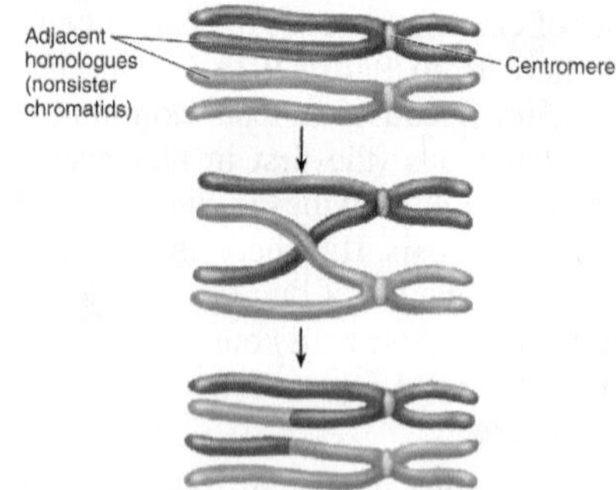

2. **Figure 9.7*a*** Referring to the homologous chromosomes shown here during prophase I, and knowing that they stay in synapsis during metaphase I, explain why it is that the sister chromatids don't separate as they do in mitosis.

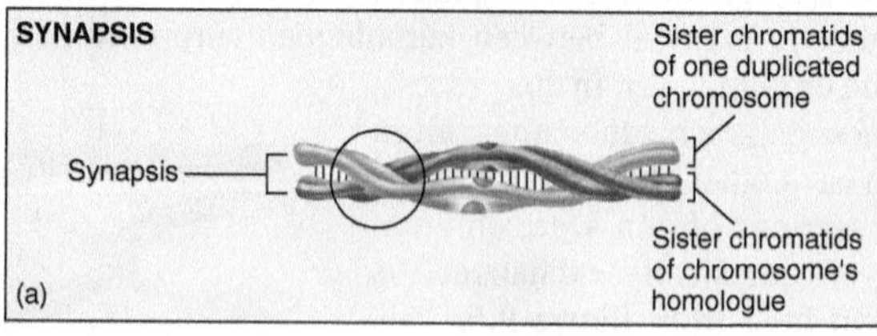

Challenge Questions

1. It would seem that you only need one set of instructions for your body to do all the jobs it needs to carry out. So why aren't organisms simply haploid all their lives?

2. Are the gamete cells of your body haploid or diploid? Why not the alternative?

3. An organism has 56 chromosomes in its diploid stage. Indicate how many chromosomes are present in the following, and explain your reasoning:
   a. somatic cells **c.** metaphase II
   b. metaphase I **d.** gametes

Chapter 10

Foundations of Genetics

CHAPTER AT A GLANCE

Mendel

10.1 Mendel and the Garden Pea

CONCEPT PREVIEW: Mendel studied heredity by crossing true-breeding garden peas that differed in easily scored alternative traits and then allowing the offspring to self-fertilize.

When you were born, many things about you resembled your mother or father (figure 10.1). This tendency for traits to be passed from parent to offspring is called **heredity.** *Traits* are the expressions of a character, or a heritable feature. How does heredity happen? Before DNA and chromosomes were discovered, this puzzle was one of the greatest mysteries of science. The key to understanding the puzzle of heredity was found in the garden of an Austrian monastery over a century ago by a monk named Gregor Mendel. Mendel used the scientific process described in chapter 1 as a powerful way of analyzing the problem. Crossing pea plants with one another, Mendel made observations that allowed him to form a simple but powerful hypothesis that accurately predicted patterns of heredity—that is, how many offspring would be like one parent and how many like the other. When Mendel's rules, introduced in chapter 1 as the theory of heredity, became widely known, investigators all over the world set out to discover the physical mechanism responsible for them. They learned that hereditary traits are instructions carefully laid out in the DNA a child receives from each parent. Mendel's solution to the puzzle of heredity was the first step on this journey of understanding and one of the greatest intellectual accomplishments in the history of science.

Figure 10.1 Families look alike.

These two young women are mother and daughter. It is no accident that they look so much alike, as the daughter shares half her mother's genes.

IMPLICATION Not all members of families look as much alike as this. In your family, do your brothers and sisters resemble you a lot? See if you can learn in this chapter why all the children in your family might not look alike.

Early Ideas About Heredity

Mendel was not the first person to try to understand heredity by crossing pea plants (figure 10.2). Over 200 years earlier British farmers had performed similar crosses and obtained results similar to Mendel's. They observed that in crosses between two types—tall and short plants, for example—one type would disappear in one generation, only to reappear in the next. In the 1790s, for example, the British farmer T. A. Knight crossed a variety of the garden pea that had purple flowers with one that had white flowers. All the offspring of the cross had purple flowers. If two of these offspring were crossed, however, some of *their* offspring were purple and some were white. Knight noted that the purple had a "stronger tendency" to appear than white, but he did not count the numbers of each kind of offspring.

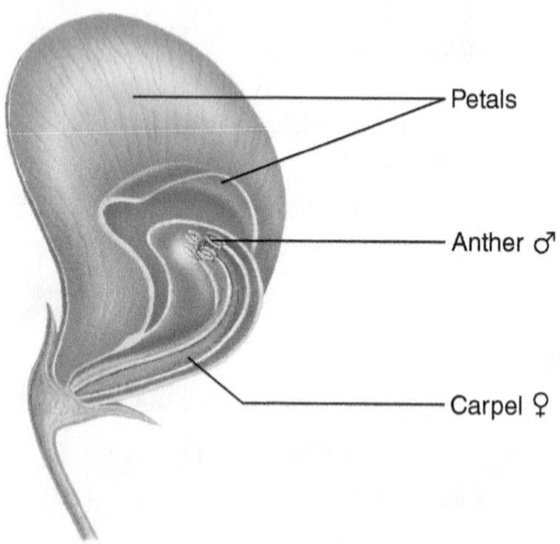

Figure 10.2 The garden pea flower.

Because it is easy to cultivate and because there are many distinctive varieties, the garden pea, *Pisum sativum,* was a popular choice as an experimental subject in investigations of heredity for as long as a century before Mendel's studies. The flower shown here is partially cut away to show internal structures.

Mendel's Experiments

Gregor Mendel was born in 1822 to peasant parents and was educated in a monastery. He became a monk and was sent to the University of Vienna to study science and mathematics. Although he aspired to become a scientist and teacher, he failed his university exams for a teaching certificate and returned to the monastery, where he spent the rest of his life, eventually becoming abbot. Upon his return, Mendel joined an informal neighborhood science club, a group of farmers and others interested in science. Under the patronage of a local nobleman, each member set out to undertake scientific investiga-

Gregor Mendel

tions, which were then discussed at meetings and published in the club's own journal. Mendel undertook to repeat the classic series of crosses with pea plants done by Knight and others, but this time he intended to count the numbers of each kind of offspring in the hope that the numbers would give some hint of what was going on. Quantitative approaches to science—measuring and counting—were just becoming fashionable in Europe.

Mendel's Experimental System: The Garden Pea

Mendel chose to study the garden pea because several of its characteristics made it easy to work with:

1. Many varieties were available. Mendel selected seven pairs of lines that differed in easily distinguished traits (including the white versus purple flowers that Knight had studied 60 years earlier).
2. Mendel knew from the work of Knight and others that he could expect the infrequent version of a character to disappear in one generation and reappear in the next. He knew, in other words, that he would have something to count.
3. Pea plants are small, easy to grow, produce large numbers of offspring, and mature quickly.
4. The reproductive organs of peas are enclosed within their flowers (see figure 10.2). Left alone, the flowers do not open. They simply fertilize themselves with their own pollen (male gametes). To carry out a cross, Mendel had only to pry the petals apart, reach in with a scissors, and snip off the male organs (anthers); he could then dust the female organs (the tip of the carpel) with pollen from another plant to make the cross.

Flowers are the reproductive structures in a group of plants called angiosperms. Angiosperm reproduction, through the pollination and fertilization of flowers, is discussed in more detail on pages 634 through 637.

Mendel's Experimental Design

Mendel's experimental design was the same as Knight's, only Mendel counted his plants. The crosses were carried out in three steps that are presented in figure 10.3:

1. Mendel began by letting each variety self-fertilize for several generations (step 1). This ensured that each variety was **true-breeding,** meaning that it contained no other varieties of the trait, and so would produce only offspring of the same variety when it self-pollinated. The white flower variety, for example, produced only white flowers and no purple ones in each generation. Mendel called these lines the **P generation** (P for parental).
2. Mendel then conducted his experiment: He crossed two pea varieties exhibiting alternative traits, such as white versus purple flowers in step 2. The offspring that resulted he called the **F_1 generation** (F_1 for "first filial" generation, from the Latin word for "son" or "daughter").
3. Finally, Mendel allowed the plants produced in the crosses of step 2 to self-fertilize, and he counted the numbers of each kind of offspring that resulted in this **F_2** ("second filial") **generation.** As reported by Knight and shown in step 3, the white flower trait reappeared in the F_2 generation, although not as frequently as the purple flower trait.

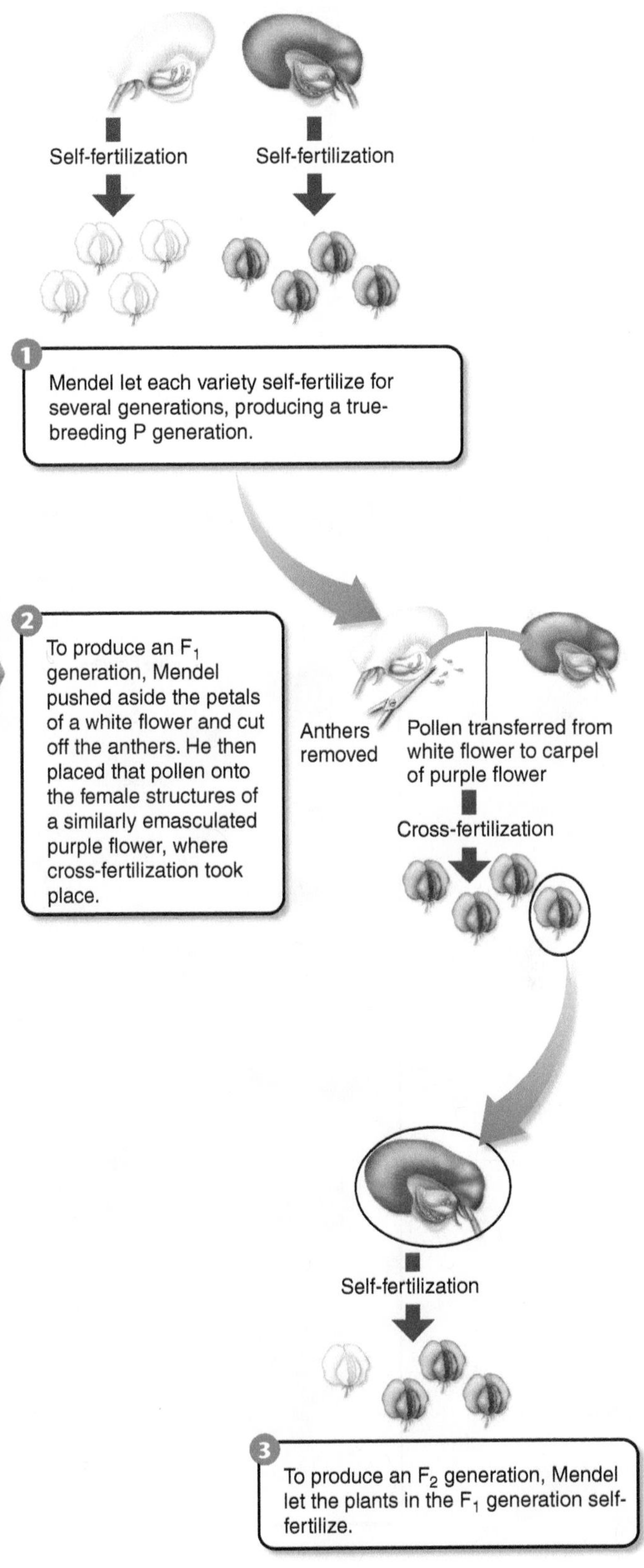

Self-fertilization
Self-fertilization
1
Mendel let each variety self-fertilize for several generations, producing a true-breeding P generation.
2
To produce an F1 generation, Mendel pushed aside the petals of a white flower and cut off the anthers. He then placed that pollen onto the female structures of a similarly emasculated purple flower, where cross-fertilization took place.
Anthers removed
Pollen transferred from white flower to carpel of purple flower
Cross-fertilization
Self-fertilization
3
To produce an F2 generation, Mendel let the plants in the F1 generation self-fertilize.

Figure 10.3 How Mendel conducted his experiments.

10.2 What Mendel Observed

CONCEPT PREVIEW: When Mendel crossed two contrasting traits and counted the offspring in the subsequent generations, he observed that all of the offspring in the first generation (F_1) exhibited one (dominant) trait, and none exhibited the other (recessive) trait. In the following generation (F_2), 25% were true-breeding for the dominant trait, 50% were not-true-breeding and appeared dominant, and 25% were true-breeding for the recessive trait.

Mendel experimented with a variety of traits in the garden pea and repeatedly made similar observations. In all, Mendel examined seven pairs of contrasting traits as shown in table 10.1. For each pair of contrasting traits that Mendel crossed he observed the same result, shown in figure 10.3, where a trait disappeared in the F_1 generation only to reappear in the F_2 generation. We will examine in detail Mendel's crosses with flower color.

TABLE 10.1 Seven Characters Mendel Studied in His Experiments

Dominant Form	Character ×	Recessive Form	F_2 Generation Dominant: Recessive	Ratio
Purple flowers	×	White flowers	705:224	3.15:1 (3/4:1/4)
Yellow seeds	×	Green seeds	6022:2001	3.01:1 (3/4:1/4)
Round seeds	×	Wrinkled seeds	5474:1850	2.96:1 (3/4:1/4)
Green pods	×	Yellow pods	428:152	2.82:1 (3/4:1/4)
Inflated pods	×	Constricted pods	882:299	2.95:1 (3/4:1/4)
Axial flowers	×	Terminal flowers	651:207	3.14:1 (3/4:1/4)
Tall plants	×	Dwarf plants	787:277	2.84:1 (3/4:1/4)

The F_1 Generation

In the case of flower color, when Mendel crossed purple and white flowers, all the F_1 generation plants he observed were purple; he did not see the contrasting trait, white flowers. Mendel called the trait expressed in the F_1 plants **dominant** and the trait not expressed **recessive.** In this case, purple flower color was dominant and white flower color recessive. Mendel studied several other characters in addition to flower color, and for every pair of contrasting traits Mendel examined, one proved to be dominant and the other recessive. The dominant and recessive traits for each character he studied are indicated in table 10.1.

Figure 10.4 Round versus wrinkled seeds.

One of the differences among varieties of pea plants that Mendel studied was the shape of the seed. In some varieties the seeds were round, whereas in others they were wrinkled.

The F_2 Generation

After allowing individual F_1 plants to mature and self-fertilize, Mendel collected and planted the seeds from each plant to see what the offspring in the F_2 generation would look like. Mendel found (as Knight had earlier) that some F_2 plants exhibited white flowers, the recessive trait. The recessive trait had disappeared in the F_1 generation, only to reappear in the F_2 generation. It must somehow have been present in the F_1 individuals but unexpressed!

At this stage Mendel instituted his radical change in experimental design. He *counted* the number of each type among the F_2 offspring. He believed the proportions of the F_2 types would provide some clue about the mechanism of heredity. In the cross between the purple-flowered F_1 plants, he counted a total of 929 F_2 individuals (see table 10.1). Of these, 705 (75.9%) had purple flowers and 224 (24.1%) had white flowers. Approximately one-fourth of the F_2 individuals exhibited the recessive form of the trait. Mendel carried out similar experiments with other traits, such as round versus wrinkled seeds (figure 10.4) and obtained the same result: Three-fourths of the F_2 individuals exhibited the dominant form of the character, and one-fourth displayed the recessive form. In other words, the dominant:recessive ratio among the F_2 plants was always approximately 3:1.

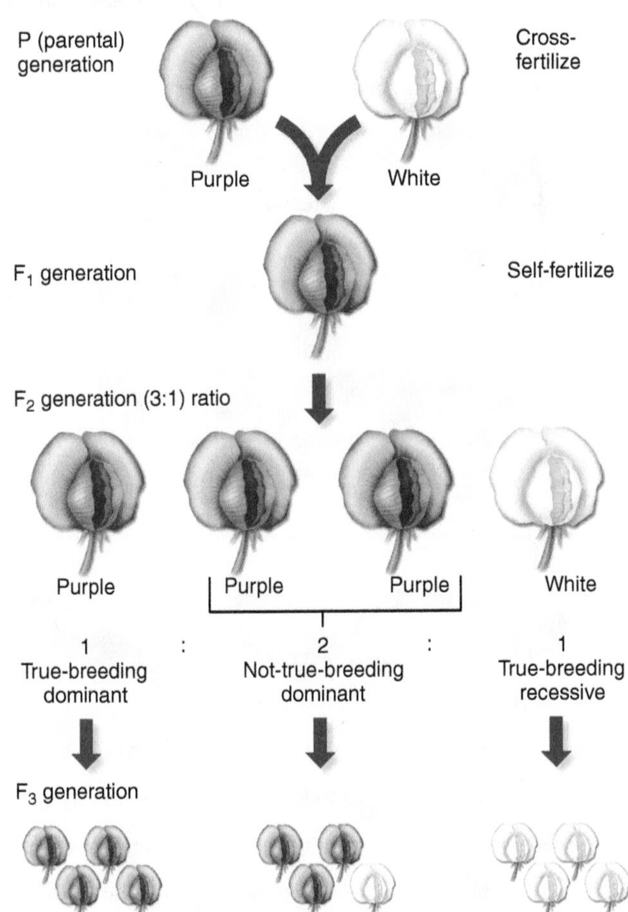

Figure 10.5 The F_2 generation is a disguised 1:2:1 ratio.

By allowing the F_2 generation to self-fertilize, Mendel found from the offspring (F_3) that the ratio of F_2 plants was one true-breeding dominant, two not-true-breeding dominant, and one true-breeding recessive.

A Disguised 1:2:1 Ratio

Mendel let the F_2 plants self-fertilize for another generation and found that the one-fourth that were recessive were true-breeding—future generations showed nothing but the recessive trait. Thus, the white F_2 individuals described previously showed only white flowers in the F_3 generation (as shown on the right in figure 10.5). Among the three-fourths of the plants that had shown the dominant trait in the F_2 generation, only one-third of the individuals were true-breeding in the F_3 generation (as shown on the left). The others showed both traits in the F_3 generation (as shown in the center)—and when Mendel counted their numbers, he found the ratio of dominant to recessive to again be 3:1! From these results Mendel concluded that the 3:1 ratio he had observed in the F_2 generation was in fact a disguised 1:2:1 ratio:

1		2		1
true-breeding dominant	:	not-true-breeding dominant	:	true-breeding recessive

BIOLOGY & YOU

Look-alike Meter. Have you ever wondered who you resemble more, your mother or your father? Using state-of-the-art face recognition technology, internet services now allow you to answer this question in a very objective way. You upload a photo of your face, looking straight into the camera, and similar photos of your mom and dad, and the service analyzes them to provide you with your own personal "look-alike meter." Typically your mother's photo is shown on the left end of the meter scale, your father's on the right. If you resemble both parents equally, the meter's needle points to the middle (straight up). If, on the other hand, you look more like one parent than the other, then the needle will swing over toward the side of that parent. The more you resemble her or him, the closer to that side of the meter the needle points. When the baby girl of Tom Cruise and Katie Holmes was analyzed in this way with the look-alike meter shown below, Suri proved to look more like Tom, by 15%. Why do you think it is possible for Suri to look more like her father than her mother? Didn't she get half her genes from each parent?

TABLE 10.2	Some Dominant and Recessive Traits in Humans
Recessive Traits	**Phenotypes**
Common Baldness	M-shaped hairline receding with age
Albinism	Lack of melanin pigmentation
Alkaptonuria	Inability to metabolize homogenistic acid
Red-green color blindness	Inability to distinguish red and green wavelengths of light
Dominant Traits	**Phenotypes**
Mid-digital hair	Presence of hair on middle segment of finger
Brachydactyly	Short fingers
Phenylthiocarbamide (PTC) sensitivity	Ability to taste PTC as bitter
Camptodactyly	Inability to straighten the little finger
Polydactyly	Extra fingers and toes

10.3 Mendel Proposes a Theory

CONCEPT PREVIEW: The genes that an individual has are referred to as its genotype; the outward appearance of the individual is referred to as its phenotype. The phenotype is determined by the alleles inherited from the parents. Analyses using Punnett squares determine all possible genotypes and phenotypes of a particular cross. A test cross determines the genotype of a dominant trait.

To explain his results, Mendel proposed a simple set of hypotheses that would faithfully predict the results he had observed. Now called Mendel's theory of heredity, it has become one of the most famous theories in the history of science. Mendel's theory is composed of five simple hypotheses:

Hypothesis 1: *Parents do not transmit traits directly to their offspring.* Rather, they transmit information about the traits, what Mendel called *merkmal* (the German word for "factor"). These factors act later, in the offspring, to produce the trait. In modern terminology, we call Mendel's factors **genes.**

Hypothesis 2: *Each parent contains two copies of the factor governing each trait.* The two copies may or may not be the same. If the two copies of the factor are the same (both encoding purple or both white flowers, for example) the individual is said to be **homozygous.** If the two copies of the factor are different (one encoding purple, the other white, for example), the individual is said to be **heterozygous.**

Hypothesis 3: *Alternative forms of a factor lead to alternative traits.* Alternative forms of a factor are called **alleles.** Mendel used lowercase letters to represent recessive alleles and uppercase letters to represent dominant ones. In modern terms, we call the appearance of an individual its **phenotype.** Appearance is determined by which alleles of the flower-color gene the plant receives from its parents, and we call those particular alleles the individual's **genotype.** Thus a pea plant might have the phenotype "white flower" and the genotype *pp.*

Hypothesis 4: *The two alleles that an individual possesses do not affect each other,* any more than two letters in a mailbox alter each other's contents. Each allele is passed on unchanged when the individual matures and produces its own gametes (egg and sperm). At the time, Mendel did not know that his factors were carried from parent to offspring on chromosomes.

Hypothesis 5: *The presence of an allele does not ensure that a trait will be expressed in the individual that carries it.* In heterozygous individuals, only the dominant allele achieves expression; the recessive allele is present but unexpressed.

These five hypotheses, taken together, constitute Mendel's model of the hereditary process. Many traits in humans exhibit dominant or recessive inheritance similar to the traits Mendel studied in peas (table 10.2).

Analyzing Mendel's Results

To analyze Mendel's results, it is important to remember that each trait is determined by the inheritance of alleles from the parents, one allele from the mother and the other from the father. These alleles, present on chromosomes, are distributed to gametes during meiosis. Each gamete receives one copy of each chromosome, and therefore one copy of an allele.

During sexual reproduction, discussed on page 144, haploid gametes, that contain one allele for each trait, combine to form a diploid offspring. The genetic make up of the offspring is thus half maternal and half paternal.

Consider again Mendel's cross of purple-flowered with white-flowered plants. Like Mendel, we will assign the symbol *P*, written in uppercase, to the dominant allele associated with the production of purple flowers, and the symbol *p*, written in lowercase, to the recessive allele associated with the production of white flowers.

In this system, the genotype of an individual true-breeding for the recessive white-flowered trait would be designated *pp*, as both copies of the allele specify the white phenotype. Similarly, the genotype of a true-breeding purple-flowered individual would be designated *PP*, and a heterozygote would be designated *Pp* (dominant allele first). Using these conventions, and denoting a cross between two strains with ×, we can symbolize Mendel's original cross as *pp* × *PP*.

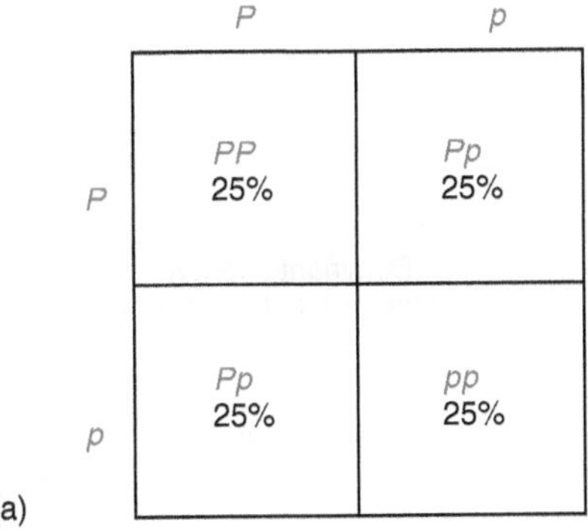

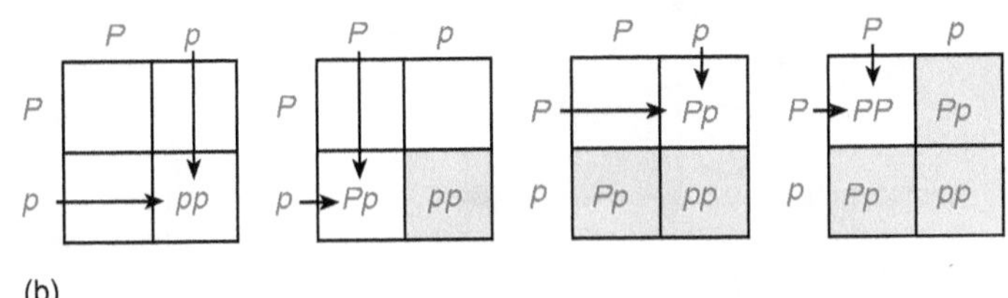

Figure 10.6 A Punnett square analysis.

(a) Each square represents 1/4 or 25% of the offspring from the cross. The squares in (b) show how the square is used to predict the genotypes of all potential offspring.

Punnett Squares

The possible results from a cross between a true-breeding, white-flowered plant (*pp*) and a true-breeding, purple-flowered plant (*PP*) can be visualized with a **Punnett square.** In a Punnett square, the possible gametes of one individual are listed along the horizontal side of the square, while the possible gametes of the other individual are listed along the vertical side. The genotypes of potential offspring are represented by the cells within the square. Figure 10.6 walks you through the set-up of a Punnett square crossing two individual plants that are heterozygous for flower color (*Pp* × *Pp*). The genotypes of the parents are placed along the top and side and the genotypes of potential offspring appear in the cells.

The frequency that these genotypes occur in the offspring is usually expressed by a **probability.** For example, in a cross between a homozygous white-flowered plant (*pp*) and a homozygous purple-flowered plant (*PP*), *Pp* is the only possible genotype for all individuals in the F_1 generation as shown by the Punnett square on the left of figure 10.7. Because *P* is dominant to *p*, all individuals in the F_1 generation have purple flowers. When individuals from the F_1 generation are crossed, as shown by the Punnett square on the right, the probability of obtaining a homozygous dominant (*PP*) individual in the F_2 is 25% because one-fourth of the possible genotypes are *PP*. Similarly, the probability of an individual in the F_2 generation being homozygous recessive (*pp*) is 25%. Because the heterozygous genotype has two possible ways of occurring (*Pp* and *pP*, but both written as *Pp*), it occurs in half of the cells within the square; the probability of obtaining a heterozygous (*Pp*) individual in the F_2 is 50% (25% + 25%).

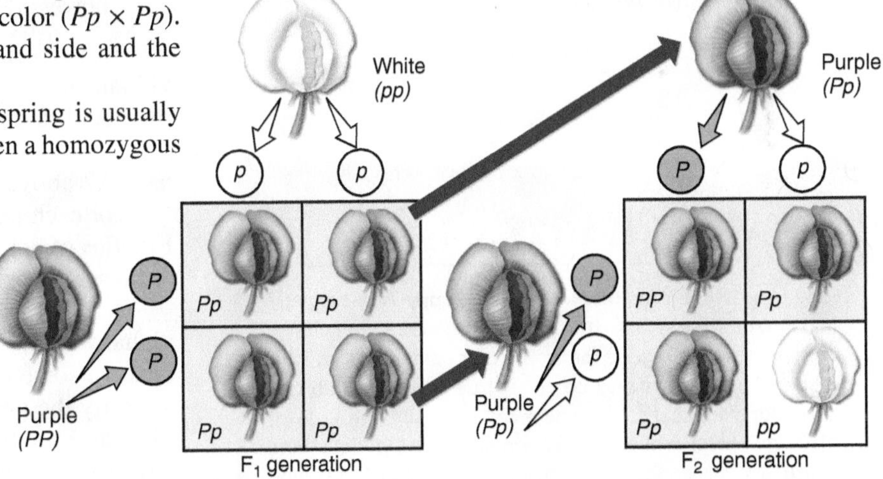

Figure 10.7 How Mendel analyzed flower color.

The only possible offspring of the first cross are *Pp* heterozygotes, purple in color. These individuals are known as the F_1 generation. When two heterozygous F_1 individuals cross, three kinds of offspring are possible: *PP* homozygotes (purple flowers); *Pp* heterozygotes (also purple flowers), which may form two ways; and *pp* homozygotes (white flowers). Among these individuals, known as the F_2 generation, the ratio of dominant phenotype to recessive phenotype is 3:1.

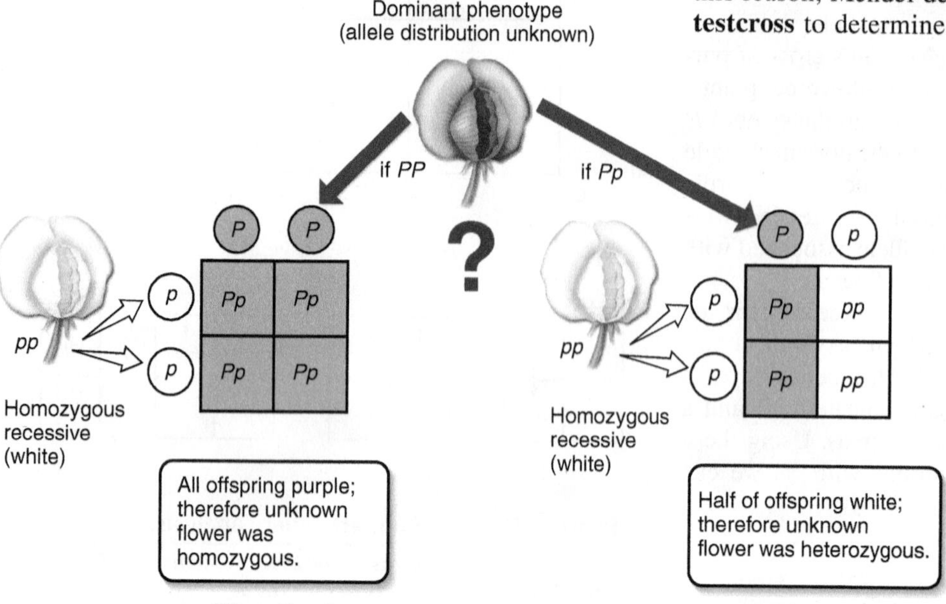

Figure 10.8 How Mendel used the testcross to detect heterozygotes.

To determine whether an individual exhibiting a dominant phenotype, such as purple flowers, was homozygous (*PP*) or heterozygous (*Pp*) for the dominant allele, Mendel devised the testcross. He crossed the individual in question with a known homozygous recessive (*pp*)—in this case, a plant with white flowers.

The Testcross

How did Mendel know which of the purple-flowered individuals in the F_2 generation (or the P generation) were homozygous (*PP*) and which were heterozygous (*Pp*)? It is not possible to tell simply by looking at them. For this reason, Mendel devised a simple and powerful procedure called the **testcross** to determine an individual's actual genetic composition. Consider a purple-flowered plant. It is impossible to determine such a plant's genotype simply by looking at its phenotype. To learn its genotype, you must cross it with some other plant. What kind of cross would provide the answer? If you cross it with a homozygous dominant individual, all of the progeny will show the dominant phenotype whether the test plant is homozygous or heterozygous. It is also difficult (but not impossible) to distinguish between the two possible test plant genotypes by crossing with a heterozygous individual. However, if you cross the test plant with a homozygous recessive individual, the two possible test plant genotypes will give totally different results. To see how this works, step through a testcross of a purple-flowered plant with a white-flowered plant. Figure 10.8 shows you the two possible alternatives:

Alternative 1 (on left): unknown plant is homozygous (*PP*). *PP* × *pp:* all offspring have purple flowers (*Pp*) as shown by the four purple squares.

Alternative 2 (on right): unknown plant is heterozygous (*Pp*). *Pp* × *pp:* one-half of offspring have white flowers (*pp*) and one-half have purple flowers (*Pp*) as shown by the two white and two purple squares.

To perform his testcross, Mendel crossed heterozygous F_1 individuals back to the parent homozygous for the recessive trait. He predicted that the dominant and recessive traits would appear in a 1:1 ratio, and that is what he observed, as you can see illustrated in alternative 2 above.

For each pair of alleles he investigated, Mendel observed phenotypic F_2 ratios of 3:1 (see table 10.1) and testcross ratios very close to 1:1, just as his model predicted.

Testcrosses can also be used to determine the genotype of an individual when two genes are involved. Mendel carried out many two-gene crosses, some of which we will soon discuss. He often used testcrosses to verify the genotypes of particular dominant-appearing F_2 individuals. Thus an F_2 individual showing both dominant traits (*A_ B_*) might have any of the following genotypes: *AABB, AaBB, AABb,* or *AaBb.* By crossing dominant-appearing F_2 individuals with homozygous recessive individuals (that is, *A_ B_* × *aabb*), Mendel was able to determine if either or both of the traits bred true among the progeny and so determine the genotype of the F_2 parent.

AABB	trait A breeds true	trait B breeds true
AaBB		trait B breeds true
AABb	trait A breeds true	
AaBb		

Is Your Black Labrador Puppy Homozygous?

In Labrador retrievers, the gene for black coat color is dominant over the gene for brown coat color. A puppy with a black-colored coat may be either true-breeding, with two alleles for black coat color, or heterozygous, with one allele for black coat color and one for brown coat color. To determine which genetic endowment your black lab puppy has, you can mate it (when it grows up) to a so-called chocolate lab, which has brown fur and two alleles for brown coat color. If all the offspring of this mating are black, your dog must be true-breeding and have both alleles for black coat color. If some of the young are chocolate brown, your dog must be heterozygous and have one allele for black coat color and one for brown coat color. Yellow labs, on the other hand, lack the allele for pigmentation, so they have light-colored coats.

10.4 Mendel's Laws

CONCEPT PREVIEW: Mendel's theories of segregation and independent assortment are well supported and are considered "laws."

Mendel's First Law: Segregation

Mendel's model brilliantly predicts the results of his crosses, accounting in a neat and satisfying way for the ratios he observed. Similar patterns of heredity have since been observed in countless other organisms. Traits exhibiting this pattern of heredity are called *Mendelian traits.* Because of its overwhelming importance, Mendel's theory is often referred to as Mendel's first law, or the **law of segregation.** In modern terms, Mendel's first law states that *the two alleles of a trait separate during the formation of gametes, so that half of the gametes will carry one copy and half will carry the other copy.*

Mendel's Second Law: Independent Assortment

Mendel went on to ask if the inheritance of one factor, such as flower color, influences the inheritance of other factors, such as plant height. To investigate this question, he followed the inheritance of two separate traits, called a **dihybrid** cross (*di* meaning two; a *monohybrid* cross examines one trait). He first established a series of true-breeding lines of peas that differed from one another with respect to two of the seven pairs of characteristics, and then crossed them. Figure 10.9 shows an experiment in which the P generation consists of homozygous individuals with round, yellow seeds (*RRYY* in the figure) that are crossed with individuals that are homozygous for wrinkled, green seeds (*rryy*). This cross produces F_1 individuals that have round, yellow seeds and are heterozygous for both of these traits (*RrYy*). The chromosomes are allocated to the gametes during meiosis such that there are four types of gametes for these two traits.

Mendel then allowed the dihybrid individuals to self-fertilize. If the segregation of alleles affecting seed shape and alleles affecting seed color were independent, the probability that a particular pair of seed-shape alleles would occur together with a particular pair of seed-color alleles would simply be a product of the two individual probabilities that each pair would occur separately. For example, the probability of an individual with wrinkled, green seeds appearing in the F_2 generation would be equal to the probability of an individual with wrinkled seeds (1 in 4) multiplied by the probability of an individual with green seeds (1 in 4), or 1 in 16.

In his dihybrid crosses, Mendel found that the frequency of phenotypes in the F_2 offspring closely matched the 9:3:3:1 ratio predicted by the Punnett square analysis shown in figure 10.9. He concluded that for the pairs of traits he studied, the inheritance of one trait does not influence the inheritance of the other trait, a result often referred to as Mendel's second law, or the **law of independent assortment.** We now know that this result is only valid for genes not located near one another on the same chromosome. Thus in modern terms, Mendel's second law is often stated as follows: *genes located on different chromosomes are inherited independently of one another.*

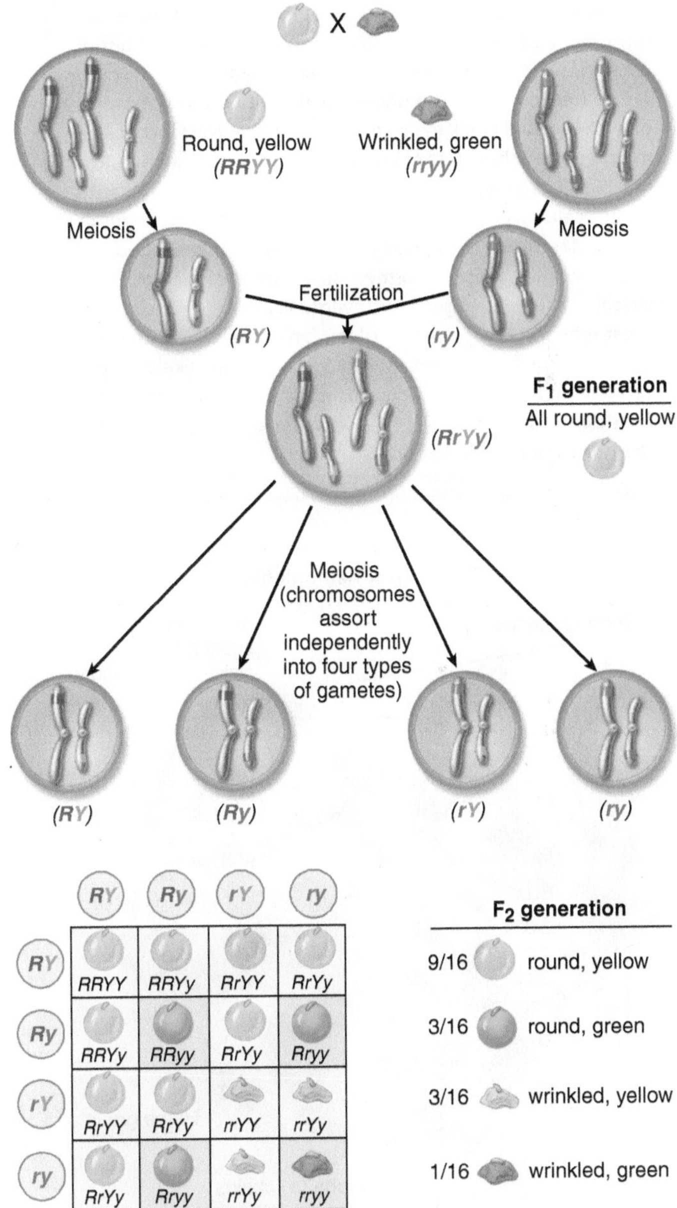

Figure 10.9 Analysis of a dihybrid cross.

This dihybrid cross shows round (*R*) versus wrinkled (*r*) seeds and yellow (*Y*) versus green (*y*) seeds. The ratio of the four possible phenotypes in the F_2 generation is predicted to be 9:3:3:1.

Concept Check

1. In Mendel's crosses, the offspring of the F_1 generation self-fertilized to produce the F_2 generation. Why didn't Mendel allow the parent plants to self-fertilize like this in making the F_1 generation?
2. Mendel's model of inheritance rests on five hypotheses. Name them.
3. How did Mendel know which F_2 generation peas were heterozygous?

From Genotype to Phenotype

10.5 How Genes Influence Traits

CONCEPT PREVIEW: Genes determine phenotypes by specifying the amino acid sequences, and thus the functional shapes, of the proteins that carry out cell activities.

It is useful, before considering Mendelian genetics further, to gain a brief understanding of how genes work. With this in mind, we will sketch, in broad strokes, a picture of how a Mendelian trait is influenced by a particular gene. We will use the protein hemoglobin as our example—you can follow along on figure 10.10.

From DNA to Protein

Each body cell of an individual contains the same set of DNA molecules, called the genome of that individual. The human genome contains about 20,000 to 25,000 genes, parcelled out into 23 pairs of chromosomes. You can see on figure 10.10 that the hemoglobin gene (*Hb*) is located on chromosome 11.

Individual genes are "read" from the chromosomal DNA by enzymes that create an RNA strand of the same sequence. After editing out unnecessary bits, this RNA transcript of the hemoglobin gene leaves the nucleus as messenger RNA (mRNA) and is delivered to ribosomes in the cytoplasm. Each ribosome is a tiny protein-assembly plant, and uses the nucleotide sequence of the mRNA to determine the amino acid sequence of a particular polypeptide. In the case of beta-hemoglobin, the mRNA encodes a strand of 146 amino acids.

How Proteins Determine the Phenotype

The beta-hemoglobin amino acid chain, that resembles beads on a string in the figure, spontaneously folds into a complex three-dimensional shape. This beta-hemoglobin associates with another beta chain and two alpha chains to form the active four-subunit hemoglobin protein (shown to the left) that binds oxygen in red blood cells. As a general rule, genes influence the phenotype by specifying the kind of proteins present in the body, which determines in large measure how that body looks and functions.

How Mutation Alters Phenotype

A change in the identity of a single nucleotide within a gene, called a mutation, can have a profound effect if the new version of the protein folds differently, as this may alter or destroy its function. How well hemoglobin performs its oxygen transport duties depends on the precise shape that the protein subunits assume when they fold. A change in the sixth amino acid of beta-hemoglobin from glutamic acid to valine causes the hemoglobin molecules to aggregate into long chains that cause the blood cells to deform into a sickle shape which can no longer carry oxygen efficiently. The resulting sickle-cell disease can be fatal, as discussed further on page 176.

Populations usually contain several versions of a gene, most of them rare. Sometimes one of the rare versions functions better under new conditions. When that happens, natural selection (see chapter 1, page 26) will favor the rare allele, which will then become more common in the population. The sickle-cell version of the beta-hemoglobin gene, rare throughout most of the world, is common in Central Africa because heterozygous individuals are resistant to malaria, a deadly disease common there.

BIOLOGY & YOU

Sickle-Cell Disease. The inherited blood disorder sickle-cell disease occurs among African Americans in 3 of every 1,000 (or about 1 in 375) live births. In its severe form it affects more than 50,000 people. The first account of what was then called "sickle-cell anemia" was in 1910 when James Herrick, a Chicago physician, described the symptoms of a 20-year-old black male student from the West Indies. The man reported shortness of breath and had severe anemia (low red blood cell count). In a 1904 examination of the patient's blood cells under a microscope, Dr. Ernest Iron, Herrick's intern, described "elongated and irregular, sickle-shaped red cells." Because these deformed sickle cells can clog blood vessels, organ damage often eventually results. One of the most affected organs is the spleen (an organ of the immune system), and so affected individuals are more likely to get serious infections. The single nucleotide change responsible for sickle-cell disease thus has widespread effects that affect the health of the whole body.

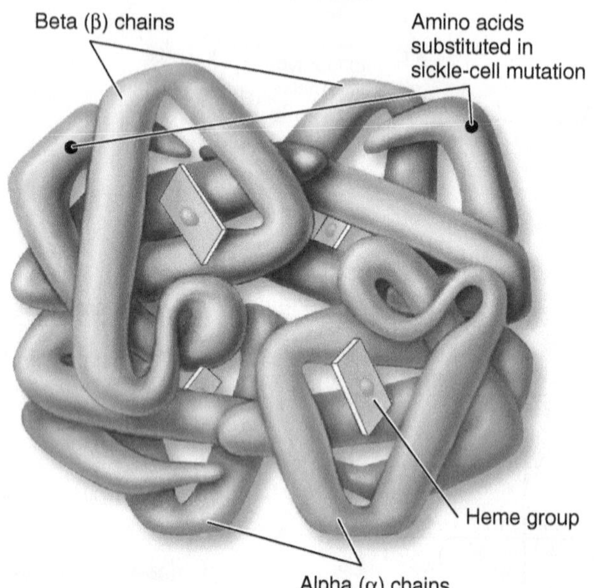

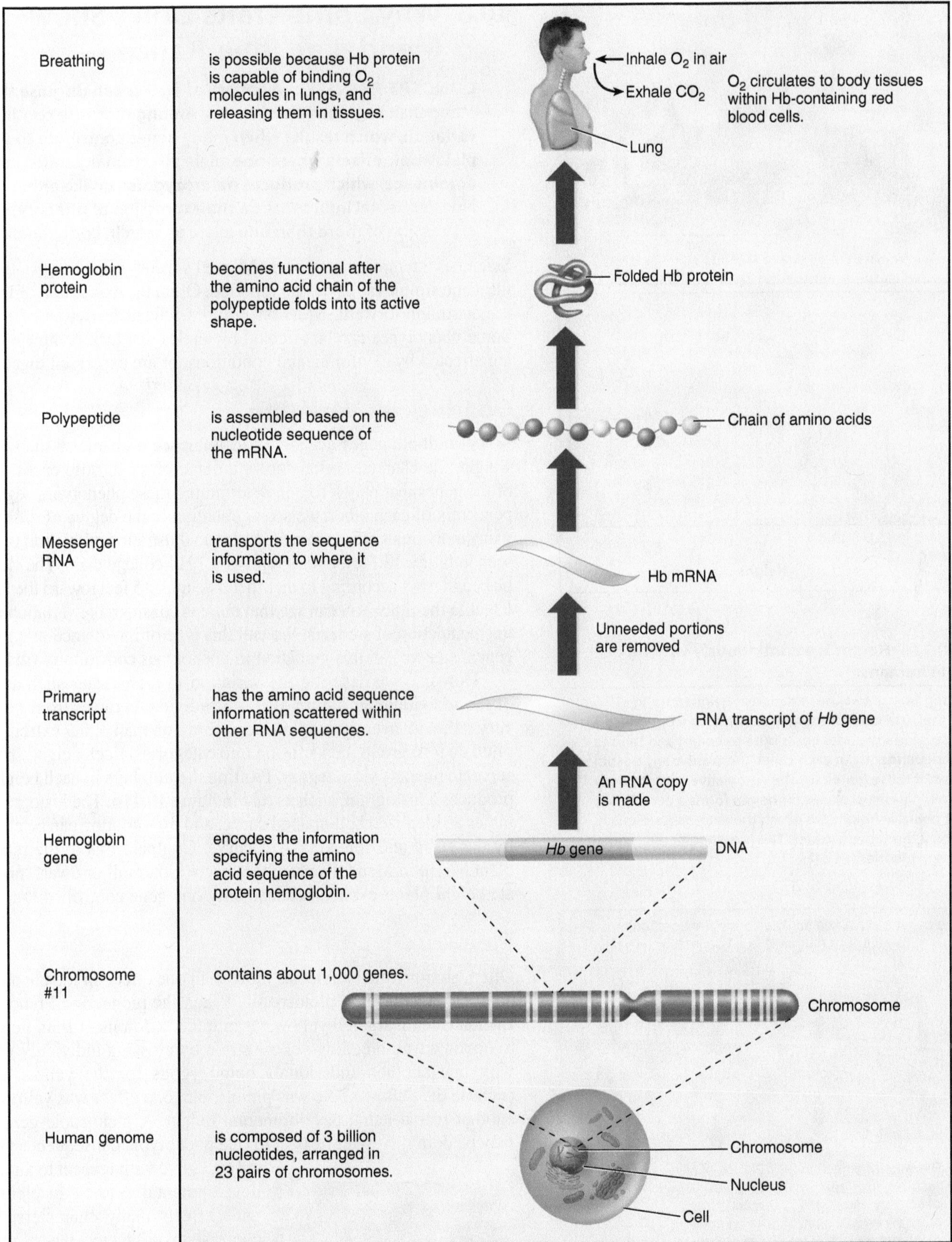
Breathing
is possible because Hb protein is capable of binding O_2 molecules in lungs, and releasing them in tissues.
Inhale O_2 in air
Exhale CO_2
O_2 circulates to body tissues within Hb-containing red blood cells.
Lung
Hemoglobin protein
becomes functional after the amino acid chain of the polypeptide folds into its active shape.
Folded Hb protein
Polypeptide
is assembled based on the nucleotide sequence of the mRNA.
Chain of amino acids
Messenger RNA
transports the sequence information to where it is used.
Hb mRNA
Unneeded portions are removed
Primary transcript
has the amino acid sequence information scattered within other RNA sequences.
RNA transcript of *Hb* gene
An RNA copy is made
Hemoglobin gene
encodes the information specifying the amino acid sequence of the protein hemoglobin.
Hb gene
DNA
Chromosome #11
contains about 1,000 genes.
Chromosome
Human genome
is composed of 3 billion nucleotides, arranged in 23 pairs of chromosomes.
Chromosome
Nucleus
Cell

Figure 10.10 The journey from DNA to phenotype.

What an organism is like is determined in large measure by its genes. Here you see how one gene of the 20,000 to 25,000 in the human genome plays a key role in allowing oxygen to be carried throughout your body. The many steps on the journey from gene to trait are the subject of chapters 11 and 12.

(a)

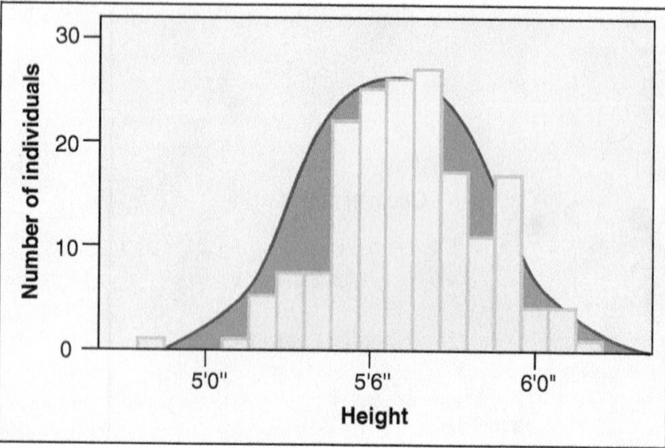

(b)

Figure 10.11 Height is a continuously varying character in humans.

(a) This photograph shows the variation in height among students of the 1914 class of the Connecticut Agricultural College. Because many genes contribute to height and tend to segregate independently of each other, there are many possible combinations of those genes. (b) The cumulative contribution of different combinations of alleles for height forms a continuous spectrum of possible heights, in which the extremes are much rarer than the intermediate values. This is quite different from the 3:1 ratio seen in Mendel's F_2 peas.

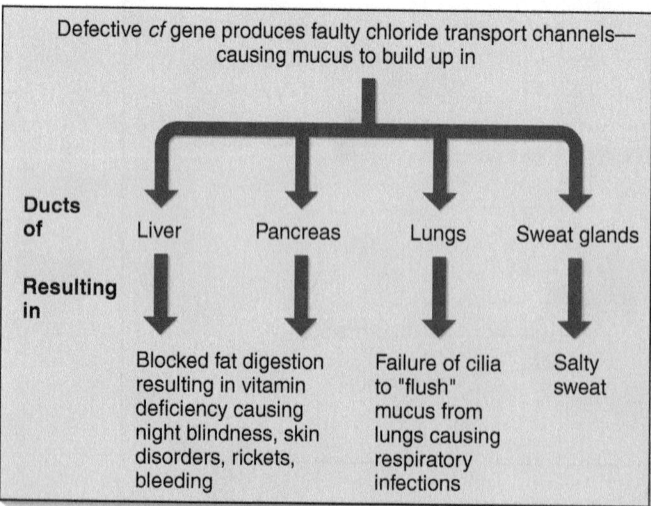

Figure 10.12 Pleiotropic effects of the cystic fibrosis gene, *cf*.

10.6 Why Some Traits Don't Show Mendelian Inheritance

CONCEPT PREVIEW: A variety of factors can disguise the Mendelian segregation of alleles. Among them are continuous variation, which results when many genes contribute to a trait; pleiotropic effects where one allele affects many traits; incomplete dominance, which produces heterozygotes unlike either parent; environmental influences on the expression of phenotypes; and the expression of more than one allele as seen in codominance.

Scientists attempting to confirm Mendel's theory often had trouble obtaining the same simple ratios he had reported. Often the expression of the genotype is not straightforward. Most phenotypes reflect the action of many genes. Some phenotypes can be affected by alleles that lack complete dominance, are affected by environmental conditions, or are expressed together.

Continuous Variation

When multiple genes act jointly to influence a character such as height or weight, the character often shows a range of small differences. Because all of the genes that play a role in determining these phenotypes segregate independently of each other, we see a gradation in the degree of difference when many individuals are examined. A classic illustration of this sort of variation is seen in figure 10.11, a photograph of a 1914 college class. The students were placed in rows according to their heights, under 5 feet toward the left and over 6 feet to the right. You can see that there is considerable variation in height in this population of students. We call this type of inheritance **polygenic** (many genes) and we call this gradation in phenotypes **continuous variation.**

How can we describe the variation in a character such as the height of the individuals in figure 10.11*a*? Individuals range from quite short to very tall, with average heights more common than either extreme. What we often do is to group the variation into categories. Each height, in inches, is a separate phenotypic category. Plotting the numbers in each height category produces a histogram, such as that in figure 10.11*b*. The histogram approximates an idealized bell-shaped curve, and the variation can be characterized by the mean and spread of that curve. Compare this to the inheritance of plant height in Mendel's peas; they were either tall or dwarf, no intermediate height plants existed because only one gene controlled that trait.

Pleiotropic Effects

Often, an individual allele has more than one effect on the phenotype. Such an allele is said to be **pleiotropic.** When the pioneering French geneticist Lucien Cuenot studied yellow fur in mice, a dominant trait, he was unable to obtain a true-breeding yellow strain by crossing individual yellow mice with one another. Individuals homozygous for the yellow allele died, because the yellow allele was pleiotropic: one effect was yellow color, but another was a lethal developmental defect. A pleiotropic gene alteration may be dominant with respect to one phenotypic consequence (yellow fur) and recessive with respect to another (lethal developmental defect). In pleiotropy, one gene affects many characters, in marked contrast to polygeny, where many genes affect one character. Pleiotropic effects are difficult to predict, because the genes that affect a character often perform other functions we may know nothing about.

Cystic fibrosis, discussed on page 82, is caused by a mutation in a single gene that disrupts the functions of a chloride channel in the plasma membrane. This allele has pleiotropic effects because the chloride channel is found in many different types of cells in the body.

Figure 10.13 Incomplete dominance.

In a cross between a red-flowered Japanese four o'clock, genotype C^RC^R, and a white-flowered one (C^WC^W), neither allele is dominant. The heterozygous progeny have pink flowers and the genotype C^RC^W. If two of these heterozygotes are crossed, the phenotypes of their progeny occur in a ratio of 1:2:1 (red:pink:white).

IMPLICATION Palomino is a golden coat color in horses. The color is created by the action of one allele of a gene called "cream" working on a red (chestnut) base coat. Two cream alleles create an almost white horse called "cremello." Is it possible to breed a true-breeding line of palomino horses? Explain.

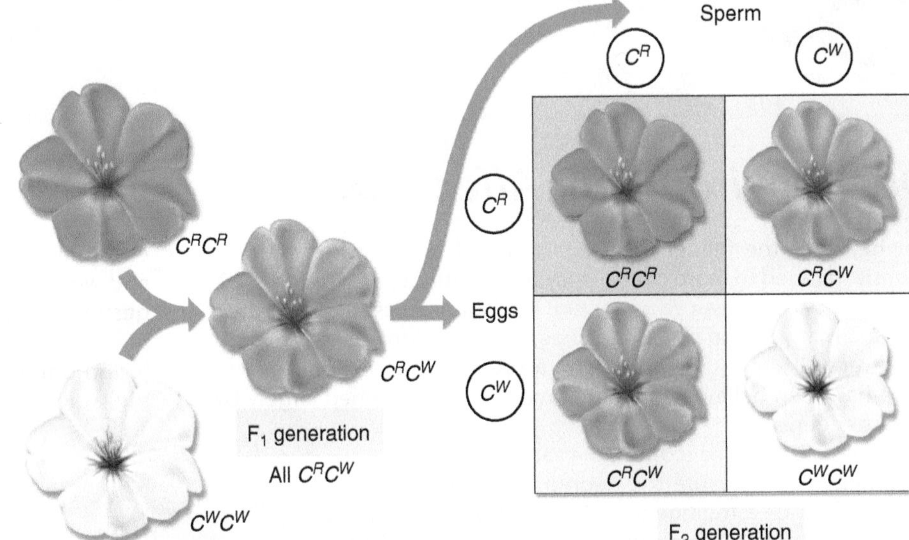

Pleiotropic effects are characteristic of many inherited disorders, such as cystic fibrosis and sickle-cell disease, discussed later in this chapter. In these disorders, multiple symptoms can be traced back to a single gene defect. As shown in figure 10.12, cystic fibrosis patients exhibit overly sticky mucus, salty sweat, liver and pancreas failure, and a battery of other symptoms. All are pleiotropic effects of a single defect, a mutation in a gene that encodes a chloride ion transmembrane channel. In sickle-cell disease, a defect in the oxygen-carrying hemoglobin molecule causes anemia, heart failure, increased susceptibility to pneumonia, kidney failure, enlargement of the spleen, and many other symptoms.

Incomplete Dominance

Not all alternative alleles are fully dominant or fully recessive in heterozygotes. Some pairs of alleles exhibit **incomplete dominance** and produce a heterozygous phenotype that is intermediate between those of the parents. For example, the cross of red- and white-flowered Japanese four o'clocks described in figure 10.13 produced red-, pink-, and white-flowered F_2 plants in a 1:2:1 ratio—heterozygotes are intermediate in color. This is different than in Mendel's pea plants that didn't exhibit incomplete dominance; the heterozygotes expressed the dominant phenotype.

Environmental Effects

The degree to which many alleles are expressed depends on the environment. Some alleles are heat-sensitive, for example. Traits influenced by such alleles are more sensitive to temperature or light than are the products of other alleles. The arctic foxes in figure 10.14, for example, make fur pigment only when the weather is warm. Can you see why this trait would be an advantage for the fox? Imagine a fox that didn't possess this trait and was white all year round. It would be very visible to predators in the summer, standing out against its darker surroundings. Similarly, the *ch* allele in Himalayan rabbits and Siamese cats encodes a heat-sensitive version of tyrosinase, one of the enzymes mediating the production of melanin, a dark pigment. The ch version of the enzyme is inactivated at temperatures above about 33°C. At the surface of the main body and head, the temperature is above 33°C and the tyrosinase enzyme is inactive, while it is more active at body extremities such as the tips of the ears and tail, where the temperature is below 33°C. The dark melanin pigment this enzyme produces causes the ears, snout, feet, and tail to be black.

(a)

(b)

Figure 10.14 Environmental effects on an allele.

(a) An arctic fox in winter has a coat that is almost white, so it is difficult to see the fox against a snowy background. (b) In summer, the same fox's fur darkens to a reddish brown, so that it resembles the color of the surrounding tundra. Heat-sensitive alleles control this color change.

Does Environment Affect I.Q.?

Nowhere has the influence of environment on the expression of genetic traits led to more controversy than in studies of I.Q. scores. I.Q. is a controversial measure of general intelligence based on a written test that many feel to be biased toward white middle-class America. However well or poorly I.Q. scores measure intelligence, a person's I.Q. score has been believed for some time to be determined largely by his or her genes.

How did science come to that conclusion? Scientists measure the degree to which genes influence a multigene trait by using an off-putting statistical measure called the *variance*. Variance is defined as the square of the standard deviation (a measure of the degree-of-scatter of a group of numbers around their mean value), and has the very desirable property of being additive—that is, the total variance is equal to the sum of the variances of the factors influencing it.

What factors can contribute to the total variance of I.Q. scores? There are three: 1. The first factor is variation at the gene level, some gene combinations leading to higher I.Q. scores than others. 2. The second factor is variation at the environmental level, some environments leading to higher I.Q. scores than others. 3. The third factor is what a statistician calls the covariance, the degree to which environment affects genes.

The degree to which genes influence a trait like I.Q., the *heritability* of I.Q., is given the symbol H and is defined simply as the fraction of the total variance that is genetic.

So how heritable is I.Q.? Geneticists estimate the heritablity of I.Q. by measuring the environmental and genetic contributions to the total variance of I.Q. scores. The environmental contributions to variance in I.Q. can be measured by comparing the I.Q. scores of identical twins reared together with those reared apart (any differences should reflect environmental influences). The genetic contributions can be measured by comparing identical twins reared together (which are 100% genetically identical) with fraternal twins reared together (which are 50% genetically identical). Any differences should reflect genes, as twins share identical prenatal conditions in the womb and are raised in virtually identical environmental circumstances, so when traits are more commonly shared between identical twins than fraternal twins, the difference is likely genetic.

When these sorts of "twin studies" have been done in the past, researchers have uniformly reported that I.Q. is highly heritable, with values of H typically reported as being around 0.7 (a very high value). While it didn't seem significant at the time, almost all the twins available for study over the years have come from middle-class or wealthy families.

The study of I.Q. has proven controversial, because I.Q. scores are often different when social and racial groups are compared. What is one to make of the observation that I.Q. scores of poor children measure lower as a group than do scores of children of middle-class and wealthy families? This difference has led to the controversial suggestion by some that the poor are genetically inferior.

What should we make of such a harsh conclusion? To make a judgment, we need to focus for a moment on the fact that these measures of the heritability of I.Q. have all made a critical assumption, one to which population geneticists, who specialize in these sorts of things, object strongly. The assumption is that environment does not affect gene expression, so that covariance makes no contribution to the total variance in I.Q. scores—that is, that the covariance contribution to H is zero.

Studies have allowed a direct assessment of this assumption. Importantly, it proves to be flat wrong.

In November of 2003, researchers reported an analysis of twin data from a study carried out in the late 1960s. The National Collaborative Prenatal Project, funded by the National Institutes of Health, enrolled nearly 50,000 pregnant women, most of them black and quite poor, in several major U.S. cities. Researchers collected abundant data, and gave the children I.Q. tests seven years later. Although not designed to study twins, this study was so big that many twins were born, 623 births. Seven years later, 320 of these pairs were located and given I.Q. tests. This thus constitutes a huge "twin study," the first ever conducted of I.Q. among the poor.

When the data were analyzed, the results were unlike any ever reported. The heritability of I.Q. was different in different environments! Most notably, the influence of genes on I.Q. was far less in conditions of poverty, where environmental limitations seem to block the expression of genetic potential. Specifically, for families of high socioeconomic status, H = 0.72, much as reported in previous studies, but for families raised in poverty, H = 0.10, a very low value, indicating genes were making little contribution to observed I.Q. scores. The lower a child's socioeconomic status, the less impact genes had on I.Q.

These data say, with crystal clarity, that the genetic contributions to I.Q. don't mean much in an impoverished environment.

How does poverty in early childhood affect the brain? Neuroscientists reported in 2008 that many children growing up in very poor families experience poor nutrition and unhealthy levels of stress hormones, both of which impair their neural development. This affects language development and memory for the rest of their lives.

Clearly, improvements in the growing and learning environments of poor children can be expected to have a major impact on their I.Q. scores. Additionally, these data argue that the controversial differences reported in mean I.Q. scores between racial groups may well reflect no more than poverty, and are no more inevitable.

Codominance

A gene may have more than two alleles in a population, and in fact most genes possess several different alleles. Often in heterozygotes there isn't a dominant allele; instead, the effects of both alleles are expressed. In these cases, the alleles are said to be **codominant.** Codominance is seen in the color patterning of some animals, such as the "roan" pattern exhibited by some varieties of horses and cattle. A roan animal expresses both white and colored hairs because both alleles are being expressed. The gray horse in figure 10.15 is exhibiting the roan pattern. It looks like it has gray hairs, but if you were able to examine its coat closely, you would see both white hairs and black hairs.

A human gene that exhibits more than one dominant allele is the gene that determines ABO blood type. This gene encodes an enzyme that adds sugar molecules to lipids on the surface of red blood cells. These sugars act as recognition markers for cells in the immune system and are called cell surface antigens. The gene that encodes the enzyme, designated *I*, has three common alleles: I^B, whose product adds galactose; I^A, whose product adds galactosamine; and *i*, whose product does not add a sugar.

Different combinations of the three *I* gene alleles occur in different individuals because each person may be homozygous for any allele or heterozygous for any two. An individual heterozygous for the I^A and I^B alleles produces both forms of the enzyme and adds both galactose and galactosamine to the surfaces of red blood cells. Because both alleles are expressed simultaneously in heterozygotes, the I^A and I^B alleles are codominant. Both I^A and I^B are dominant over the *i* allele because both I^A or I^B alleles lead to sugar addition and the *i* allele does not. The different combinations of the three alleles produce four different phenotypes (figure 10.16):

1. Type A individuals add only galactosamine. They are either I^AI^A homozygotes or I^Ai heterozygotes (the three darkest boxes).
2. Type B individuals add only galactose. They are either I^BI^B homozygotes or I^Bi heterozygotes (the three lightest-colored boxes).
3. Type AB individuals add both sugars and are I^AI^B heterozygotes (the two intermediate-colored boxes).
4. Type O individuals add neither sugar and are *ii* homozygotes (the one white box).

These four different cell surface phenotypes are called the **ABO blood groups.** A person's immune system can distinguish between these four phenotypes. If a type A individual receives a transfusion of type B blood, the recipient's immune system recognizes that the type B blood cells possess a "foreign" antigen (galactose) and attacks the donated blood cells, causing the cells to clump or agglutinate. This also happens if the donated blood is type AB. However, if the donated blood is type O, it contains no galactose or galactosamine antigens on the surfaces of its blood cells, and so elicits no immune response to these antigens. For this reason, the type O individual is often referred to as a "universal donor." Because neither galactose nor galactosamine is foreign to type AB individuals (whose red blood cells have both sugars), those individuals ("universal recipients") may receive any type of blood.

Figure 10.15 Codominance in color patterning.

This roan horse is heterozygous for coat color. The offspring of a cross between a white homozygote and a black homozygote, it expresses both phenotypes. Some of the hairs on its body are white and some are black.

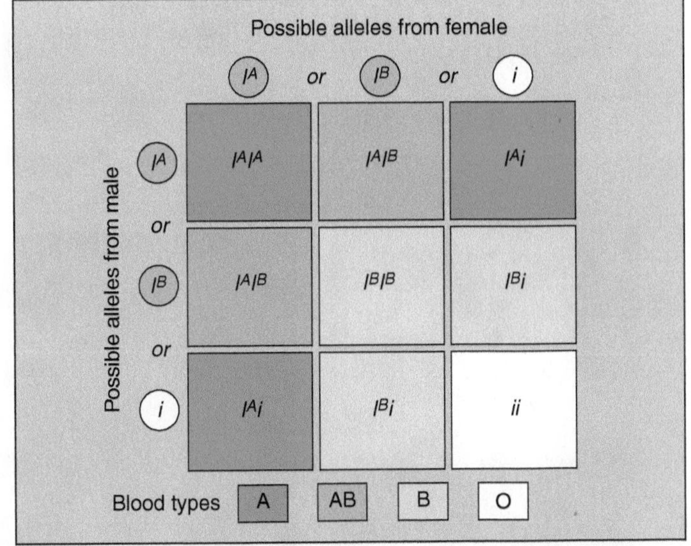

Figure 10.16 Multiple alleles controlling the ABO blood groups.

Three common alleles control the ABO blood groups. The different combinations of the three alleles result in four different blood type phenotypes: type A (either I^AI^A homozygotes or I^Ai heterozygotes), type B (either I^BI^B homozygotes or I^Bi heterozygotes), type AB (I^AI^B heterozygotes), and type O (*ii* homozygotes).

Concept Check

1. Explain how a single nucleotide change in the gene for beta-hemoglobin can lead to organ damage and death.
2. Why is human height not a dominant/recessive trait?
3. Is human blood type A dominant over blood type B? Explain.

Chromosomes and Heredity

IN THE NEWS

Adding an Artificial Chromosome to Treat Disease. Attempts to treat inherited disorders with gene therapy (that is, adding a healthy copy of the defective gene, discussed in chapter 13) have been largely unsuccessful. One of the problems is that the virus used to carry the gene into the cells of the patient can insert the gene into the wrong place on a human chromosome, which can cause cancer. In a new approach, researchers are creating artificial chromosomes to deliver the therapeutic genes. Because this method avoids using viruses, the genes are not inserted into a patient's chromosomes, and so do not cause cancer. Scientists in British Columbia have built up an artificial chromosome from the key elements of a normal mouse chromosome, and added the gene for the human hormone erythropoietin (a blood hormone which triggers red blood cell production). When they injected cells that carry the artificial chromosome into mice, the mice produced the human hormone, leading to elevated levels of red blood cells. The artificial chromosome behaves like a normal one: It is duplicated when cells divide and is passed from generation to generation. Trials of this approach in humans are planned.

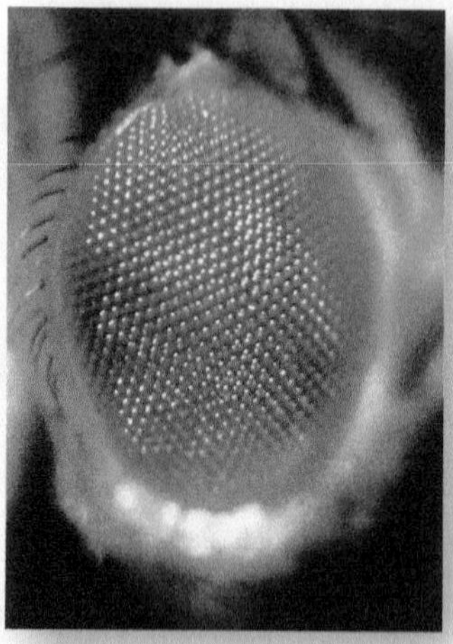
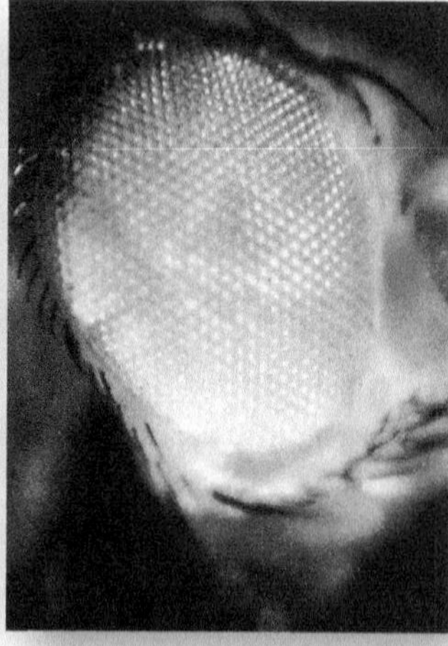

Figure 10.17 Red-eyed (wild type) and white-eyed (mutant) *Drosophila*.

The white-eye defect (shown on the *right*) is hereditary, the result of a mutation in a gene located on the X chromosome. By studying this mutation, Morgan first demonstrated that genes are on chromosomes.

10.7 Chromosomes Are the Vehicles of Mendelian Inheritance

CONCEPT PREVIEW: Mendelian traits segregate because they are determined by genes located on chromosomes that segregate into the gametes during meiosis.

The Chromosomal Theory of Inheritance

A central role for chromosomes in heredity was first suggested in 1900 by the German geneticist Karl Correns, in one of the papers announcing the rediscovery of Mendel's work. Soon observations that similar chromosomes paired with one another during meiosis led to the *chromosomal theory of inheritance,* first formulated by American Walter Sutton in 1902.

Several pieces of evidence supported Sutton's theory. One was that reproduction involves the initial union of only two cells, egg and sperm. If Mendel's model was correct, then these two gametes must make equal hereditary contributions. Sperm, however, contain little cytoplasm, suggesting that the hereditary material must reside within the nuclei of the gametes. Furthermore, while diploid individuals have two copies of each pair of homologous chromosomes, gametes have only one. This observation was consistent with Mendel's model, in which diploid individuals have two copies of each heritable gene and gametes have one. Finally, chromosomes segregate during meiosis, and each pair of homologues orients on the metaphase plate independently of every other pair. Segregation and independent assortment were two characteristics of the genes in Mendel's model.

Problems with the Chromosomal Theory

Investigators soon pointed out one problem with this theory, however. If Mendelian traits are determined by genes located on the chromosomes, and if the independent assortment of Mendelian traits reflects the independent assortment of chromosomes in meiosis, why does the number of traits that assort independently in a given kind of organism often greatly exceed the number of chromosome pairs the organism possesses? This seemed a fatal objection, and it led many early researchers to have serious reservations about Sutton's theory.

Morgan's White-Eyed Fly

The essential correctness of the chromosomal theory of heredity was demonstrated by a single small fly. In 1910 Thomas Hunt Morgan, studying the fruit fly *Drosophila melanogaster,* detected a mutant male fly that differed strikingly from normal fruit flies: Its eyes were white instead of red (figure 10.17).

Morgan immediately set out to determine if this new trait would be inherited in a Mendelian fashion. He first crossed the mutant male with a normal female to see if red or white eyes were dominant. All of the F_1 progeny had red eyes, so Morgan concluded that red eye color was dominant over white. Following the experimental procedure that Mendel had established long ago, Morgan then crossed the red-eyed flies from the F_1 generation with each other. Of the 4,252 F_2 progeny Morgan examined, 782 (18%) had white eyes. Although the ratio of red eyes to white eyes in the F_2 progeny was greater than 3:1, the results of the cross nevertheless provided clear evidence that eye color segregates. However, there was something about the outcome that was strange and totally unpredicted by Mendel's theory—*all of the white-eyed F_2 flies were males!*

How could this result be explained? Perhaps it was impossible for a white-eyed female fly to exist; such individuals might not be viable for some unknown reason. To test this idea, Morgan testcrossed the female F_1 progeny with the original white-eyed male. He obtained white-eyed and red-eyed males and females in a 1:1:1:1 ratio, just as Mendelian theory predicted. Hence, a female could have white eyes. Why, then, were there no white-eyed females among the progeny of the original cross?

Sex Linkage Confirms the Chromosomal Theory

The solution to this puzzle involved sex. In *Drosophila,* the sex of an individual is determined by the number of copies of a particular chromosome, the X chromosome, that an individual possesses. A fly with two X chromosomes is a female, and a fly with only one X chromosome is a male. In males, the single X chromosome pairs in meiosis with a large, dissimilar partner called the Y chromosome. The female thus produces only X gametes, while the male produces both X and Y gametes. When fertilization involves an X sperm, the result is an XX zygote, which develops into a female; when fertilization involves a Y sperm, the result is an XY zygote, which develops into a male.

The solution to Morgan's puzzle is that the gene causing the white-eye trait in *Drosophila* resides only on the X chromosome—it is absent from the Y chromosome. (We now know that the Y chromosome in flies carries almost no functional genes.) A trait determined by a gene on the sex chromosome is said to be **sex-linked.** Knowing the white-eye trait is recessive to the red-eye trait, we can now see that Morgan's result was a natural consequence of the Mendelian assortment of chromosomes (figure 10.18). In this experiment, the F_1 generation all had red eyes, while the F_2 generation contained flies with white eyes—but they were all males. This at-first-surprising result happens because the segregation of the white-eye trait has a one-to-one correspondence with the segregation of the X chromosome. In other words, the white-eye gene is on the X chromosome. In humans, traits such as color-blindness (see chapter 29) and hemophilia (a blood-clotting disease discussed later in this chapter) are sex-linked.

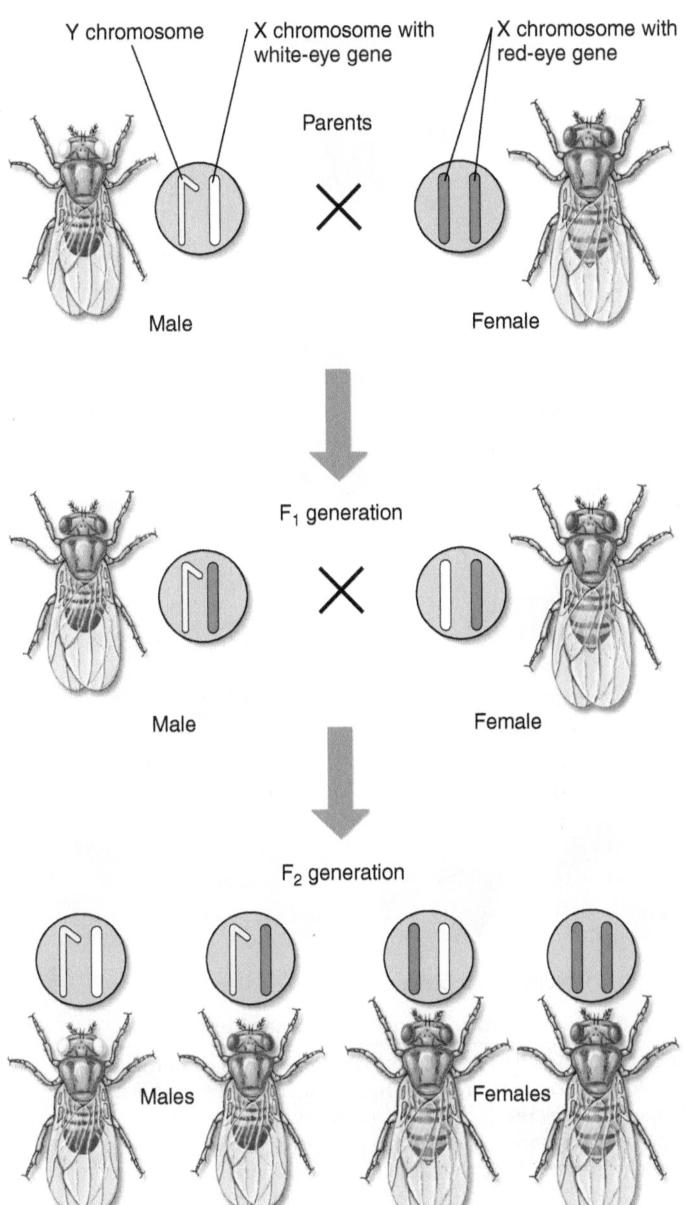

Figure 10.18 Morgan's experiment demonstrating the chromosomal basis of sex linkage.

Morgan's experiment presented the first clear evidence that the genes determining Mendelian traits reside on chromosomes, just as Sutton had proposed. Now we can see that the reason Mendelian traits segregate is because chromosomes segregate. When Mendel observed the segregation of alternative traits in pea plants, he was observing a reflection of the meiotic segregation of the chromosomes, which contained the characters he was observing.

If genes are located on chromosomes, you might expect that two genes on the same chromosome would segregate together. However, if the two genes are located far from each other on the chromosome, like genes *A* and *I* in figure 10.19, the likelihood of crossing over occurring between them is very high, leading to independent assortment. Conversely, the closer two genes are to each other on a chromosome, like genes *I* and *T*, the less likely it is that a cross over event will occur between them. Genes that are located quite close to each other almost always segregate together, and so are inherited together. The tendency of close-together genes to segregate together is called **linkage.**

Crossing over, discussed on page 146, occurs during meiosis when homologous chromosomes physically exchange segments. As a result, an allele located on one chromosome may be transferred to its homologue, causing the alleles to segregate independently.

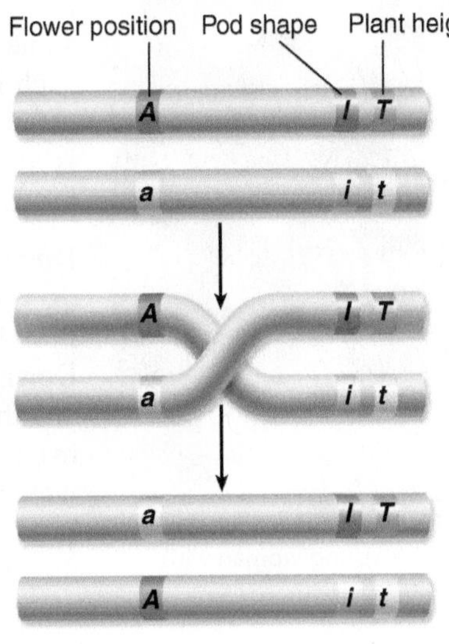

Figure 10.19 Linkage.

Genes that are located farther apart on a chromosome, like the genes for flower position (*A*) and pod shape (*I*) in Mendel's peas, will assort independently because crossing over results in recombination of these alleles. Pod shape (*I*) and plant height (*T*), however, are positioned very near each other, such that crossing over usually would not occur. These genes are said to be linked and do not undergo independent assortment.

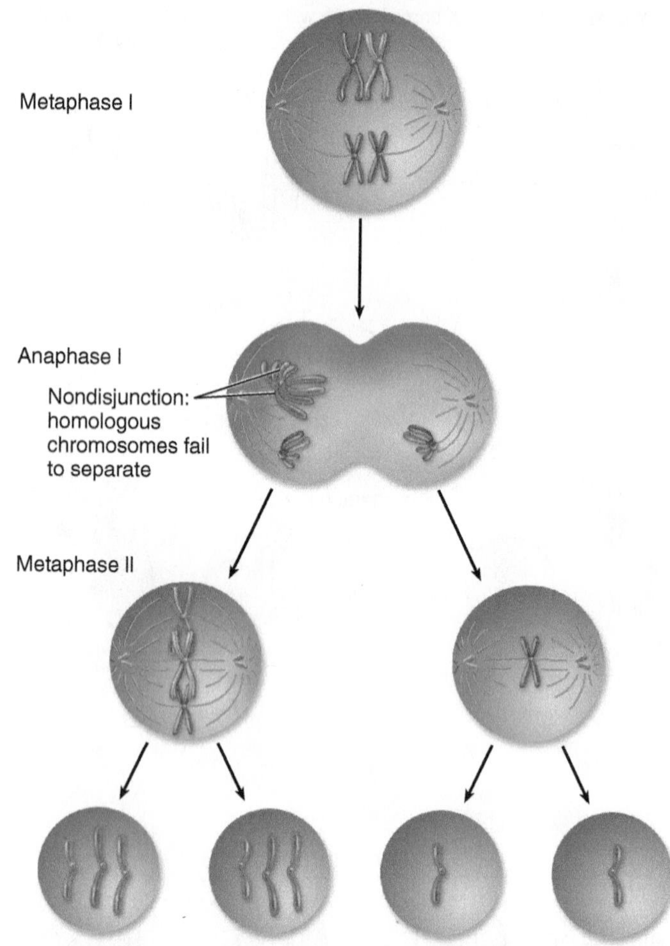

Figure 10.20 Nondisjunction in anaphase I.

In nondisjunction that occurs during meiosis I, one pair of homologous chromosomes fails to separate in anaphase I, and the gametes that result have one too many or one too few chromosomes. Nondisjunction can also occur in meiosis II, when sister chromatids fail to separate during anaphase II.

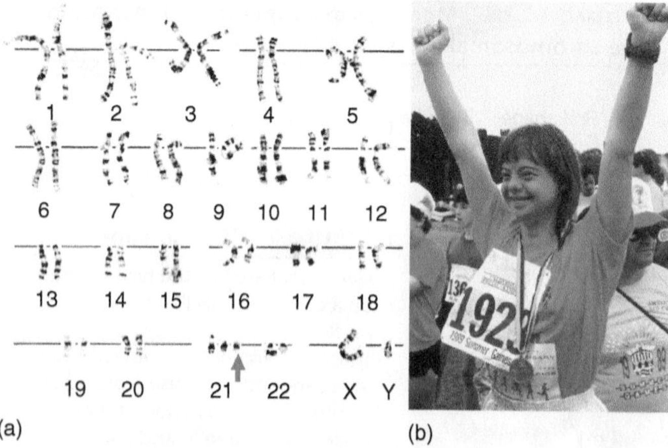

Figure 10.21 Down syndrome.

(a) In this karyotype of a male individual with Down syndrome, the trisomy at position 21 can be clearly seen. (b) A young woman with Down syndrome.

10.8 Human Chromosomes

CONCEPT PREVIEW: Autosome loss is always lethal and an extra autosome is, with few exceptions, lethal too. Additional sex chromosomes have less serious consequences, although they can lead to sterility.

Each human somatic cell normally has 46 chromosomes, which in meiosis form 23 pairs. Homologous chromosomes can be identified, according to size, shape, and appearance. Of the 23 pairs of human chromosomes, 22 are perfectly matched in both males and females and are called **autosomes.** The remaining pair, the **sex chromosomes,** consist of two similar chromosomes in females and two dissimilar chromosomes in males. In humans, females are designated XX and males are XY. The genes present on the Y chromosome determine "maleness" and therefore humans who inherit the Y chromosome develop into males.

Recent evidence suggests that a gene called *SRY* for "Sex-determining Region of the *Y* chromosome" may be responsible for the development of "maleness." This is discussed in more detail on page 595.

Nondisjunction

Sometimes during meiosis, homologous chromosomes or sister chromatids that paired up during metaphase remain stuck together instead of separating. The failure of chromosomes to separate correctly during either meiosis I or II is called **nondisjunction.** Nondisjunction leads to **aneuploidy,** an abnormal number of chromosomes. The nondisjunction you see in figure 10.20 occurs because the homologous pair of larger chromosomes failed to separate in anaphase I. The gametes that result from this division have unequal numbers of chromosomes. Under normal meiosis (refer back to *Essential Biological Process 9A*), all gametes would be expected to have two chromosomes, but as you can see two of these gametes have three chromosomes, while the others have just one.

Almost all humans of the same sex have the same karyotype (refer back to figure 8.3) simply because other arrangements don't work well. Humans who have lost even one copy of an autosome (called **monosomics**) do not survive development. In all but a few cases, humans who have gained an extra autosome (called **trisomics**) also do not survive. However, five of the smallest chromosomes—those numbered 13, 15, 18, 21, and 22—can be present in humans as three copies and still allow the individual to survive for a time. The presence of an extra chromosome 13, 15, or 18 causes severe developmental defects, and infants with such a genetic makeup die within a few months. In contrast, individuals who have an extra copy of chromosome 21 or, more rarely, chromosome 22, usually survive to adulthood. In such individuals, the maturation of the skeletal system is delayed, so they generally are short and have poor muscle tone. Their mental development is also affected, and children with trisomy 21 or trisomy 22 are always mentally impaired.

Down Syndrome. The developmental defect produced by trisomy 21, an extra copy of chromosome 21 seen in the karyotype in figure 10.21, was first described in 1866 by J. Langdon Down; for this reason, it is called Down syndrome. About 1 in every 750 children exhibits Down syndrome, and the frequency is similar in all racial groups. It is much more common in children of older mothers. The graph in figure 10.22 shows the increasing incidence in older mothers. In mothers under 30 years old, the incidence is only about 0.6 per 1,000 (or 1 in 1,500 births), while in mothers 30 to 35 years old, the incidence doubles to about 1.3 per 1,000 births (or 1 in

750 births). In mothers over 45, the risk is as high as 63 per 1,000 births (or 1 in 16 births). The reason that older mothers are more prone to Down syndrome babies is that all the eggs that a woman will ever produce are present in her ovaries by the time she is born, and as she gets older they may accumulate damage that can result in nondisjunction.

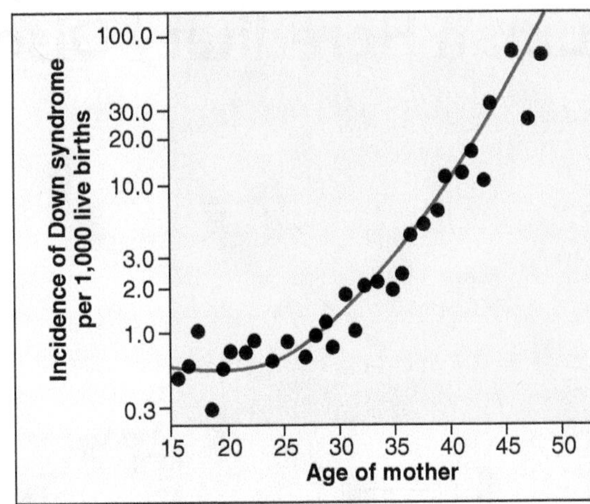

Figure 10.22 Correlation between maternal age and the incidence of Down syndrome.

As women age, the chances they will bear a child with Down syndrome increase. After a woman reaches age 35, the frequency of Down syndrome increases rapidly.

Nondisjunction Involving the Sex Chromosomes

As noted, 22 of the 23 pairs of human chromosomes are perfectly matched in both males and females and are called autosomes. The remaining pair are the sex chromosomes, X and Y. In humans, as in *Drosophila* (but by no means in all diploid species), females are XX and males XY; any individual with at least one Y chromosome is male. The Y chromosome is highly condensed and bears few functional genes in most organisms. Some of the active genes the Y chromosome does possess are responsible for the features associated with "maleness." Individuals who gain or lose a sex chromosome do not generally experience the severe developmental abnormalities caused by changes in autosomes. Such individuals may reach maturity, but with somewhat abnormal features.

Nondisjunction of the X Chromosome. When X chromosomes fail to separate during meiosis, some of the gametes that are produced possess both X chromosomes and so are XX gametes; the other gametes that result from such an event have no sex chromosome and are designated "O."

Figure 10.23 shows what happens if gametes from X chromosome nondisjunction combine with sperm. If an XX egg combines with an X sperm, the resulting XXX zygote develops into a female who is taller than average but other symptoms can vary greatly. Some are normal in most respects, others may have lower reading and verbal skills, and still others are mentally retarded. If an XX egg combines with a Y sperm, the XXY zygote develops into a sterile male who has many female body characteristics and, in some cases, diminished mental capacity. This condition, called *Klinefelter syndrome,* occurs in about 1 in 500 male births.

If an O egg fuses with a Y sperm, the OY zygote is nonviable and fails to develop further because humans cannot survive when they lack the genes on the X chromosome. If an O egg fuses with an X sperm, the XO zygote develops into a sterile female of short stature, with a webbed neck and immature sex organs that do not undergo changes during puberty. The mental abilities of XO individuals are normal in verbal learning but lower in nonverbal/math-based problem solving. This condition, called *Turner syndrome,* occurs roughly once in every 5,000 female births.

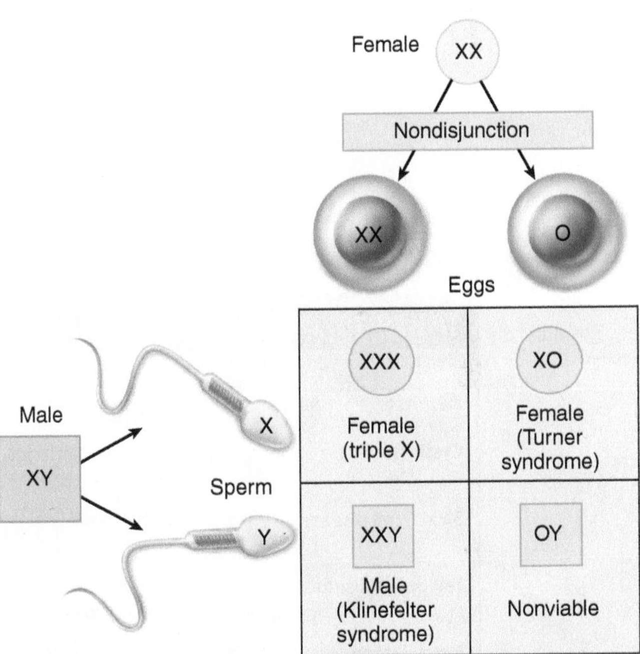

Figure 10.23 Nondisjunction of the X chromosome.

Nondisjunction of the X chromosome can produce sex chromosome aneuploidy—that is, abnormalities in the number of sex chromosomes.

Nondisjunction of the Y Chromosome. The Y chromosome can also fail to separate in meiosis, leading to the formation of YY sperm. When these sperm combine with X eggs, the XYY zygotes develop into fertile males of normal appearance. The frequency of the XYY genotype is about 1 per 1,000 newborn males.

Concept Check

1. Mendel reported that flower position and pod shape, traits located on the same chromosome, segregated independently in dihybrid crosses. Explain how this can occur.
2. What is the cause of Down syndrome?
3. Is it possible for a female to have Klinefelter syndrome? Explain.

Human Hereditary Disorders

KEY:
Affected
Carrier
Unaffected
Female
Male

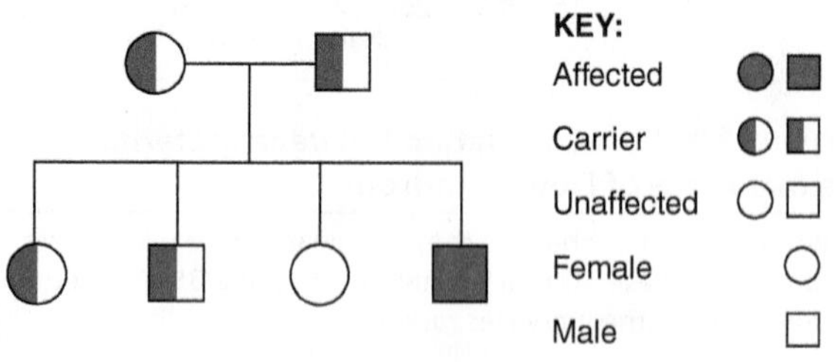

Figure 10.24 A general pedigree.

This pedigree is consistent with the inheritance of a recessive trait.

10.9 The Role of Mutations in Human Heredity

CONCEPT PREVIEW: Many human hereditary disorders reflect the presence of rare (and sometimes not so rare) mutations within human populations.

The proteins encoded by most of your genes must function in a very precise fashion for you to develop properly and for the many complex processes of your body to function correctly. Unfortunately, genes sometimes sustain damage or are copied incorrectly. We call these accidental changes in genes **mutations.** Mutations occur only rarely, because your cells police your genes and attempt to correct any damage they encounter. Still, some mutations get through. Many of them are bad for you in one way or another. It is easy to see why. Mutations hit genes at random—imagine that you randomly changed the number of a part on the design of a jet fighter. Sometimes it won't matter critically—a seat belt becomes a radio, say. But what if a key rivet in the wing becomes a roll of toilet paper? The chance of a random mutation in a gene improving the performance of its protein is about the same as that of a randomly selected part making the jet fly faster.

Mutations can occur in somatic cells or in germ-line cells. Both can have dramatic effects, but as discussed on page 193, only mutations in germ-line tissues are passed on to offspring and affect future generations.

Most mutations are rare in human populations. Almost all result in recessive alleles, and so they are not eliminated from the population by evolutionary forces—because they are not expressed in most individuals (heterozygotes) in which they occur. Do you see why they occur mostly in heterozygotes? Because mutant alleles are rare, it is unlikely that a person carrying a copy of the mutant allele will marry someone who also carries

TABLE 10.3 Some Important Genetic Disorders

Disorder	Symptom	Defect	Dominant/ Recessive	Frequency Among Human Births
Cystic fibrosis	Mucus clogs lungs, liver, and pancreas	Failure of chloride ion transport mechanism	Recessive	1/2,500 (Caucasians)
Sickle-cell disease	Poor blood circulation	Abnormal hemoglobin molecules	Recessive	1/625 (African Americans)
Tay-Sachs disease	Deterioration of central nervous system in infancy	Defective enzyme (hexosaminidase A)	Recessive	1/3,500 (Ashkenazi Jews)
Phenylketonuria (PKU)	Brain fails to develop in infancy	Defective enzyme (phenylalanine hydroxylase)	Recessive	1/12,000
Hemophilia	Blood fails to clot	Defective blood-clotting factor VIII	Sex-linked recessive	1/10,000 (Caucasian males)
Huntington's disease	Brain tissue gradually deteriorates in middle age	Production of an inhibitor of brain cell metabolism	Dominant	1/24,000
Muscular dystrophy (Duchenne)	Muscles waste away	Degradation of myelin coating of nerves stimulating muscles	Sex-linked recessive	1/3,700 (males)
Congenital hypothyroidism	Increased birth weight, puffy face, constipation, lethargy	Failure of proper thyroid development	Recessive	1/1,000 (Hispanics) 1/700 (Native Americans)
Hypercholesterolemia	Excessive cholesterol levels in blood, leading to heart disease	Abnormal form of cholesterol cell surface receptor	Dominant	1/500

it. Instead, he or she will typically marry someone homozygous dominant, and so none of their children would be homozygous for the mutant allele. While most mutations are harmful to normal functions and are usually recessive, that is not to say all mutations are undesirable; some mutations can lead to enhanced function. Nor are all mutations recessive; rarely they can occur as dominant alleles.

In some cases, particular mutant alleles have become more common in human populations. In these cases, the harmful effects that they produce are called *genetic disorders.* Some of the most common genetic disorders are listed in table 10.3. To study human heredity, scientists look at the results of crosses that have already been made. They study family trees, or **pedigrees,** to identify which relatives exhibit a trait. Figure 10.24 shows a general pedigree. Females are indicated with circles and males with squares. The lines connect the parents and display the offspring. Solid shapes indicate an individual affected by a disorder; half-filled shapes indicate a carrier (someone who is heterozygous); open shapes indicate an individual not affected. Pedigrees can often indicate whether the gene producing the trait is sex-linked or autosomal and whether the trait's phenotype is dominant or recessive. Frequently, they can infer which individuals are homozygous and which are heterozygous for the allele specifying the trait.

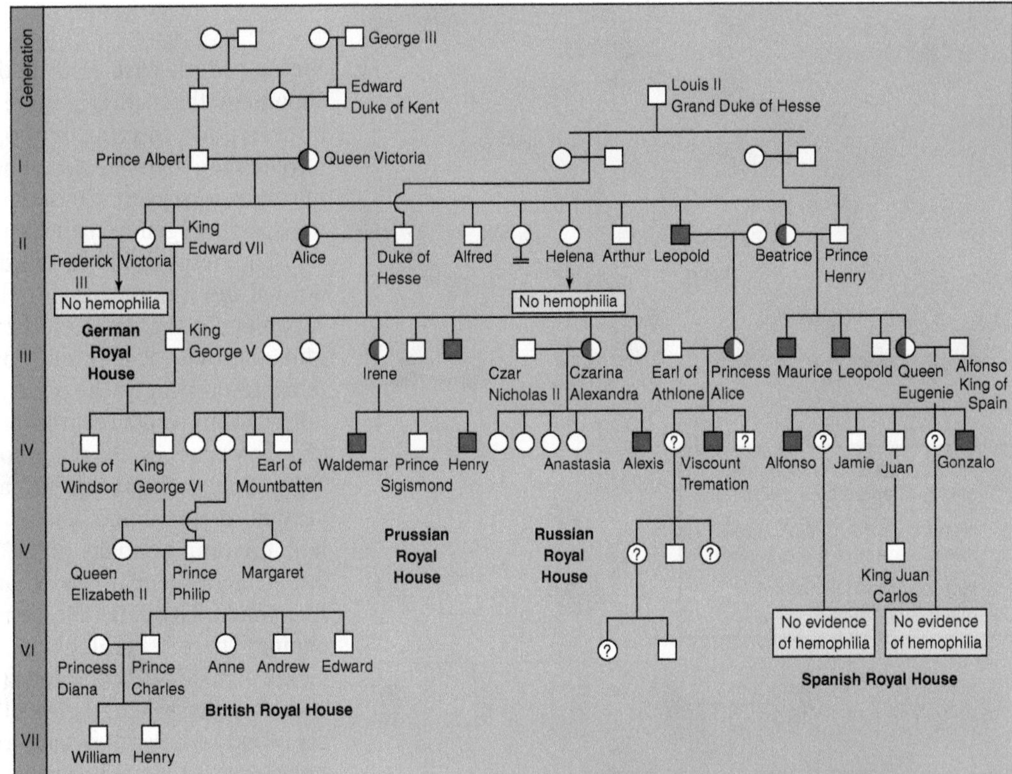

Figure 10.25 The Royal hemophilia pedigree.

Queen Victoria's daughter Alice introduced hemophilia into the Russian and Prussian royal houses, and her daughter Beatrice introduced it into the Spanish royal house. Victoria's son Leopold, himself a victim, also transmitted the disorder in a third line of descent. Half-shaded symbols represent carriers with one normal allele and one defective allele; fully shaded symbols represent affected individuals. Squares represent males; circles represent females. In this photo, Queen Victoria of England is surrounded by some of her descendants in 1894. Standing behind Victoria and wearing feathered boas are two of Victoria's granddaughters, Alice's daughter's: Princess Irene of Prussia *(right),* and Alexandra *(left),* who would soon become Czarina of Russia. Both Irene and Alexandra were also carriers of hemophilia.

Hemophilia: A Sex-Linked Trait

Blood in a cut clots as a result of the polymerization of protein fibers circulating in the blood. A dozen proteins are involved in this process, and all must function properly for a blood clot to form. A mutation causing any of these proteins to lose their activity leads to a form of **hemophilia,** a hereditary condition in which the blood clots slowly or not at all.

Hemophilias are recessive disorders, expressed only when an individual does not possess any copy of the normal allele and so cannot produce one of the proteins necessary for clotting. Most of the genes that encode the blood-clotting proteins are on autosomes, but two (designated VIII and IX) are on the X chromosome. These two genes are sex-linked (see section 10.7). Any male who inherits a mutant allele will develop hemophilia, because his other sex chromosome is a Y chromosome that lacks any alleles of those genes.

The most famous instance of hemophilia, often called the Royal hemophilia, is a sex-linked form that arose in the royal family of England. This hemophilia was caused by a mutation in gene IX that occurred in one of the parents of Queen Victoria of England (1819–1901). The pedigree in figure 10.25 shows that in the six generations since Queen Victoria, 10 of her male descendants have had hemophilia (the solid squares). The present British royal family has escaped the disorder because Queen Victoria's son, King Edward VII, did not inherit the defective allele, and all the subsequent rulers of England are his descendants. Three of Victoria's nine children did receive the defective allele, however, and they carried it by marriage into many of the other royal families of Europe.

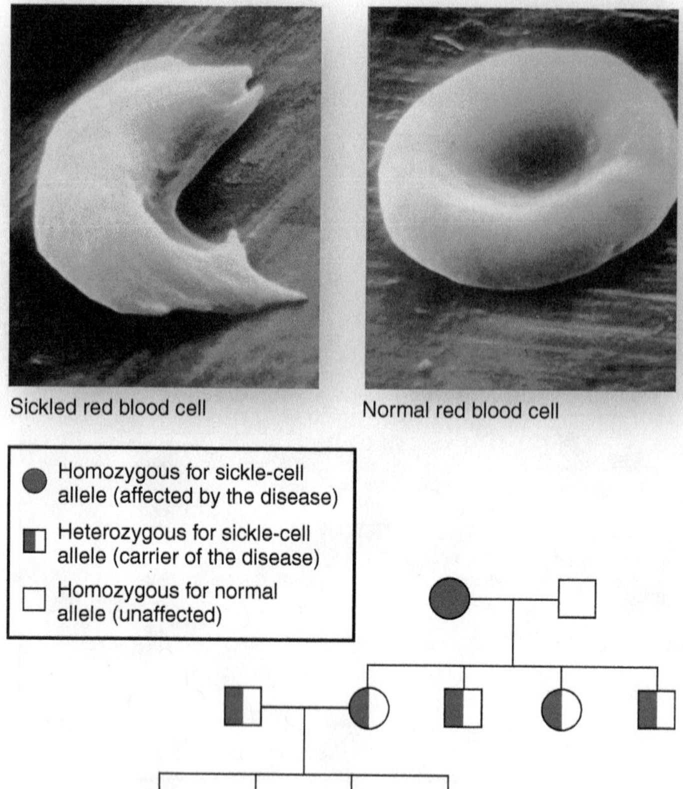

Figure 10.26 Inheritance of sickle-cell disease.

Sickle-cell disease is a recessive autosomal disorder. If one parent is homozygous for the recessive trait, all of the offspring will be carriers (heterozygotes) like the F_1 generation of Mendel's testcross. A normal red blood cell is shaped like a flattened sphere. In individuals homozygous for the sickle-cell trait, many of the red blood cells have sickle shapes.

IMPLICATION If the sickle-cell allele (*S*) when heterozygous with the normal allele (*A*) confers resistance to malaria, then the phenotype of homozygous individuals (*AA*) is different from the phenotype of heterozygous individuals (*AS*). *AS* individuals are resistant to malaria while *AA* individuals are not. In light of this, how can the *S* allele be considered recessive to the *A* allele? Discuss.

Sickle-Cell Disease: Recessive Trait

Sickle-cell disease is a recessive hereditary disorder. Its inheritance is shown in the pedigree in figure 10.26, where affected individuals are homozygous, carrying two copies of the mutated gene. Affected individuals have defective molecules of hemoglobin, the protein within red blood cells that carries oxygen. Consequently, these individuals are unable to properly transport oxygen to their tissues.

The hemoglobin in the defective red blood cells differs from that in normal red blood cells in only one of beta-hemoglobin's 146 amino acid subunits. In the defective hemoglobin, the amino acid valine replaces a glutamic acid at a single position in each of the two beta-subunit proteins. Interestingly, the position of the change is far from the active site of hemoglobin where the iron-bearing heme group binds oxygen. Instead, the change occurs on the outer corners of the 4-subunit hemoglobin molecule. Why then is the result so catastrophic? The sickle-cell mutation puts a very nonpolar amino acid (valine) on the surface of the hemoglobin protein, creating a "sticky patch" that sticks to other such patches—nonpolar amino acids tend to associate with one another in polar environments like water. The defective hemoglobin molecules adhere to one another in chains. These hemoglobin chains form stiff, rodlike structures that result in sickle-shaped red blood cells (see figure 10.26). As a result of their stiffness and irregular shape, these cells have difficulty moving through the smallest blood vessels; they tend to accumulate in those vessels and form clots. People who have large proportions of sickle-shaped red blood cells tend to have intermittent illness and a shortened life span.

Individuals heterozygous for the sickle-cell allele are generally indistinguishable from normal persons. However, some of their red blood cells show the sickling characteristic when they are exposed to low levels of oxygen. The allele responsible for sickle-cell disease is particularly common among people of African descent because the sickle-cell allele is more common in Africa. About 9% of African Americans are heterozygous for this allele, and about 0.2% are homozygous and therefore have the disorder. In some groups of people in Africa, up to 45% of all individuals are heterozygous for this allele, and fully 6% are homozygous and express the disorder. What factors determine the high frequency of sickle-cell disease in Africa? It turns out that heterozygosity for the sickle-cell allele increases resistance to malaria, a common and serious disease in Central Africa. Comparing the two maps shown in figure 10.27, you can see that the area of the sickle-cell trait matches well with the incidence of malaria. The interactions of sickle-cell disease and malaria are discussed further in chapter 14.

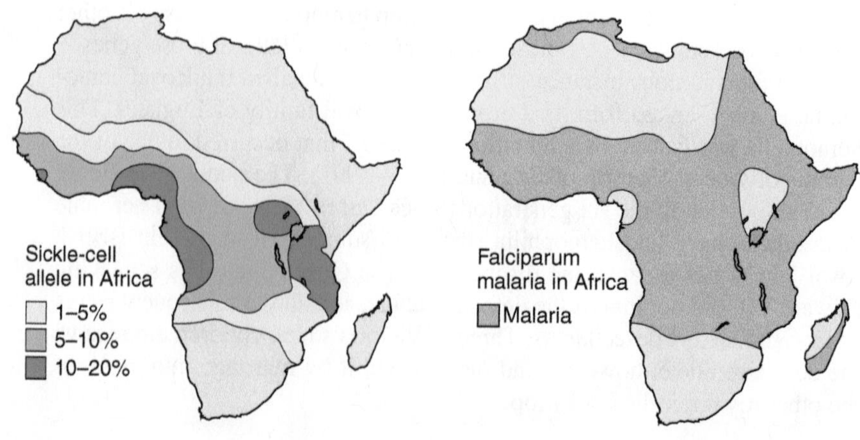

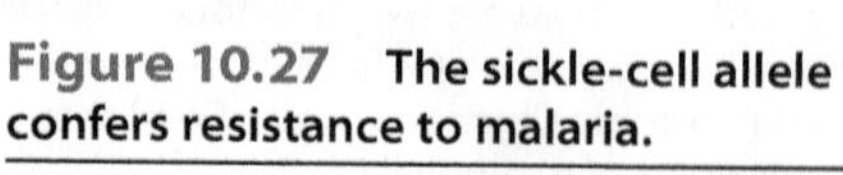

Figure 10.27 The sickle-cell allele confers resistance to malaria.

The distribution of sickle-cell disease closely matches the occurrence of malaria in central Africa. This is not a coincidence. The sickle-cell allele, when heterozygous, confers resistance to malaria, a very serious disease.

Tay-Sachs Disease: Recessive Trait

Tay-Sachs disease is an incurable hereditary disorder in which the brain deteriorates. Affected children appear normal at birth and usually do not develop symptoms until about the eighth month, when signs of mental deterioration appear. The children are blind within a year after birth, and they rarely live past five years of age.

The Tay-Sachs allele produces the disease by encoding a nonfunctional form of the enzyme hexosaminidase A. This enzyme breaks down *gangliosides,* a class of lipids occurring within the lysosomes of brain cells. As a result, the lysosomes fill with gangliosides, swell, and eventually burst, releasing oxidative enzymes that kill the cells. There is no known cure for this disorder.

Lysosomes are a component of the endomembrane system, as discussed on page 73. They are membrane-bounded vesicles that contain powerful enzymes that break down cellular debris. If the lysosome enzymes leak out, they will kill the cell from within.

Tay-Sachs disease is rare in most human populations, occurring in only 1 in 300,000 births in the United States. However, the disease has a high incidence among Jews of Eastern and Central Europe (Ashkenazi) and among American Jews, 90% of whom trace their ancestry to Eastern and Central Europe. In these populations, it is estimated that 1 in 28 individuals is a heterozygous carrier of the disease, and approximately 1 in 3,500 infants has the disease. Because the disease is caused by a recessive allele, most of the people who carry the defective allele do not themselves develop symptoms of the disease because, as shown by the middle bar in figure 10.28, their one normal gene produces enough enzyme activity (50%) to keep the body functioning normally.

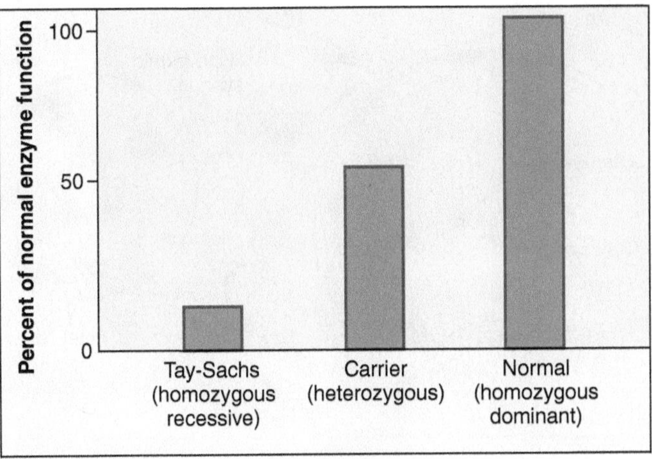

Figure 10.28 Tay-Sachs disease.

Homozygous individuals (*left bar*) typically have less than 10% of the normal level of hexosaminidase A (*right bar*), while heterozygous individuals (*middle bar*) have about 50% of the normal level—enough to prevent deterioration of the central nervous system.

IMPLICATION Tay-Sachs disease is named for Warren Tay, an eye doctor who first described the cherry-red spot on the retina that is now the marker for the disease, and Bernard Sachs, a neurologist who first described the changes in the brain and the prevalence among Ashkenazi Jews. Can you think of another disease named for its discoverer?

Huntington's Disease: Dominant Trait

Not all hereditary disorders are recessive. **Huntington's disease** is a hereditary condition caused by a dominant allele that causes the progressive deterioration of brain cells. Perhaps 1 in 24,000 individuals develops the disorder. Because the allele is dominant, every individual who carries the allele expresses the disorder. Nevertheless, the disorder persists in human populations because its symptoms usually do not develop until the affected individuals are more than 30 years old, and by that time most of those individuals have already had children. Consequently, as illustrated by the pedigree in figure 10.29, the allele is often transmitted before the lethal condition develops.

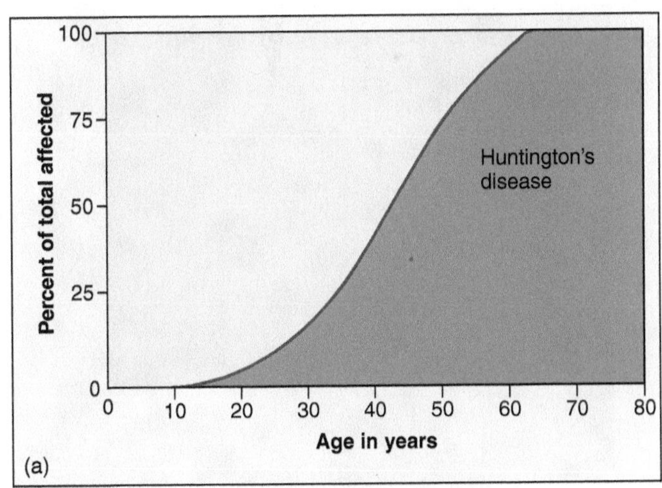

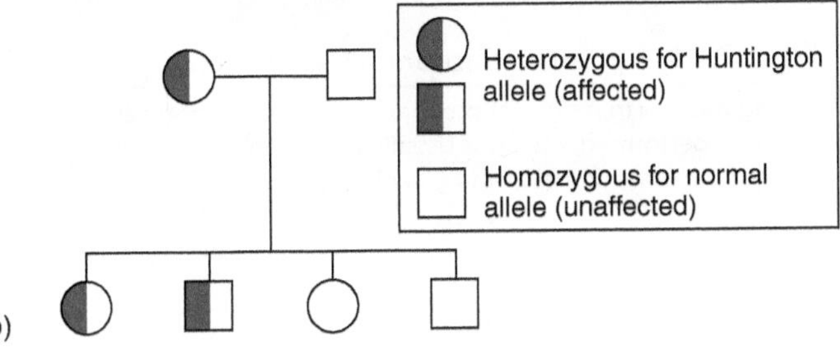

Figure 10.29 Huntington's disease is a dominant genetic disorder.

(a) Because of the late age of onset of Huntington's disease, the allele causing it persists despite being both dominant and fatal. (b) The pedigree illustrates how a dominant lethal allele can be passed from one generation to the next. Although the mother was affected, we can tell that she was heterozygous because if she were homozygous dominant, all of her children would have been affected. However, by the time she found out that she had the disease, she had probably already given birth to her children. In this way the trait passes on to the next generation even though it is fatal.

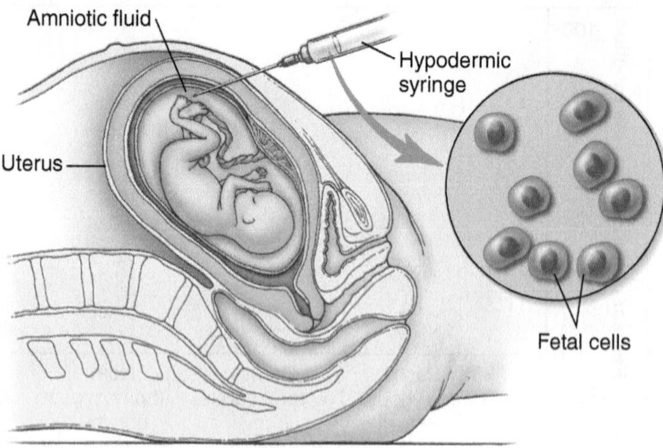

Figure 10.30 Amniocentesis.

A needle is inserted into the amniotic cavity, and a sample of amniotic fluid, containing some free cells derived from the fetus, is withdrawn into a syringe. The fetal cells are then grown in culture and their karyotype and many of their metabolic functions are examined.

IMPLICATION The risk of amniocentesis-related miscarriage due to infection, puncture leakage, or other complications is estimated to be as low as 1 in 600. In contrast, the risk of miscarriage for chorionic villus sampling is approximately 1 in 100, although the sampling may be done up to four weeks earlier. If you have a child, would you carry out genetic screening? If so, which procedure would you use? Why?

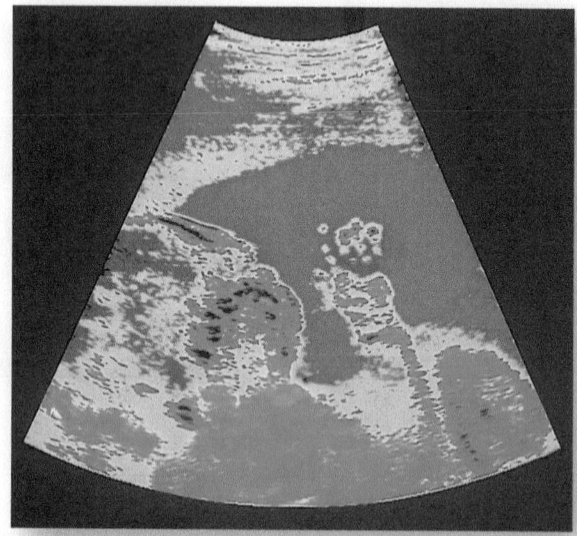

Figure 10.31 An ultrasound view of a fetus.

During the fourth month of pregnancy, when amniocentesis is normally performed, the fetus usually moves about actively. The head of the fetus (visualized in *green*) is to the *left*.

10.10 Genetic Counseling and Therapy

CONCEPT PREVIEW: It has recently become possible to detect genetic defects early in pregnancy, allowing appropriate planning by prospective parents.

The process of identifying parents at risk of producing children with genetic defects and of assessing the genetic state of early embryos is called **genetic counseling.** Genetic counseling can help prospective parents determine their risk of having a child with a genetic disorder, and advise them on medical treatments or options if a genetic disorder is determined to exist in an unborn child.

Genetic Screening

When a pregnancy is diagnosed as being high risk, many women elect to undergo **amniocentesis,** a procedure that permits the prenatal diagnosis of many genetic disorders. Figure 10.30 shows how an amniocentesis is performed. In the fourth month of pregnancy, a sterile hypodermic needle is inserted into the expanded uterus of the mother, and a small sample of the amniotic fluid bathing the fetus is removed. Within the fluid are free-floating cells derived from the fetus; once removed, these cells can be grown in cultures in the laboratory. During amniocentesis, the position of the needle and that of the fetus are usually observed by means of **ultrasound.** The ultrasound image in figure 10.31 clearly reveals the fetus's position in the uterus.

In recent years, physicians have increasingly turned to another invasive procedure for genetic screening called **chorionic villus sampling.** In this procedure, the physician removes cells from the chorion, a membranous part of the placenta that nourishes the fetus. This procedure can be used earlier in pregnancy (by the eighth week) and yields results much more rapidly than does amniocentesis, but can increase the risk of miscarriage.

Genetic counselors look at three things in the cultures of cells obtained from amniocentesis or chorionic villus sampling:

1. **Chromosomal karyotype.** Analysis of the karyotype can reveal aneuploidy (extra or missing chromosomes) and gross alterations.
2. **Enzyme activity.** In many cases, it is possible to test directly for the proper functioning of enzymes involved in genetic disorders. The lack of normal enzymatic activity signals the presence of the disorder.
3. **Genetic markers.** Genetic counselors can look for an association with known genetic markers. For sickle-cell disease, Huntington's disease, and one form of muscular dystrophy (a genetic disorder characterized by weakened muscles), investigators have found other mutations on the same chromosomes that, by chance, occur at about the same place as the mutations that cause those disorders. By testing for the presence of these other mutations, a genetic counselor can identify individuals with a high probability of possessing the disorder-causing mutations.

Concept Check

1. If most recessive mutations disrupt genes and so are bad for you, why aren't they eliminated from the human population by natural selection?
2. If Huntington's disease is caused by a dominant allele and is lethal, why doesn't the disease disappear from the human population?
3. Why not use ultrasound instead of amniocentesis for prenatal diagnosis? Isn't it safer?

Why Woolly Hair Runs in Families

The woman in the photo on the right does not cut her hair. Her hair breaks off naturally as it grows, keeping it from getting long. Other members of her family have the same sort of hair, suggesting it is a hereditary trait. Because of its curly, fuzzy texture, this trait has been given the name "woolly hair."

While the woolly hair trait is rare, it flares up in certain families. The extensive pedigree below (drawn curved so as to fit in the large families produced by the second and subsequent generations) records the incidence of woolly hair in five generations (indicated by the Roman numerals on the left) of a Norwegian family. As is the convention, affected individuals are indicated by solid symbols, with circles indicating females and squares indicating males. The pedigree will provide you with all the information you need to discover how this trait is inherited within human families.

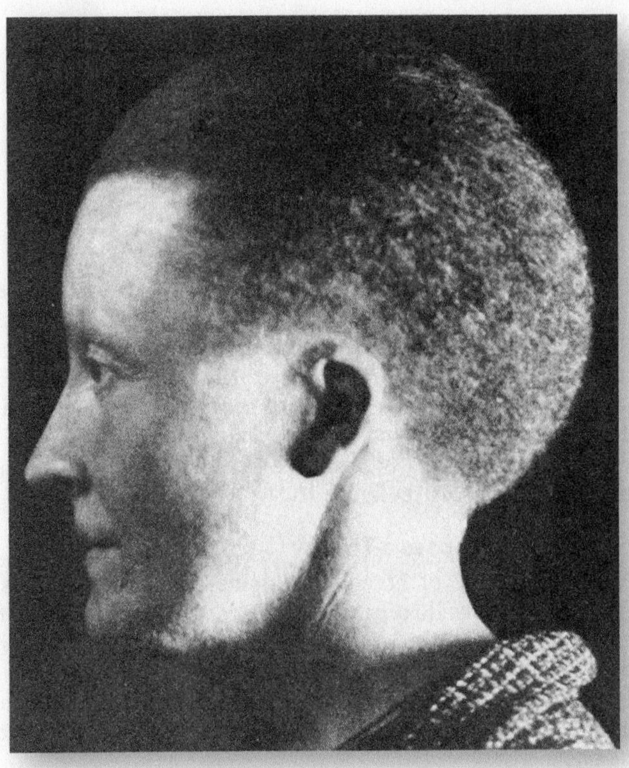

Analysis

1. **Applying Concepts** In the diagram below, how many individuals are documented? Are all of them related?
2. **Interpreting Data**
   a. Does the woolly hair trait appear in both sexes equally?
   b. Does every woolly hair child have a woolly hair parent?
   c. What percentage of the offspring born to a woolly haired parent are also woolly haired?
3. **Making Inferences**
   a. Is woolly hair sex-linked or autosomal?
   b. Is woolly hair dominant or recessive?
   c. Is the woolly hair trait determined by a single gene, or by several?
4. **Drawing Conclusions**
   a. How many copies of the woolly hair allele are necessary to produce a detectable change in a person's hair?
   b. Are there any woolly hair homozygous individuals in the pedigree? Explain.

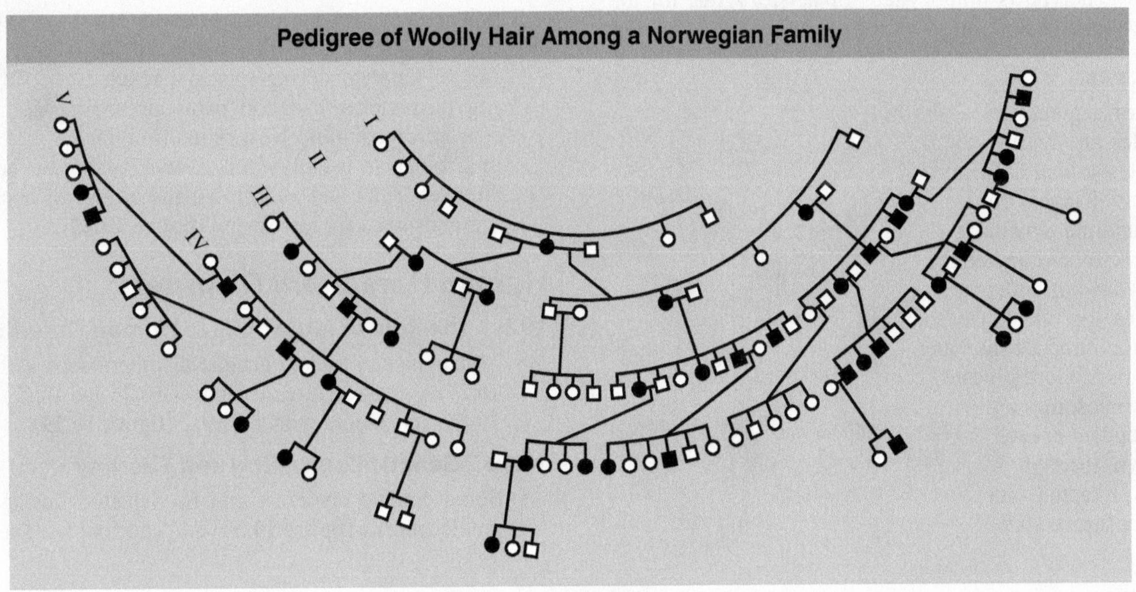

Concept Summary

Mendel

10.1 Mendel and the Garden Pea

- Mendel studied inheritance using the garden pea (**figure 10.2**) and an experimental system that included counting his results.
- Mendel used plants that were true-breeding for a particular characteristic; these plants were the P generation. He then crossed two P generation plants that expressed alternate traits (different forms of a characteristic). Their offspring were called the F_1 generation. He then allowed the F_1 plants to self-fertilize, giving rise to the F_2 generation (**figure 10.3**).

10.2 What Mendel Observed

- In Mendel's experiments, the F_1 generation plants all expressed the same alternative form, called the dominant trait. In the F_2 generation, 3/4 of the offspring expressed the dominant trait and 1/4 expressed the other form, called the recessive trait. Mendel found this 3:1 ratio in the F_2 generation in all the seven traits he studied (**table 10.1**). Mendel then found that this 3:1 ratio was actually a 1:2:1 ratio—1 true-breeding dominant: 2 not-true-breeding dominant: 1 true-breeding recessive (**figure 10.5**).

10.3 Mendel Proposes a Theory

- Mendel's theory of heredity explains that characteristics are passed from parent to offspring as alleles, one allele inherited from each parent. If both of the alleles are the same the individual is homozygous for the trait. If the individual has one dominant and one recessive allele, it is heterozygous for the trait. An individual's alleles are its genotype, and the expression of those alleles is its phenotype.
- A Punnett square can be used to predict the probabilities of inheriting certain genotypes and phenotypes in the offspring of a cross. The alleles are assigned letters: an uppercase letter for the dominant allele and a lowercase letter for the recessive allele (**figures 10.6** and **10.7**).
- A testcross is the mating of an individual of unknown genotype with an individual that is homozygous recessive. It is done to determine if the unknown genotype is homozygous or heterozygous for the dominant trait (**figure 10.8**).

10.4 Mendel's Laws

- Mendel's law of segregation states that alleles are distributed into gametes so that half of the gametes will carry one copy of a trait and the remaining gametes carry the other copy of the trait. Mendel's law of independent assortment states that the inheritance of one trait does not influence the inheritance of other traits. Genes located on different chromosomes are inherited independent of each other, as shown through a dihybrid cross, like the one shown here from **figure 10.9.**

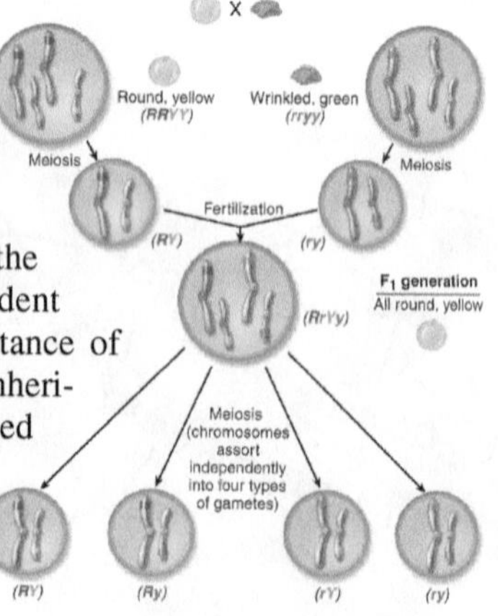

From Genotype to Phenotype

10.5 How Genes Influence Traits

- Genes coded in DNA determine phenotype because DNA encodes the amino acid sequences of proteins, and proteins are the outward expression of genes (**figure 10.10**). Alleles, which are alternative forms of a gene, result from mutations.

10.6 Why Some Traits Don't Show Mendelian Inheritance

- Not all traits follow the inheritance patterns outlined by Mendel. Continuous variation results when more than one gene contributes in a cumulative way to a phenotype, resulting in a continuous array of phenotypes. This pattern of inheritance is called polygenic (**figure 10.11**). Pleiotropic effects result when one gene influences more than one trait (**figure 10.12**). Incomplete dominance results when alternative alleles are not fully dominant or fully recessive such that heterozygous individuals express a phenotype that is intermediate between the dominant and recessive phenotypes. An example is the Japanese four o'clock flowers shown here from **figure 10.13.** The expression of some genes is influenced by environmental factors, such as the changing of fur color triggered by heat-sensitive alleles (**figure 10.14**). Codominance occurs when there isn't a dominant allele—two alleles are expressed resulting in phenotypic expression of both alleles (**figures 10.15** and **10.16**).

Chromosomes and Heredity

10.7 Chromosomes Are the Vehicles of Mendelian Inheritance

- Genes segregate because they are located on chromosomes that segregate during meiosis. Morgan demonstrated this using an X-linked gene in fruit flies (**figure 10.18**). However, the farther apart two genes are on a chromosome, the more likely they are to assort independently because of crossing over (**figure 10.19**).

10.8 Human Chromosomes

- Humans have 23 pairs of homologous chromosomes, for a total of 46 chromosomes. They have 22 pairs of autosomes and one pair of sex chromosomes. Nondisjunction occurs when sister chromatids or homologous pairs, as shown here from **figure 10.20**, fail to separate during meiosis, resulting in gametes with too many or too few chromosomes. Nondisjunction of autosomes is usually fatal, Down syndrome being an exception (**figures 10.21** and **10.22**), but the effects of nondisjunction of sex chromosomes are less severe (**figure 10.23**).

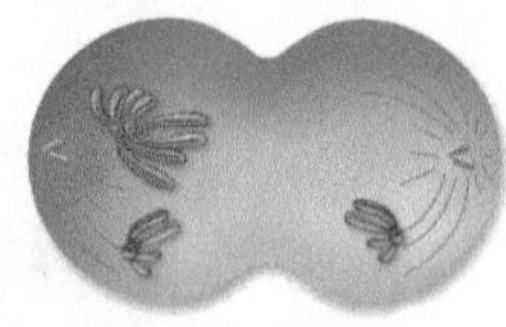

Human Hereditary Disorders

10.9 The Role of Mutations in Human Heredity

- Mutations can lead to genetic disorders such as hemophilia (**figure 10.25**), sickle-cell disease (**figures 10.26** and **10.27**), Tay-Sachs (**figure 10.28**), and Huntington's disease (**figure 10.29**).

10.10 Genetic Counseling and Therapy

- Some genetic disorders can be detected during pregnancy using amniocentesis (**figure 10.30**) and chorionic villus sampling.

Self-Test

1. Gregor Mendel studied the garden pea plants because
   a. pea plants are small, easy to grow, grow quickly, and produce lots of flowers and seeds.
   b. he knew about studies with the garden pea that had been done for hundreds of years, and wanted to continue them, using math—counting and recording differences.
   c. he knew that there were many varieties available with distinctive characteristics.
   d. all of these.
2. Mendel examined seven characteristics, such as flower color. He crossed plants with two different forms of a character (purple flowers and white flowers). In every case the first generation of offspring (F_1) were
   a. all purple flowers.
   b. half purple flowers and half white flowers.
   c. 3/4 purple and 1/4 white flowers.
   d. all white flowers.
3. Following question 2, when Mendel allowed the F_1 generation to self-fertilize, the offspring in the F_2 generation were
   a. all purple flowers.
   b. half purple flowers and half white flowers.
   c. 3/4 purple and 1/4 white flowers.
   d. all white flowers.
4. Mendel then studied his results, and proposed a set of hypotheses to explain them. The basis of these hypotheses is that parents transmit
   a. traits directly to their offspring, and they are expressed.
   b. some factor, or information, about traits to their offspring, and it may or may not be expressed.
   c. some factor, or information, about traits to their offspring, and it will always be expressed.
   d. some factor, or information, about traits to their offspring, and both traits expressed in every generation, perhaps in a "blended" form with information from the other parent.
5. A cross between two individuals results in a ratio of 9:3:3:1 for four possible phenotype combinations. This is an example of a
   a. dihybrid cross.
   b. monohybrid cross.
   c. testcross.
   d. None of these are correct.
6. Human height shows a continuous variation from the very short to the very tall. Height is most likely controlled by
   a. a single gene.
   b. environmental factors.
   c. sex-linked genes.
   d. multiple genes.
7. In the human ABO blood grouping, the four basic blood types are type A, type B, type AB, and type O. The enzymes that produce types A and B are
   a. simple dominant and recessive traits.
   b. incomplete dominant traits.
   c. codominant traits.
   d. sex-linked traits.
8. What finding finally determined that genes were carried on chromosomes?
   a. heat sensitivity of certain enzymes that determined coat color
   b. sex-linked eye color in fruit flies
   c. the finding of complete dominance
   d. establishing pedigrees
9. Nondisjunction
   a. occurs when homologous chromosomes or sister chromatids fail to separate during meiosis.
   b. may lead to Down syndrome.
   c. results in aneuploidy.
   d. all of the above.
10. Which of the following analyses can detect aneuploidy?
    a. enzyme activity
    b. chromosomal karyotyping
    c. pedigrees
    d. genetic markers

Visual Understanding

1. **Figure 10.9** Using the four gametes shown from the F_1 generation, how many possible crosses are there? Remember that a gamete type could cross with another of the same type (such as $RY \times RY$). Draw a Punnett square for each cross, and list the ratios of genotypes and phenotypes for the F_2 generation of that cross.

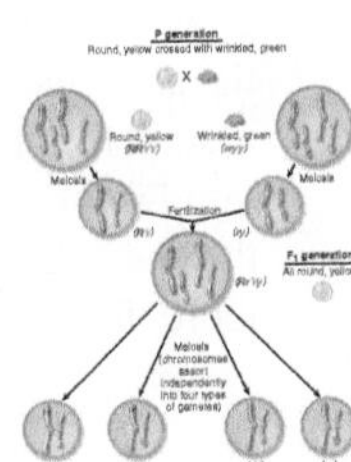

2. **Figure 10.16** Referring to this figure, use Punnett squares to illustrate whether a type A female and a type B male can have a child with type O blood.

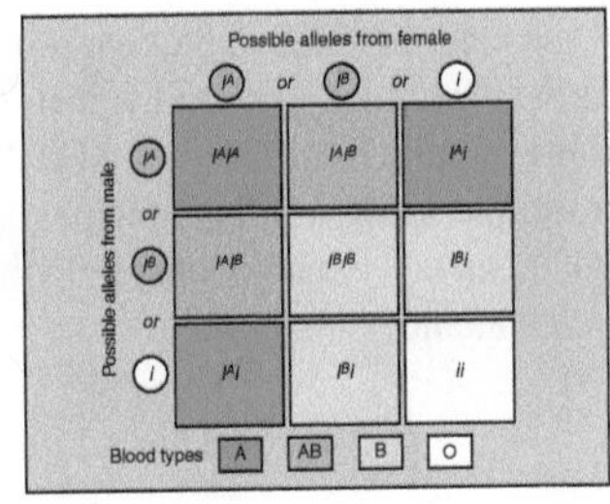

Challenge Questions

1. As Mendel struggled with understanding inheritance and formed his laws, how would the outcome have been different if he had chosen two traits that are carried on the same chromosome, with loci that are in close proximity to each other?

2. Kim and Su-Ling are doing fruit fly crosses in their biology class. Kim wants to test whether the female they have is homozygous or heterozygous for red eyes by mating with a red-eyed male. How should Su-Ling explain the difficulty to him?

3. Your biology class is collecting information on heredity. Michael realizes that he, along with three of his four brothers, are color blind, but his four sisters are not, and neither are his parents nor his grandparents. Can you help Michael understand what happened?

4. Kuzungu is a child orphaned by civil war in her country and raised in a group home. She has sickle-cell disease, and type AB blood. Two couples who believe they are her grandparents ask you, a genetic counselor, to help them determine who her real grandparents are. What do you suggest?

Additional Genetics Problems

These genetics problems will help you see the far-reaching effects of Mendel's experiments. If you need help, the answers appear at www.mhhe.com/tlwessentials3.

1. Silky feathers in chickens is a single-gene recessive trait whose effect is to produce shiny plumage.
  a. If 108 birds were raised from a cross between individuals heterozygous for this gene, how many would be expected to be silky and how many normal?
  b. If you had a normal-feathered bird, what would be the easiest cross to perform in order to determine if the bird is homozygous or heterozygous for the silky allele?

2. Among Hereford cattle there is a dominant allele called *polled;* the individuals that have this allele lack horns. Suppose you acquire a herd consisting entirely of polled cattle, and you carefully determine that no cow in the herd has horns. Some of the calves born that year, however, grow horns. You remove them from the herd and make certain that no horned adult has gotten into your pasture. Despite your efforts, more horned calves are born the next year. What is the reason for the appearance of the horned calves? If your goal is to maintain a herd consisting entirely of polled cattle, what should you do?

3. An inherited trait among humans in Norway causes affected individuals to have very curly hair, not unlike that of a sheep. The trait, called *woolly,* is very evident when it occurs in families (see *Inquiry & Analysis*); no child possesses woolly hair unless at least one parent does. Imagine you are a Norwegian judge, and you have before you a woolly haired man suing his normal-haired wife for divorce because their first child has woolly hair but their second child has normal hair. The husband claims this constitutes evidence of his wife's infidelity. Do you accept his claim? Justify your decision.

4. Brachydactyly is a rare human trait that causes a shortening of the length of the fingers by a third. A review of medical records reveals that the progeny of marriages between a brachydactyl person and a normal person are approximately half brachydactylous. What proportion of offspring in matings between two brachydactylous individuals would be expected to be brachydactylous?

5. Many animals and plants bear recessive alleles for *albinism,* a condition in which homozygous individuals lack certain pigments. An albino plant, for example, lacks chlorophyll and is white, and an albino human lacks melanin. If two normally pigmented persons heterozygous for the same albinism allele marry, what proportion of their children would you expect to be albino?

6. You inherit a racehorse and decide to put him out to stud. In looking over the stud book, however, you discover that the horse's grandfather exhibited a rare disorder that causes brittle bones. The disorder is hereditary and results from homozygosity for a recessive allele. If your horse is heterozygous for the allele, it will not be possible to use him for stud because the genetic defect may be passed on. How would you determine whether your horse carries this allele?

7. Your instructor presents you with a *Drosophila* (fruit fly) with red eyes, as well as a stock of white-eyed flies and another stock of flies homozygous for the red-eye allele. You know that the presence of white eyes in *Drosophila* is caused by homozygosity for a recessive allele. How would you determine whether the single red-eyed fly was heterozygous for the white-eye allele?

8. Hemophilia is a recessive sex-linked human blood disease that leads to failure of blood to clot normally. One form of hemophilia has been traced to the royal family of England, from which it spread throughout the royal families of Europe. For the purposes of this problem, assume that it originated as a mutation either in Prince Albert or in his wife, Queen Victoria.
  a. Prince Albert did not have hemophilia. If the disease is a sex-linked recessive abnormality, how could it have originated in Prince Albert, a male, who would have been expected to exhibit sex-linked recessive traits?
  b. Alexis, the son of Czar Nicholas II of Russia and Empress Alexandra (a granddaughter of Victoria), had hemophilia, but their daughter Anastasia did not. Anastasia died, a victim of the Russian revolution, before she had any children. Can we assume that Anastasia would have been a carrier of the disease? Would your answer be different if the disease had been present in Nicholas II or in Alexandra?

9. A normally pigmented man marries an albino woman. They have three children, one of whom is an albino. What is the genotype of the father?

10. A man works in an atomic energy plant, and he is exposed daily to low-level background radiation. After several years, he has a child who has Duchenne muscular dystrophy, a recessive genetic defect caused by a mutation on the X chromosome. Neither the parents nor the grandparents have the disease. The man sues the plant, claiming that the abnormality in their child is the direct result of radiation-induced mutation of his gametes, and that the company should have protected him from this radiation. Before reaching a decision, the judge hearing the case insists on knowing the sex of the child. Which sex would be more likely to result in an award of damages, and why?

Chapter 11

DNA: The Genetic Material

CHAPTER AT A GLANCE

Genes Are Made of DNA

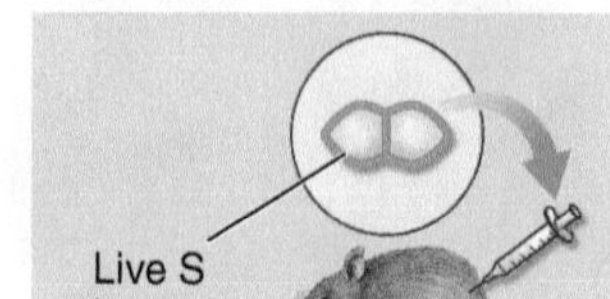

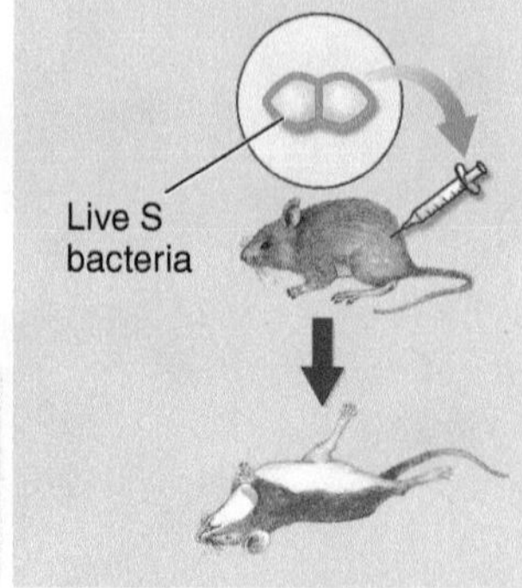

Live S bacteria
1
S bacteria have a polysaccharide capsule and are pathogenic. When they are injected into mice, the mice die.

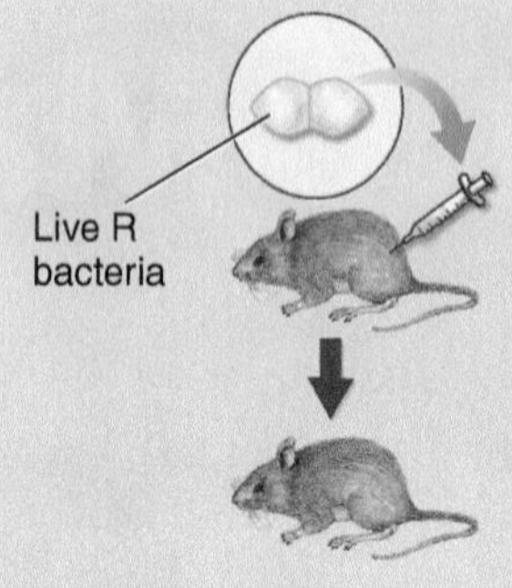

Live R bacteria
2
R bacteria do not have the capsule and do not kill mice.

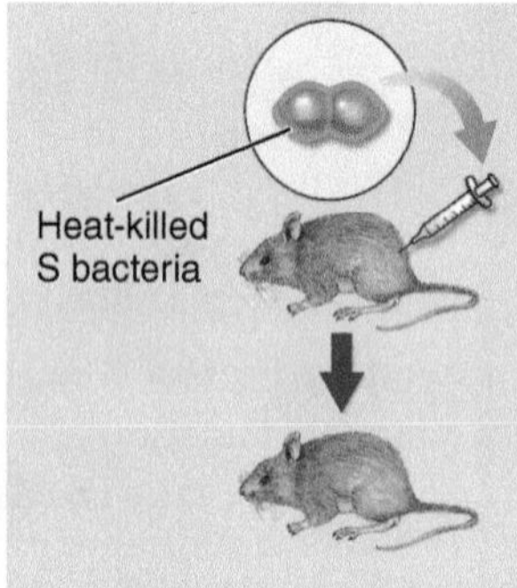

Heat-killed S bacteria
3
Heat-killed bacteria are dead but still have the capsule. They do not kill mice.

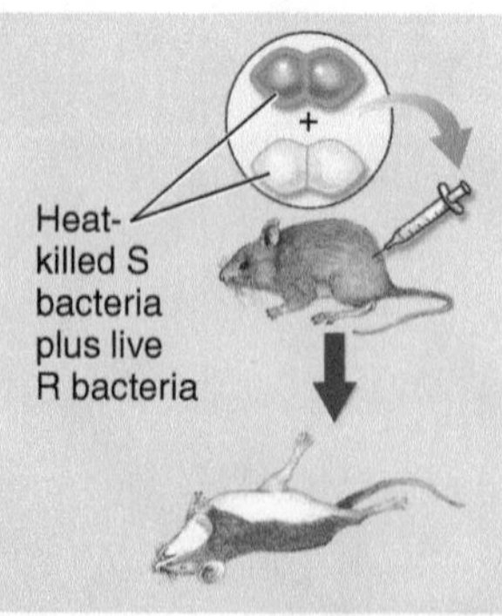

Heat-killed S bacteria plus live R bacteria
4
A mixture of live R bacteria and heat-killed S bacteria does cause mice to die.

Figure 11.1 How Griffith discovered transformation.

Transformation, the movement of a gene from one organism to another, provided some of the key evidence that DNA is the genetic material. Griffith found that extracts of dead pathogenic strains of the bacterium *Streptococcus pneumoniae* can "transform" live harmless strains into live pathogenic strains.

11.1 The Griffith Experiment

CONCEPT PREVIEW: Hereditary information can pass from dead cells to living ones and transform them.

As we learned in chapters 8, 9, and 10, chromosomes contain genes, which, in turn, contain hereditary information. However, Mendel's work left a key question unanswered: What *is* a gene?

When biologists began to examine chromosomes in their search for genes, they soon learned that chromosomes are made of two kinds of macromolecules, both of which you encountered in chapter 3: **proteins** (long chains of *amino acid subunits* linked together in a string) and **DNA** (deoxyribonucleic acid—long chains of *nucleotide* subunits linked together in a string). It was possible to imagine that either of the two was the stuff that genes are made of—information might be stored in a sequence of different amino acids, or in a sequence of different nucleotides. But which one is the stuff of genes, protein or DNA? This question was answered clearly in a variety of different experiments, all of which shared the same basic design: If you separate the DNA in an individual's chromosomes from the protein, which of the two materials is able to change another individual's genes?

In a key experiment in 1928, British microbiologist Frederick Griffith made a series of unexpected observations while experimenting with pathogenic (disease-causing) bacteria. Figure 11.1 takes you stepwise through his discoveries. When he infected mice with a virulent strain of *Streptococcus pneumoniae* bacteria (then known as *Pneumococcus*), the mice died of blood poisoning ❶. However, when he infected similar mice with a mutant strain of *S. pneumoniae* that lacked the virulent strain's polysaccharide capsule, the mice showed no ill effects ❷. The capsule was apparently necessary for infection. The normal pathogenic form of this bacterium is referred to as the S form because it forms smooth colonies in a culture dish. The mutant form, which lacks an enzyme needed to manufacture the polysaccharide capsule, is called the R form because it forms rough colonies.

To determine whether the polysaccharide capsule itself had a toxic effect, Griffith injected dead bacteria of the virulent S strain into mice, and the mice remained perfectly healthy ❸. Finally, he injected mice with a mixture containing dead S bacteria (the virulent strain) and live, capsuleless R bacteria, each of which by itself did not harm the mice. Unexpectedly, the mice developed disease symptoms and many of them died ❹. The blood of the dead mice was found to contain high levels of live, virulent *Streptococcus* type S bacteria, which had surface proteins characteristic of the live (previously R) strain. Somehow, the information specifying the polysaccharide capsule had passed from the dead, virulent S bacteria to the live, capsuleless R bacteria in the mixture, permanently transforming the capsuleless R bacteria into the virulent S variety. Griffith called this process, **transformation.**

11.2 The Avery and Hershey-Chase Experiments

CONCEPT PREVIEW: Several key experiments demonstrated conclusively that DNA, not protein, is the hereditary material.

The Avery Experiments

The agent responsible for transforming *Streptococcus* went undiscovered until 1944. In a classic series of experiments, Oswald Avery and his coworkers Colin MacLeod and Maclyn McCarty characterized what they referred to as the "transforming principle." Avery and his colleagues prepared the same mixture of dead S *Streptococcus* and live R *Streptococcus* that Griffith had used, but first they removed as much of the protein as they could from their preparation of dead S *Streptococcus,* eventually achieving 99.98% purity. Despite the removal of nearly all protein from the dead S *Streptococcus,* the transforming activity was not reduced. Moreover, the chemical properties of the transforming principle resembled those of DNA, and protein-digesting enzymes did not affect the principle's activity, while a DNA-digesting enzyme destroyed all transforming activity. They concluded that "a nucleic acid of the deoxyribose type is the fundamental unit of the transforming principle of *Pneumococcus* Type III"—in essence, that DNA is the hereditary material.

The Hershey-Chase Experiment

Avery's result was not widely appreciated at first, because most biologists still preferred to think that genes were made of proteins. In 1952, however, a simple experiment carried out by Alfred Hershey and Martha Chase was impossible to ignore. The team studied the genes of viruses that infect bacteria. These viruses attach themselves to the surface of bacterial cells and inject their genes into the interior; once inside, the genes take over the genetic machinery of the cell and conduct the manufacturing of hundreds of new viruses. When mature, the progeny viruses burst out to infect other cells. These bacteria-infecting viruses have a very simple structure: a core of DNA surrounded by a coat of protein.

In this experiment shown in figure 11.2, Hershey and Chase used radioactive isotopes to "label" the DNA and protein of the viruses. Radioactively tagged molecules are indicated in red in the figure. In the preparation on the right, the viruses were grown so that their DNA contained radioactive phosphorus (^{32}P), which is present in DNA but not in proteins; in another preparation on the left side of the figure, the viruses were grown so that their protein coats contained radioactive sulfur (^{35}S), present in proteins but not in DNA. After the labeled viruses were allowed to infect bacteria, Hershey and Chase shook the suspensions forcefully to dislodge attacking viruses from the surface of bacteria. They then used a rapidly spinning centrifuge to isolate the bacteria, and asked a very simple question: What did the viruses inject into the bacterial cells, protein or DNA? They found that the bacterial cells infected by viruses containing the ^{32}P label had labeled tracer in their interiors; cells infected by viruses containing the ^{35}S labeled tracer did not. The conclusion was clear: The genes that viruses use to specify new viruses are made of DNA and not protein.

Isotopes, as discussed on page 34, are atoms of an element that contain varying numbers of neutrons. Some isotopes are unstable, undergoing radioactive decay, which can be detected when the isotopes are incorporated into DNA or proteins.

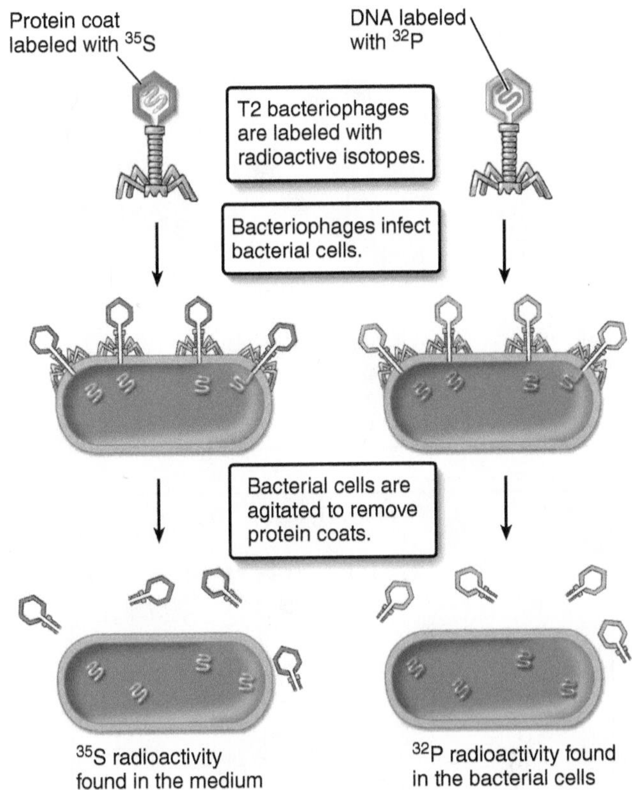
Protein coat labeled with ^{35}S
DNA labeled with ^{32}P
T2 bacteriophages are labeled with radioactive isotopes.
Bacteriophages infect bacterial cells.
Bacterial cells are agitated to remove protein coats.
^{35}S radioactivity found in the medium
^{32}P radioactivity found in the bacterial cells

Figure 11.2 The Hershey-Chase experiment.

The experiment that convinced most biologists that DNA is the genetic material was carried out soon after World War II, when radioactive isotopes were first becoming commonly available to researchers. Hershey and Chase used different radioactive labels to "tag" and track protein and DNA. They found that when bacterial viruses inserted their genes into bacteria to guide the production of new viruses, it was DNA and not protein that was inserted. More specifically, ^{35}S radioactivity did not enter infected bacterial cells and ^{32}P radioactivity did. Clearly the virus DNA, not the virus protein, was responsible for directing the production of new viruses.

IMPLICATION Household smoke detectors contain a very small amount (3 millionths of a gram) of the radioactive isotope Americium-241, a decay product of plutonium. Am-241 emits a stream of alpha particles which ionize oxygen and nitrogen atoms in the air, creating a small steady electric current. When smoke enters the smoke detector, smoke particles absorb the alpha radiation; this halts ion production, causing the current to fall and setting off the alarm. Why do you think Am-241 is used, rather than some other, possibly less expensive radioisotope?

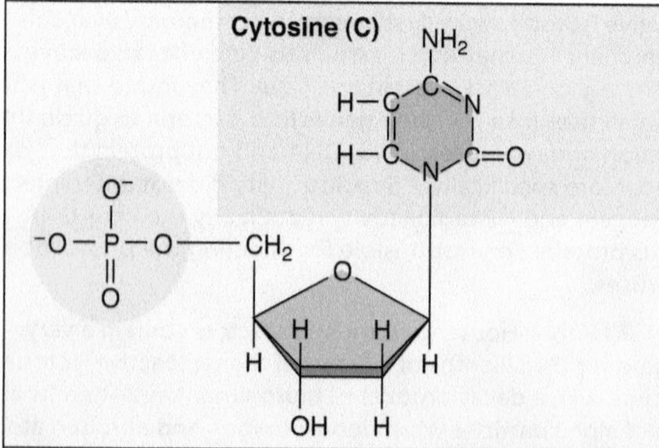

Figure 11.3 The four nucleotide subunits that make up DNA.

The nucleotide subunits of DNA are composed of three parts: a central five-carbon sugar called deoxyribose, a phosphate group, and an organic, nitrogen-containing base.

11.3 Discovering the Structure of DNA

CONCEPT PREVIEW: The DNA molecule has two strands of nucleotides held together by hydrogen bonds between bases. The two strands wind into a double helix.

As it became clear that DNA stored the hereditary information, researchers began to question how a molecule like DNA could carry out the complex function of inheritance. Scientists at that time did not know what the DNA molecule looked like.

We now know that DNA is a long, chainlike molecule made up of subunits called **nucleotides.** As you can see in figure 11.3, each nucleotide has three parts: a central sugar called deoxyribose to which a phosphate (PO_4) group and an organic base are attached. The sugar (lavender pentagon structure) and the phosphate group (yellow-circled structure) are the same in every nucleotide of DNA. However, there are four different kinds of bases: two large ones with double-ring structures, and two small ones with single rings. The large bases, called **purines,** are **A** (adenine) and **G** (guanine). The small bases, called **pyrimidines,** are **C** (cytosine) and **T** (thymine). The carbon atoms that make up the sugar of the deoxyribose are numbered from 1′ to 5′, as shown in the top panel. The phosphate group binds to the 5′ carbon and the organic base binds to the 1′ carbon. You will learn about the significance of this numbering system later.

Early in the analysis of DNA, a key observation was made by Erwin Chargaff. He noted that DNA molecules always had equal amounts of purines and pyrimidines. In fact, with slight variations due to imprecision of measurement, the amount of A always equals the amount of T, and the amount of G always equals the amount of C. This observation (A = T, G = C), known as **Chargaff's rule,** suggested that DNA had a regular structure.

In 1953 the British chemist Rosalind Franklin carried out the first X-ray diffraction experiments on DNA. In her experiments, DNA molecules bombarded with X-ray beams created a pattern on photographic film, as shown in figure 11.4*a*, that looked like the ripples created by tossing a rock into a smooth lake. Franklin's results suggested that the DNA molecule had the shape of a coiled spring or a corkscrew, a form called a **helix.**

Franklin's work was shared with two researchers at Cambridge University, Francis Crick and James Watson, before it was published. Using Tinkertoy-like models of the bases, Watson and Crick deduced the structure of DNA (figure 11.4*b*): The DNA molecule is a **double helix,** a structure that resembles a winding staircase (figure 11.4*c*). The sugar and phosphate groups form the stringers of the staircase, and the bases of the nucleotides form the steps. The significance of Chargaff's rule is now clear, a direct reflection of this structure—every bulky purine on one strand is paired with a slender pyrimidine on the other strand. Specifically, A (blue bases) pairs with T (orange bases), and G (purple bases) pairs with C (pink bases).

The constant distance between the strands in DNA could also be explained by A pairing with C. The reason why A doesn't pair with C, or G with T, is because of how hydrogen bonds form between the nitrogen bases, described on page 53.

Concept Check

1. If dead S bacteria and live R bacteria are each harmless when injected into mice, why is injecting them both together lethal to the mouse?
2. How could Hershey and Chase conclude that DNA was the hereditary material based on their results?
3. What subunits make up the DNA nucleotides and which nucleotides contain purine bases and which contain pyrimidine bases?

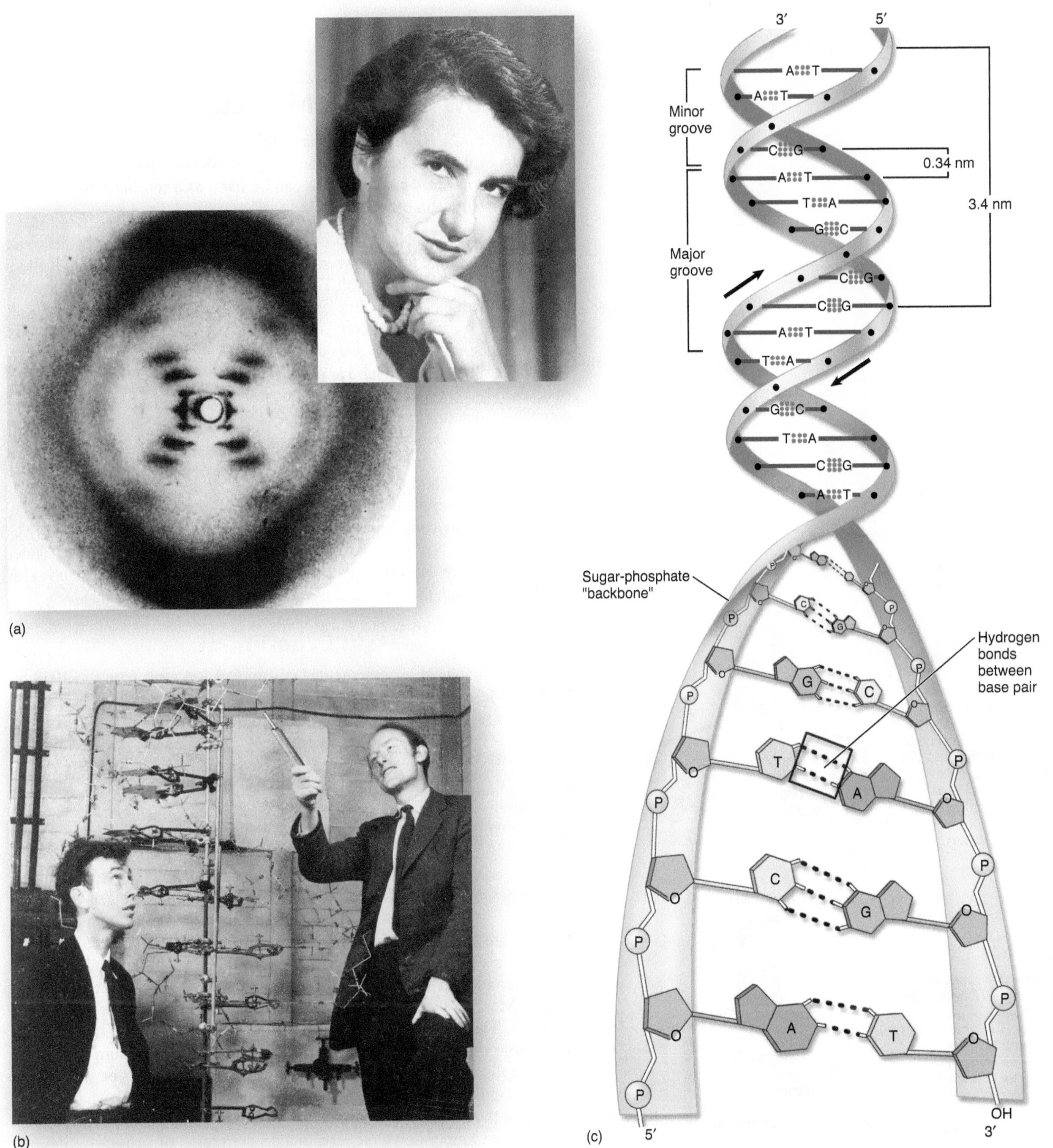

Figure 11.4 The DNA double helix.

(a) This X-ray diffraction photograph was made in 1953 by Rosalind Franklin (inset) in the laboratory of Maurice Wilkins. It suggested to Watson and Crick that the DNA molecule was a helix, like a winding staircase. (b) In 1953 Watson and Crick deduced the structure of DNA. James Watson (seated and peering up at their homemade model of the DNA molecule) was a young American postdoctoral student, and Francis Crick (pointing) was an English scientist. (c) The dimensions of the double helix were suggested by the X-ray diffraction studies. In a DNA duplex molecule, only two base pairs are possible: adenine (A) with thymine (T) and guanine (G) with cytosine (C). A G–C base pair has three hydrogen bonds; an A–T base pair has only two.

DNA Replication

Parent DNA

Replicating DNA

Conservative replication: The two strands of the double helix separate and serve as templates for the assembly of two new strands by base pairing A with T and G with C. After replicating, the original strands rejoin, preserving the parent DNA and forming an entirely new duplex.

Rejoined original DNA

Daughter DNA composed of two new strands

Semiconservative replication: The double helix need only "unzip" and assemble a new complementary chain along each single strand. The sequence of the original duplex is conserved after one round of replication, but the duplex itself is not. Instead, each strand of the parent duplex becomes part of another duplex.

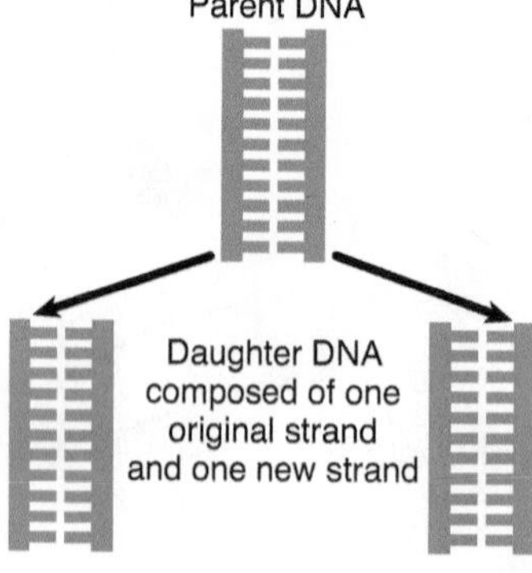

Parent DNA

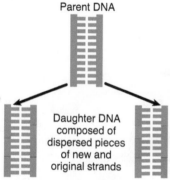

Dispersive replication: The original DNA serves as a template for the formation of new DNA strands, but the new and old DNA are dispersed among the two daughter strands. Each daughter strand is made up of sections of original strands and new strands.

Daughter DNA composed of dispersed pieces of new and original strands

Figure 11.5 Alternative mechanisms of DNA replication.

There are three possible alternatives as to how the DNA could serve as a template for the assembly of new DNA molecules. In all three, the original strands of DNA are colored blue, and the newly synthesized strands are colored red.

11.4 How the DNA Molecule Copies Itself

CONCEPT PREVIEW: The basis for the great accuracy of DNA replication is complementarity. DNA's two strands are complementary so either one can be used as a template to reconstruct the other.

What holds the two DNA strands together? The "glue" is provided by the weak hydrogen bonds that form between the bases that face each other from the two strands. That is why A pairs with T and not C. The A base can only form hydrogen bonds with the T base. Similarly, G can form hydrogen bonds with C but not T. In the Watson-Crick model of DNA, the two strands of the double helix are said to be *complementary* to each other.

One chain of the helix can have any sequence of bases, of A, T, G, and C, but this sequence completely determines that of its partner in the helix. If the sequence of one chain is ATTGCAT, the sequence of its partner in the double helix must be TAACGTA. Each chain in the helix is a complementary mirror image of the other. This complementarity makes it possible for the DNA molecule to copy itself during cell division in a very direct manner; but there are several different ways that this could occur. Figure 11.5 walks you through three possible mechanisms of DNA replication.

The complementarity of the DNA structure is universal, with all living cells showing the same complementarity in their DNA. As you will see on page 220, this allows the DNA of different organisms to be combined, which is the basis for genetic engineering.

The Meselson-Stahl Experiment

The three alternative hypotheses of DNA replication were tested in 1958 by Matthew Meselson and Franklin Stahl of the California Institute of Technology. These two scientists grew bacteria in a medium containing the heavy isotope of nitrogen, ^{15}N, which became incorporated into the bases of the bacterial DNA (figure 11.6). After several generations, samples were taken from this culture and grown in a medium containing the normal lighter isotope ^{14}N, which became incorporated into the newly replicating DNA. Bacterial samples were taken from the ^{14}N media at 20 minute intervals (❷ through ❹). DNA was extracted from all three samples and from a fourth sample, ❶, that served as a control.

Isotopes, as discussed on page 34, are atoms that contain varying numbers of neutrons. Isotopes have the same atomic number but different masses. In this experiment, ^{15}N contains one more neutron than ^{14}N and so it is heavier; DNA that contains ^{15}N is heavier.

By dissolving the DNA they had collected in a heavy salt called cesium chloride, and then spinning the solution at very high speeds in an ultracentrifuge, Meselson and Stahl were able to separate DNA strands of different densities. The centrifugal forces caused the cesium ions to migrate toward the bottom of the centrifuge tube, creating a gradient of cesium concentration, and thus a gradation of density. Each DNA strand floats or sinks in the gradient until it reaches the position where its density exactly matches the density of the cesium there. Because ^{15}N strands are denser than ^{14}N strands, they migrate farther down the tube to a denser region of cesium.

The DNA collected immediately after the transfer was all dense, as shown in test tube ❷. However, after the bacteria completed their first round of DNA replication in the ^{14}N medium, the density of their DNA had decreased to a value intermediate between ^{14}N-DNA and ^{15}N-DNA, as shown in test tube ❸. After the second round of replication, two density classes of DNA were observed, one intermediate and one equal to that of ^{14}N-DNA, as shown in test tube ❹.

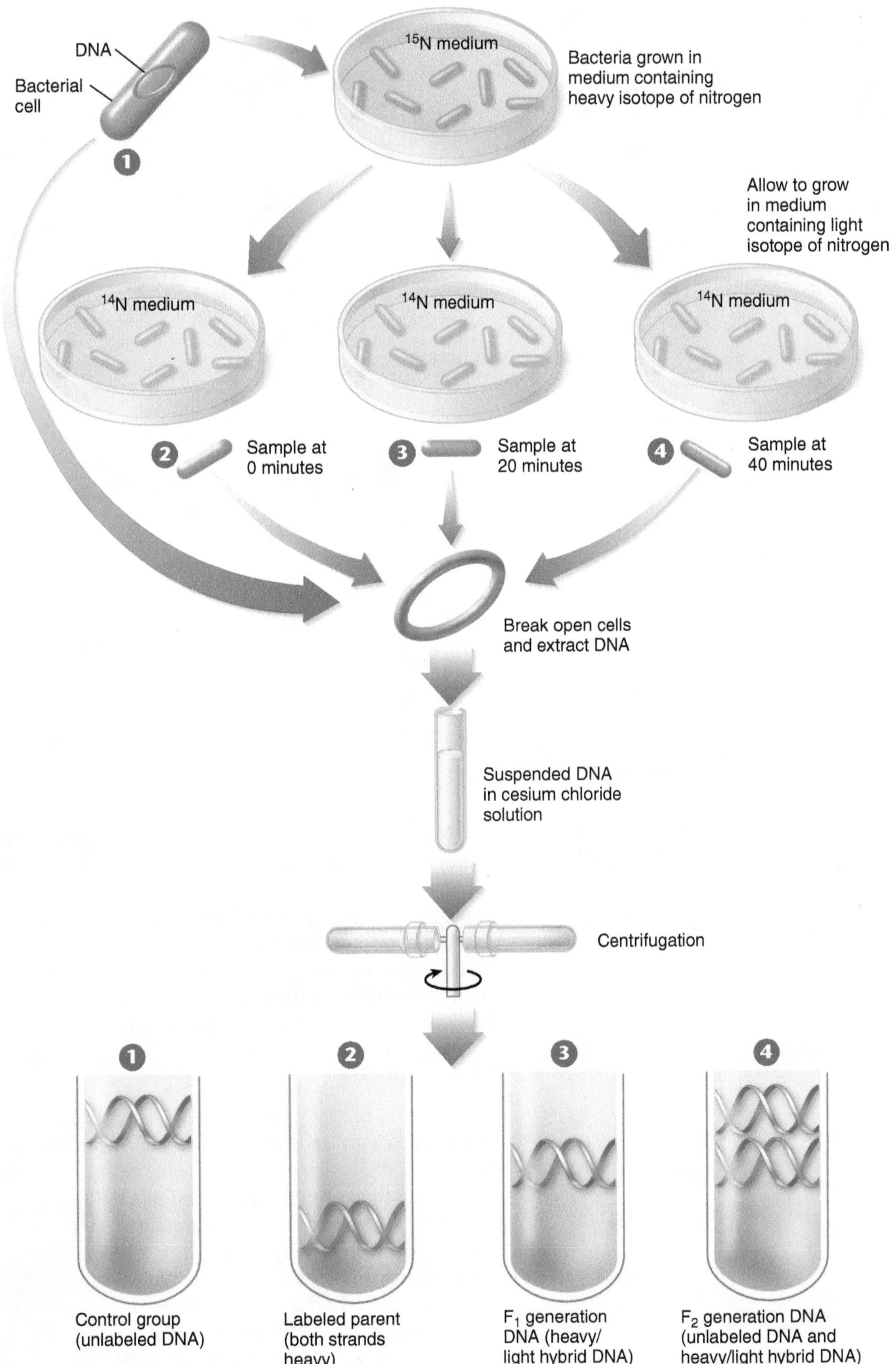

Figure 11.6 The Meselson-Stahl experiment.

Bacterial cells were grown for several generations in a medium containing a heavy isotope of nitrogen (^{15}N) and then were transferred to a new medium containing the normal lighter isotope (^{14}N). At various times thereafter, samples of the bacteria were collected, and their DNA was dissolved in a solution of cesium chloride, which was spun rapidly in a centrifuge. The labeled and unlabeled DNA settled in different areas of the tube because they differed in weight. The DNA with two heavy strands settled down toward the bottom of the tube. The DNA with two light strands settled higher up in the tube. The DNA with one heavy and one light strand settled in between the other two.

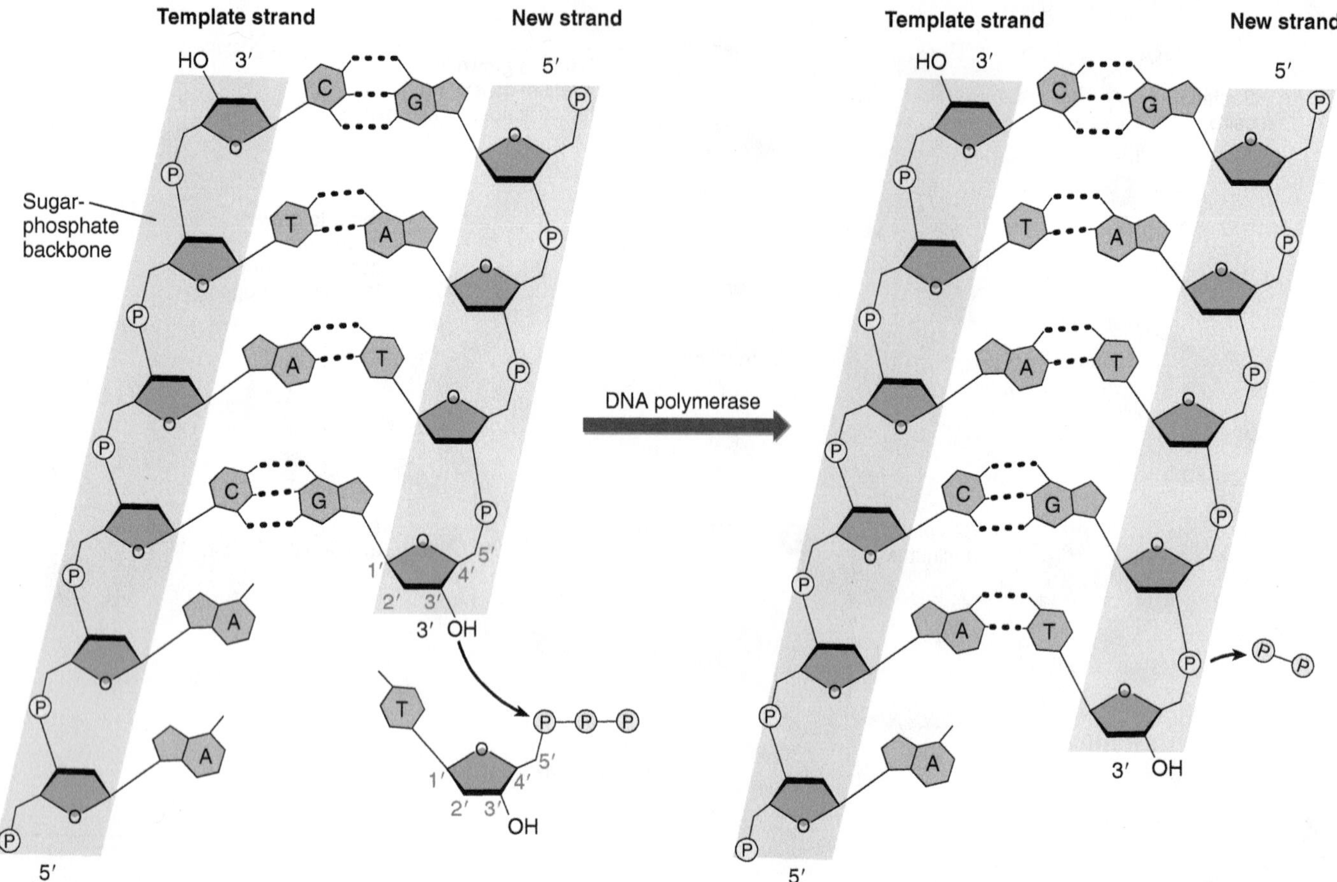

Figure 11.7 How nucleotides are added in DNA replication.

Nucleotides are added to the new growing strand of DNA by DNA polymerase. The addition of the nucleotides follows base pairing.

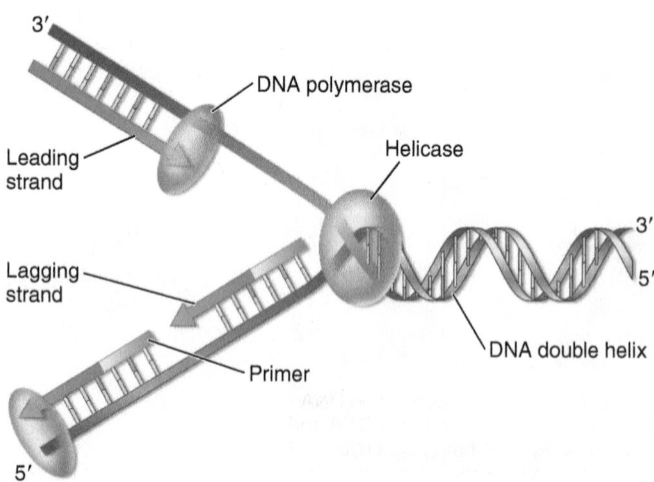

Figure 11.8 Building the leading and lagging strands.

DNA polymerase builds the leading strand as a continuous strand moving into the replication fork growing 5′ to 3′, but the lagging strand, also growing 5′ to 3′, is assembled moving away from the replication fork, in segments, each beginning with a primer.

Meselson and Stahl interpreted their results as follows: After the first round of replication, each daughter DNA duplex was a hybrid possessing one of the heavy strands of the parent molecule and one light strand; when this hybrid duplex replicated, it contributed one heavy strand to form another hybrid duplex and one light strand to form a light duplex. Thus, this experiment clearly ruled out conservative and dispersive DNA replication, and confirmed the prediction of the Watson-Crick model that DNA replicates in a semiconservative manner.

How DNA Copies Itself

The copying of DNA before cell division is called **DNA replication** and is carried out by an enzyme called *DNA polymerase.* An enzyme called *helicase* first unwinds the DNA double helix, then DNA polymerase reads along each single strand (the blue strand in figure 11.7) and adds the correct complementary nucleotide (A pairs with T, G with C) at each position as it moves, creating a complementary strand (the pink strand).

This process of unwinding and separating the two strands of the DNA molecule happens again during protein synthesis. A section of the DNA that contains a gene is opened during transcription, discussed on page 200, and an RNA copy of the DNA is made by a different enzyme.

However, there are some limitations of the actions of DNA polymerase. First, it can only add to an existing strand; it cannot begin a strand. Another enzyme circumvents this difficulty by beginning the new strand with a section of nucleotides called a *primer.* These are the green segments in figure 11.8. This happens at the place where the parent DNA molecule becomes unzipped, called the *replication fork.* At the replication fork, the polymerase very actively shuttles several hundred nucleotides up one strand, building a new strand of DNA called the **leading strand,** adding on to the primer in a continuous fashion. The leading strand is the upper red strand in figure 11.8, the primer is off further to the left out of the frame of the diagram. The new strand is built when the phosphate group of a nucleotide, called the 5′ end, attaches to the sugar end, called the 3′ end, of the nucleotide at the end of the growing strand. The carbon atoms in the sugar component of a nucleotide have a numbering scheme, shown in figure 11.7 (or refer back to figure 11.3). In a nucleotide, the phosphate group is attached to the 5′ carbon atom of the sugar, and an OH group is attached to the 3′ carbon atom. So, each nucleotide has a 5′ end and a 3′ end, and when the nucleotides attach to each other in a long chain, there will be a 5′ phosphate end to the chain on one side and a 3′ OH end on the other side. In the DNA double helix, the two strands of nucleotides pair up in opposite orientations, with one strand running 5′ to 3′ and the other running 3′ to 5′.

The directionality of building the new strand is apparent in figure 11.7, where the phosphate group of the incoming T nucleotide attaches to the OH group of the sugar of the G nucleotide. The new strand assembles in a 5′ to 3′ direction, and new nucleotides can only be added to the 3′ end of an existing strand. This reveals a second limitation: DNA polymerase can only build a strand of DNA in one direction, and so it assembles the other DNA strand, called the **lagging strand,** in segments. Each lagging strand segment begins with a primer (the green segments you saw in figure 11.8), and the DNA polymerase then builds it away from the replication fork until it encounters the previous section.

Eukaryotic chromosomes each contain a single, very long molecule of DNA, one far too long to copy all the way from one end to the other with a single replication fork. Each eukaryotic chromosome is instead copied in sections of about 100,000 nucleotides, each with its own replication origin and fork.

Before the newly formed DNA molecules wind back into the double helix shape, the primers must be removed and the segments of DNA assembled in sections on the lagging strand need to be covalently linked together. The enzyme that performs this sealing function is *DNA ligase.* DNA ligase joins the ends of newly synthesized segments of DNA after the primers have been removed, resulting in one continuous strand of DNA. This process is summarized in *Essential Biological Process 11A*, with the DNA ligase in panel 3 sealing the gaps between the DNA sections of the lagging strand.

The enormous amount of DNA that resides within the cells of your body represents a long series of DNA replications, starting with the DNA of a single cell—the fertilized egg. Living cells have evolved many mechanisms to avoid errors during DNA replication and to preserve the DNA from damage. These mechanisms of DNA repair proofread the strands of each DNA molecule against one another for accuracy and correct any mistakes. But the proofreading is not perfect. If it were, no mistakes such as mutations would occur. Mutation will be discussed in more detail in the next section and in chapter 14, where we consider mutation as the raw material of evolution.

Concept Check

1. Explain complementarity and why it occurs.
2. In Meselson and Stahl's experiment, what would be the expected result if DNA replication had been conservative, as illustrated in figure 11.5?
3. If DNA polymerase cannot begin a strand, explain how DNA replication gets started.

Essential Biological Process 11A

DNA Replication

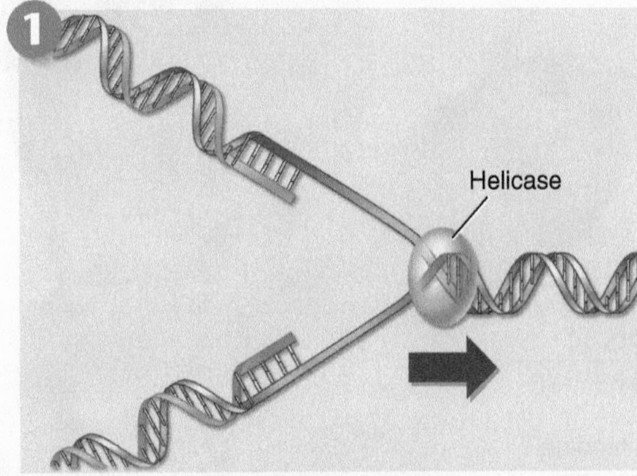

Helicase unwinds the DNA double helix for about 1,000 nucleotides.

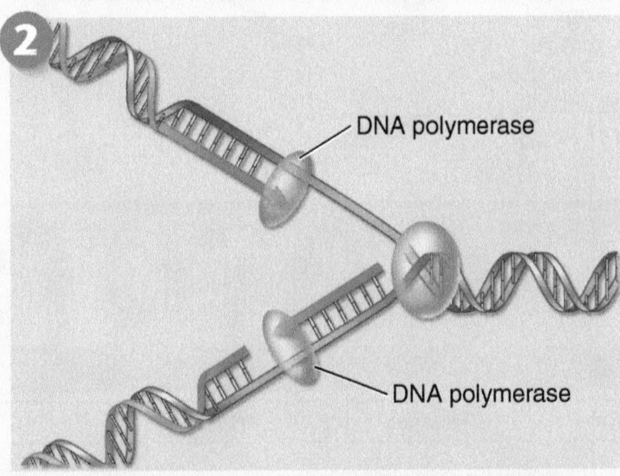

DNA polymerase assembles a complementary new strand on each old one, building the two strands in opposite directions.

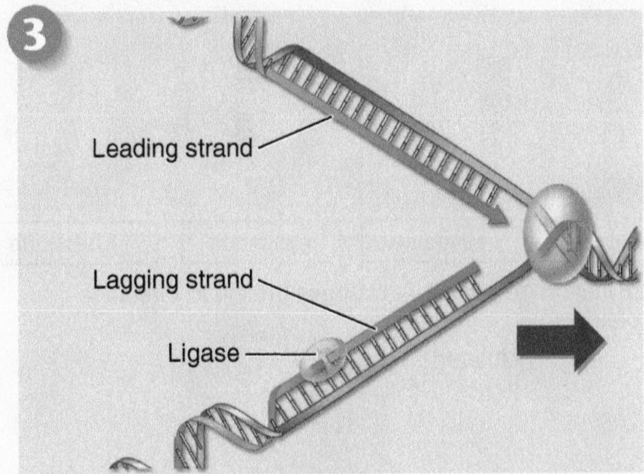

DNA ligase attaches one new strand to the previously replicated segment on the lagging strand, and helicase unwinds another segment.

Altering the Genetic Message

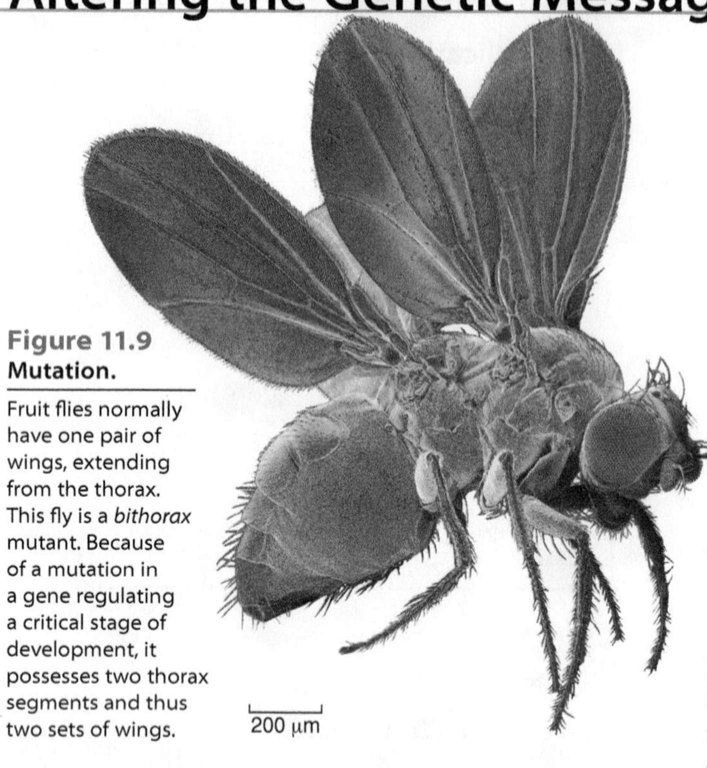

Figure 11.9 Mutation.

Fruit flies normally have one pair of wings, extending from the thorax. This fly is a *bithorax* mutant. Because of a mutation in a gene regulating a critical stage of development, it possesses two thorax segments and thus two sets of wings.

11.5 Mutation

CONCEPT PREVIEW: Rare changes in genes, called mutations, can have significant effects on the individual when they occur in somatic tissue, but they are inherited only if they occur in germ-line tissue. Inherited changes provide the raw material for evolution.

A change in the content of the genetic message—the base sequence of one or more genes—is referred to as a **mutation.** As you learned in the previous section, DNA copies itself by forming complementary strands along single strands of DNA when they are separated. The template strand directs the formation of the new strand. However, this replication process is not foolproof. Sometimes errors are made and these are called mutations. Some mutations alter the identity of a particular nucleotide, while others remove or add nucleotides to a gene. The cells of eukaryotes contain an enormous amount of DNA, and the mechanisms that protect and proofread the DNA are not perfect. If they were, no variation would be generated.

Mistakes Happen

In fact, cells do make mistakes during replication, as shown in figure 11.9. Other mutations occur because of DNA alteration by chemicals like those in cigarette smoke, or by radiation like the ultraviolet light from the sun or in tanning beds. However, mutations are rare. Typically, a particular gene is altered in only one of a million gametes. Limited as it might seem, however, this steady trickle of change is the very stuff of evolution. Every difference in the genetic messages that specify different organisms arose as the result of genetic change.

Kinds of Mutation

The message that DNA carries in its genes is the "instructions" of how to make proteins. The sequence of nucleotides in a strand of DNA translates into the sequence of amino acids that makes up a protein. This process was introduced in section 10.5 on page 164. If the core message in the DNA is altered through mutation as shown in figure 11.10, where an A nucleotide (in red) is inserted instead of a C nucleotide during DNA replication, then the protein product can also be altered, sometimes to the point where it can no longer function properly. Because mutations can occur randomly in a cell's DNA, most mutations are detrimental, just as making a random change in a computer program usually worsens performance. The consequences of a detrimental mutation may be minor or catastrophic, depending on the function of the altered gene.

Gene expression occurs in two steps: transcription, discussed on page 200 transfers the nucleotide message in the DNA to a molecule of RNA. In translation, discussed on page 201, the nucleotide message is converted into a string of amino acids that make up the protein.

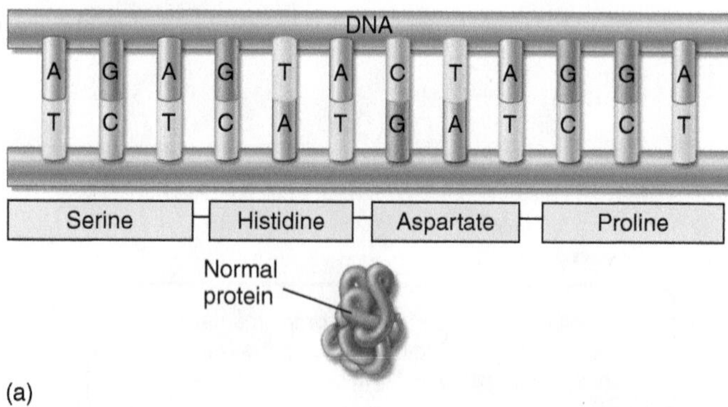

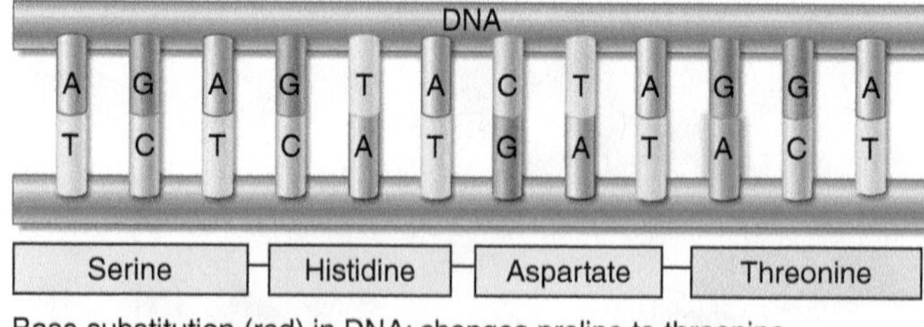

Base substitution (red) in DNA: changes proline to threonine in the protein.

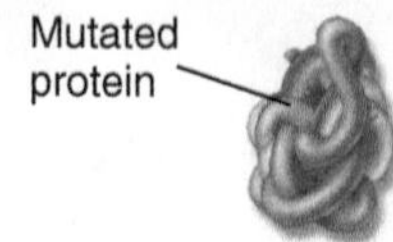

Figure 11.10 Base substitution mutation.

(a) Often, DNA sequences code for a particular protein. (b) A mutation that substitutes one base for another can result in a change in a single amino acid. This can produce a mutated protein that may not function the same as the normal protein.

Mutations in Germ-Line Tissues. The effect of a mutation depends critically on the identity of the cell in which the mutation occurs. During the embryonic development of all multicellular organisms, there comes a point when cells destined to form gametes (germ-line cells) are segregated from those that will form the other cells of the body (somatic cells). Only when a mutation occurs within a germ-line cell is it passed to subsequent generations as part of the hereditary endowment of the gametes derived from that cell. Mutations in germ-line tissue are of enormous biological importance because they provide the raw material from which natural selection produces evolutionary change.

Mutations in Somatic Tissues. Change can occur only if there are new, different allele combinations available to replace the old. Mutation produces new alleles, and recombination puts the alleles together in different combinations. In animals, it is the occurrence of these two processes in germ-line tissue that is important to evolution, because mutations in somatic cells (somatic mutations) are not passed from one generation to the next. However, a somatic mutation may have drastic effects on the individual organism in which it occurs, because it is passed on to all of the cells that are descended from the original mutant cell. Thus, if a mutant lung cell divides, all cells derived from it will carry the mutation. Somatic mutations of lung cells are the principal cause of lung cancer.

Altering the Sequence of DNA. One category of mutational changes affects the message itself, producing alterations in the sequence of DNA nucleotides (table 11.1). If alterations involve only one or a few base pairs in the coding sequence, they are called **point mutations.** Sometimes the identity of a nucleotide changes (*base substitution*), while other times one or a few nucleotides are added (*insertion*) or lost (*deletion*). If an insertion or deletion throws the reading of the gene message out of register, a **frame-shift mutation** results. Figure 11.10 shows a base substitution mutation that results in the change of an amino acid, from proline to threonine. This could be a minor change or catastrophic. However, suppose that this had been the deletion of a nucleotide, that the cytosine base nucleotide had been skipped during replication. This would shift the register of the DNA message (imagine removing the "w" from this sentence, yielding "*This oulds hiftt her egistero fth eDN Amessag*") and you can see the problem.

Many point mutations result from damage to the DNA caused by mutagens, usually radiation or chemicals. The latter is of particular importance because modern industrial societies often release many chemical mutagens into the environment.

TABLE 11.1 Some Categories of Mutation

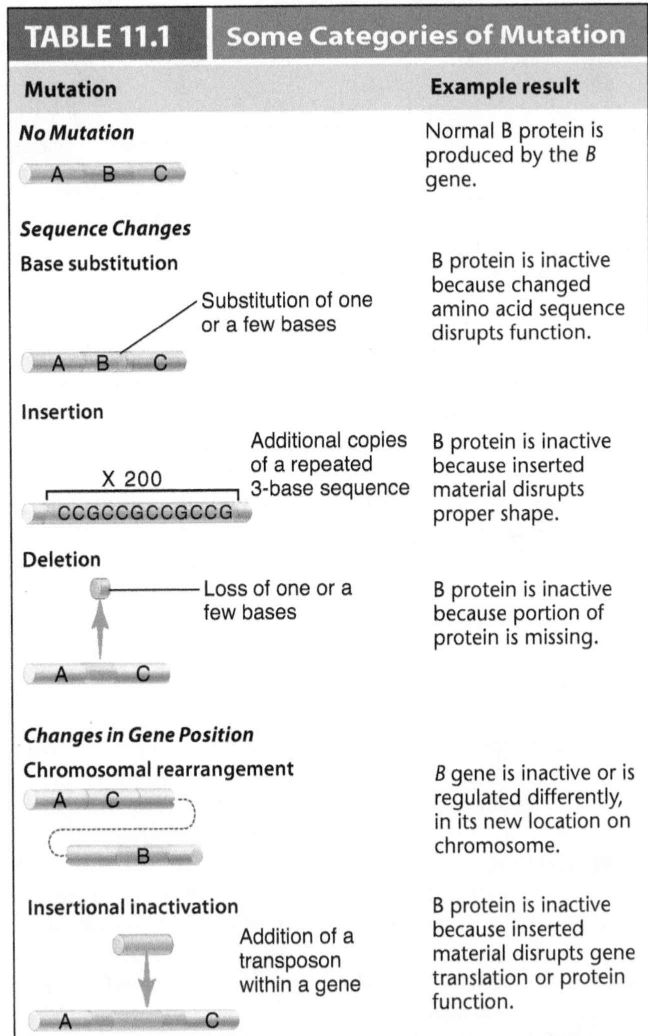

Mutation		Example result
No Mutation	A B C	Normal B protein is produced by the *B* gene.
Sequence Changes		
Base substitution	Substitution of one or a few bases A B C	B protein is inactive because changed amino acid sequence disrupts function.
Insertion	Additional copies of a repeated 3-base sequence X 200 CCGCCGCCGCCG	B protein is inactive because inserted material disrupts proper shape.
Deletion	Loss of one or a few bases A C	B protein is inactive because portion of protein is missing.
Changes in Gene Position		
Chromosomal rearrangement	A C B	*B* gene is inactive or is regulated differently, in its new location on chromosome.
Insertional inactivation	Addition of a transposon within a gene A C	B protein is inactive because inserted material disrupts gene translation or protein function.

The Importance of Genetic Change

All evolution begins with alterations in the genetic message that create new alleles or alter the organization of genes on chromosome. Some changes in germ-line tissue produce alterations that enable an organism to leave more offspring, and those changes tend to be preserved as the genetic endowment of future generations. Other changes reduce the ability of an organism to leave offspring. Those changes tend to be lost, as the organisms that carry them contribute fewer members to future generations. Evolution can be viewed as the selection of particular combinations of alleles from a pool of alternatives. The rate of evolution is ultimately limited by the rate at which these alternatives are generated. Genetic change through mutation and recombination provides the raw material for evolution.

Concept Check

1. In order for a mutation to be passed on to offspring, it has to occur in germ-line tissue. What cells are these in the body?
2. What type of mutation would most likely cause major changes in the cell?
3. If somatic mutations are not inherited, why are they important?

BIOLOGY & YOU

Almost All Inherited Mutations Occur in Males. Molecular analysis of DNA allows us to determine whether a mutation occurred in the mother or the father. The results are dramatic. In studies to determine the parent of origin, a total of 92 new human mutations were analyzed, and ALL were paternal. How can we account for a far higher mutation rate in males than in females? The explanation seems to lie in the far greater number of cell divisions in the male germ line. In females germ cell divisions stop by the time of birth, while in males cell divisions are continuous, so that many divisions have occurred before an adult male's sperm is produced. Because most germ-line mutations are replication errors, the far greater number of replications in males leads to a much bigger opportunity for mistakes. This predicts that human mutation rates should increase with the age of the father. They do. At age 20, the mutation rate for a man is about 8 times the female rate. The difference is some 30-fold by age 30, and as much as 100-fold by age 40.

Biology and Staying Healthy

Protecting Your Genes

This text's discussion of changes in genes—mutations—has largely focused on heredity, how changes in the information encoded in DNA can affect offspring. It is important, however, to realize that inherited mutations occur only in germ-line tissue, in the cells that generate your eggs or sperm. Mutations in the other cells of your body, in so-called somatic tissues, are not inherited. This does not, however, mean that such mutations are not important. In fact, somatic mutations can have a disastrous impact upon your health, because they can lead to cancer. Protecting the DNA of your body's cells from damaging mutation is perhaps the most important thing you can do to prolong your life. Here we will examine two potential threats.

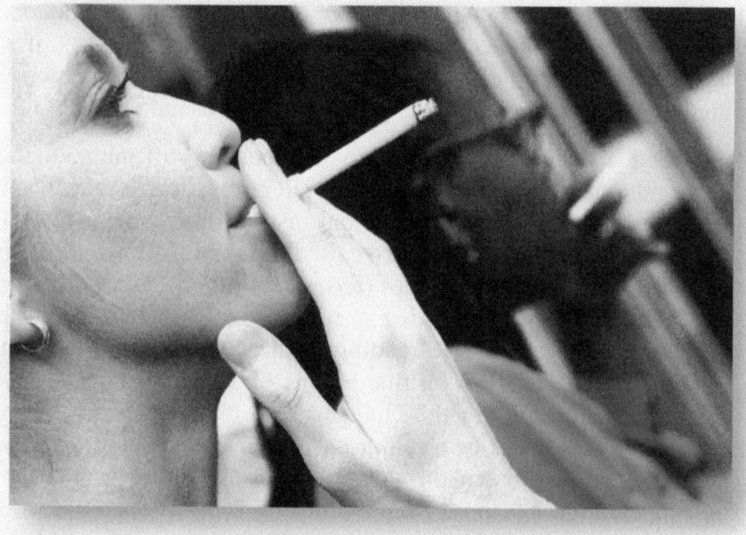

Smoking and Lung Cancer

The association of particular chemicals in cigarette smoke with lung cancer, particularly chemicals that are potent mutagens (see chapters 8 and 25), led researchers early on to suspect that lung cancer might be caused, at least in part, by the action of chemicals on the cells lining the lung.

The hypothesis that chemicals in tobacco cause cancer was first advanced over 200 years ago in 1761 by Dr. John Hill, an English physician. Hill noted unusual tumors of the nose in heavy snuff users and suggested tobacco had produced these cancers. In 1775, a London surgeon, Sir Percivall Pott, made a similar observation, noting that men who had been chimney sweeps exhibited frequent cancer of the scrotum. He suggested that soot and tars might be responsible. These observations led to the hypothesis that lung cancer results from the action of tars and other chemicals in tobacco smoke.

It was over a century before this hypothesis was directly tested. In 1915, Japanese doctor Katsusaburo Yamagiwa applied extracts of tar to the skin of 137 rabbits every two or three days for three months. Then he waited to see what would happen. After a year, cancers appeared at the site of application in seven of the rabbits. Yamagiwa had induced cancer with the tar, the first direct demonstration of chemical carcinogenesis. In the decades that followed, this approach demonstrated that many chemicals can cause cancer.

But do these lab studies apply to people? Do tars in cigarette smoke in fact induce lung cancer in humans? In 1949, the American physician Ernst Winder and the British epidemiologist Richard Doll independently reported that lung cancer showed a strong link to the smoking of cigarettes, which introduces tars into the lungs. Winder interviewed 684 lung cancer patients and 600 normal controls, asking whether each had ever smoked. Cancer rates were 40 times higher in heavy smokers than in nonsmokers. From these studies, it seemed likely as long as 50 years ago that tars and other chemicals in cigarette smoke induce cancer in the lungs of persistent smokers. While this suggestion was resisted by the tobacco industry, the evidence that has accumulated since these pioneering studies makes a clear case, and there is no longer any real doubt. Chemicals in cigarette smoke cause cancer.

As you will learn in chapter 25 (page 498), tars and other chemicals in cigarette smoke cause lung cancer by mutating DNA, disabling genes that in normal lung cells restrain cell division. Lacking these restraints, the altered lung cells begin to divide ceaselessly, and lung cancer results. Over 160,000 Americans died of lung cancer last year, and almost all of them were cigarette smokers.

If cigarette smoking is so dangerous, why do so many Americans smoke? Fully 23% of American men smoke, and 18% of women. Are they not aware of the danger? Of course they are. But they are not able to quit. Tobacco smoke, you see, also contains another chemical, nicotine, which is highly addictive. The nature of drug addiction is discussed in chapter 29 (page 557). Basically, what happens is that a smoker's brain makes physiological compensations to overcome the effects of nicotine, and once these adjustments are made the brain does not function normally without nicotine. The body's physiological response to nicotine is profound and unavoidable; there is no way to prevent addiction to nicotine with willpower.

Many people attempting to quit smoking use patches containing nicotine to help them, the idea being that providing nicotine removes the craving for cigarettes. This is true, it does—as long as you keep using the patch. Actually, using such patches simply substitutes one (admittedly less dangerous) nicotine source for another. If you are going to quit smoking, there is no way to avoid the necessity of eliminating the drug to which you are addicted, nicotine. There is no easy way out. The only way to quit is to quit.

Clearly, if you do not smoke, you should not start. When asked what three things were most important to improve Americans' health, a prominent physician replied: "Don't smoke. Don't smoke. Don't smoke."

Tanning and Skin Cancer

Almost all cells in the human body undergo cell division, replacing themselves as they wear out. Some adult cells do this very frequently, others rarely if ever. Skin cells divide quite frequently. Exposed to a lot of wear and tear, they divide about every 27 days to replace dead or damaged cells. The skin sloughs off dead cells from the surface and replaces these with new cells from beneath. The average person will lose about 105 pounds of skin by the time he or she turns 70.

While skin can become damaged in many ways, the damage that seems to have the most long-term affect is caused by the sun. The skin contains cells called melanocytes that produce a pigment called melanin when exposed to UV light. Melanin produces a yellow-to-brown color in the skin. The type of melanin and the amount produced is genetically determined. People with darker skin types have more melanocytes and produce a melanin that is dark brown in color. Protected by UV-absorbing melanin, they almost never sunburn. Fair skinned people have fewer melanocytes and produce melanin that is more yellow in color. Unprotected by melanin, these people sunburn easily and rarely tan. When cells on the body's surface are badly damaged by the sun, called a sunburn, the cells slough off. Recall the peeling that you experience if you have ever had a bad sunburn.

Up until the early 20th century, a tan was a condition that people went to great lengths to avoid. A tanned body was a sign of the working class, people who had to work in the sun. The wealthy elite avoided the sun with pale skin being in fashion. All of this changed in the 1920s, when tans became a status symbol, with the wealthy able to travel to warm, sunny destinations, even in the middle of winter. That tan, bronzed glow that people would sit in the sun for hours to achieve was thought to be both healthy and attractive.

During the 1970s, doctors started to see an uptick in the number of cases of melanoma, a deadly form of skin cancer. New cases were increasing about 6% each year. Researchers proposed that UV rays from the sun were the underlying cause of this epidemic of skin cancer and warned people to avoid the sun when possible and protect themselves with sunscreen.

Malignant melanoma is the most deadly of skin cancers, although treatable if caught early. Melanoma is cancer of melanocyte cells. Melanoma lesions usually appear as shades of tan, brown, and black and often begin in or near a mole, and so changes in a mole is a symptom of melanoma. Melanoma is most prevalent in fair-skinned people, but unlike the other forms of skin cancer, it can also affect people with darker complexions.

The public has been slow to respond to warnings about avoiding sun exposure, perhaps because the cosmetic benefits of tanning are immediate while the health hazards are much delayed. The desire to achieve that tanned, bronzed body is as strong as ever.

A good tan requires regular exposure to the sun to maintain it, so indoor tanning salons have become popular. Tanning beds emit concentrated UV rays from two sides, allowing a person to tan in less time and in all weather conditions (sun, rain, snow). The indoor tanning business has grown in the U.S. to a $2-billion-a-year industry with an estimated 28 million Americans tanning annually.

People thought that building up a tan through the use of tanning beds would protect a person's skin from burning and would reduce the time exposed to the UV radiation; both leading to a reduced risk of skin cancer. However, recent research does not support these assumptions. A 2003 study of 106,000 Scandinavian women showed that exposure to UV rays in a tanning bed as little as once a month can increase your risk of melanoma by 55%, especially when the exposure is during early adulthood. Those women who were in their 20s and used sun lamps to tan were at the highest risk, about 150% higher than those who didn't use a tanning bed. As with other studies, fair-skinned women were at the greatest risk. In fact, tanning beds, even for those people who tan more easily, heighten the risk for skin cancer because people use the tanning beds year-round, increasing their cumulative exposure.

It is difficult to avoid the conclusion that to protect your genes you should avoid tanning beds. Like smoking cigarettes, excessive tanning is gambling with your life.

Inquiry & Analysis

Are Mutations Random or Directed By the Environment?

Once biologists appreciated that Mendelian traits were in fact alternative versions of DNA sequences, which resulted from mutations, a very important question arose and needed to be answered—Are mutations random events that might happen anywhere on a DNA chromosome, or are they directed to some degree by the environment? Do the mutagens in cigarettes, for example, damage DNA at random locations, or do they preferentially seek out and alter specific sites such as those regulating the cell cycle?

This key question was addressed and answered in an elegant and deceptively simple experiment carried out in 1943 by two of the pioneers of molecular genetics, Salvadore Luria and Max Delbruck. They chose to examine a particular mutation that occurs in laboratory strains of the bacterium *E. coli*. These bacterial cells are susceptible to T1 viruses, tiny chemical parasites that infect, multiply within, and kill the bacteria. If 10^5 bacterial cells are exposed to 10^{10} T1 viruses, and the mixture spread on a culture dish, not one cell grows—every single *E. coli* cell is infected and killed. However, if you repeat the experiment using 10^9 bacterial cells, lots of cells survive! When tested, these surviving cells prove to be mutants, resistant to T1 infection. The question is, did the T1 virus cause the mutations, or were the mutations present all along, too rare to be present in a sample of only 10^5 cells but common enough to be present in 10^9 cells?

To answer this question, Luria and Delbruck devised a simple experiment they called a "fluctuation test," illustrated here. Five cell generations are shown for each of four independent bacterial cultures, all tested for resistance in the fifth generation. If the T1 virus causes the mutations (top row), then each culture will have more or less the same number of resistant cells, with only a little fluctuation (that is, variation among the four). If, on the other hand, mutations are spontaneous and so equally likely to occur in any generation, then bacterial cultures in which the T1 resistance mutation occurs in earlier generations will possess far more resistant cells by the fifth generation than cultures in which the mutation occurs in later generations, resulting in wide fluctuation among the four cultures. The table presents the data they obtained for 20 individual cultures.

Number of Bacteria Resistant to T1 Virus

Culture number	Resistant colonies found	Culture number	Resistant colonies found
1	1	11	107
2	0	12	0
3	3	13	0
4	0	14	0
5	0	15	1
6	5	16	0
7	0	17	0
8	5	18	64
9	0	19	0
10	6	20	35

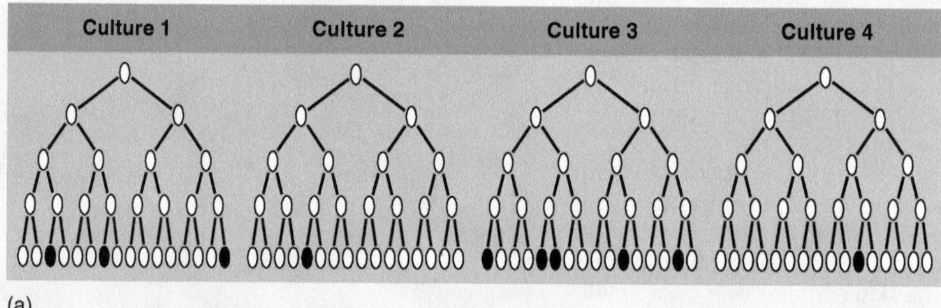

(a)

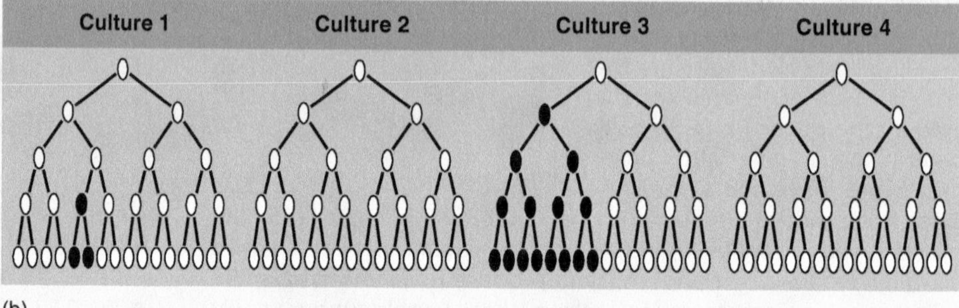

(b)

Analysis

1. **Interpreting Data** What is the mean number of T1-resistant bacteria found in the 20 individual cultures?

2. **Making Inferences**
   a. Comparing the twenty individual cultures, do the cultures exhibit similar numbers of T1-resistant bacterial cells?
   b. Which of the two alternative outcomes illustrated above, (*a*) or (*b*), is more similar to the outcome obtained by Luria and Delbruck in this experiment?

3. **Drawing Conclusions** Are these data consistent with the hypothesis that the mutation for T1 resistance among *E. coli* bacteria is caused by exposure to T1 virus? Explain.

Concept Summary

Genes Are Made of DNA

11.1 The Griffith Experiment

- Using *Streptococcus pneumoniae* bacteria, Griffith showed that information that controls physical characteristics can be passed from one bacterium to another, even from a dead bacterium.
- By injecting mice with different strains of *S. pneumoniae,* Griffith determined that some strains were pathogenic, resulting in the mice's deaths. Bacteria of the pathogenic strains contained polysaccharide capsules (S strain), like the bacteria shown here from **figure 11.1,** while those without the capsules (R strain) were nonlethal. When he mixed dead pathogenic bacteria (S), which usually would not cause death, and live nonpathogenic bacteria (R) and injected them into mice, the mice died. The dead mice contained living S strains.

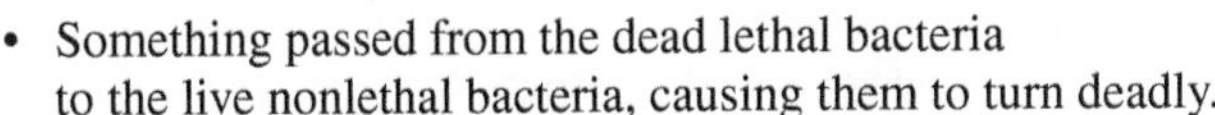

- Something passed from the dead lethal bacteria to the live nonlethal bacteria, causing them to turn deadly.

11.2 The Avery and Hershey-Chase Experiments

- Avery and colleagues showed that protein was not the source of this transformation. They replicated Griffith's experiment but removed all protein from the preparation. The virulent strain with its protein coat removed was still able to transform nonvirulent bacteria. This experimental result supported the hypothesis that DNA, not protein, was the transforming principle.
- Using bacterial viruses, Hershey and Chase showed that genes were carried on DNA and not proteins. They used two different radioactively tagged preparations, DNA in one, as shown here from **figure 11.2,** and protein in the other. Each preparation was used to infect bacteria. When they screened the two bacterial cultures, they discovered that the infected bacteria contained radioactively tagged DNA.

11.3 Discovering the Structure of DNA

- The structure of DNA was not known. The basic chemical components of DNA were determined to be nucleotides. Each nucleotide has a similar structure: a deoxyribose sugar attached to a phosphate group and one of four organic bases (**figure 11.3**).
- Erwin Chargaff observed that two sets of bases are always present in equal amounts in a molecule of DNA (the amount of A nucleotides equals the amount of T nucleotides, and C nucleotides equals G nucleotides). This observation, called Chargaff's rule, gave some insight into the structure of DNA—that there was some regularity to the structure.
- Using X-ray diffraction, Rosalind Franklin was able to form a "picture" of DNA. The image suggested that the DNA molecule was coiled, a form called a helix.
- Using Chargaff's and Franklin's research, Watson and Crick determined that DNA is a double helix, two strands that are connected by base pairing between the nucleotide bases. An A nucleotide on one strand pairs with T on the other, and similarly G pairs with C (**figure 11.4**).

DNA Replication

11.4 How the DNA Molecule Copies Itself

- The complementarity of DNA (A pairs with T and C with G) implies a method of replication where a single strand of DNA can serve as the template for production of another strand, but there are several ways in which this could occur (**figure 11.5**).
- Meselson and Stahl showed that DNA replicates semiconservatively, using each of the original strands as templates to form new strands. In semiconservative replication, each new strand of DNA consists of a template strand from the parent DNA and a newly synthesized strand that is complementary to the template stand (**figure 11.6**).
- In replication, the DNA molecule first unwinds by the actions of an enzyme called helicase. Each DNA strand is then copied by the actions of an enzyme called DNA polymerase. The two original strands serve as templates to the new DNA strands. DNA polymerase adds nucleotides to the new DNA strands that are complementary to the original single strands. DNA polymerase can only add on to an existing strand, and so the new strand begins after a section of nucleic acids called a primer is added. A different enzyme builds the primer. Nucleotides are added to the growing strand in a 5′ to 3′ direction (**figure 11.7**).
- The point where the DNA separates is called the replication fork. Because nucleotides can only be added onto the 3′ end of the growing DNA strand, DNA copies in a continuous manner on one of the strands, called the leading strand, and in a discontinuous manner on the other strand, called the lagging strand (**figure 11.8**). On the lagging strand, primers are inserted at the replication fork, and nucleotides are added in sections, as shown here on the lower strand from ***Essential Biological Process 11A.*** Before the new DNA strands rewind, the primers are removed and the DNA segments are linked together with another enzyme called DNA ligase.

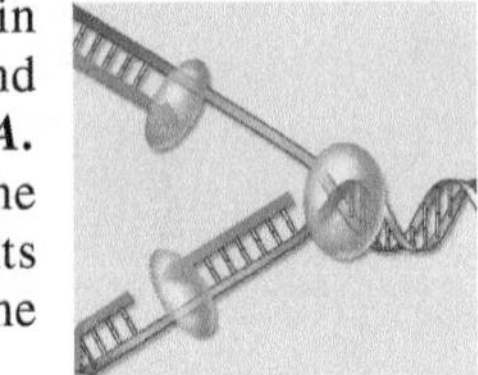

- Errors can occur during the replication of DNA. The cell has many mechanisms to correct damage to the DNA or mistakes made during replication. This proofreading process compares one strand against its complementary strand and corrects errors, but this system is not foolproof.

Altering the Genetic Message

11.5 Mutation

- A mutation is a change in the nucleotide sequence of the genetic message. Mutations that change one or only a few nucleotides are called point mutations (**figure 11.10**). Some mutations cause only minor changes while others can have dramatic consequences (**table 11.1**).

Self-Test

1. In the experiments performed by Frederick Griffith, they found that
   a. hereditary information within a cell cannot be changed.
   b. hereditary information can be added to cells from other cells.
   c. mice infected with live R strains die.
   d. mice infected with heat-killed S strains die.
2. The experiment performed by Alfred Hershey and Martha Chase showed that the molecule viruses use to specify new viruses is
   a. a protein. **c.** ATP.
   b. a carbohydrate. **d.** DNA.
3. Erwin Chargaff, Rosalind Franklin, Francis Crick, and James Watson all worked on pieces of information relating to the
   a. structure of DNA. **c.** inheritance of DNA.
   b. function of DNA. **d.** mutations of DNA.
4. The four DNA nucleotides are all different in terms of
   a. their sizes.
   b. the number of hydrogen bonds they can form with their base pair.
   c. the type of nitrogen base.
   d. the type of sugar.
5. Which of the following lists the organic bases found in the purine nucleotide bases?
   a. adenine and cytosine **c.** cytosine and thymine
   b. guanine and thymine **d.** adenine and guanine
6. If one strand of a DNA molecule has the base sequence ATTGCAT, its complementary strand will have the sequence
   a. ATTGCAT. **c.** GCCATGC.
   b. TAACGTA. **d.** CGGTACG.
7. Regarding the duplication of DNA, we now know that each double helix
   a. reforms after replicating.
   b. splits down the middle into two single strands, and each one then acts as a template to build its complement.
   c. fragments into small chunks that duplicate and reassemble.
   d. All of these are true for different types of DNA.
8. DNA polymerase can only add nucleotides to an existing chain, so ______________ is required.
   a. a primer **c.** a lagging strand
   b. helicase **d.** a leading strand
9. Genetic messages can be altered in two ways:
   a. through semiconservative replication or conservative replication.
   b. through the chromosome or through the protein.
   c. by mutation or by transformation.
   d. by activation or by repression.
10. Mutations can occur in
    a. germ-line tissues and are passed on to future generations.
    b. somatic tissues and are passed on to future generations.
    c. germ-line tissues but not in somatic tissues.
    d. somatic tissues but not in germ-line tissues.

Visual Understanding

1. **Figure 11.4c** What are some of the possible problems that could occur if the cytosine nucleotide indicated with the red arrow is accidentally replaced with an adenine nucleotide?

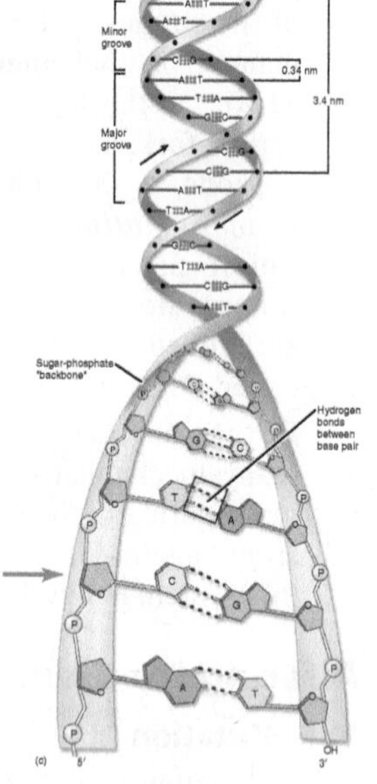

2. **Table 11.1** What types of mutations in the table result in a shift in the reading frame of the DNA? Explain.

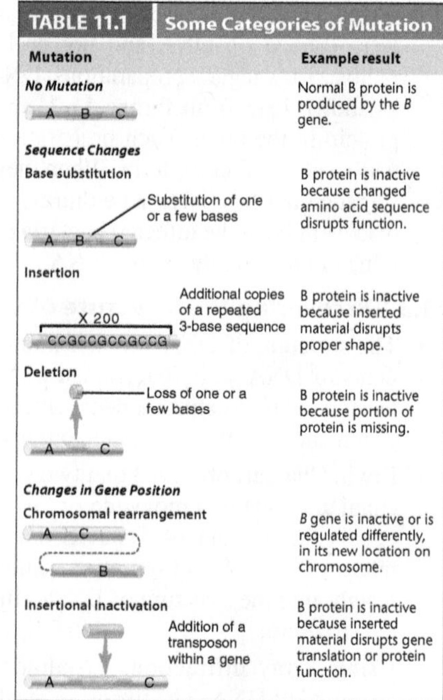

TABLE 11.1 Some Categories of Mutation

Mutation		Example result
No Mutation	A B C	Normal B protein is produced by the B gene.
Sequence Changes		
Base substitution	Substitution of one or a few bases; A B C	B protein is inactive because changed amino acid sequence disrupts function.
Insertion	X 200; CCGCCGCCGCCG; Additional copies of a repeated 3-base sequence	B protein is inactive because inserted material disrupts proper shape.
Deletion	Loss of one or a few bases; A C	B protein is inactive because portion of protein is missing.
Changes in Gene Position		
Chromosomal rearrangement	A C; B	B gene is inactive or is regulated differently, in its new location on chromosome.
Insertional inactivation	Addition of a transposon within a gene; A C	B protein is inactive because inserted material disrupts gene translation or protein function.

Challenge Questions

1. Based on the experiments and discoveries discussed in chapter 10 and here in chapter 11, defend the statement, attributed to Sir Isaac Newton in 1676 (though some say that Bernard of Chartres said it first, way back in about 1130!) that scientists build new ideas in science by "standing on the shoulders of giants."
2. Mutations can occur in somatic (body) cells or in germ-line cells. What problems or opportunities does each kind of mutated cell face?

Chapter 12

How Genes Work

CHAPTER AT A GLANCE

From Gene to Protein

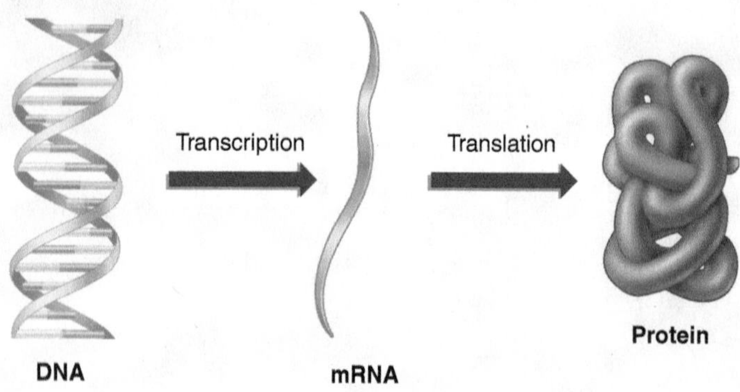

Figure 12.1 The central dogma: DNA to RNA to protein.

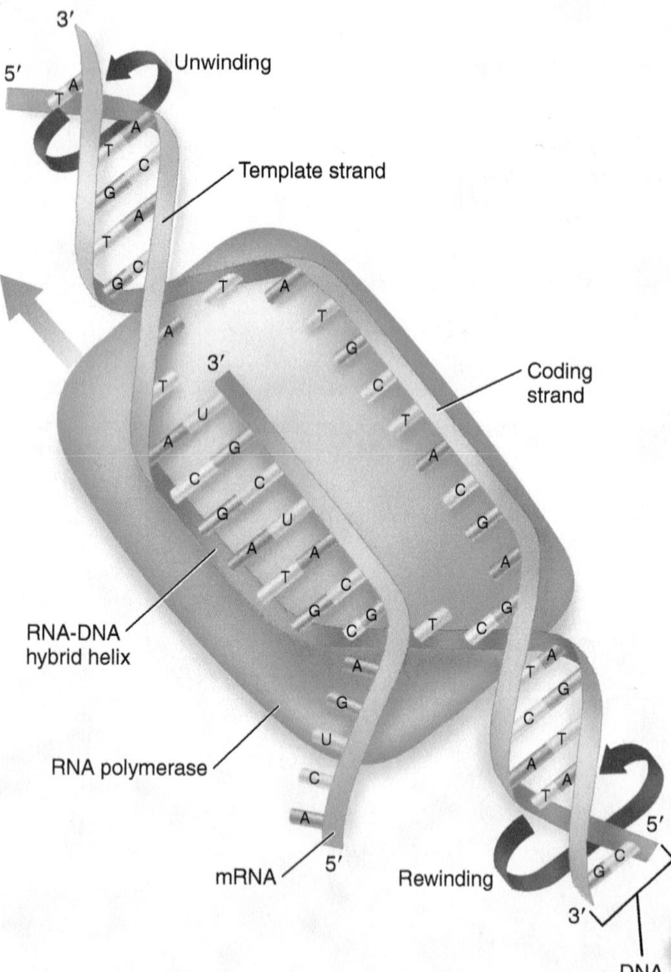

Figure 12.2 Transcription.

One of the strands of DNA functions as a template on which nucleotide building blocks are assembled into mRNA by RNA polymerase as it moves along the DNA strand.

12.1 Transcription

CONCEPT PREVIEW: Transcription is the production of an mRNA copy of a gene by the enzyme RNA polymerase.

The discovery that genes are made of DNA, discussed in chapter 11, left unanswered the question of how the information in DNA is used. How does a string of nucleotides in a spiral molecule determine if you have red hair or green eyes? We now know that the information in DNA is arrayed in little blocks, like entries in a dictionary, and each block is a gene that specifies the sequence of amino acids for a polypeptide. These polypeptides form the proteins that determine what a particular cell will be like.

Just as an architect protects building plans from loss or damage by keeping them safe in a central place and issuing only blueprint copies to on-site workers, so your cells protect their DNA instructions by keeping them safe within a central DNA storage area, the nucleus. The DNA never leaves the nucleus. Instead, "blueprint" copies of particular genes within the DNA instructions are sent out into the cell to direct the assembly of proteins. These working copies of genes are made of ribonucleic acid (RNA) rather than DNA. Recall that RNA, like DNA, is made of nucleotides except that the sugars in RNA have an extra oxygen atom and T is replaced by a similar pyrimidine base called uracil, U (see figure 3.11). The path of information is thus: **DNA ⟶ RNA ⟶ protein.** This information path is often called the *central dogma,* because it describes the key organization used by your cells to express their genes (figure 12.1).

A cell uses three kinds of RNA in the synthesis of proteins: messenger RNA (mRNA), ribosomal RNA (rRNA), and transfer RNA (tRNA). The use of information in DNA to direct the production of particular proteins is called **gene expression.** Gene expression occurs in two stages: in the first stage, called **transcription,** mRNA molecules are synthesized from genes within the DNA; in the second stage, called **translation,** the mRNA is used to direct the production of polypeptides, the components of proteins.

The Transcription Process

The RNA copy of a gene used in the cell to produce a polypeptide is called **messenger RNA (mRNA)**—it is the messenger that conveys the information from the nucleus to the cytoplasm. The copying process that makes the mRNA is called transcription—just as monks in monasteries used to make copies of manuscripts by faithfully transcribing each letter, so enzymes make mRNA copies of your genes by faithfully complementing each nucleotide.

In cells, the transcriber is a large and very sophisticated protein called **RNA polymerase.** It binds to the DNA double helix at a particular site called a *promoter*. It separates the two strands and then moves along one of the DNA strand like a train engine on a track. Although DNA is double-stranded, the two strands have complementary rather than identical sequences, so RNA polymerase is only able to bind one of the two DNA strands (the one with the promoter-site sequence it recognizes). As RNA polymerase goes along the DNA strand, it pairs each nucleotide with its complementary RNA version (G with C, A with U—recall that RNA uses a nucleotide with uracil, U, in place of thymine), building an mRNA chain in the 5′ to 3′ direction (figure 12.2).

The production of an RNA molecule during transcription is similar to the process of DNA replication, with the RNA chain of nucleotides growing in a 5′ to 3′ direction as is seen in DNA synthesis in figure 11.7 on page 190.

12.2 Translation

CONCEPT PREVIEW: The genetic code dictates how a nucleotide sequence specifies a particular amino acid sequence. A gene is transcribed into mRNA, which is then translated into a polypeptide. The sequence of mRNA codons dictates the corresponding sequence of amino acids in a growing polypeptide chain.

The Genetic Code

The essence of Mendelian genetics is that the information determining hereditary traits, traits passed from parent to child, is encoded information, written within the chromosomes in blocks called genes. To correctly read a gene, a cell must translate the information encoded in DNA into the language of proteins—that is, it must convert the order of the gene's nucleotides into the order of amino acids in a polypeptide, a process called **translation.** The rules that govern this translation are called the **genetic code.**

Genes and the proteins they encode underlie the expression of phenotypes, as described on page 164. RNAs are used to make proteins encoded in the DNA, and the proteins determine phenotype. A mutation in DNA can result in an error in the mRNA and its protein product.

The mRNA nucleotide sequence is "read" by a ribosome in three nucleotide units called **codons.** Each codon, with the exception of three, codes for a particular amino acid. Biologists worked out which codon corresponds to which amino acid by trial-and-error experiments carried out in test tubes. In these experiments, investigators used artificial mRNAs to direct the synthesis of polypeptides in the tube, and then looked to see the sequence of amino acids in the newly formed polypeptides. An mRNA that was a string of UUUUUU . . . , for example, produced a polypeptide that was a string of phenylalanine (Phe) amino acids, telling investigators that the codon UUU corresponded to the amino acid Phe. Most amino acids are specified by more than one codon. The entire genetic code dictionary is presented in figure 12.3.

Amino acids, discussed on page 49, are the monomers that make up a protein. They form long chains, held together with peptide bonds. The 20 amino acids are similar in structure except for their functional groups that give each amino acid its unique characteristics.

Figure 12.3 The genetic code (RNA codons).

A codon consists of three nucleotides read in sequence. For example, ACU codes for threonine. To determine which amino acid corresponds to a codon you read the chart first down the left side, then across the top, then down the right side. For the codon ACU, find the first letter, A, in the First Letter column; then follow the row over to the second letter, C, in the Second Letter row across the top; and then in that column trace down to the third letter, U, in the Third Letter column. Most amino acids are specified by more than one codon. For example, threonine is specified by four codons, which differ only in the third nucleotide (ACU, ACC, ACA, and ACG).

The Genetic Code

First Letter	Second Letter: U		C		A		G		Third Letter
U	UUU	Phenylalanine	UCU	Serine	UAU	Tyrosine	UGU	Cysteine	U
	UUC		UCC		UAC		UGC		C
	UUA	Leucine	UCA		UAA	Stop	UGA	Stop	A
	UUG		UCG		UAG	Stop	UGG	Tryptophan	G
C	CUU	Leucine	CCU	Proline	CAU	Histidine	CGU	Arginine	U
	CUC		CCC		CAC		CGC		C
	CUA		CCA		CAA	Glutamine	CGA		A
	CUG		CCG		CAG		CGG		G
A	AUU	Isoleucine	ACU	Threonine	AAU	Asparagine	AGU	Serine	U
	AUC		ACC		AAC		AGC		C
	AUA		ACA		AAA	Lysine	AGA	Arginine	A
	AUG	Methionine; Start	ACG		AAG		AGG		G
G	GUU	Valine	GCU	Alanine	GAU	Aspartate	GGU	Glycine	U
	GUC		GCC		GAC		GGC		C
	GUA		GCA		GAA	Glutamate	GGA		A
	GUG		GCG		GAG		GGG		G

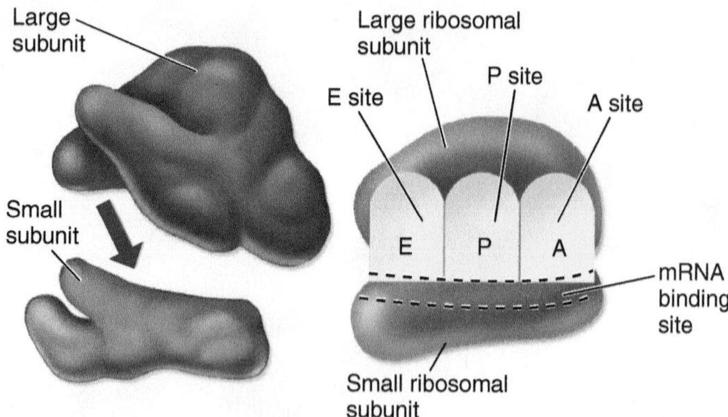

Figure 12.4 A ribosome is composed of two subunits.

The smaller subunit fits into a depression on the surface of the larger one. The A, P, and E sites on the ribosome play key roles in protein synthesis.

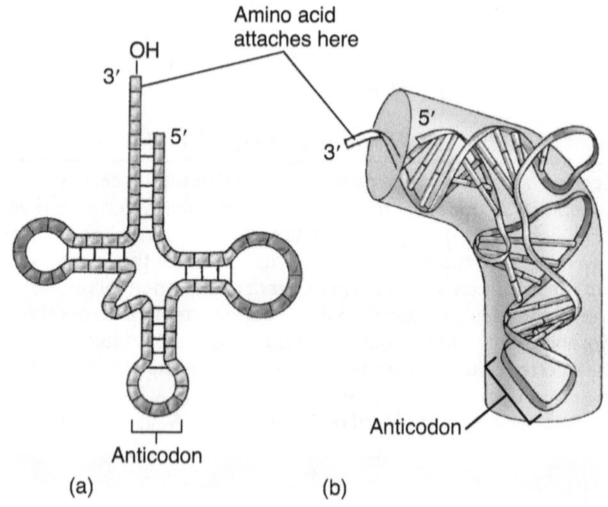

Figure 12.5 The structure of tRNA.

tRNA, like mRNA, is a long strand of nucleotides. However, unlike mRNA, hydrogen bonding occurs between its nucleotides, causing the strand to form hairpin loops, as seen in (a). The loops then fold up on each other to create the compact, three-dimensional shape seen in (b). Amino acids attach to the free, single-stranded —OH end of a tRNA molecule. A three-nucleotide sequence called the anticodon in the lower loop of tRNA interacts with a complementary codon on the mRNA.

The genetic code is universal, the same in practically all organisms. GUC codes for valine in bacteria, in fruit flies, in eagles, and in your own cells. The only exception biologists have ever found to this rule is in the way in which cell organelles that contain DNA (mitochondria and chloroplasts) and a few microscopic protists read the "stop" codons. In every other instance, the same genetic code is employed by all living things.

Translating the RNA Message into Proteins

The final result of the transcription process is the production of an mRNA copy of a gene. Like a photocopy, the mRNA can be used without damage or wear and tear on the original. After transcription of a gene is finished, the mRNA passes out of the nucleus into the cytoplasm through pores in the nuclear envelope. There, translation of the genetic message occurs. In translation, organelles called **ribosomes** use the mRNA produced by transcription to direct the synthesis of a polypeptide following the genetic code.

The Protein-Making Factory. Ribosomes are the polypeptide-making factories of the cell. Ribosomes use mRNA, the "blueprint" copies of nuclear genes, to direct the assembly of polypeptides, which are then combined into proteins.

Ribosomes are very complex, containing over 50 different proteins (shown in gold in the image on page 199) and three chains of **ribosomal RNA (rRNA)** of some 3,000 nucleotides (shown in gray). It had been traditionally assumed that the proteins in a ribosome act as enzymes to catalyze the assembly process, with the RNA acting as a scaffold to position the proteins. In the year 2000 powerful atomic-resolution X-ray diffraction studies unexpectedly revealed the many proteins of a ribosome to be scattered over its surface like decorations on a Christmas tree. The role of these proteins seems to be to stabilize the many bends and twists of the RNA chains, the proteins acting like spot-welds between RNA strands. Importantly, there are no proteins on the inside of the ribosome where the chemistry of protein synthesis takes place—just twists of RNA. Thus it is the ribosome's RNA, not its proteins, that catalyzes the synthesis of polypeptides!

Ribosomes are composed of two parts, or subunits, one nested into the other like a fist in the palm of your hand. The "fist" is the smaller of the two subunits, the pink structure in figure 12.4. Its rRNA has a short nucleotide sequence exposed on the surface of the subunit. This exposed sequence is identical to a sequence called the leader region that occurs at the beginning of all genes. Because of this, an mRNA molecule binds to the exposed rRNA of the small subunit like a fly sticking to flypaper.

The Key Role of tRNA. Directly adjacent to the exposed rRNA sequence are three small pockets or dents, designated the A, P, and E sites, in the surface of the ribosome (shown in figure 12.4 and discussed shortly). These sites have just the right shape to bind yet a third kind of RNA molecule, **transfer RNA (tRNA).** It is tRNA molecules that bring amino acids to the ribosome used in making proteins. tRNA molecules are chains about 80 nucleotides long. The string of nucleotides folds back on itself, forming a 3-looped structure shown in figure 12.5*a*. The looped structure further folds into a compact shape shown in figure 12.5*b*, with a three-nucleotide sequence at the bottom (the pink loop) and an amino acid attachment site at the top (the 3′ end).

The three-nucleotide sequence on the tRNA, called the **anticodon,** is very important: It is the complementary sequence to 1 of the 64 codons of the genetic code! Special enzymes, called *activating enzymes,* match amino acids in the cytoplasm with their proper tRNAs. The anticodon determines which amino acid will attach to a particular tRNA.

Essential Biological Process 12A

Translation

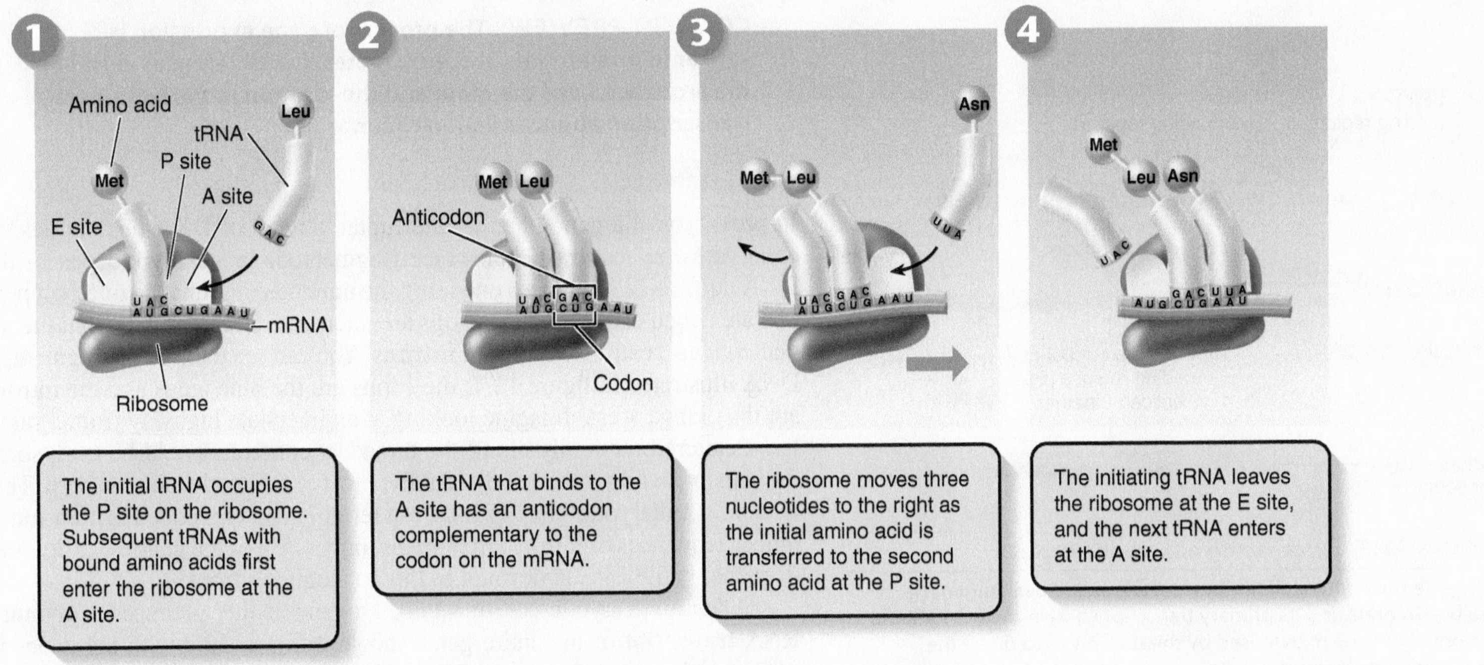

1
Amino acid
tRNA
Leu
P site
Met
A site
E site
mRNA
Ribosome
The initial tRNA occupies the P site on the ribosome. Subsequent tRNAs with bound amino acids first enter the ribosome at the A site.
2
Met Leu
Anticodon
Codon
The tRNA that binds to the A site has an anticodon complementary to the codon on the mRNA.
3
Asn
Met Leu
The ribosome moves three nucleotides to the right as the initial amino acid is transferred to the second amino acid at the P site.
4
Met
Leu Asn
The initiating tRNA leaves the ribosome at the E site, and the next tRNA enters at the A site.

Because the first dent in the ribosome, called the A site (the attachment site where amino-acid-bearing tRNAs will bind) is directly adjacent to where the mRNA binds to the rRNA, three nucleotides of the mRNA are positioned directly facing the anticodon of the tRNA. Like the address on a letter, the anticodon ensures that an amino acid is delivered to its correct "address" on the mRNA where the ribosome is assembling the polypeptide.

Making the Polypeptide. Once an mRNA molecule has bound to the small ribosomal subunit, the other larger ribosomal subunit binds as well, forming a complete ribosome. The ribosome then begins the process of translation, shown in *Essential Biological Process 12A*. Panel 1 of the figure shows how the mRNA begins to thread through the ribosome like a string passing through the hole in a doughnut. The mRNA passes through in short spurts, three nucleotides at a time, and at each burst of movement a new three-nucleotide codon on the mRNA is positioned opposite the A site in the ribosome, where a tRNA molecule first binds, as shown in panel 2.

As each new tRNA brings in an amino acid to each new codon presented at the A site, the old tRNA paired with the previous codon is passed over to the P site where peptide bonds form between the incoming amino acid and the growing polypeptide chain. The tRNA in the P site eventually shifts to the E site (the exit site), as shown in panel 3, and the amino acid it carried is attached to the end of a growing amino acid chain. The tRNA is then released in panel 4. So as the ribosome proceeds down the mRNA, one tRNA after another is selected to match the sequence of mRNA codons. In figure 12.6 you can see the ribosome traveling along the length of the mRNA, the tRNAs bringing the amino acids into the ribosome and the growing polypeptide chain extending out from the ribosome. Translation continues until a "stop" codon is encountered, which signals the end of the polypeptide. The ribosome complex falls apart, and the newly made polypeptide is released into the cell.

A peptide bond is the name given to the chemical bond that forms between two amino acids in a polypeptide, as discussed on page 49. Two amino acids are linked together through a dehydration reaction where a water molecule is a by-product of the reaction as described on page 47.

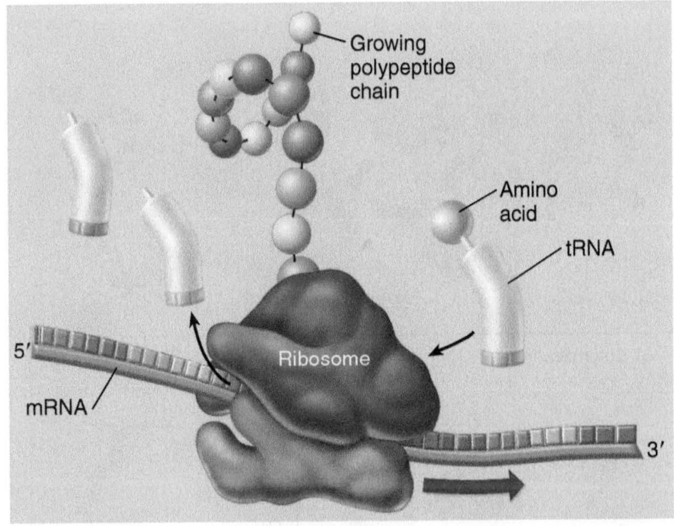

Figure 12.6 Ribosomes guide the translation process.

tRNA binds to an amino acid as determined by the anticodon sequence. Ribosomes bind the loaded tRNAs to their complementary sequences on the strand of mRNA. tRNA adds its amino acid to the growing polypeptide chain, which is released as the completed protein. The overall flow of genetic information is from DNA to mRNA to protein. For example, the polypeptide that is being formed in *Essential Biological Process 12A* began with the DNA nucleotide sequence TACGACTTA, which was transcribed into the mRNA sequence AUGCUGAAU. This sequence is then translated into a polypeptide composed of the amino acids methionine—leucine—asparagine.

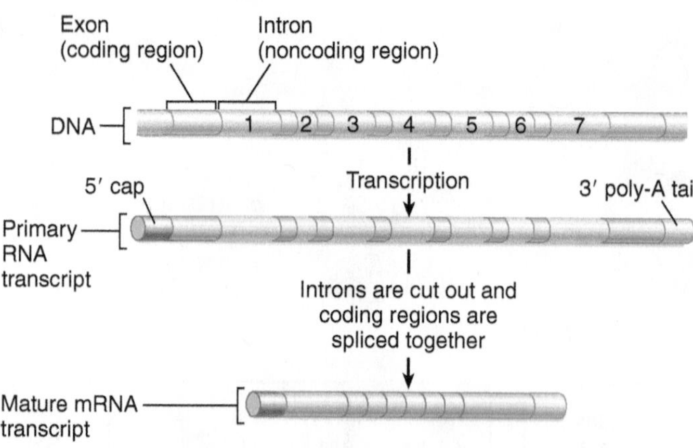

Figure 12.7 Processing eukaryotic RNA.

The gene shown here codes for a protein called ovalbumin. The ovalbumin gene and its primary transcript contain seven segments not present in the mRNA used by the ribosomes to direct the synthesis of the protein.

IMPLICATION Some mutations alter the sequence of DNA bases in a gene but do not produce a noticeable change in the gene's polypeptide product. Explain how this can happen.

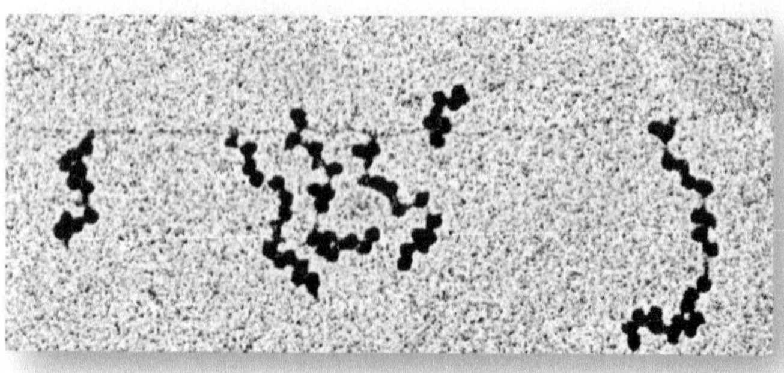

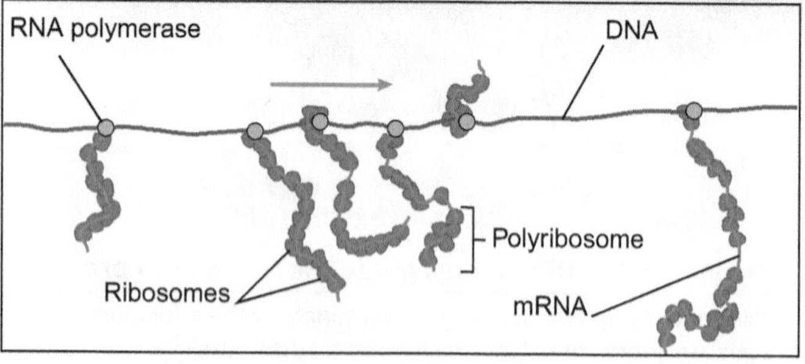

Figure 12.8 Transcription and translation in prokaryotes.

Ribosomes attach to an mRNA as it is formed, producing polyribosomes that translate the gene soon after it is transcribed.

12.3 Gene Expression

CONCEPT PREVIEW: The process of gene expression is similar in prokaryotes and eukaryotes, but differences exist in the architecture of the gene and the location in the cell where transcription and translation occur.

Architecture of the Gene

In prokaryotes, a gene is an uninterrupted stretch of DNA nucleotides. In eukaryotes, by contrast, genes are fragmented. In eukaryotic genes, the DNA nucleotide sequences encoding the amino acid sequence of a polypeptide are called **exons,** and the exons are interrupted frequently by extraneous nucleotides, "extra stuff" called **introns.** You can see them in the segment of DNA illustrated in figure 12.7; the exons are the blue areas and the introns are the orange areas. Imagine looking at an interstate highway from a satellite. Scattered randomly along the thread of concrete would be cars, some moving in clusters, others individually; most of the road would be bare. That is what a eukaryotic gene is like: scattered exons embedded within much longer sequences of introns. In humans, only 1.5% of the genome is devoted to exons, while 24% is devoted to the noncoding introns.

When a eukaryotic cell transcribes a gene, it first produces a **primary RNA transcript** of the entire gene, shown in figure 12.7 with the exons in green and the introns in orange. Enzymes add modifications called a *5´cap* and a *3´ poly-A* tail, which protect the RNA transcript from degradation. The primary transcript is then "processed," the introns removed and the exons joined together to form the shorter mRNA transcript that is actually translated into an amino acid chain. Notice that the mRNA transcript in figure 12.7 contains only exons (green segments).

Why have introns at all? It appears that many human genes exons are functional modules that can be spliced together in more than one way. One exon might encode a straight stretch of protein, another a curve, yet another a flat place. Like mixing Tinkertoy parts, you can construct quite different assemblies by employing the same exons in different combinations and orders. With this process called **alternative splicing,** the 20,000 to 25,000 genes of the human genome seem to encode as many as 120,000 different messenger RNAs.

Protein Synthesis

Prokaryotic cells lack a nucleus and so there is no barrier between where mRNA is synthesized during transcription and where proteins are formed during translation. Consequently, a gene can be translated as it is being transcribed (figure 12.8). In eukaryotic cells, a nuclear membrane separates the process of transcription from translation, making protein synthesis much more complicated. Figure 12.9 walks you through the entire process. Transcription (step ❶) and RNA processing (step ❷) occur within the nucleus. In step ❸, the mRNA travels to the cytoplasm where it binds to the ribosome. In step ❹, tRNAs bind to their appropriate amino acids, that correspond to their anticodons. In steps ❺ and ❻, the tRNAs bring the amino acids to the ribosome and the mRNA is translated into a polypeptide.

Concept Check

1. What process produces an mRNA molecule, transcription or translation?
2. Of the 64 codons, how many do not code for an amino acid?
3. How does an RNA transcript differ in prokaryotes and eukaryotes?

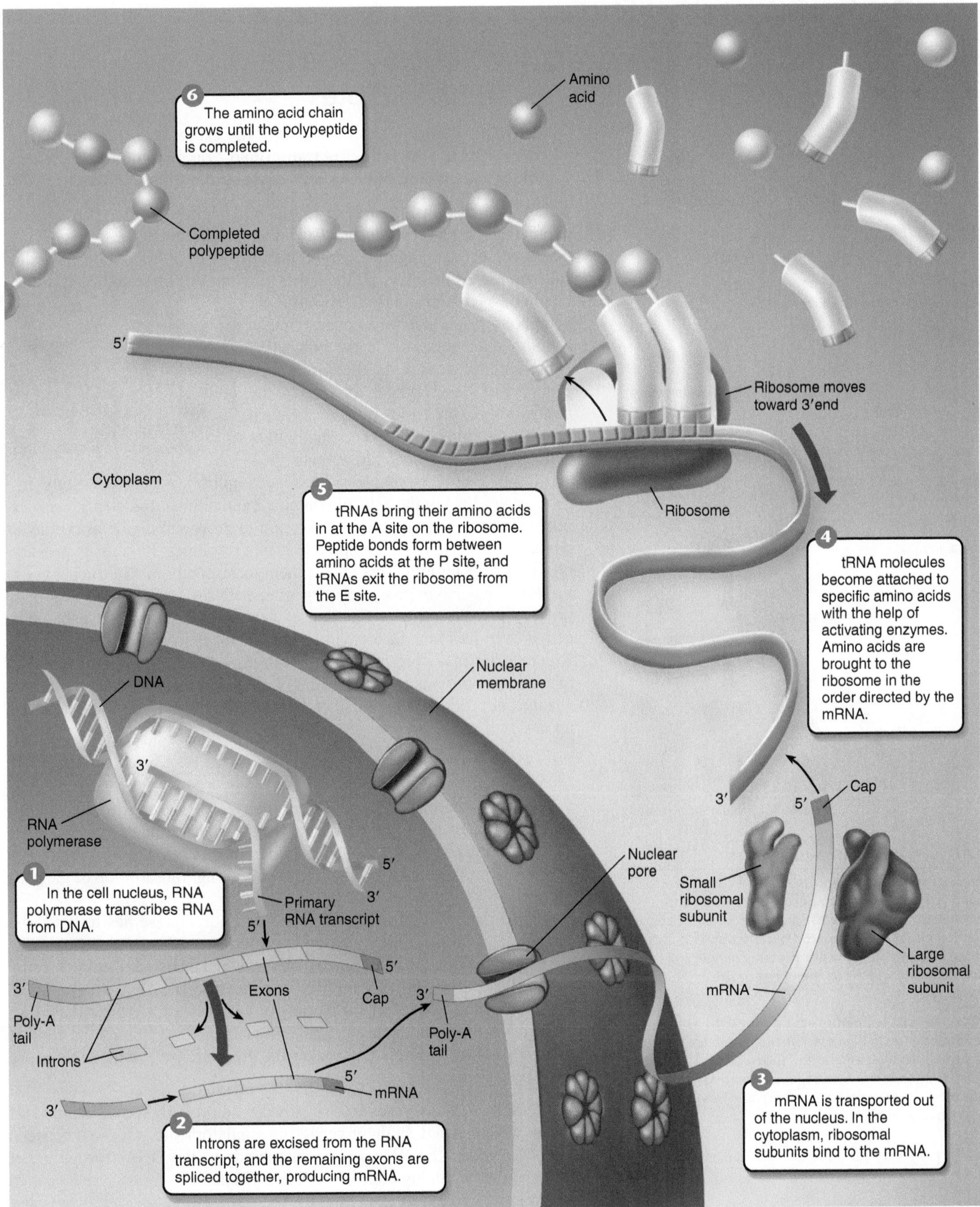

Figure 12.9 How protein synthesis works in eukaryotes.

Regulating Gene Expression

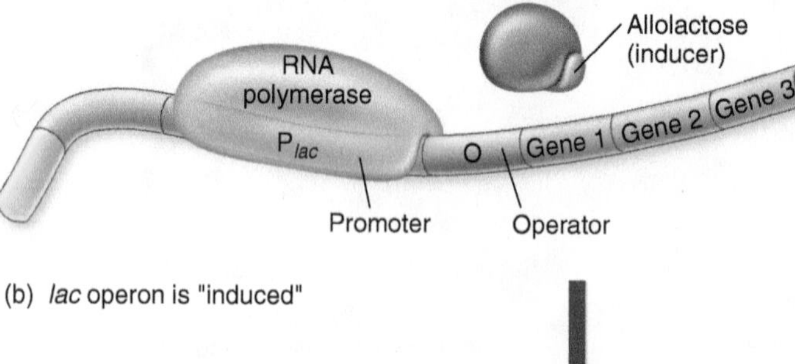

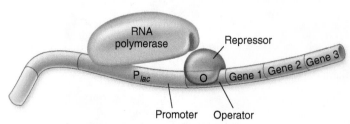

(a) *lac* operon is "repressed"

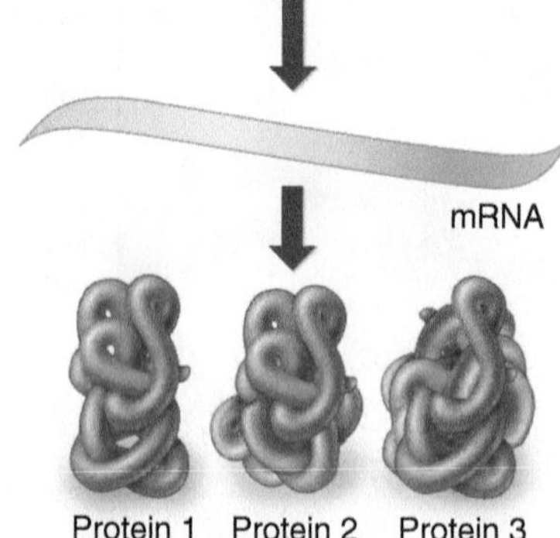

(b) *lac* operon is "induced"

Figure 12.10 How the lac operon works.

(a) The *lac* operon is shut down ("repressed") when the repressor protein is bound to the operator site. Because promoter and operator sites overlap, RNA polymerase and the repressor cannot bind at the same time. (b) The *lac* operon is transcribed ("induced") when allolactose binds to the repressor protein changing its shape so that it can no longer sit on the operator site and block polymerase binding.

IMPLICATION Certain antibiotics act by interfering with transcription or translation in bacteria. The rifamycins are a group of drugs that are used in the treatment of tuberculosis. Unlike the repressor in the *lac* operon that binds to the operator site on the DNA, rifamycin binds to bacterial RNA polymerase. How can this effectively treat a bacterial infection?

12.4 Transcriptional Control in Prokaryotes

CONCEPT PREVIEW: **Cells control the expression of genes by determining when they are transcribed. Some regulatory proteins block the binding of RNA polymerase, and others facilitate it.**

Being able to translate a gene into a polypeptide is only part of gene expression. Every cell must also be able to regulate when particular genes are used. Imagine if every instrument in a symphony played at full volume all the time, all the horns blowing full blast and each drum beating as fast and loudly as it could! No symphony plays that way, because music is more than noise—it is the controlled expression of sound. In the same way, growth and development are due to the controlled expression of genes, each brought into play at the proper moment to achieve precise and delicate effects.

Scientist can determine which genes are expressed by measuring what proteins are present in the cell. Another way is to determine the identity of the mRNA molecules present in the cell. This can be accomplished with the use of gene microarrays, as discussed on page 224.

Control of gene expression is accomplished very differently in prokaryotes than in the cells of complex multicellular organisms. Prokaryotic cells have been shaped by evolution to grow and divide as rapidly as possible, enabling them to exploit transient resources. Proteins in prokaryotes turn over rapidly. This allows them to respond quickly to changes in their external environment by changing patterns of gene expression. In prokaryotes, the primary function of gene control is to adjust the cell's activities to its immediate environment. Changes in gene expression alter which enzymes are present in the cell in response to the quantity and type of available nutrients and the amount of oxygen present. Almost all of these changes are fully reversible, allowing the cell to adjust its enzyme levels up or down as the environment changes.

How Prokaryotes Turn Genes Off and On

Prokaryotes control the expression of their genes largely by saying *when* individual genes are to be transcribed. At the beginning of each gene are special regulatory sites that act as points of control. Specific regulatory proteins within the cell bind to these sites, turning transcription of the gene off or on.

For a gene to be transcribed, the RNA polymerase has to bind to a **promoter,** a specific sequence of nucleotides on the DNA that signals the beginning of a gene. In prokaryotes, gene expression is controlled by either blocking or allowing the RNA polymerase access to the promoter. Genes can be turned off by the binding of a **repressor,** a protein that binds to the DNA blocking the promoter. Genes can be turned on by the binding of an **activator,** a protein that makes the promoter more accessible to the RNA polymerase.

Repressors. Many genes are "negatively" controlled: They are turned off except when needed. In these genes, the regulatory site is located between the place where the RNA polymerase binds to the DNA (the promoter site) and the beginning edge of the gene. When a regulatory protein called a repressor is bound to its regulatory site, called the *operator,* its presence blocks the movement of the polymerase toward the gene (figure 12.10).

Imagine if you went to sit down to eat dinner and someone was already sitting in your chair—you could not begin your meal until this person was removed from your chair. In the same way, the polymerase cannot begin transcribing the gene until the repressor protein is removed.

To turn on a gene whose transcription is blocked by a repressor, all that is required is to remove the repressor. Cells do this by binding special "signal" molecules to the repressor protein; the binding causes the repressor protein to contort into a shape that doesn't fit DNA, and it falls off, removing the barrier to transcription. A specific example demonstrating how repressor proteins work is the set of genes called the *lac* operon in the bacterium *Escherichia coli.* An **operon** is a segment of DNA containing a cluster of genes that are transcribed as a unit. The *lac* operon, shown in figure 12.10, consists of both polypeptide-encoding genes (labeled genes 1, 2, and 3, which code for enzymes involved in breaking down the sugar lactose) and associated regulatory elements—the operator (the purple segment) and promoter (the orange segment). Transcription is turned off when a repressor molecule binds to the operator such that RNA polymerase cannot bind to the promoter. When *E. coli* encounters the sugar lactose, a metabolite of lactose called allolactose binds to the repressor protein and induces a twist in its shape that causes it to fall from the DNA. As you can see in figure 12.10*b*, RNA polymerase is no longer blocked, so it starts to transcribe the genes needed to break down the lactose to get energy.

Activators. Because RNA polymerase binds to a specific promoter site on one strand of the DNA double helix, it is necessary that the DNA double helix unzip in the vicinity of this site for the polymerase protein to be able to sit down properly. This unzipping requires the assistance of a regulatory protein called an activator that binds to the DNA nearby and helps it unwind. Cells can turn the genes on and off by binding "signal" molecules to this activator protein. In the *lac* operon, a protein called catabolite activator protein (CAP) acts as an activator. CAP has to bind a signal molecule, cAMP, before it can associate with the DNA. Once the CAP/cAMP complex forms, as seen in figure 12.11, it binds to the DNA and makes the promoter more accessible to RNA polymerase.

Recall from the discussion on page 190 that the DNA is unwound by an enzyme called helicase. When the DNA is unwound, DNA polymerase has access to the DNA and can replicate it. Similarly, an activator allows RNA polymerase access to the gene.

Why bother with activators? Imagine if you had to eat every time you encountered food! Activator proteins enable a cell to cope with this sort of problem. Activators and repressors work together to control transcription. To understand how, let's consider the *lac* operon again, now shown in figure 12.12. When a bacterium encounters the sugar lactose, it may already have lots of energy in the form of glucose, as shown in panel ❶, and so does not need to break down more lactose. CAP can only bind and activate gene transcription when glucose levels are low. Because RNA polymerase requires the activator to function, the *lac* operon is not expressed. Also if glucose is present and lactose is absent, not only is the activator CAP unable to bind, but also a repressor blocks the promoter, as shown in panel ❷. In the absence of both glucose and lactose, cAMP, the "low glucose" signal molecule (the green pie-shaped piece in panels ❸ and ❹) binds to CAP, and CAP is able to bind to the DNA. However, the repressor is still blocking transcription, as shown in panel ❸. Only in the absence of glucose and in the presence of lactose, the repressor is removed, the activator (CAP) is bound, and transcription proceeds, as shown in panel ❹.

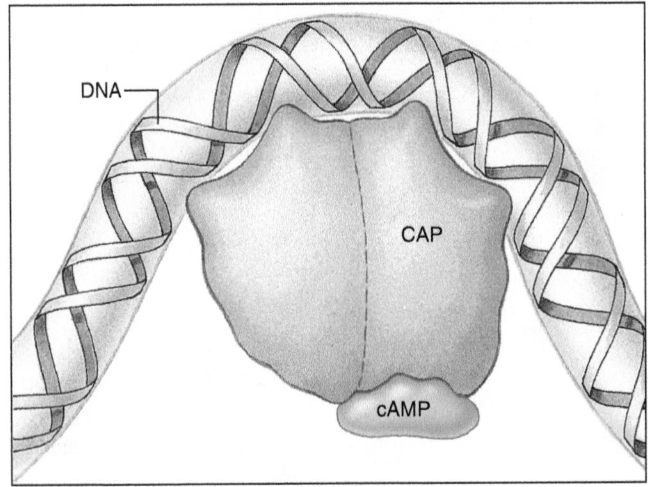

Figure 12.11 How an activator works.

Binding of the catabolite activator protein complex to DNA causes the DNA to bend around it. This increases the activity of RNA polymerase.

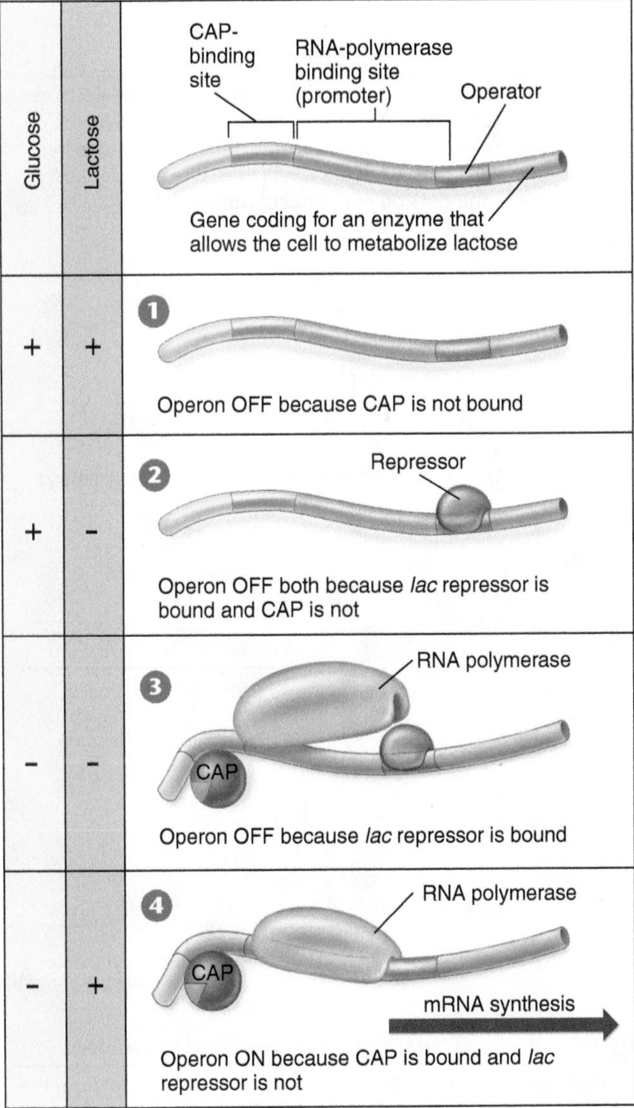

Figure 12.12 Activators and repressors at the *lac* operon.

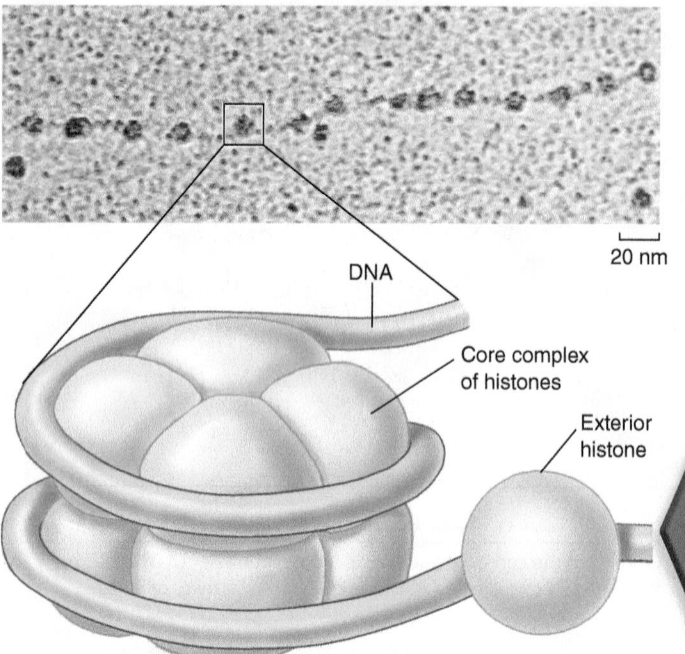

Figure 12.13 DNA coils around histones.

In chromatin, DNA is packaged into nucleosomes. In the electron micrograph (*top*), the DNA is partially unwound, and individual nucleosomes can be seen. In a nucleosome, the DNA double helix coils around a core complex of eight histones; one additional histone binds to the outside of the nucleosome.

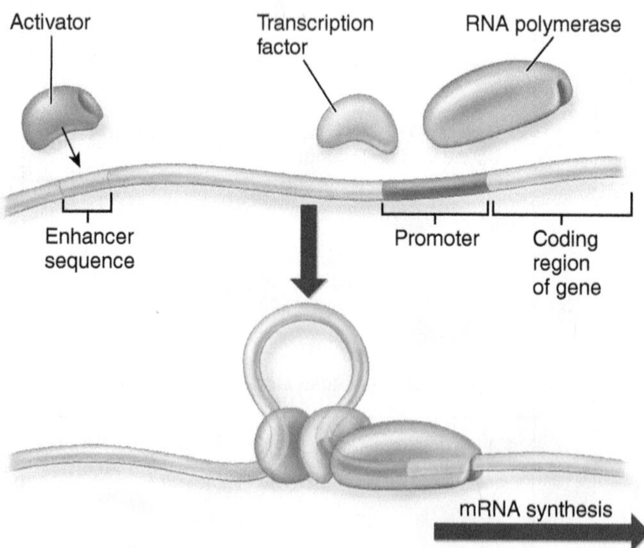

Figure 12.14 Transcription factors and enhancers.

The activator binding site, or enhancer, is often located far from the gene. The binding of an activator protein to the transcription factor is required for polymerase initiation.

12.5 Transcriptional Control in Eukaryotes

CONCEPT PREVIEW: Transcriptional control in eukaryotes can be effected by the tight packaging of DNA into nucleosomes. Transcription factors and enhancers also give these cells great flexibility in controlling gene expression.

Chromatin Structure

In multicellular organisms with relatively constant internal environments, the primary function of gene control in a cell is not to respond to that cell's immediate environment, like a prokaryote does, but rather to participate in regulating the body as a whole. Some of these changes in gene expression compensate for changes in the physiological condition of the body. Others mediate the decisions that ultimately produce the body, ensuring that the right genes are expressed in the right cells at the right time during development. In multicellular organisms, changes in gene expression serve the needs of the whole organism, rather than the survival of individual cells.

An understanding of gene expression helps explain the gene theory, discussed on page 24. All cells in an organism have the same DNA, but not all of the cells express the same genes; different cells need different proteins to function. Many genes are never turned on in a given cell.

The first hurdle faced by RNA polymerase in transcribing a eukaryotic gene is gaining access to it. As described in chapter 8, eukaryotic chromosomes consist of chromatin, a complex of DNA and protein. In chromatin, the DNA is packaged with histone proteins into nucleosomes (figure 12.13). During mitosis, nucleosomes wind, twist, and coil into chromosomes, but even during interphase when transcription is occurring, some sections of DNA remain as part of nucleosomes. These nucleosomes seem to block the binding of RNA polymerase and other proteins called transcription factors to the promoter site. Histones can be chemically modified to result in a greater condensation of the chromatin, making it even less accessible. Another chemical modification of the DNA—adding a methyl group ($—CH_3$) to cytosine nucleotides—blocks accidental transcription of "turned-off" genes. DNA methylation ensures that once a gene is turned off, it stays off.

Transcription Factors and Enhancers

Eukaryotic transcription requires not only the RNA polymerase molecule, but also a variety of other proteins, called *transcription factors,* that interact with the polymerase to form an *initiation complex*. Transcription factors are necessary for the assembly of the initiation complex and recruitment of RNA polymerase to a promoter. While these factors, colored green in figure 12.14, are required for transcription to occur, they do not increase the rate of transcription.

While prokaryotic gene control regions, such as the operator, are positioned immediately upstream of the coding region, this is not true in eukaryotes, in which far away sites called **enhancers** can have a major impact on the rate of transcription. The ability of enhancers to act over large distances is accomplished by DNA bending to form a loop. In figure 12.14, the DNA loops, bringing the activator in contact with the RNA polymerase/initiation complex so that transcription can begin.

This complex transcriptional control is only one aspect of gene regulation in eukaryotic cells. Other processes associated with translation, such as gene silencing, protein synthesis, and post-translational modifications are described in *Essential Biological Process 12B* and provide the cell the ability to produce finely graded responses to environmental and developmental signals.

Essential Biological Process 12B

Control of Eukaryotic Gene Expression

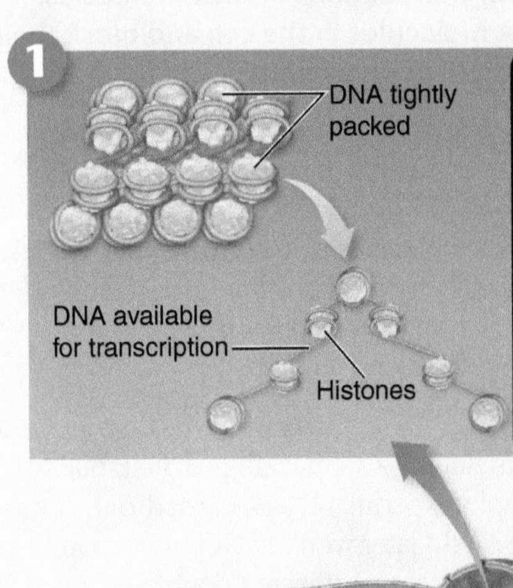

Chromatin structure
Access to many genes is affected by the packaging of DNA and by chemically altering the histone proteins.

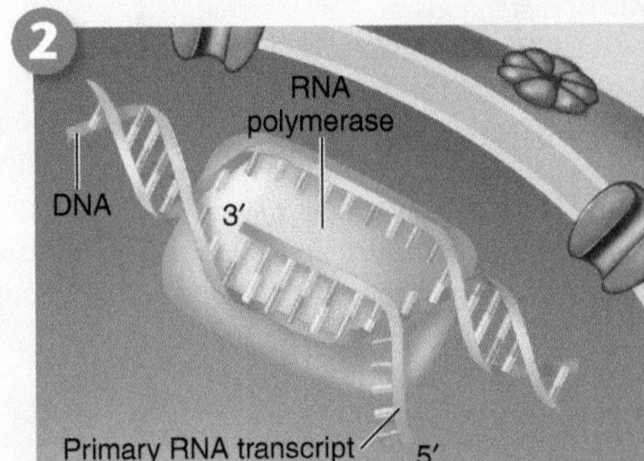

Initiation of transcription
Most control of gene expression is achieved by regulating the frequency of transcription initiation.

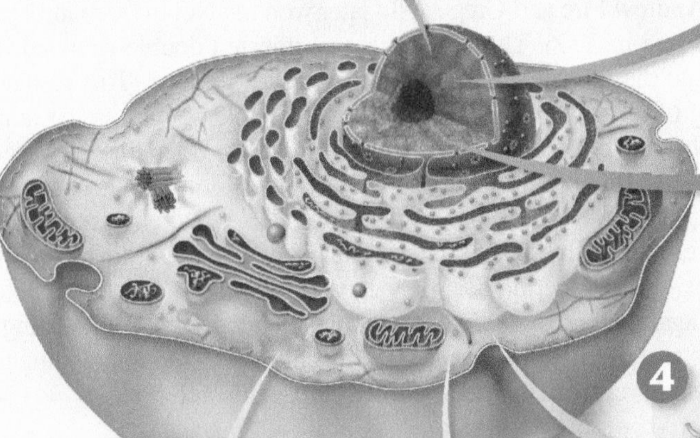

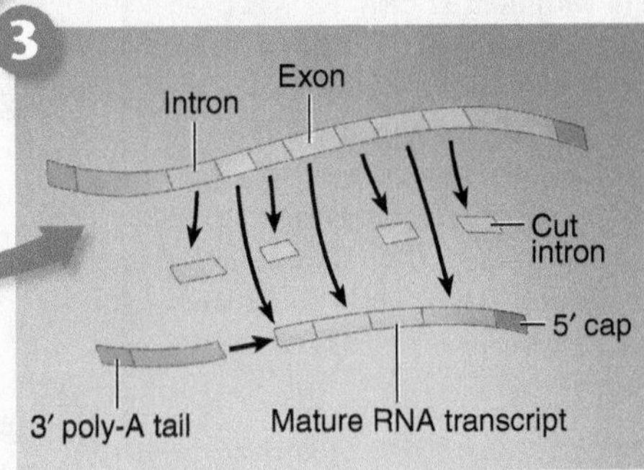

RNA splicing
Gene expression can be controlled by altering the rate of splicing in eukaryotes. Alternative splicing can produce multiple mRNAs from one gene.

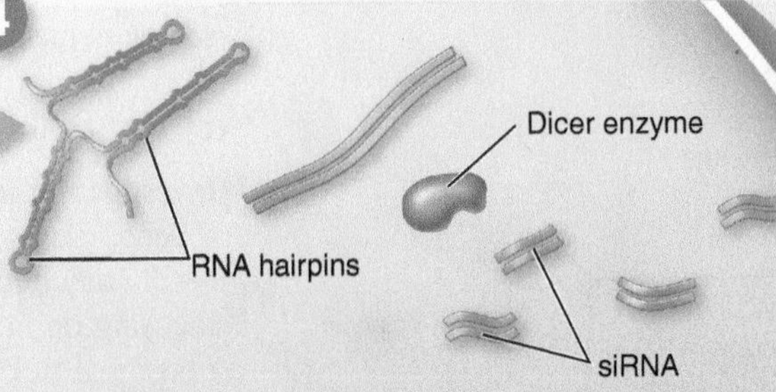

Gene silencing
Cells can silence genes with siRNAs, which are cut from inverted sequences that fold into double-stranded loops. siRNAs bind to mRNAs and block their translation.

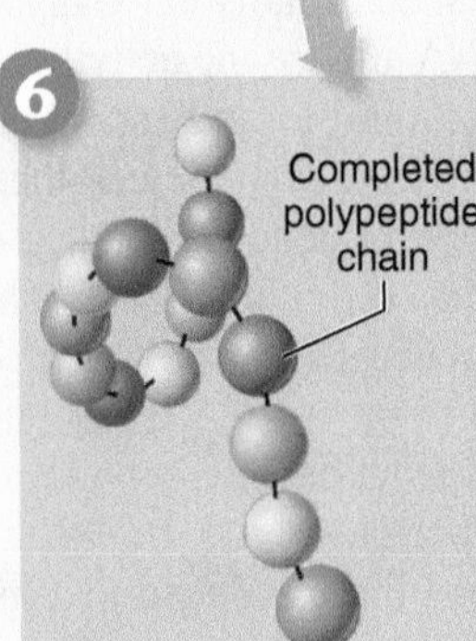

Post-translational modification
Phosphorylation or other chemical modifications can alter the activity of a protein after it is produced.

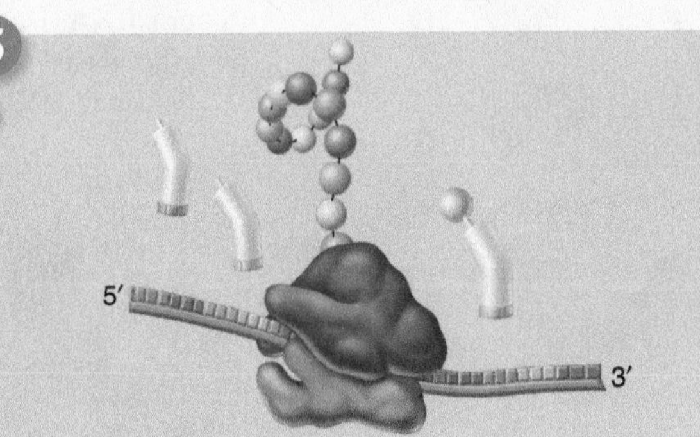

Protein synthesis
Many proteins take part in the translation process, and regulation of the availability of any of them alters the rate of gene expression by speeding or slowing protein synthesis.

IN THE NEWS

Silencing AIDS. After decades of searching unsuccessfully for an effective AIDS vaccine, researchers are turning to other approaches. One of the most promising centers on a 42-year-old American resident of Germany, who in 2008 was completely cured of AIDS. How? First, his immune system was wiped out with radiation and drugs, then he received blood stem cells (which make both circulating blood cells and immune system cells) from a person homozygous for a gene mutation known as *delta 32*. This mutation destroys the cell surface receptors that allow HIV to invade the immune system, so that people homozygous for it are immune to HIV infection and AIDS. Because the patient's own blood stem cells had been destroyed, these new ones reconstituted his blood supply and immune system with *delta 32* cells. He has been free of the HIV virus for 20 months and it appears he has been permanently cured of AIDS. Wiping out a person's immune system is far too dangerous as a general therapy (10%–30% die), but the success in this instance has encouraged researchers to try using RNA "scissors" as described on this page to cut out the *delta 32* gene from a patient's own blood stem cells and reinject them after wiping out only the patient's blood stem cells, not the entire immune system. Researchers report that the concept is working in monkeys.

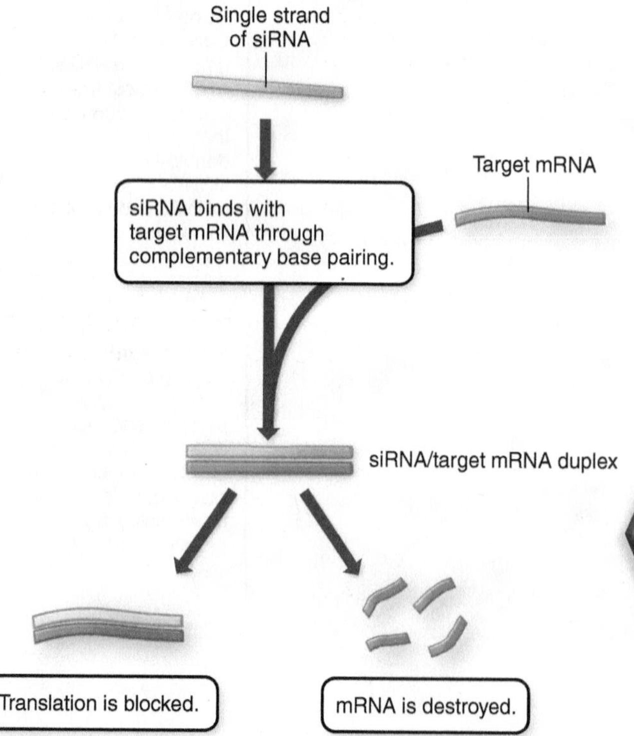
Single strand
of siRNA
Target mRNA
siRNA binds with
target mRNA through
complementary base pairing.
siRNA/target mRNA duplex
Translation is blocked.
mRNA is destroyed.

Figure 12.15 RNA interference.

RNA interference stops gene expression either by blocking the translation of the gene (on the left) or by targeting the mRNA for destruction before it can be translated.

12.6 RNA-Level Control

CONCEPT PREVIEW: Small interfering RNAs, called siRNAs, are formed from double-stranded sections of RNA molecules. These siRNAs bind to mRNA molecules in the cell and block their translation in a process called RNA interference.

Thus far we have discussed gene regulation entirely in terms of proteins that regulate the start of transcription by blocking or activating the "reading" of a particular gene by RNA polymerase. Within the last decade, however, it has become increasingly clear that RNA molecules also regulate gene expression, acting after transcription as a second equally important level of control.

Discovery of RNA Interference

As will be discussed in detail in chapter 13, the bulk of the eukaryotic genome is not translated into proteins. This finding was puzzling at first, but began to make sense in 1998, when a simple experiment was carried out, for which Americans Andrew Fire and Greg Mello later won the Nobel Prize in Physiology or Medicine in 2006. These investigators injected double-stranded RNA molecules into the nematode worm *Caenorhabditis elegans*. This resulted in the silencing of the gene whose sequence was complementary to the double-stranded RNA, and of no other gene. The investigators called this very specific effect **gene silencing,** or **RNA interference.** What is going on here? A group of viruses called RNA viruses, those that contain RNA as their hereditary storage molecule rather than DNA, replicate themselves through double-stranded intermediates. RNA interference may have evolved as a cellular defense mechanism against these viruses with double-stranded viral RNAs being targeted for destruction by RNA interference machinery. Without intending to do so, the nematode researchers had stumbled across this defense.

How RNA Interference Works

Investigating interference, researchers noted that in the process of silencing a gene, plants produced short RNA molecules (ranging in length from 21 to 28 nucleotides) that matched the gene being silenced. Earlier researchers focusing on far larger messenger RNA (mRNA), transfer RNA (tRNA), and ribosomal RNA (rRNA) had not noticed these far smaller bits, tossing them out during experiments. These bits of RNA are called "small interfering RNA" or siRNA. How do these small fragments of RNA silence the activity of specific genes? In a complex way we are just beginning to understand clearly, the small RNA fragments bind to any mRNA molecules in the cell that have a complementary sequence. Silencing of the gene that produced this mRNA is achieved in one of two ways (figure 12.15): either the expression of the mRNA is inhibited by blocking its translation into protein, or the mRNA is simply destroyed. In either case, the specific gene that produced that mRNA fails to be expressed—it is silenced.

mRNA molecules are single-stranded, as described on page 52. During translation, the codon in the mRNA is exposed so it can bind to the complementary anticodon of the tRNA. If the mRNA codons are blocked by siRNA, the codons can't be read to make a polypeptide.

Concept Check

1. If lactose is added to their growth medium, bacteria begin to transcribe the *lac* operon. How is transcription possible now, when it wasn't before?
2. Enhancers are located far from the genes they regulate but in order to function they need to be in contact with the gene. How is that achieved?
3. How can RNA be used to regulate gene expression?

Silencing Genes to Treat Disease

The recent discovery that eukaryotes control their genes by selectively "silencing" particular gene transcripts has electrified biologists, as it opens exciting possibilities for treating disease and infection. Many diseases are caused by expression of one or more genes. AIDS for example requires the expression of several genes of the HIV virus. Many chronic human diseases result from excessively active genes. What if doctors could somehow shut these genes off? The expression of the diseases could be halted in their tracks.

The idea is simple. If you can isolate a gene involved in the disorder and determine its sequence, then in principle you could synthesize an RNA molecule with the sequence of the opposite or "antisense" strand. This RNA would thus have a sequence complementary to the messenger RNA produced by that gene. Introduced into cells, this synthesized RNA might be able to bind to the mRNA, creating a double-stranded RNA that could not be read by ribosomes. If an antisense therapy could be made to work and be delivered practically and inexpensively, the AIDS epidemic could be halted in its tracks. Indeed, any viral infection could be combatted in this way. Influenza is perhaps the greatest killer of all infectious diseases. A workable antisense therapy could provide a means of stamping out a bird flu epidemic before the virus spreads.

By far the most exciting promise of antisense gene silencing therapy is the possibility of a practical cancer therapy. Discussed in chapter 8, cancer kills more Americans than any other disease. We now know in considerable detail how cancer comes about. It results from damage to genes that regulate the cell cycle. The great promise of RNA gene silencing therapy comes from those cancer-causing gene mutations that increase the effectiveness of one or more "divide" signals. If these mutant genes could be silenced, the cancer could be shut down.

The prospect of using complementary RNA to silence troublesome genes has gotten a huge boost in the last few years from the discovery of a unique virus defense system in eukaryotes. In order to protect themselves from RNA virus infection, cells have a complex system for detecting, attacking, and destroying viral RNA. The system takes advantage of a subtle vulnerability of the infecting virus: at some point, in order to multiply within the infected cell, the virus must express its genes—it must make complementary copies of them that can serve as messenger RNAs to direct production of viral proteins. At that point, while the viral RNA molecule is double-stranded, the virus is vulnerable to attack: at no place in the cell is double-stranded RNA usually found, so by targeting double-stranded RNAs for immediate destruction, a cell can defeat viral infections.

Silencing genes with complementary RNA, dubbed "RNA interference," offers the exciting hope that successful treatment of many diseases may be literally at our doorstep. First, however, scientists must figure out how to make RNA interference therapies work. They are facing some formidable technical problems, not the least of which is to find a way to deliver the interfering RNA to, and into, the target cells. The problem is that RNA is rapidly broken down in the bloodstream, and most of the body's cells don't readily absorb it, even if it does reach them. Some researchers are attempting to package the RNA into viruses, although gene therapies that have attempted this approach can trigger an immune response and could even cause cancer. Gene therapy researchers have been seeking safer virus gene-delivery vehicles; what they learn will surely be put to good effect.

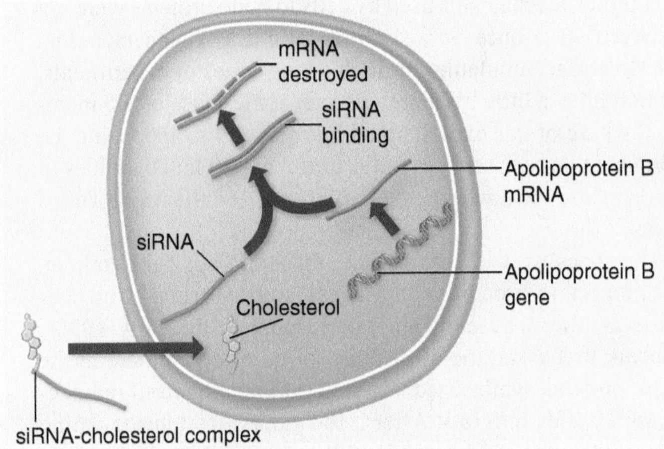

One interesting alternative approach is to modify the RNA to protect it and make it more easily taken up by cells. This work focuses on the mRNA that encodes apolipoprotein B, a molecule involved in the metabolism of cholesterol. High levels of apolipoprotein are found in people with high levels of cholesterol, associated with increased risk of coronary heart disease. Interfering RNAs that target apolipoprotein B mRNA result in destruction of the mRNA, and lower levels of cholesterol. To effectively deliver it to the body's tissues, researchers simply attached a molecule of cholesterol to each interfering RNA molecule (see diagram above). Levels of apolipoprotein B were reduced 50–70%, and blood cholesterol levels plummeted downward, to the same levels seen in cells from which the apolipoprotein B gene had been deleted. It is not clear if this approach will work for many other RNAs, but it looks promising.

A second major problem confronting those seeking to develop successful therapies based on RNA silencing of troublesome genes is one of specificity. It is very important that only the target gene be silenced. Before carrying out clinical trials involving large numbers of people, it is imperative that we be sure the interfering RNA will not shut down vital human genes as well as the targeted virus or cancer genes. Some studies suggest this will not be a problem, while in others, a range of "off-target" genes seem to be affected. This possibility will have to be carefully evaluated for each new therapy being developed.

Inquiry & Analysis

Building Proteins in a Test Tube

The complex mechanisms used by cells to build proteins were not discovered all at once, in a flash of insight. Our understanding came slowly, accumulating through a long series of experiments, each telling us a little bit more. To gain some sense of the incremental nature of this experimental journey, and to appreciate the excitement that each step gave, it is useful to step into the shoes of an investigator back when little was known and the way forward was not clear.

The shoes we will step into are those of Paul Zamecnik, an early pioneer in protein synthesis research. Working with colleagues at Massachusetts General Hospital in the early 1950s, Zamecnik first asked the most direct of questions: Where in the cell are proteins synthesized? To find out, they injected radioactive amino acids into rats. After a few hours, the labeled amino acids could be found as part of newly made proteins in the livers of the rats. And, if the livers were removed and checked only minutes after injection, radioactive-labeled proteins were found only associated with small particles in the cytoplasm. Composed of protein and RNA, these particles, later named ribosomes, had been discovered years earlier by electron microscope studies of cell components. This experiment identified them as the sites of protein synthesis in the cell.

After several years of trial-and-error tinkering, Zamecnik and his colleagues had worked out a "cell-free" protein-synthesis system that would lead to the synthesis of proteins in a test tube. It included ribosomes, mRNA, and ATP to provide energy. It also included a collection of required soluble "factors" isolated from homogenized rat cells that somehow worked with the ribosome to get the job done. When Zamecnik's team characterized these required factors, they found most of them to be proteins, as expected, but also present in the mix was a small RNA, very unexpected.

To see what this small RNA was doing, they performed the following experiment. In a test tube, they added various amounts of ^{14}C-leucine (that is, the radioactively labeled amino acid leucine) to the cell-free system containing the soluble factors, ribosomes, and ATP. After waiting a bit, they then isolated the small RNA from the mixture and checked it for radioactivity. You can see the results in graph (a) above.

In a follow-up experiment, they mixed the radioactive leucine-small RNA complex that this experiment had generated with cell extracts containing intact endoplasmic reticulum (that is, a cell system of ribosomes on membranes quite capable of making protein). Looking to see where the radioactive label now went, they then isolated the newly-made protein [red in graph (b)] as well as the small RNA [blue in graph (b)].

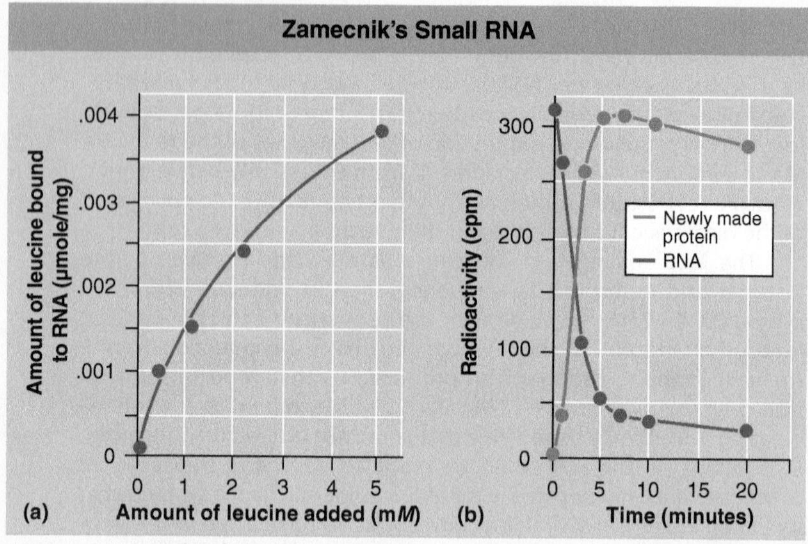

Analysis

EXPERIMENT A, shown in graph (a)

1. **Interpreting Data** Does the amount of leucine added to the test tube have an effect on the amount of leucine found bound to the small RNA?
2. **Making Inferences** Is the amount of leucine bound to small RNA proportional to the amount of leucine added to the mixture?
3. **Drawing Conclusions** Can you reasonably conclude from this result that the amino acid leucine is binding to the small RNA?

EXPERIMENT B, shown in graph (b)

1. **Interpreting Data**
   a. Monitoring radioactivity for 20 minutes after the addition of the radioactive leucine-small RNA complex to the cell extract, what happens to the level of radioactivity in the small RNA (blue)?
   b. Over the same period, what happens to the level of radioactivity in the newly made protein (red)?
2. **Making Inferences** Is the same amount of radioactivity being lost from the small RNA that is being gained by the newly made protein?
3. **Drawing Conclusions**
   a. Is it reasonable to conclude that the small RNA is donating its amino acid to the growing protein? [Hint: As a result of this experiment, the small RNA was called transfer RNA.]
   b. If you were to isolate the protein from this experiment made after 20 minutes, which amino acids would be radioactively labeled? Explain.

Concept Summary

From Gene to Protein

12.1 Transcription

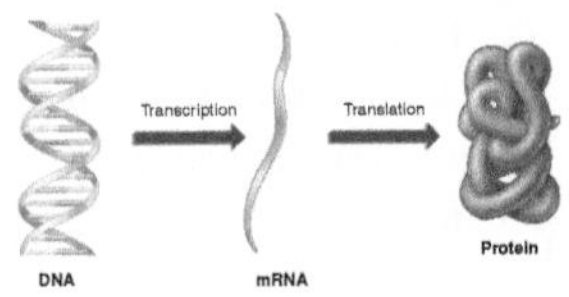

- DNA is the storage site of genetic information in the cell. The process of gene expression, DNA to RNA to protein, is called the central dogma, shown here from **figure 12.1.**
- Gene expression occurs in two stages using three types of RNA: transcription, where an mRNA copy is made from the DNA, and translation, where the information on the mRNA is translated into a protein using rRNA and tRNA.
- In transcription, DNA serves as a template for mRNA synthesis by a protein called RNA polymerase. RNA polymerase binds to one strand of the DNA at a site called the promoter. RNA polymerase adds complementary nucleotides onto the growing mRNA in a way that is similar to the actions of DNA polymerase (**figure 12.2**).

12.2 Translation

- The message within the mRNA is coded in its sequence of nucleotides, which are read in three nucleotide units called codons. Codons correspond to particular amino acids. The rules that govern the translation of codons on the mRNA into amino acids is called the genetic code (**figure 12.3**).
- In translation, the mRNA carries the message to the cytoplasm. rRNA combines with proteins to form a structure called a ribosome (**figure 12.4**), the platform on which proteins are assembled.
- A ribosome contains a small and a large subunit. Translation begins when the mRNA binds to the small ribosomal subunit, which triggers the binding of the large subunit to the small subunit, forming a complete ribosome. The ribosome has three sites, called A, P, and E, to which a third type of RNA, called transfer RNA (tRNA) binds.
- tRNA molecules, like one shown here from **figure 12.5,** carry amino acids to the ribosome to build the polypeptide chain. The amino acid that attaches to the tRNA is determined by a three-nucleotide sequence on the tRNA called the anticodon.
- A ribosome moves along mRNA, while the tRNA molecules that contain anticodon sequences that are complementary to the codons bring the appropriate amino acids to the ribosome. An incoming tRNA first attaches to the A site, then moves to the P and E sites as the ribosome moves, leaving the A site open for the next tRNA. The amino acids add to the growing polypeptide chain (***Essential Biological Process 12A*** and **figure 12.6**).
- When a "stop" codon is reached, the ribosome dissociates and releases the polypeptide into the cell.

12.3 Gene Expression

- Prokaryotic genes are contained within a stretch of DNA that is transcribed and translated in its entirety.
- Eukaryotic genes are fragmented, containing coding regions called exons, and noncoding regions called introns. The entire eukaryotic gene is transcribed into RNA, but the introns are spliced out before translation (**figure 12.7**).

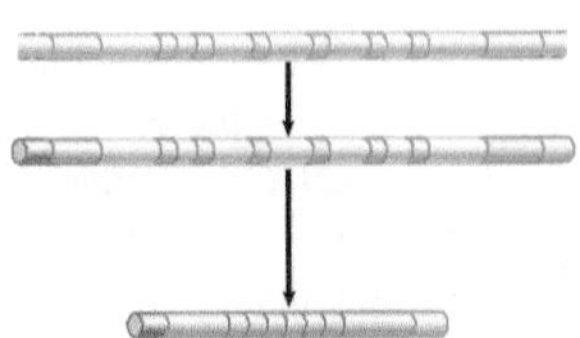

- Exons can be spliced together in different ways, a process called alternative splicing, producing different protein products from the same sections of DNA.
- The process of protein synthesis is different in eukaryotes compared to prokaryotes. In prokaryotes, transcription and translation can occur simultaneously. Ribosomes attach to the mRNA as it is transcribed, beginning translation before transcription is completed (**figure 12.8**). In eukaryotes, the RNA transcript is first produced and then processed (introns spliced out) in the nucleus. The mRNA then travels to the cytoplasm, where it is translated into a polypeptide (**figure 12.9**).

Regulating Gene Expression

12.4 Transcriptional Control in Prokaryotes

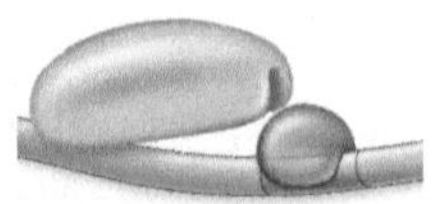

- In prokaryotic cells, genes are turned off when a repressor protein blocks the promoter, as shown here from **figure 12.10,** binding to a site called an operator.
- Some genes can be turned on only when a protein called an activator binds to the DNA and opens up the double helix so that RNA polymerase can bind to the promoter.
- The *lac* operon contains a cluster of genes that are involved in the breakdown of the sugar lactose. When the proteins produced by the *lac* operon genes are needed, an inducer molecule will bind to the repressor protein so it can't attach to the DNA, thereby freeing the promoter so that RNA polymerase can bind (**figure 12.10**).
- The *lac* operon is also controlled by an activator. The activator alters the shape of DNA, which allows the RNA polymerase to bind to the DNA (**figure 12.11**). It is only when the activator binds to the DNA and the repressor is removed that the RNA polymerase can bind to the promoter (**figure 12.12**).

12.5 Transcriptional Control in Eukaryotes

- The coiling of DNA around histones (**figure 12.13**) restricts RNA polymerase's access to the DNA. Controlling gene expression may involve chemical modification of histones, that make the DNA more accessible, or methylation of the DNA itself that keeps a gene turned off.
- In eukaryotic cells, transcription requires the binding of transcription factors before RNA polymerase can bind to the promoter. Eukaryotic genes are controlled from distant locations called enhancers. A regulatory protein binds to the enhancer region far from the gene and the DNA forms a loop, as shown here from **figure 12.14,** bringing the distant enhancer region into contact with the transcription factors. Eukaryotic cells have several levels of gene expression (***Essential Biological Process 12B***).

12.6 RNA-Level Control

- RNA interference blocks translation. Small sections of RNA, called siRNA, bind to mRNA in the cytoplasm, which blocks the expression of the gene (**figure 12.15**).

Self-Test

1. Which of the following is not a type of RNA?
   a. nRNA (nuclear RNA) c. rRNA (ribosomal RNA)
   b. mRNA (messenger RNA) d. tRNA (transfer RNA)
2. Each amino acid in a polypeptide is specified by
   a. an enhancer. c. an rRNA molecule.
   b. a promoter. d. a codon.
3. Which of the following statements is correct about the genetic code?
   a. Every codon encodes an amino acid.
   b. Each amino acid is encoded by only one codon.
   c. A codon consists of three nuceotides.
   d. A codon and its complementary anticodon have the same sequences.
4. The process of obtaining a copy of the information in a gene as a strand of messenger RNA is called
   a. polymerase. c. transcription.
   b. expression. d. translation.
5. The site where RNA polymerase attaches to the DNA molecule to start the formation of an RNA molecule is called a(n)
   a. promoter. c. intron.
   b. exon. d. enhancer.
6. The process of taking the information on a strand of messenger RNA and building an amino acid chain, which will become all or part of a protein molecule, is called
   a. polymerase. c. transcription.
   b. expression. d. translation.
7. If an mRNA codon reads UAC, its complementary anticodon will be
   a. TUC. c. AUG.
   b. ATG. d. UAC.
8. Which of the following accurately describes gene expression in prokaryotic cells?
   a. All genes are on all the time in all cells, making the needed amino acid sequences.
   b. Some genes are always off unless a promoter turns them on.
   c. Some genes are always on unless a promoter turns them off.
   d. Some genes remain off as long as a repressor is bound.
9. Which of the following statements is correct about eukaryotic gene expression?
   a. mRNAs must have introns spliced out.
   b. mRNAs contain the transcript of only one gene.
   c. Enhancers act from a distance.
   d. All of these statements are correct.
10. Which of the following is *not* a mechanism of controlling gene expression in eukaryotic cells?
    a. Blocking translation with siRNA.
    b. Activating an enhancer.
    c. Translating a gene as it is being transcribed.
    d. Alternative splicing of the primary RNA transcript.

Visual Understanding

1. **Figure 12.1** This figure of the central dogma represents the general process of gene expression in prokaryotes and eukaryotes, however the process is slightly more complex in eukaryotic cells. What step is missing here that occurs in eukaryotic cells but not in prokaryotic cells?

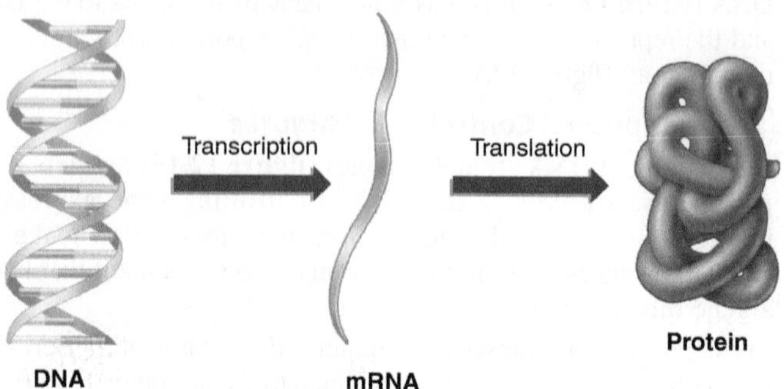

2. **Figure 12.10** Can genes 1, 2, and 3 be transcribed? What would happen if an inducer molecule was present in the cell?

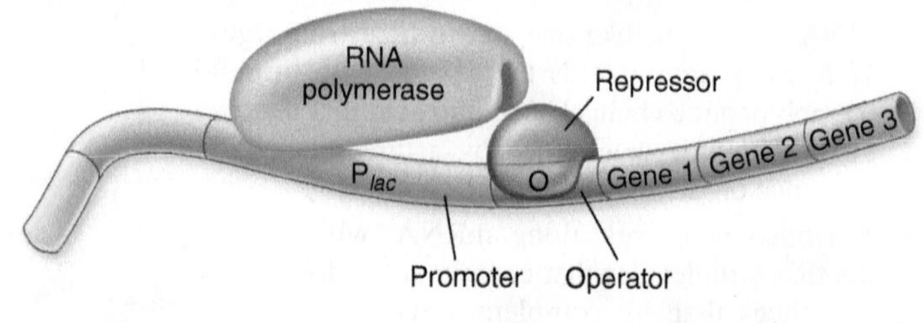

Challenge Questions

1. Compare DNA to a cookbook. The book is kept in a library and cannot be checked out (removed). Start with the letters and words in the cookbook compared with the bases and codons in DNA; end with the amino acid chain being folded into a protein compared to a cake being baked.
2. What would happen if all the genes in a cell were always active?
3. If you travel to a foreign country where you don't speak the language, you might hire a translator to translate what you want to say from your language to the language used in the country you are visiting. The central dogma works in a similar way: The language of nucleic acids (which uses nucleotides) is translated into the language of proteins (which uses amino acids). That being the case, which molecule serves as the translator?
4. The nucleotide sequence of a hypothetical gene is:

   TACATACTTAGTTACGTCGCCCGGAAATAT

   a. What will be the sequence on the mRNA when it is transcribed?
   b. What will be the amino acid sequence of the protein when it's translated?
   c. What would happen to the amino acid chain if the highlighted nucleotide underwent a mutation and was changed to an A nucleotide?

Chapter 13

The New Biology

CHAPTER AT A GLANCE

Sequencing Entire Genomes

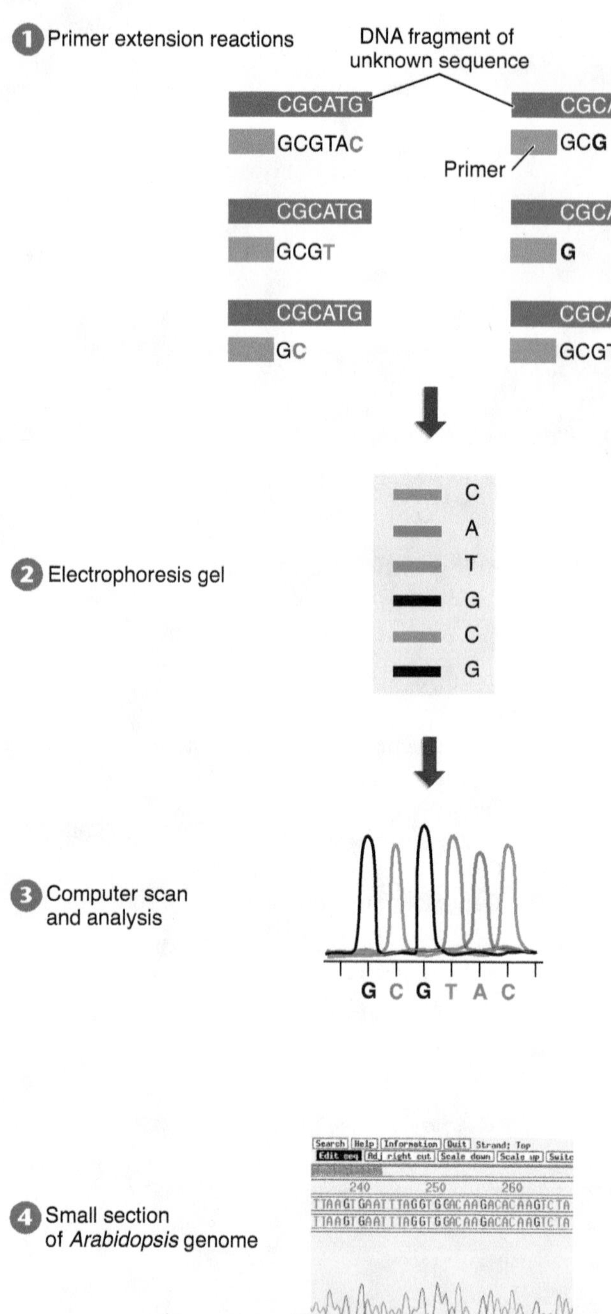

Figure 13.1 How to sequence DNA.

1 DNA is sequenced by adding complementary bases to a single-stranded fragment. DNA synthesis stops when a chemical tag is inserted instead of a nucleotide, resulting in different sizes of DNA fragments. 2 The DNA fragments of varying lengths are separated by gel electrophoresis, the smaller fragments migrating farther down the gel. (The letters indicate the chemical tags added in step 1 that stopped the replication process.) 3 Computers scan the gel, from smallest to largest fragments, and display the DNA sequence as a series of colored peaks. 4 Data from an automated DNA-sequencing run show the nucleotide sequence for a small section of the *Arabidopsis* (plant) genome.

13.1 Genomics

CONCEPT PREVIEW: Powerful automated DNA sequencing technology is now revealing the DNA sequences of entire genomes.

The full complement of genetic information of an organism—all of its genes and other DNA—is called its **genome.** To study a genome the DNA is first sequenced, a process that allows each nucleotide of a DNA strand to be read in order. The first genome to be sequenced was a very simple one: a small bacterial virus called ϕ-X174 (ϕ is the Greek letter phi). Frederick Sanger, inventor of the first practical way to sequence DNA, obtained the sequence of this 5,375-nucleotide genome in 1977. This was followed by the sequencing of dozens of prokaryotic genomes. The advent of automated DNA sequencing machines in recent years has made the DNA sequencing of much larger eukaryotic genomes practical, including our own (table 13.1).

Sequencing DNA

In sequencing DNA, the DNA of unknown sequence is first cut into fragments. Each DNA fragment is then copied (amplified), so there are thousands of copies of the fragment. The DNA fragments are then mixed with copies of DNA polymerase, copies of a primer (recall from chapter 11 that DNA polymerase can only add nucleotides onto an existing strand of nucleotides), a supply of the four nucleotide bases, and a supply of four different chain-terminating chemical tags. The chemical tags act as one of the four nucleotide bases in DNA synthesis, undergoing complementary base pairing. First, heat is applied to denature the double-stranded DNA fragments. The solution is then allowed to cool, allowing the primer (the lighter blue box in figure 13.1 1) to bind to a single strand of the DNA, and synthesis of the complementary strand proceeds. Whenever a chemical tag is added instead of a nucleotide base, the synthesis stops, as shown in the figure. For example, the terminating red "T" was added after three normal nucleotides and synthesis stopped. Because of the relatively low concentration of the chemical tags compared with the nucleotides, a tag that binds to G on the DNA fragment, for example, will not necessarily be added to the first G site. Thus, the mixture will contain a series of double-stranded DNA fragments of different lengths, corresponding to the different distances the polymerase traveled from the primer before a chain-terminating tag was incorporated (six are shown in 1).

To better understand DNA sequencing it would be helpful to review the process of DNA replication on page 190. For example, if the T nucleotide being added in figure 11.7 was a chain-terminating nucleotide, replication would stop before any more nucleotides were added.

The series of fragments are then separated according to size by gel electrophoresis. The fragments become arrayed like the rungs of a ladder, each rung being one base longer than the one below it. Compare the lengths of the fragments in 1 and their positions on the gel in 2. The shortest fragment has only one nucleotide (G) added to the primer, so it is the lowest rung on the gel. In automated DNA sequencing, fluorescently colored chemical tags are used to label the fragments, one color for each type of nucleotide. Computers read the colors on the gel to determine the DNA sequence and display this sequence as a series of colored peaks (3 and 4). The development of automated sequencers in the mid-1990s made the sequencing of large eukaryotic genomes practical. A research institute with several hundred such instruments can sequence 100 million base pairs every day, with only 15 minutes of human attention!

TABLE 13.1 Some Eukaryotic Genomes

Organism		Estimated Genome Size (Mbp)	Number of Genes (×1,000)	Nature of Genome
Vertebrates				
	Homo sapiens (human)	3,200	20–25	The first large genome to be sequenced; the number of transcribable genes is far less than expected; much of the genome is occupied by repeated DNA sequences.
	Pan troglodytes (chimpanzee)	2,800	20–25	There are few base substitutions between chimp and human genomes, less than 2%, but many small sequences of DNA have been lost as the two species diverged, often with significant effects.
	Mus musculus (mouse)	2,500	25	Roughly 80% of mouse genes have a functional equivalent in the human genome; importantly, large portions of the noncoding DNA of mouse and human have been conserved; overall, rodent genomes (mouse and rat) appear to be evolving more than twice as fast as primate genomes (humans and chimpanzees).
	Gallus gallus (chicken)	1,000	20–23	One-third the size of the human genome; genetic variation among domestic chickens seems much higher than the genetic variation seen in humans.
	Fugu rubripes (pufferfish)	365	35	The *Fugu* genome is only one-ninth the size of the human genome, yet it contains 10,000 more genes.
Invertebrates				
	Caenorhabditis elegans (nematode)	97	21	The fact that every cell of *C. elegans* has been identified makes its genome a particularly powerful tool in developmental biology.
	Drosophila melanogaster (fruit fly)	137	13	*Drosophila* telomere regions lack the simple repeated segments that are characteristic of most eukaryotic telomeres. About one-third of the genome consists of gene-poor centric heterochromatin.
	Anopheles gambiae (mosquito)	278	15	The extent of similarity between *Anopheles* and *Drosophila* is approximately equal to that between human and pufferfish.
	Nematostella vectensis (sea anemone)	450	18	The genome of this cnidarian is much more like vertebrate genomes than nematode or insect genomes that appear to have become streamlined by evolution.
Plants				
	Oryza sativa (rice)	430	33–50	The rice genome contains only 13% as much DNA as the human genome, but roughly twice as many genes; like the human genome, it is rich in repetitive DNA.
	Populus trichocarpa (cottonwood tree)	500	45	This fast-growing tree is widely used by the timber and paper industries. Its genome, fifty times smaller than the pine genome, is one-third heterochromatin.
Fungi				
	Saccharomyces cerevisiae (brewer's yeast)	13	6	*S. cerevisiae* was the first eukaryotic cell to have its genome fully sequenced.
Protists				
	Plasmodium falciparum (malaria parasite)	23	5	The *Plasmodium* genome has an unusually high proportion of adenine and thymine. Scarcely 5,000 genes contain the bare essentials of the eukaryotic cell.

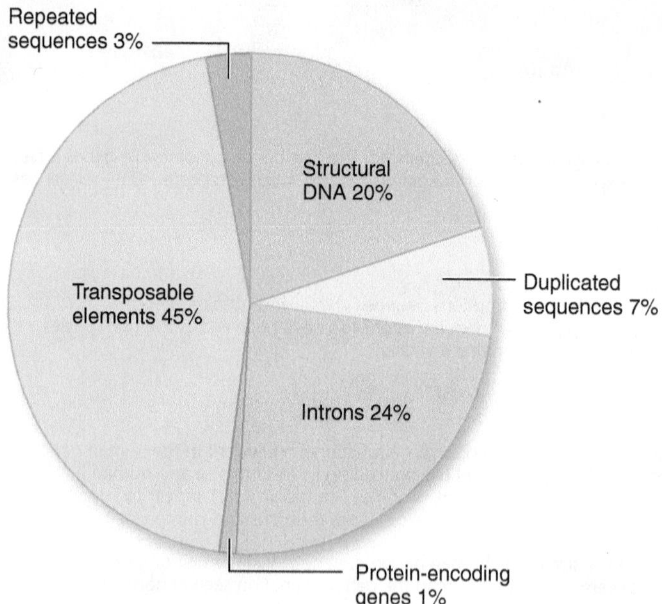

Figure 13.2 The human genome.

Very little of the human genome is devoted to protein-encoding genes, indicated by the light blue section in this pie chart.

13.2 The Human Genome

CONCEPT PREVIEW: The entire 3.2-billion-base-pair human genome has been sequenced. Only about 1% to 1.5% of the human genome is devoted to protein-encoding genes. Much of the rest is composed of transposable elements.

On June 26, 2000, geneticists announced that the entire human genome had been sequenced. This effort presented no small challenge, as the human genome is huge—more than 3 billion base pairs, which is the largest genome sequenced to date. To get an idea of the magnitude of the task, consider that if all 3.2 billion base pairs were written down on the pages of this book, the book would be 500,000 pages long, and it would take you about 60 years, working eight hours a day, every day, at five bases a second, to read it all.

Reading the human genome for the first time, geneticists encountered three big surprises.

The Number of Genes Is Surprisingly Low

The human genome sequence contains only 20,000 to 25,000 protein-encoding genes, only 1% of the genome (figure 13.2). As you can see in table 13.1, this is scarcely more genes than in a nematode worm (21,000 genes), not quite double the number in a fruit fly (13,000 genes). Researchers had confidently anticipated at least four times as many genes, because over 100,000 unique messenger RNA (mRNA) molecules can be found in human cells—surely, they argued, it would take as many genes to make them.

How can human cells contain more mRNAs than genes? Recall from chapter 12 that in a typical human gene, the sequence of DNA nucleotides that specifies a protein is broken into many bits called exons, scattered among much longer segments of nontranslated DNA called introns. Imagine this paragraph was a human gene; all the occurrences of the letter "e" could be considered exons, while the rest would be noncoding introns, which make up 24% of the human genome.

When a cell uses a human gene to make a protein, it first manufactures mRNA copies of the gene, then splices the exons together, getting rid of the intron sequences in the process. Now here's the turn of events researchers had not anticipated: The transcripts of human genes are often spliced together in different ways, called *alternative splicing*. As we discussed in chapter 12, each exon is actually a module; one exon may code for one part of a protein, another for a different part of a protein. When the exon transcripts are mixed in different ways, very different protein shapes can be built.

Alternative splicing, described on page 204 explains how fewer genes can encode many mRNA molecules. The mRNA shown in figure 12.7 consists of all the exons. You can imagine how a different mRNA would be produced if only half of the exons were used to make the mRNA.

With alternative splicing, it is easy to see how 25,000 genes can encode four times as many proteins. The added complexity of human proteins occurs because the gene parts are put together in new ways. Great music is made from simple tunes in much the same way.

Some Chromosomes Have Very Few Genes

In addition to the fragmenting of genes by the scattering of exons throughout the genome, there is another interesting "organizational" aspect of the genome. Genes are not distributed evenly over the genome. The small chromosome number 19 is packed densely with genes, transcription factors, and other functional elements.

Transcription factors are proteins involved in eukaryotic gene expression as discussed on page 208. Transcription cannot occur without the involvement of transcription factors.

BIOLOGY & YOU

Sequencing the Genome of a Cancer Patient. In 2008 scientists at Washington University in Saint Louis sequenced the entire genome of a cancer patient, a woman who had acute myeloid leukemia (AML). This was the first time all the genes of a cancer patient had been examined—a very important milestone because for the first time medical researchers could see exactly what genes had been changed to cause the cancer and aid its progression. The researchers discovered genetic mutations in the cells of the patient's cancerous tumor; mutations present in every tumor cell but not present in any other body cells. Two of these mutations were expected, as they had been linked to AML in many other patients. Importantly, however, there were eight other mutations, rare among humans and never before linked to AML. Most work on cancer has focused on the few hundred genes known to be directly involved in the disease, not the 20,000 others that make up the full human genome. Using this new approach, scientists can identify which mutations are relevant to a particular patient's cancer and determine which therapy would be most suitable for that patient. Because one-third of the students reading these words will someday develop cancer, that's good news for all of us.

The much larger chromosome numbers 4 and 8, by contrast, have few genes, scattered like isolated hamlets in a desert. On most chromosomes, vast stretches of seemingly barren DNA fill the chromosomes between clusters rich in genes.

Most of Genome Is Noncoding DNA

The third notable characteristics of the human genome is the startling amount of noncoding DNA it possesses. Only 1% to 1.5% of the human genome is coding DNA, devoted to genes encoding proteins. Each of your cells has about six feet of DNA stuffed into it, but of that, less than one inch is devoted to genes! Nearly 99% of the DNA in your cells seems to have little or nothing to do with the instructions that make you who you are (table 13.2).

There are four major types of noncoding human DNA:

Noncoding DNA Within Genes. As discussed earlier, a human gene is made up of numerous fragments of protein-encoding information (exons) embedded within a much larger matrix of noncoding DNA (introns). Introns make up 24% of the human genome—exons only 1%!

Structural DNA. Some regions of the chromosomes remain highly condensed, tightly coiled, and untranscribed throughout the cell cycle. These portions—about 20% of the DNA—tend to be localized around the centromere, or located near the telomeres, or ends, of the chromosome.

Repeated Sequences. Scattered about chromosomes are simple sequence repeats of two or three-nucleotides like CA or CGG, repeated like a broken record thousands and thousands of times. These make up about 3% of the human genome. An additional 7% is devoted to other sorts of duplicated sequences. Repetitive sequences with excess C and G tend to be found in the neighborhood of genes, while A- and T-rich repeats dominate the nongene deserts. The light bands on chromosome karyotypes now have an explanation—they are regions rich in GC and genes. Dark bands signal neighborhoods rich in A and T which are thin on genes. Chromosome 8 in figure 13.3 contains many nongene areas that are indicated by the dark bands, while chromosome 19 is dense with genes and so it has few dark bands.

Transposable Elements. Fully 45% of the human genome consists of mobile parasitic bits of DNA called transposable elements. Discovered by Barbara McClintock in 1950 (she won the Nobel Prize in Physiology or Medicine in 1983 for her discovery), transposable elements are bits of DNA that are able to jump from one location on a chromosome to another—tiny molecular versions of Mexican jumping beans. Because they leave a copy of themselves behind when they jump, their numbers in the genome increase as generations pass. Nested within the human genome are over half a million copies of an ancient transposable element called *Alu*, composing fully 10% of the entire human genome. Often jumping right into genes, *Alu* transpositions cause many harmful mutations.

Transposable elements (also called transposons) are most harmful when they insert right in the middle of a gene, as discussed on page 193 and shown in table 11.1.

Concept Check

1. How can DNA be sequenced by listing differences in fragment size?
2. How many genes do the chromosomes of one of your skin cells contain?
3. What fraction of your DNA is composed of protein-encoding genes?

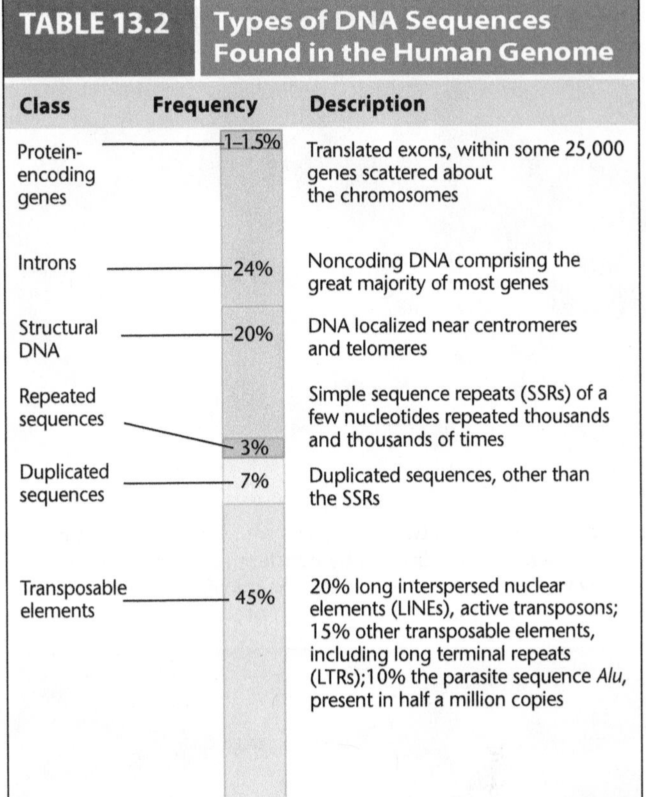

TABLE 13.2 Types of DNA Sequences Found in the Human Genome

Class	Frequency	Description
Protein-encoding genes	1–1.5%	Translated exons, within some 25,000 genes scattered about the chromosomes
Introns	24%	Noncoding DNA comprising the great majority of most genes
Structural DNA	20%	DNA localized near centromeres and telomeres
Repeated sequences	3%	Simple sequence repeats (SSRs) of a few nucleotides repeated thousands and thousands of times
Duplicated sequences	7%	Duplicated sequences, other than the SSRs
Transposable elements	45%	20% long interspersed nuclear elements (LINEs), active transposons; 15% other transposable elements, including long terminal repeats (LTRs);10% the parasite sequence *Alu*, present in half a million copies

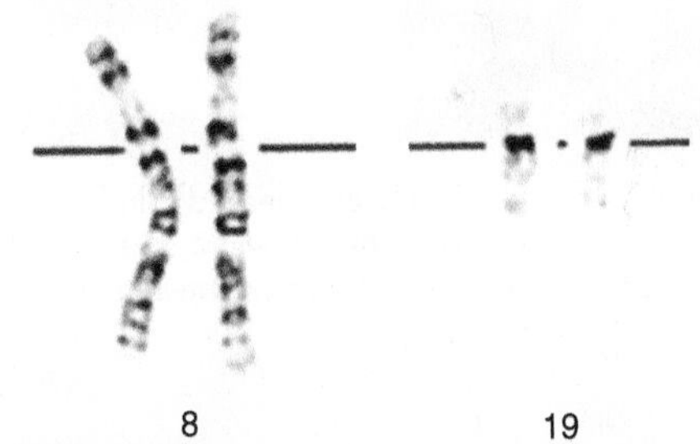

Figure 13.3 Banding on karyotype chromosomes. The dark bands are areas rich in A and T nucleotides, which indicate nongene areas. Lighter gene-heavy areas of the chromosome indicate repetitive sequences containing C and G nucleotides.

Genetic Engineering

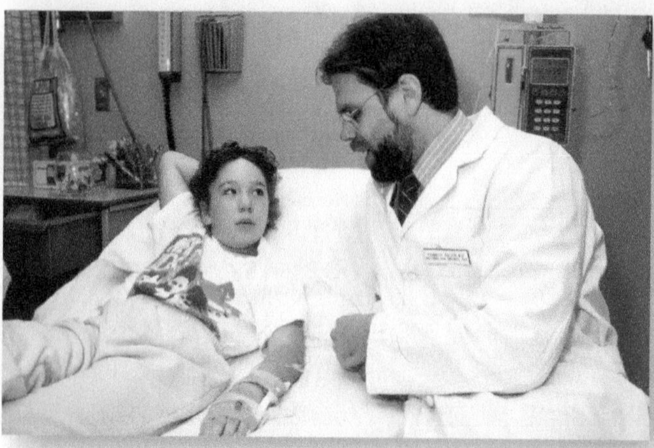

Curing disease. One of two young girls who were the first humans "cured" of a hereditary disorder by transferring into their bodies healthy versions of a defective gene. The transfer was successfully carried out in 1990, and the girls remain healthy.

Increasing yields. The genetically engineered salmon on the *right* have shortened production cycles and are heavier than the nontransgenic salmon of the same age on the *left*.

Pest-proofing plants. The genetically engineered cotton plants on the *right* have a gene that inhibits feeding by weevils; the cotton plants on the *left* lack this gene, and produce far fewer cotton bolls.

Figure 13.4 Examples of genetic engineering.

13.3 A Scientific Revolution

CONCEPT PREVIEW: Restriction enzymes, the key tools that make genetic engineering possible, bind to specific short sequences of DNA and cut the DNA. This produces fragments with "sticky ends," which can be rejoined in different combinations.

In recent years, **genetic engineering**—the ability to manipulate genes and move them from one organism to another—has led to great advances in medicine and agriculture (figure 13.4). Most of the insulin used to treat diabetes is now obtained from bacteria that contain a human insulin gene. In late 1990, the first transfers of genes from one human to another were carried out to correct the effects of defective genes in a rare genetic immune disorder called severe combined immunodeficiency (SCID)—often called the Bubble Boy disorder based on a young boy who lived out his life in an enclosed, germ-free environment. In addition, cultivated plants and animals can be genetically engineered to resist pests, grow bigger, or grow faster.

Restriction Enzymes

The first stage in any genetic engineering experiment is to chop up the "source" DNA to get a copy of the gene you wish to transfer. This first stage is the key to successful transfer of the gene, and learning how to do it is what has led to the genetic revolution. The trick is in how the DNA molecules are cut. The cutting must be done in such a way that the resulting DNA fragments have "sticky ends" that can later be joined with another molecule of DNA.

This special form of molecular surgery is carried out by **restriction enzymes,** also called *restriction endonucleases*, which are special enzymes that bind to specific short sequences (typically four to six nucleotides long) on the DNA. These sequences are very unusual in that they are symmetrical—the two strands of the DNA duplex have the same nucleotide sequence, running in opposite directions! The sequence in figure 13.5 for example, is GAATTC. Try writing down the sequence of the opposite strand: it is CTTAAG—the same sequence, written backward. This sequence is recognized by the restriction enzyme *Eco*RI. Other restriction enzyme recognize other sequences.

What makes the DNA fragments "sticky" is that most restriction enzymes do not make their incision in the center of the sequence; rather, the cut is made to one side. In the sequence in figure 13.5 ❶, the cut is made on both strands between the G and A nucleotides, G/AATTC. This produces a break, with short, single strands of DNA dangling from each end. Because the two single-stranded ends are complementary in sequence, they could pair up and heal the break, with the aid of a sealing enzyme—*or* they could pair with *any other DNA fragment cut by the same enzyme,* because all would have the same single-stranded sticky ends. Figure 13.5 ❷ shows how DNA from another source (the orange DNA) also cut with *Eco*RI has the same sticky ends as the original source DNA. Any gene in any organism cut by the enzyme that attacks GAATTC sequences will have the same sticky ends, and can be joined to any other with the aid of a sealing enzyme called *DNA ligase* ❸.

As discussed on page 53, the two strands of DNA are held together through complementary base pairing of nucleotides. Base pairing is universal, whether the DNA resides in a bacterial cell or a human cell, and that is why restriction enzymes work on any DNA.

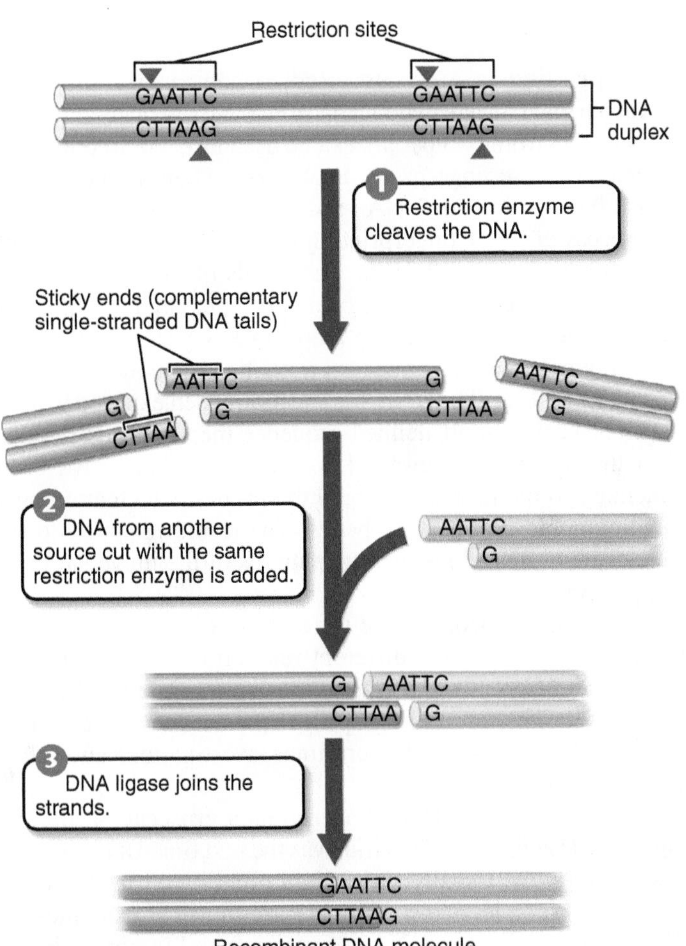

Figure 13.5 How restriction enzymes produce DNA fragments with sticky ends.

The restriction enzyme *Eco*RI always cleaves the sequence GAATTC between G and A. Because the same sequence occurs on both strands, both are cut. However, the two sequences run in opposite directions on the two strands. As a result, single-stranded tails are produced that are complementary to each other, or "sticky."

IMPLICATION Restriction enzymes evolved as a way for bacteria to destroy the DNA of invading viruses. Some 2,500 different restriction enzymes have been isolated from bacteria, using over 200 different 4–8 base recognition sequences. In each instance, the bacterium also contains an enzyme that adds a methyl group (—CH_3) to that same 4–8 base sequence. Why do you suppose bacteria always possess the pair of enzymes, and never just the restriction enzyme alone? *Hint:* There is a lot of viral DNA that the restriction enzyme has to "look through" to find the recognition sequence. Could something speed up this process?

Formation of cDNA

As you will recall from chapter 12, eukaryotic genes are encoded in segments called *exons* separated from one another by numerous nontranslated sequences called *introns.* The entire gene is transcribed by RNA polymerase, producing what is called the *primary RNA transcript* (figure 13.6). Before a eukaryotic gene can be translated into a protein, the introns must be cut out of this primary transcript. The fragments that remain are then spliced together to form the *mRNA,* which is eventually translated in the cytoplasm. When transferring eukaryotic genes into bacteria (discussed in section 13.4), it is necessary to transfer DNA that has had the intron information removed because bacteria lack the enzymes to carry out this processing. Bacterial genes do not contain introns. To produce eukaryotic DNA without introns, genetic engineers first isolate from the cytoplasm the processed mRNA corresponding to a particular gene. The cytoplasmic mRNA has *only* exons, properly spliced together. An enzyme called *reverse transcriptase* is then used to make a complementary DNA strand of the mRNA. A double-stranded DNA molecule is then produced. Such a version of a gene is called complementary DNA, or **cDNA.**

cDNA technology is being used in other ways, such as determining the patterns of gene expression in different cells. Every cell in an organism contains the same DNA, but genes are selectively turned on and off in any given cell. Researchers can see what genes are actively expressed using cDNAs.

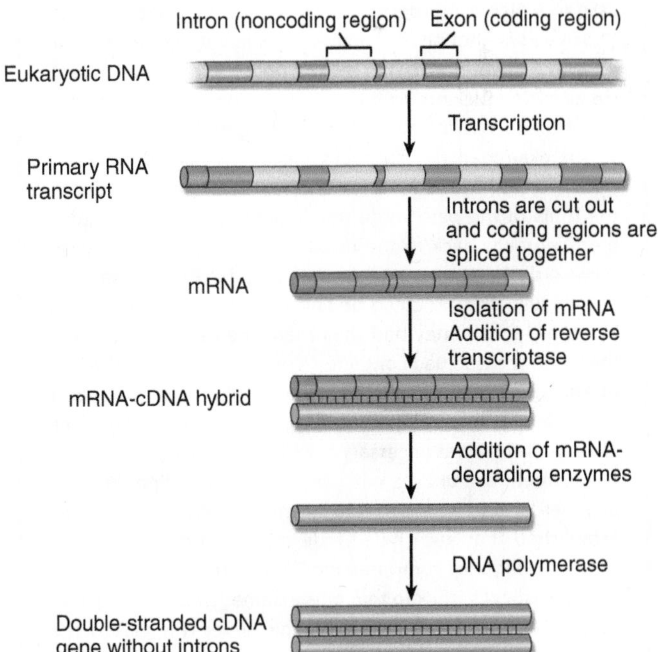

Figure 13.6 cDNA: Producing an intron-free version of a eukaryotic gene for genetic engineering.

In eukaryotic cells, a primary RNA transcript is processed into the mRNA. The mRNA is isolated and converted into cDNA.

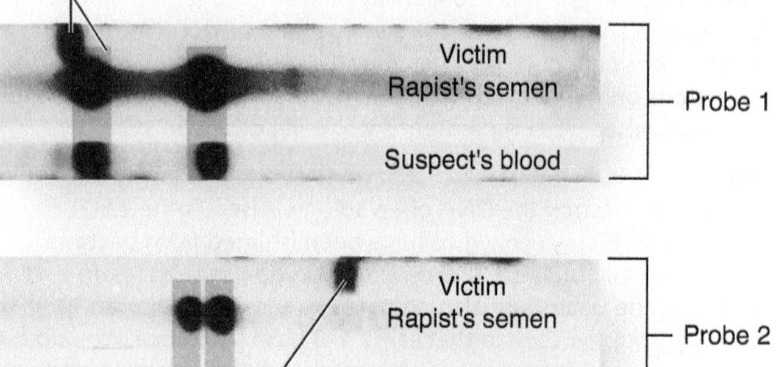
Probe 1 tags the same fragments of DNA in the rapist and the suspect but tags a different fragment of DNA in the victim. This probe indicates a match between the rapist and the suspect.
Victim
Rapist's semen
Suspect's blood
Probe 1
Victim
Rapist's semen
Suspect's blood
Probe 2
Like probe 1, probe 2 tags the same fragments of DNA in the rapist and the suspect but tags a different fragment of DNA in the victim. This probe indicates another match between the rapist and the suspect.

Figure 13.7 DNA fingerprints that led to conviction.

The two DNA probes seen here were used to characterize DNA isolated from the victim, the semen left by the rapist, and the suspect's blood. There is a clear match between the suspect's DNA and the DNA of the rapist's semen.

IN THE NEWS

Plant Witness for the Prosecution. The first case in which a murderer was convicted on plant DNA evidence was in Phoenix, Arizona. A pager left at the scene of the murder of a young woman led the police to a prime suspect. He admitted picking up the victim at a bar, but claimed she had robbed him of his wallet and pager. The crime scene squad examined the suspect's pickup truck and collected pods wedged by the front fender that were later identified as the fruits of the palo verde tree (*Cercidium spp.*). One squad member went back to the murder scene and found several palo verde trees, one recently damaged by a car. If the pods on the suspect's car could be linked to the damaged tree at the crime scene, they had their man. The detective heading the crime scene squad contacted a geneticist at the University of Arizona to establish evidence that would stand up in court that the pod indeed came from this very tree and no other. First, crucially, it was necessary to establish that individual palo verde trees have unique patterns of DNA. Sampling different palo verde trees at the murder scene and elsewhere quickly established that each palo verde tree is unique in its DNA pattern. Next, they compared the DNA pattern of a pod found on the suspect's truck to that of the damaged palo verde tree at the murder scene. They were the same. This placed the suspect at the scene of the murder beyond any doubt, and the suspect was convicted.

DNA Fingerprinting and Forensic Science

DNA fingerprinting is a process used to compare samples of DNA. Because each person differs genetically from others in many ways, comparing DNA samples from two people can be used as a tool to tell them apart, much as detectives use fingerprints. Each person is unique not only in their fingerprints, but also in their DNA sequences.

The process of DNA fingerprinting uses probes to fish out particular sequences to be compared from the thousands of other sequences in the human genome. The DNA of the person to be compared is first cut up by a restriction endonuclease, producing a host of DNA fragments of different sizes. The fragments are separated on a gel by techniques similar to that described in figure 13.1. The DNA fragments are then exposed to a "probe," a DNA fragment of a short defined sequence that has been radioactively tagged so that it can be viewed. DNA fragments that have sequences complementary to the probes will bind the probes, which are then visible on autoradiographic film as dark bands. The resulting pattern of parallel bars on X-ray film resembles the line patterns of the universal price code found on groceries.

Because different people have different DNA sequences throughout their genome, they will have different restriction enzyme cutting sites, and so produce different-sized fragments that migrate to different locations on the gel. The autoradiograph gel patterns are in essence DNA "fingerprints" that can be used in criminal investigations and other identification applications.

Figure 13.7 shows the DNA fingerprints a prosecuting attorney presented in a rape trial in 1987. This trial was the first time DNA evidence was used in a court of law. Usually six to eight probes are used to identify the source of a DNA sample, two such probes are shown as examples in figure 13.7. The probes are unique DNA sequences found in noncoding regions of human DNA that vary much more frequently from one individual to the next than do coding regions of the DNA. The chances of any two individuals, other than identical twins, having the same restriction pattern for these noncoding sequences varies from 1 in 800,000 to 1 in 1 billion, depending on the number of probes used.

The results of two probes are indicated in figure 13.7, probe 1 in the upper set of bars and probe 2 in the lower set of bars. A vaginal swab was taken from the victim within hours of her attack; from it semen was collected and the semen DNA analyzed for its restriction endonuclease patterns. The red bars compare the restriction endonuclease patterns of the semen with that of the suspect, Tommie Lee Andrews. You can see that the suspect's patterns match that of the rapist (and are not at all like those of the victim). Although a DNA fingerprint doesn't prove with 100% certainty that the semen came from the suspect, it is at least as reliable as traditional fingerprinting when several probes are used. The more probes used, the more reliable are the results. On November 6, 1987, the jury returned a verdict of guilty. Andrews became the first person in the United States to be convicted of a crime based on DNA evidence. Since the Andrews verdict, DNA fingerprinting has been admitted as evidence in thousands of court cases.

Just as fingerprinting revolutionized forensic evidence in the early 1900s, so DNA fingerprinting is revolutionizing it today. A hair, a minute speck of blood, a drop of semen, all can serve as sources of DNA to convict or clear a suspect. Of course, laboratory analyses of DNA samples must be carried out properly—sloppy procedures could lead to a wrongful conviction. After widely publicized instances of questionable lab procedures, national standards have been developed.

13.4 Genetic Engineering and Medicine

CONCEPT PREVIEW: Genetic engineering has facilitated the production of medically important proteins and led to novel vaccines.

Much of the excitement about genetic engineering has focused on its potential to improve medicine—to aid in curing and preventing illness. Major advances have been made in the production of proteins used to treat illness, and in the creation of new vaccines to combat infections.

Making "Magic Bullets"

Many genetic defects occur because our bodies fail to make critical proteins. Juvenile diabetes is such an illness. The body is unable to control levels of sugar in the blood because a critical protein, insulin, cannot be made. This failure can be overcome if the body can be supplied with the protein it lacks. The donated protein is in a very real sense a "magic bullet" to combat the body's inability to regulate itself.

Insulin is a type of chemical called a hormone that is produced in very small quantities in one area of the body and is carried throughout the body in the bloodstream. Insulin, as discussed on pages 521 and 584, helps cells take up sugar from the blood.

Until recently, the principal problem with using regulatory proteins as drugs was in manufacturing the protein. Proteins that regulate the body's functions are typically present in the body in very low amounts, and this makes them difficult and expensive to obtain in quantity. With genetic engineering techniques, the problem of obtaining large amounts of rare proteins has been largely overcome. The cDNA of genes encoding medically important proteins are now introduced into bacteria. Because the host bacteria can be grown cheaply, large amounts of the desired protein can be easily isolated. In 1982, the U.S. Food and Drug Administration approved the use of human insulin produced from genetically engineered bacteria, the first commercial product of genetic engineering.

The use of genetic engineering techniques in bacteria has provided ample sources of therapeutic proteins, but the application extends beyond bacteria. Today hundreds of pharmaceutical companies around the world are busy producing other medically important proteins expanding the use of these genetic engineering techniques. A gene added to the DNA of the mouse on the right in figure 13.8 produces human growth hormone, allowing the mouse to grow larger than its twin.

The advantage of using genetic engineering is clearly seen with factor VIII, a protein that promotes blood clotting. A deficiency in factor VIII leads to hemophilia, an inherited disorder (discussed in chapter 10), which is characterized by prolonged bleeding. For a long time, hemophiliacs received blood factor VIII that had been isolated from donated blood. Unfortunately, some of the donated blood had been infected with viruses such as HIV and hepatitis B, which were then unknowingly transmitted to those people who received blood transfusions. Today the use of genetically engineered factor VIII produced in the laboratory eliminates the risks associated with blood products obtained from other individuals.

BIOLOGY & YOU

Eliminating Tooth Decay. The human mouth is home to billions of bacteria belonging to more than 300 species, but one species, *Streptococcus mutans*, is the major cause of tooth decay. It thrives on the organic film that coats tooth surfaces, and in the process of doing so produces lots of lactic acid, a corrosive chemical that gradually dissolves the protective enamel coating of the teeth. Genetic engineers have devised a way to block this path to the dentist's chair by replacing harmful *S. mutans* with a version of the species engineered to be more friendly to your mouth. To do this, they transferred into *S. mutans* a gene to increase production of an enzyme called urease. This enzyme converts urea, plentiful in the mouth, into ammonia, a base that neutralizes acid and creates conditions that enhance the buildup of tooth enamel. When the mouths of laboratory rats were colonized with this engineered form of *S. mutans*, they got far fewer cavities. Of course, this doesn't mean it will work with people. And even if it does, did anyone check the mouth odor of the rats?

Figure 13.8 Genetically engineered human growth hormone.

These two mice are genetically identical, but the large one has one extra gene: the gene encoding human growth hormone. The gene was added to the mouse's genome by genetic engineers and is now a stable part of the mouse's genetic makeup. In humans, growth hormone is used to treat various forms of dwarfism.

Putting Your Genome to Work

Microarrays

A **gene microarray** is a glass square smaller than a postage stamp, covered with hundreds of thousands of different single strands of DNA rising from the surface like blades of grass. At each position on the glass plate, a particular DNA sequence of a hundred or more nucleotides is assembled, forming the microarray. The gene microarray chip you see to the right, called a *GeneChip* by its manufacturer, contains all known human gene sequences and can be purchased for as little as $200.

How could you use such a microarray chip to delve into a person's genes? All you would have to do is to obtain a little of the person's DNA, say from a blood sample, and denature it to form single-stranded DNA. You would then flush fluid containing the person's denatured DNA over the chip surface with known DNA sequences. Wherever the DNA has a gene matching one of the microarray strands, it will stick to it in a way a computer can detect.

Gene microarrays can also be used to determine patterns of gene expression. To do this, mRNA isolated from the cells being studied is reverse transcribed, using fluorescently labeled nucleotides, to make complementary DNA (cDNA, see page 221). Because the cDNA contains fluorescently labeled nucleotides, it is easily recognized by a computer. When this labeled cDNA is mixed with a gene microarray representing many thousands of genes, spots light up on the computer screen corresponding to those genes being transcribed in the cells.

Similarly, two different sources of DNA can be compared, such as DNA from two different individuals, to determine their levels of genetic similarities. In this case, the DNA from the two sources are labeled with different-colored fluorescent labels, typically one labeled with a green fluorescent dye and the other with a red fluorescent dye. Spots that fluoresce are places where the samples of DNA bind to DNA on the microarray; the spots are reddish where one source binds and greenish where the other source binds. Where the two sources have similar DNA sequences, they bind to the same spot on the microarray, and it shows up as yellow spots. The more yellow spots there are, the more similar the source DNAs are.

Researchers are busily comparing the "reference sequence" of the human genome with the DNA of individual people, and noting any differences they detect. In this way, they are finding SNPs (single nucleotide polymorphisms), or spot differences in the identity of particular nucleotides, which record every way in which a particular individual differs from the reference sequence. Some SNPs are associated with disorders like cystic fibrosis or sickle-cell disease. Others may give you red hair or elevated cholesterol in your blood. The human genome tells us that SNPs can be expected to occur at a frequency of about 5 per 1,000 nucleotides, scattered about randomly over the chromosomes. Each of us can be expected to differ from the standard "type sequence" by thousands of nucleotide SNPs.

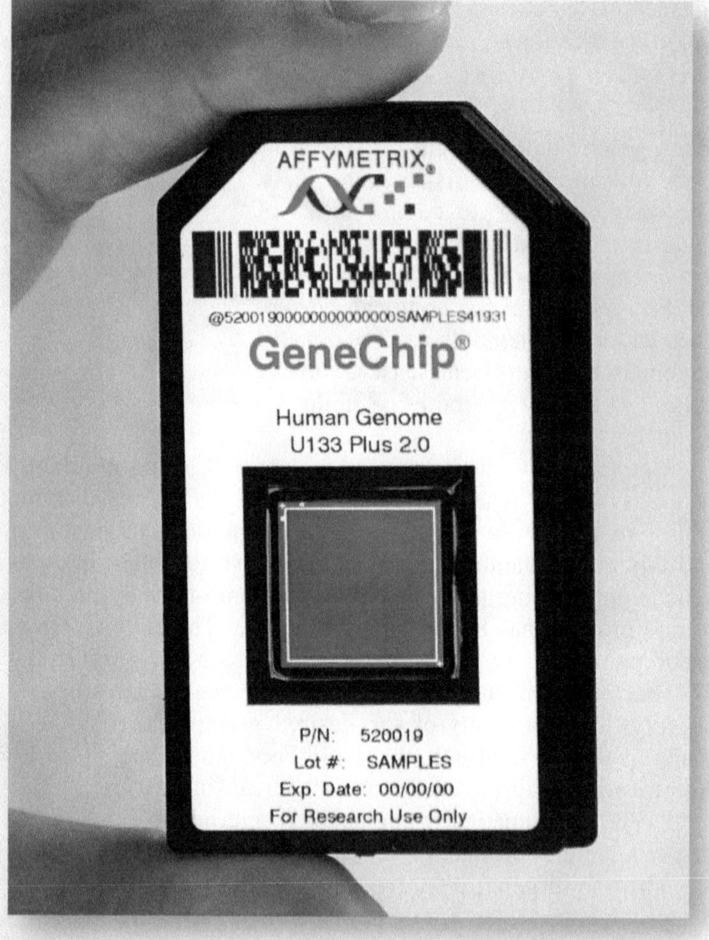

Humanity on a chip.

Microarrays such as this Affymetrix GeneChip now include all known human genes.

Microarrays Raise Critical Issues of Personal Privacy

Humans are thought to contain some 10 million different SNPs, all of which could reside on a small library of gene microarrays. When your DNA is flushed over a SNP microarray, the sequences that light up will instantly reveal your SNP profile, the genetic characteristics that make up who you are. Genes that might affect your health, your behavior, your future potential—all are there to be read. Your SNP profile will reflect all of this variation: a table of contents of your chromosomes, a molecular window to who you are.

When millions of such SNP profiles have been gathered over the coming years, computers will be able to identify other individuals with profiles like yours, and, by examining health records, standard personality tests, and the like, correlate parts of your profile with particular traits. Even behavioral characteristics involving many genes, which until now have been thought too complex to ever analyze, cannot resist a determined assault by a computer comparing SNP profiles. This raises issues of privacy—who should have access to this information and how should it be used?

DNA and the Innocence Project

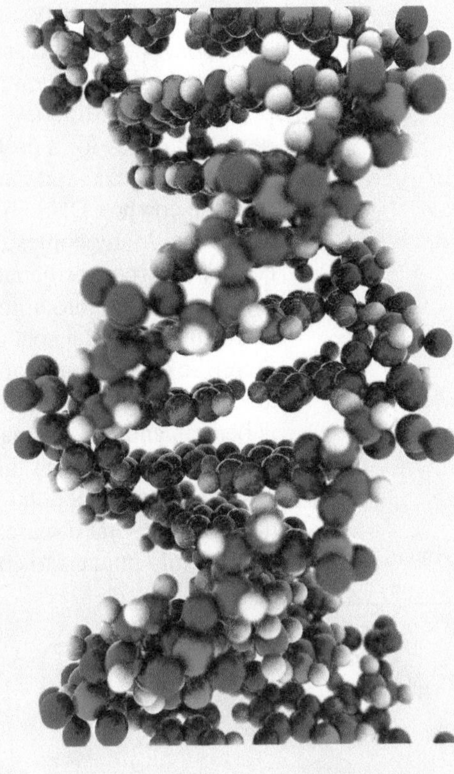

Every person's DNA is uniquely their own, a sequence of nucleotides found in no other person. Like a molecular social security number a billion digits long, the nucleotide sequence of an individual's genes can provide proof-positive identification of a rapist or murderer from DNA left at the scene of a crime—proof more reliable than fingerprints, more reliable than an eye witness, even more reliable than a confession by the suspect.

Never was this demonstrated more clearly than on May 16, 2006 in a Rochester, New York courtroom. There a judge freed convicted murderer Douglas Warney after ten years in prison.

The murder occurred on New Year's Day in 1996. The bloody body of one William Beason, a prominent community activist, was found in his bed. Police called in all the usual suspects, in this case everyone known to be an acquaintance of the victim. Warney, an unemployed 34-year-old who had dropped out of school in the eighth grade, committed robberies, and worked as a male hustler, learned that detectives wanted to speak to him about the killing, and went to the police station for questioning. Within hours he was charged with murder.

Warney's interrogation was not recorded, but it resulted in a signed confession based on the words that the detective sergeant said Warney uttered, a confession that contained accurate details about the murder scene that had not been made public. Warney said that the victim was wearing a nightgown and had been cooking chicken in a pot, and that the murderer had used a 12-inch serrated knife. The case against him in court rested almost entirely on these vivid details. Even though Warney recanted his confession at his trial, the accuracy of his confession was damning. The details that Warney provided to the sergeant could have come only from someone who was present at the crime scene.

There were problems with his confession, brought out at trial. Three elements of the signed statement's account of that night were clearly not true. It said Warney had driven to the victim's house in his brother's car, but his brother did not own a car; it said Warney disposed of his bloody clothes after the stabbing in the garbage can behind the house, but the can, buried in snow from the day of the crime, did not contain bloody clothes; it named a relative of Warney as an accomplice, but that relative was in a secure rehabilitation center on that day.

The most difficult bit of evidence to match to the written confession was blood found at the scene that was not that of the victim. Drops of a second person's blood were found on the floor and on a towel. The difficult bit was that the blood was a different blood type than Warney's.

At trial, prosecutors pointed out that the blood could have come from the accomplice mentioned in the confession, and pounded away on the point that the details in the confession could only have come from first-hand knowledge of the crime.

After a short trial, Douglas Warney was convicted of the murder of William Beason and sentenced to 25 years.

When appeals failed, Mr. Warney in 2004 sought help from the Innocence Project, a non-profit legal clinic that helps identify wrongly-convicted individuals and secure their freedom. Set up at the Benjamin N. Cardozo School of Law in New York by lawyers Barry Schech and Peter Neufeld, the Innocence Project specializes in using DNA technology to establish innocence.

The Innocence Project staff petitioned the court for additional DNA testing using new sensitive DNA probes, arguing that this might disclose evidence that would have resulted in a different verdict. The judge refused, ruling that the possibility that the blood found at the scene of the crime might match that of a criminal already in the state databank was "too speculative and improbable" to warrant the new tests.

Someone in the prosecutor's office must have been persuaded, however. Without notifying Warney's legal team, Project Innocence, or the court, this good Samaritan arranged for new DNA tests on the blood drops found at the crime scene. When compared to the New York State criminal DNA database, they hit a strong match. The blood was that of Eldred Johnson, in prison for slitting his landlady's throat in Utica two weeks before Beason was killed.

When confronted, the prisoner Johnson readily admitted to the stabbing of Beason. He said he was the sole killer, and had never met Douglas Warney.

This leaves the interesting question of how Warney's signed confession came to include such accurate information about the crime scene. It now appears he may have been fed critical details about the crime scene by the homicide detective leading the investigation, a Sergeant Gropp. It seems Gropp's partner had stepped out to get some papers when the confession was obtained. Sergeant Gropp died in March, 2006.

DNA testing has become a pillar of the American criminal justice system. It has provided key evidence that has established the guilt of thousands of suspects beyond any reasonable doubt—and, as you see here, also provided the evidence that our criminal justice system sometimes convicts and sentences innocent people. Over more than a decade, the Innocence Project and other similar efforts have cleared hundreds of convicted people, strong proof that wrongful convictions are not isolated or rare events. DNA testing opens a window of hope for the wrongly convicted.

Piggyback Vaccines

Another area of potential significance involves the use of genetic engineering to produce subunit vaccines against viruses such as those that cause herpes and hepatitis. Genes encoding part of the protein-polysaccharide coat of the herpes simplex virus or hepatitis B virus are spliced into a fragment of the vaccinia (cowpox) virus genome. The vaccinia virus, which is essentially harmless to humans and was used by British physician Edward Jenner more than 200 years ago in his pioneering vaccinations against smallpox, is now used as a vector to carry the herpes or hepatitis viral coat gene into cultured mammalian cells. The steps, highlighted in figure 13.9, begin with ❶ extracting the herpes simplex viral DNA and ❷ isolating a gene that codes for a protein on the surface of the virus. The cowpox viral DNA is extracted and cleaved in step ❸, and the herpes gene is combined with the cowpox DNA in ❹. The recombinant DNA is inserted into a cowpox virus. Many copies of the recombinant virus, which have the outside coat of a herpes (or hepatitis) virus, are produced. When this recombinant virus is injected into a human ❺, the immune system produces antibodies directed against the coat of the recombinant virus as in step ❻. The person therefore develops an immunity to the virus. Vaccines produced in this way, also known as **piggyback vaccines,** are harmless because the vaccinia virus is benign, and only a small fragment of the DNA from the disease-causing virus is introduced via the recombinant virus.

The great attraction of this approach is that it does not depend upon the nature of the viral disease. In the future, similar recombinant viruses may be injected into humans to confer resistance to a wide variety of viral diseases.

Figure 13.9 Constructing a subunit, or piggyback, vaccine for the herpes simplex virus.

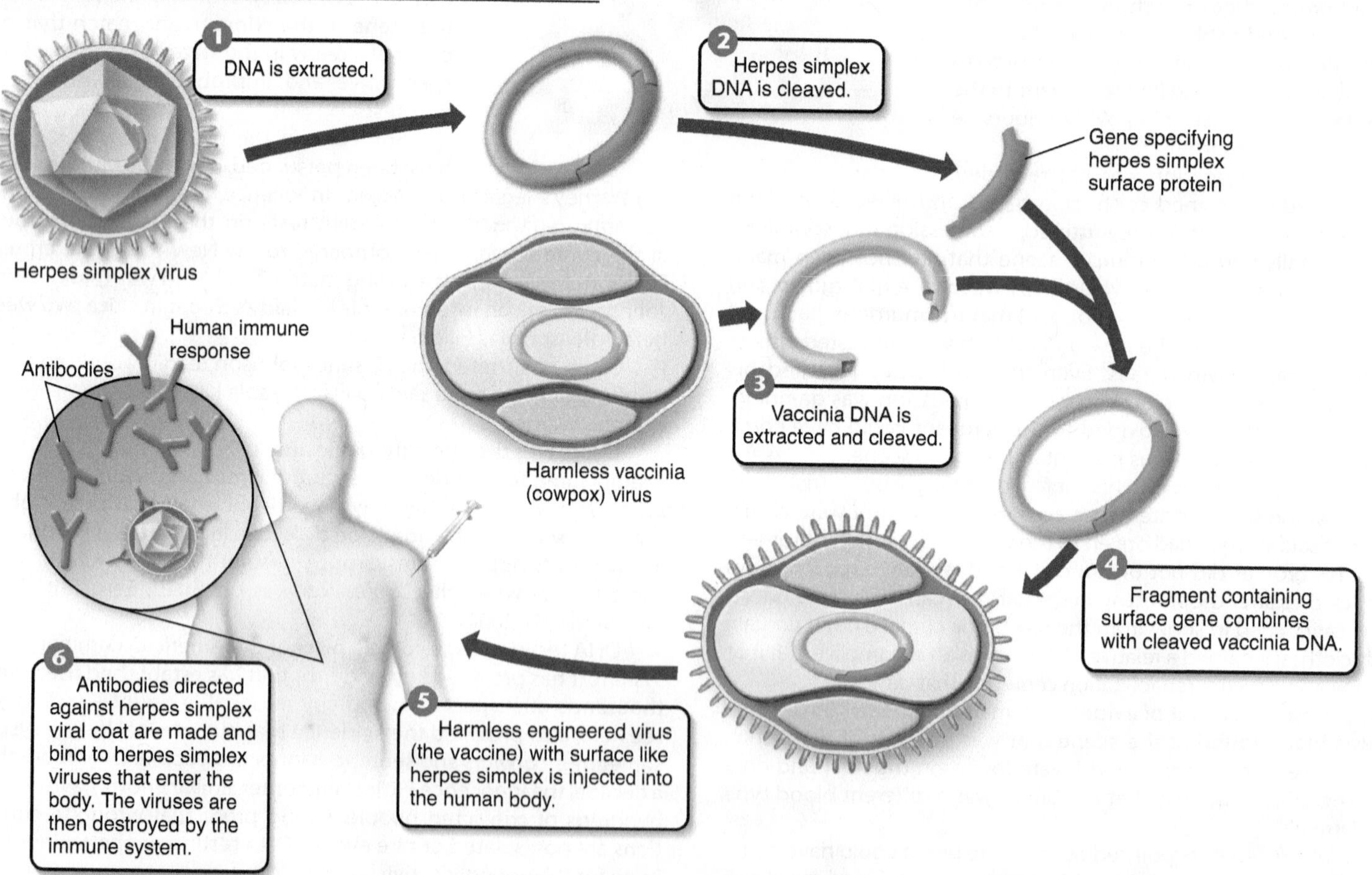
1 DNA is extracted.
Herpes simplex virus
2 Herpes simplex DNA is cleaved.
Gene specifying herpes simplex surface protein
Harmless vaccinia (cowpox) virus
3 Vaccinia DNA is extracted and cleaved.
4 Fragment containing surface gene combines with cleaved vaccinia DNA.
5 Harmless engineered virus (the vaccine) with surface like herpes simplex is injected into the human body.
Human immune response
Antibodies
6 Antibodies directed against herpes simplex viral coat are made and bind to herpes simplex viruses that enter the body. The viruses are then destroyed by the immune system.

13.5 Genetic Engineering and Agriculture

CONCEPT PREVIEW: Genetic engineering affords great opportunities for progress in food production. On balance, there are risks, but the potential benefits are substantial.

Pest Resistance

An important effort of genetic engineers in agriculture has involved making crops resistant to insect pests without spraying with pesticides, a great saving to the environment. Consider cotton. Its fibers are a major source of raw material for clothing throughout the world, yet the plant itself can hardly survive in a field because many insects attack it. Over 40% of the chemical insecticides used today are employed to kill insects that eat cotton plants. The world's environment would greatly benefit if these thousands of tons of insecticide were not needed. Biologists are now in the process of producing cotton plants that are resistant to attack by insects.

One successful approach uses a kind of soil bacterium, *Bacillus thuringiensis* (Bt) that produces a protein that is toxic when eaten by crop pests, such as larvae (caterpillars) of butterflies. When the gene producing the Bt protein was inserted into the chromosomes of tomatoes, the plants began to manufacture Bt protein. While not harmful to humans, it makes the tomatoes highly toxic to hornworms (one of the most serious pests of commercial tomato crops).

Many important plant pests also attack roots. To combat these pests, genetic engineers are introducing the *Bt* gene into different kinds of bacteria, ones that colonize the roots of crop plants. Any insects eating such roots consume the bacteria and so are lethally attacked by the Bt protein.

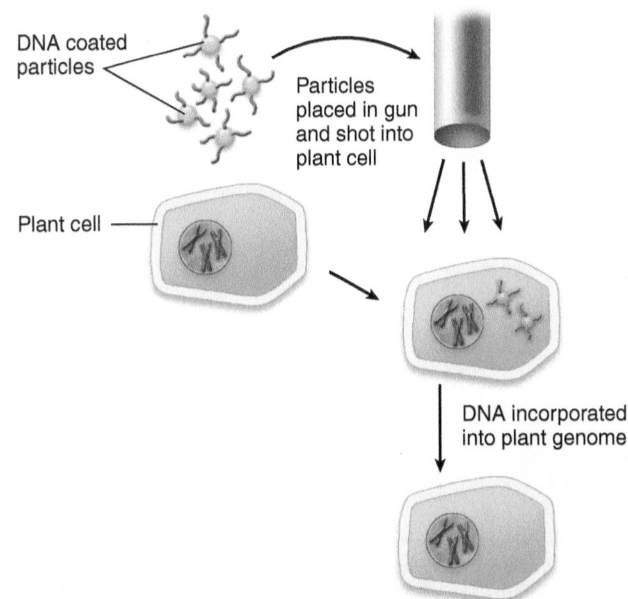

Figure 13.10 Shooting genes into cells.

A DNA particle gun, also called a gene gun, fires tungsten or gold particles coated with DNA into plant cells. The DNA coated particles pass through the cell wall and into the cell, where the DNA is incorporated into the plant cell's DNA. The gene encoded by the DNA is expressed.

Herbicide Resistance

A major advance has been the creation of crop plants that are resistant to the herbicide *glyphosate,* a powerful biodegradable herbicide that kills most actively growing plants. Glyphosate is used in orchards and agricultural fields to control weeds. Growing plants need to make a lot of protein, and glyphosate stops them from making protein by destroying an enzyme necessary for the manufacture of so-called aromatic amino acids (that is, amino acids that contain a ring structure). Humans are unaffected by glyphosate because we don't make aromatic amino acids—we obtain them from plants we eat! To make crop plants resistant to this powerful plant killer, genetic engineers screened thousands of organisms until they found a species of bacteria that could make aromatic amino acids in the presence of glyphosate. They then isolated the gene encoding the resistant enzyme and successfully introduced the gene into plants. They inserted the gene into the plants using DNA particle guns, also called gene guns. You can see in figure 13.10 how a DNA particle gun works. Small tungsten or gold pellets are coated with DNA (red in the figure) that contains the gene of interest and placed in the DNA particle gun. The DNA gun literally shoots the gene into plant cells in culture where the gene can be incorporated in the plant genome and then expressed. Plants that have been genetically engineered in this way are shown in figure 13.11. The two plants on top were genetically engineered to be resistant to glyphosate, the herbicide that killed the two plants at the bottom of the photo.

Figure 13.11 Genetically engineered herbicide resistance.

All four of these petunia plants were exposed to equal doses of an herbicide. The two on *top* were genetically engineered to be resistant to glyphosate, the active ingredient in the herbicide, whereas the two dead ones on the *bottom* were not.

More Nutritious Crops

The cultivation of genetically modified (GM) crops of corn, cotton, soybeans, and other plants (table 13.3) has become commonplace in the United States. In 2004, 85% of soybeans in the United States were planted with seeds genetically modified to be herbicide resistant. The result has been that less tillage is needed and as a consequence soil erosion is greatly lessened. Pest-resistant GM corn in 2004 comprised over 50% of all corn planted in the United States, and pest-resistant GM cotton comprised 81% of all cotton. In both cases, the change greatly lessens the amount of chemical pesticide used on the crops.

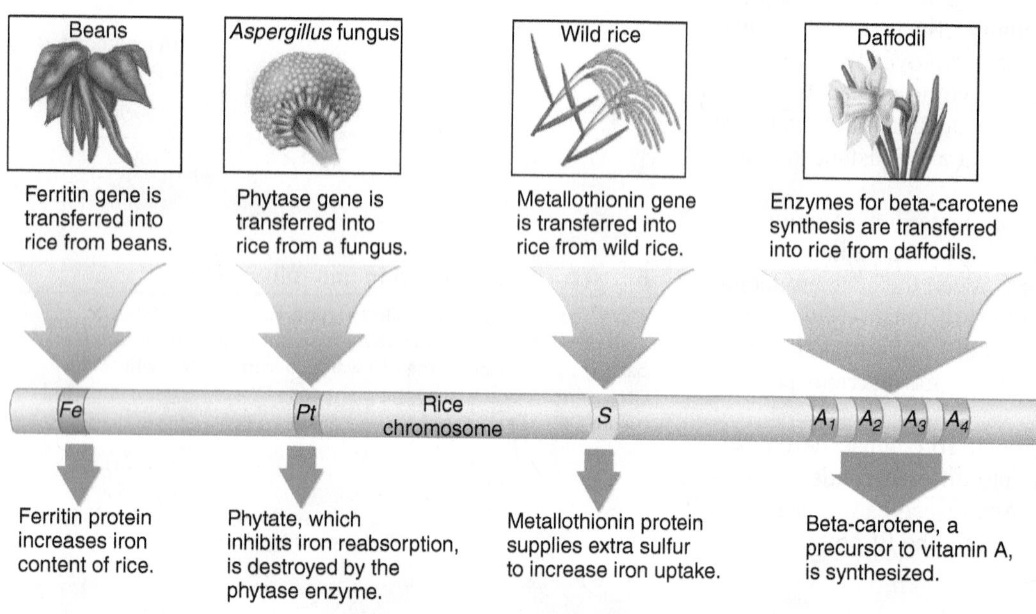
Beans
Aspergillus fungus
Wild rice
Daffodil
Ferritin gene is transferred into rice from beans.
Phytase gene is transferred into rice from a fungus.
Metallothionin gene is transferred into rice from wild rice.
Enzymes for beta-carotene synthesis are transferred into rice from daffodils.
Fe
Pt
Rice chromosome
S
A1 A2 A3 A4
Ferritin protein increases iron content of rice.
Phytate, which inhibits iron reabsorption, is destroyed by the phytase enzyme.
Metallothionin protein supplies extra sulfur to increase iron uptake.
Beta-carotene, a precursor to vitamin A, is synthesized.

Figure 13.12 Transgenic "golden" rice.

IMPLICATION The "Free Rice Game" on the internet (www.freerice.com) asks you quiz questions. For each answer you get right, 20 grains of rice are donated to the UN World Food Program to help end hunger. Since its inception in October 2007, over 50 billion grains of rice have been donated, about 20,000,000 grains a day. For each answer you get right, you then get a harder question to attempt. How many questions in a row do you think you can get right (the average is four)?

The real promise of plant genetic engineering is to produce genetically modified plants with desirable traits that directly benefit the consumer. One recent advance, nutritionally improved "golden" rice, gives us a hint of what is to come. In developing countries large numbers of people live on simple diets that are poor sources of both iron, which affects 1.4 billion women, 24% of the world population, and vitamin A, affecting 40 million children, 7% of the world population. These two deficiencies are especially severe in developing countries where the major staple food is rice. To solve the problem of dietary iron deficiency among rice eaters, gene engineers first asked why rice is such a poor source of dietary iron. The problem, and the answer, proved to have three parts:

1. *Too little iron.* The proteins of rice endosperm have unusually low amounts of iron. To solve this problem, a ferritin gene (abbreviated as *Fe* in figure 13.12) was transferred into rice from beans. Ferritin is a protein with an extraordinarily high iron content, and so greatly increased the iron content of the rice.
2. *Inhibition of iron absorption by the intestine.* Rice contains an unusually high concentration of a chemical called phytate, which inhibits iron absorption in the intestine—it stops your body from taking up the iron in the rice. To solve this problem, a gene encoding an enzyme called phytase (abbreviated as *Pt*) that destroys phytate was transferred into rice from a fungus.
3. *Too little sulfur for efficient iron absorption.* The human body requires sulfur for the uptake of iron, and rice has very little of it. To solve this problem, a gene encoding a sulfur-rich protein (abbreviated as *S*) was transferred into rice from wild rice.

To solve the problem of vitamin A deficiency, the same approach was taken. First, the problem was identified. It turns out rice only goes partway toward making vitamin A; there are no enzymes in rice to catalyze the last four steps. To solve the problem, genes encoding these four enzymes (abbreviated A_1 A_2 A_3 A_4) were added to rice from a flower, the daffodil.

The development of this transgenic rice is only the first step. Many years will be required to breed the genes into lines adapted to local conditions, but it is a promising start, hinting at the very real promise of genetic engineering.

How Do We Measure the Potential Risks of Genetically Modified Crops?

Is Eating Genetically Modified Food Dangerous? Many consumers worry that when genetic engineers introduce novel genes into genetically modified (GM) crops, there may be dangerous consequences for the food we eat. The introduction of glyphosate-resistance into soybeans is an example. Is the soybean that results nutritionally different? No. But could introduced proteins like the enzyme making the GM soybeans glyphosate tolerant cause a fatal immune reaction in some people? Because the potential danger of allergic reactions is quite real, every time a protein-encoding gene is introduced into a GM crop it is necessary to carry out extensive tests of the introduced protein's allergen potential. No GM crop currently being produced in the United States contains a protein that acts as an allergen to humans. On this score, then, the risk of genetic engineering to the food supply seems to be slight.

Are GM Crops Harmful to the Environment? Those concerned about the widespread use of GM crops raise three legitimate concerns:

1. *Harm to Other Organisms.* Results from a small laboratory experiment suggested that pollen from Bt corn could harm larvae from the Monarch butterfly. While this preliminary report received considerable publicity, subsequent studies suggest little possibility of harm. Monarch butterflies lay their eggs on milkweed, not corn, and there is little if any milkweed growing in or near cornfields.
2. *Resistance.* All insecticides used in agriculture share the problem that pests eventually evolve resistance to them, in much the same way that bacterial populations evolve resistance to antibiotics. However, despite the widespread use of Bt crops like corn, soybeans, and cotton since 1996, there are as of yet only a few cases of insects developing resistance to Bt plants in the field. Still, because of this possibility, farmers are required to plant at least 20% non-Bt crops alongside Bt crops to provide refuges where insect populations are not under selection pressure and in this way to slow the development of resistance.
3. *Gene Flow.* How about the possibility that introduced genes will pass from GM crops to their wild or weedy relatives? For the major GM crops, there is usually no potential relative around to receive the modified gene from the GM crop. There are no wild relatives of soybeans in Europe, for example. Thus there can be no gene escape from GM soybeans in Europe, any more than genes can flow from you to your pet dog or cat. However—and this is a big however—for secondary crops only now being genetically modified, studies suggest that it may be difficult to prevent GM crops from interbreeding with surrounding relatives to create new hybrids.

Concept Check

1. If a six-base restriction enzyme recognition site begins with T A G_ _ _, fill in the remaining bases.
2. Why doesn't the herbicide glyphosate hurt people?
3. The possibility of gene flow seems to be a potential problem with GM crops. With which crops? Why these?

TABLE 13.3	Genetically Modified Crops
Rice  	Genes have been added to commercial rice from daffodils for vitamin A, and from beans, fungi, and wild rice to supply dietary iron; transgenic strains that are cold-tolerant are under development.
Wheat 	New strains of wheat, resistant to the herbicide glyphosate, greatly reduce the need for tilling and so reduce loss of topsoil; these strains have not been made commercially available yet because of public resistance to GM crops.
 Soybean 	A major animal feed crop, soybeans tolerant of the herbicide glyphosate were used in 85% of U.S. soybean acreage in 2004. Varieties are being developed that contain the *Bt* gene, to protect the crop from insect pests without chemical pesticides. The nutritional value of soybean crops is being improved by genetic engineers in several ways, including transgenic varieties with high tryptophan (soybeans are poor in this essential amino acid), reduced trans-fatty acids, and enhanced omega-3 (beneficial) fatty acids, common in fish oil but low in plants.
 Corn 	Corn varieties resistant to insect pests (Bt corn) are widely planted (40% of U.S. acreage); varieties also tolerant of the herbicide glyphosate have been recently developed. Varieties that are drought-resistant are being developed, as well as nutritionally improved lines with high lysine, vitamin A, and high levels of the unsaturated fat oleic acid, which reduces harmful cholesterol and so prevents clogged arteries.
Cotton 	Cotton crops are attacked by cotton bollworm, budworm, and other lepidopteran insects; more than 40% of all chemical pesticide tonnage worldwide is applied to cotton. A form of the *Bt* gene toxic to all lepidopterans but harmless to other insects has transformed cotton to a crop that requires few chemical pesticides. 81% of U.S. acreage is Bt cotton.
Peanut 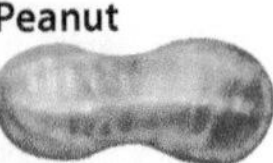	The lesser cornstalk borer causes serious damage to peanut crops. An insect-resistant variety is under development by gene engineers to control this pest.
Potato 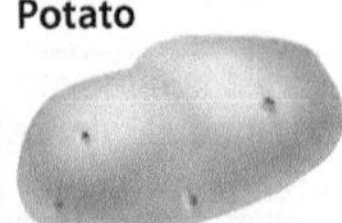	Verticillium wilt (a fungal disease) infects the water-conducting tissues of potatoes, reducing crop yields 40%. An antifungal gene from alfalfa reduces infections sixfold.
Canola 	Canola, a major vegetable oil and animal feed crop, is typically grown in narrow rows with little cultivation, requiring extensive application of chemical herbicides to keep down weeds. New glyphosate-tolerant varieties require far less chemical treatment. 80% of U.S. canola acreage planted is gene-modified canola.

The Revolution in Cell Technology

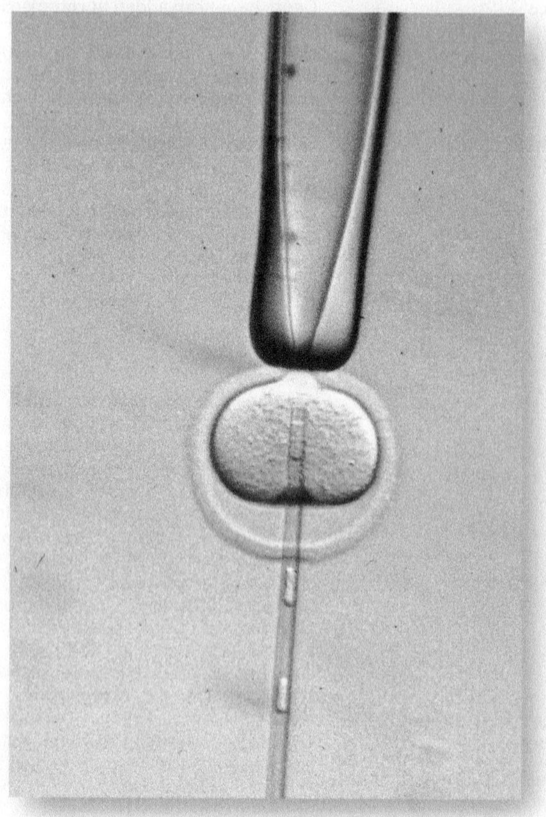

Figure 13.13 A cloning experiment.

In this photo, a nucleus is being injected from a micropipette *(bottom)* into an enucleated egg cell held in place by a pipette.

13.6 Reproductive Cloning

CONCEPT PREVIEW: Although recent experiments have demonstrated the possibility of cloning animals from adult tissue, the cloning of farm animals often fails for lack of proper genomic imprinting.

One of the most active and exciting areas of biology involves recently developed approaches to manipulating animal cells. In this section, you will encounter three areas where landmark progress is being made in cell technology: reproductive cloning of farm animals, stem cell research, and gene therapy. Advances in cell technology hold the promise of revolutionizing our lives.

The idea of cloning animals was first suggested in 1938 by German embryologist Hans Spemann (called the "father of modern embryology"), who proposed what he called a "fantastical experiment": remove the nucleus from an egg cell (an enucleated egg) and put in its place a nucleus from another cell. When attempted many years later (figure 13.13), this experiment actually succeeded in frogs, sheep, monkeys, and many other animals. However, only donor nuclei extracted from early embryos seemed to work. After repeated failures using nuclei from adult cells, many researchers became convinced that the nuclei of animal cells become irreversibly committed to a developmental pathway after the first few cell divisions of the developing embryo.

Wilmut's Lamb

Then, in the 1990s, a key insight was made in Scotland by geneticist Keith Campbell, a specialist in studying the cell cycle of agricultural animals. Recall from chapter 8 that the division cycle of eukaryotic cells progresses in several stages. Campbell reasoned, "Maybe the egg and the donated nucleus need to be at the same stage in the cell cycle." This proved to be a key insight. In 1994 researchers succeeded in cloning farm animals from advanced embryos by first starving the cells, so that they paused at the beginning of the cell cycle. Two starved cells are thus synchronized at the same point in the cell cycle.

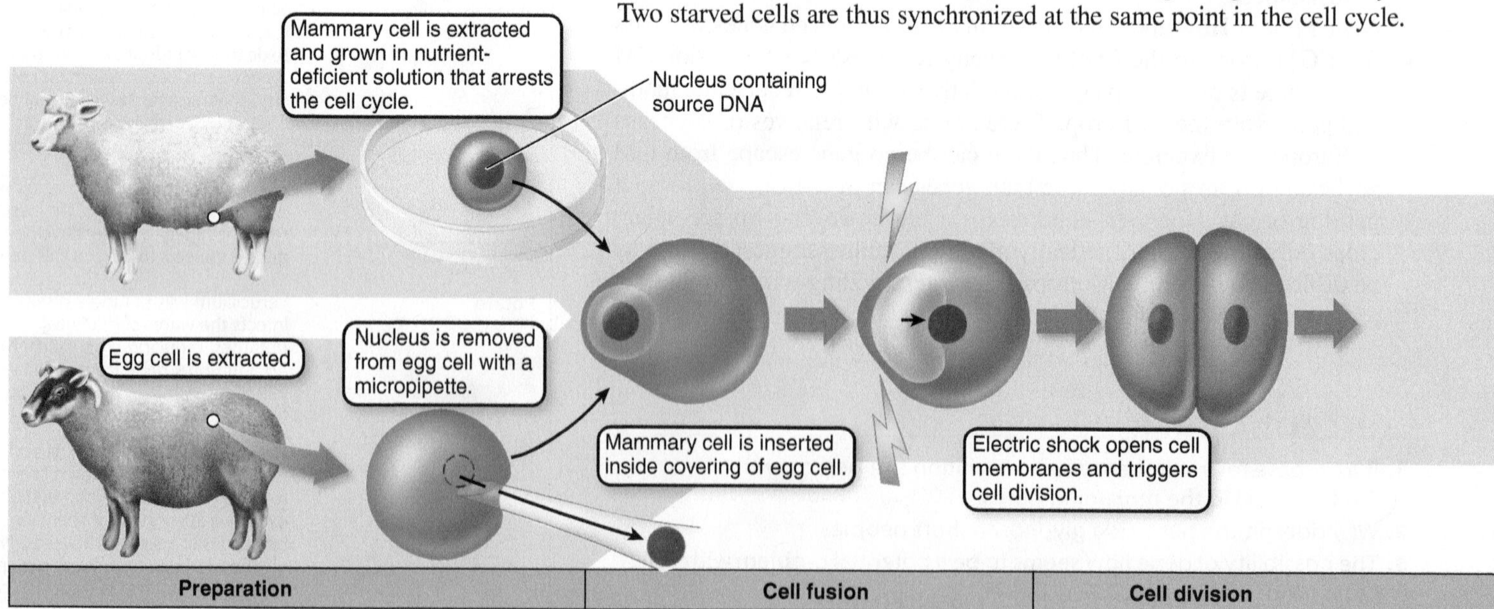

Mammary cell is extracted and grown in nutrient-deficient solution that arrests the cell cycle.
Nucleus containing source DNA
Egg cell is extracted.
Nucleus is removed from egg cell with a micropipette.
Mammary cell is inserted inside covering of egg cell.
Electric shock opens cell membranes and triggers cell division.
Preparation
Cell fusion
Cell division

Figure 13.14 Wilmut's animal cloning experiment.

Campbell's colleague Ian Wilmut then attempted the key breakthrough, the experiment that had been eluding researchers: He set out to transfer the nucleus from an adult differentiated cell into an enucleated egg, and to allow the resulting embryo to grow and develop in a surrogate mother, hopefully producing a healthy animal (figure 13.14). Approximately five months later, on July 5, 1996, the mother gave birth to a lamb. This lamb, "Dolly," was the first successful clone generated from a differentiated animal cell. Dolly grew into a healthy adult, and as you can see in the photo at the beginning of this chapter, she went on to have healthy offspring normal in every respect.

Progress with Reproductive Cloning

Since Dolly's birth in 1996, scientists have successfully cloned a wide variety of farm animals with desired characteristics, including cows, pigs, goats, horses, and donkeys, as well as pets like cats and dogs. Snuppy, the puppy in figure 13.15, was the first dog to be cloned. For most farm animals, cloning procedures have become increasingly efficient since Dolly was cloned. However, the development of clones into adults tends to go unexpectedly haywire. Almost none survive to live a normal life span. Even Dolly died prematurely in 2003, having lived only half a normal sheep life span.

The Importance of Genomic Imprinting

What is going wrong? It turns out that as mammalian eggs and sperm mature, their DNA is conditioned by the parent female or male, a process called reprogramming. Chemical changes are made to the DNA that alter when particular genes are expressed without changing the nucleotide sequences. In the years since Dolly, scientists have learned a lot about gene reprogramming, also called **genomic imprinting.** Genomic imprinting works by blocking the cell's ability to read certain genes. A gene is locked in the off position by adding a $—CH_3$ (methyl) group to some of its cytosine nucleotides. After a gene has been altered like this, the polymerase protein that is supposed to "read" the gene can no longer recognize it. The gene has been shut off.

We are only beginning to learn how to reprogram human DNA, so any attempt to clone a human is simply throwing stones in the dark, hoping to hit a target we cannot see. For this and many other reasons, any attempt at human reproductive cloning is regarded as highly unethical.

Figure 13.15 Cloning the family pet.

This puppy named "Snuppy" is the first dog cloned. Beside him to the left, is the adult male dog who provided the skin cell from which Snuppy was cloned. The dog in the photo on the right was Snuppy's surrogate mother.

IMPLICATION Do you have a dog or cat? Do you think it would be ethical for you to have your dog or cat cloned when it grows old, so you can continue to enjoy its company for many more years? Then, in later years, do you clone the clone? What, if any, limits would you place on this process? Discuss.

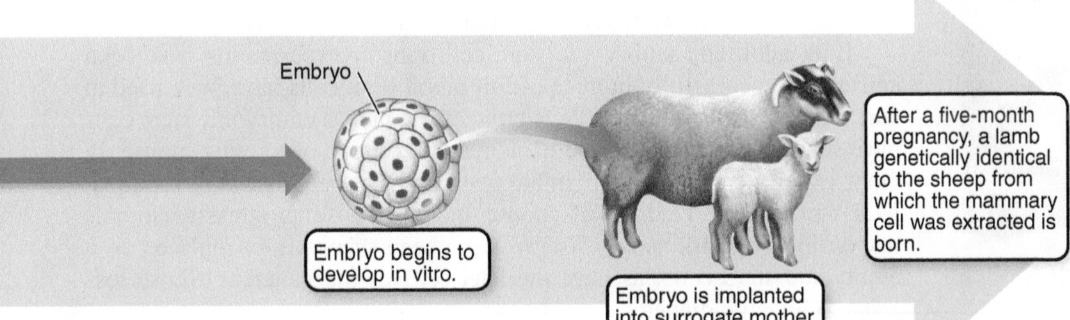

Embryo
Embryo begins to develop in vitro.
Embryo is implanted into surrogate mother.
After a five-month pregnancy, a lamb genetically identical to the sheep from which the mammary cell was extracted is born.
Development
Implantation
Birth of clone

Growth to adulthood

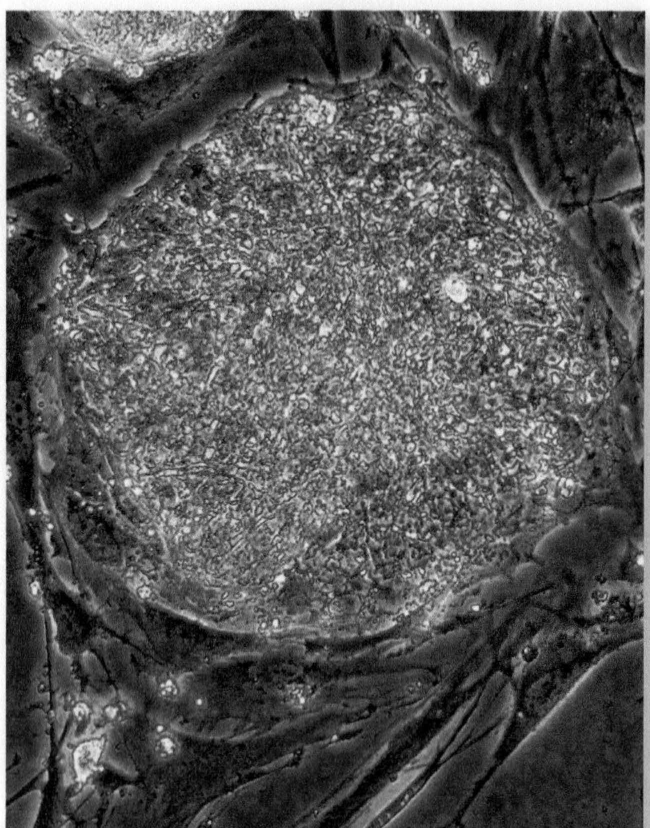

Figure 13.16 Human embryonic stem cells (×20).

This mass is a colony of undifferentiated human embryonic stem cells surrounded by fibroblasts (elongated cells) that serve as a "feeder layer." The image depicts stem cell research occurring at the University of Wisconsin–Madison.

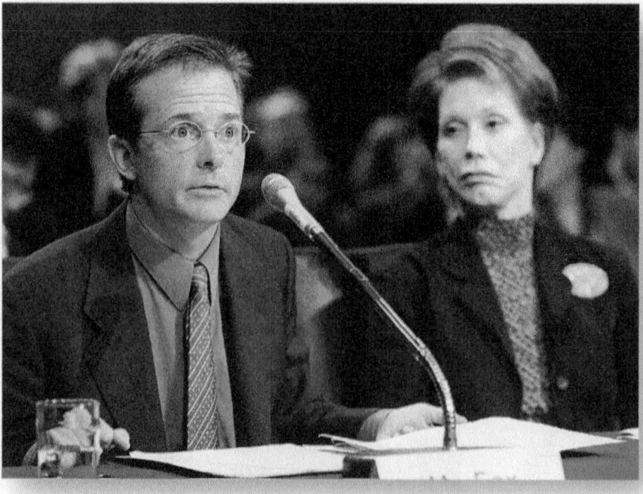

Figure 13.17 Promoting a cure for Parkinson's.

Michael J. Fox, with whom you may be familiar as a star of the *Back to the Future* film series and the TV show *Family Ties*, is a victim of Parkinson's disease, and a prominent spokesman for those who suffer from it. Here you see him testifying before the U.S. Senate (along with fellow advocate Mary Tyler Moore) on the need for vigorous efforts to support research seeking a cure.

13.7 Stem Cell Therapy

CONCEPT PREVIEW: Human adult and embryonic stem cells offer the possibility of replacing damaged or lost human tissues.

You can see a colony of human embryonic stem cells in figure 13.16. Each is **totipotent**—able to form any body tissue, and even an entire adult animal. What is an embryonic stem cell, and why is it totipotent? To answer this question, we need to consider for a moment where an embryo comes from. At the dawn of a human life, a sperm fertilizes an egg to create a single cell destined to become a child. As development commences, that cell begins to divide, producing after five or six days a small ball of a few hundred cells called a blastocyst, enclosing an inner cell mass of up to 200 **embryonic stem cells.** Each embryonic stem cell has all of the genes needed to produce a normal individual. In cattle breeding, for example, these cells are frequently separated by the breeder and used to produce multiple clones of valuable offspring.

As development proceeds, some of these embryonic stem cells become committed to forming specific types of tissues, such as nerve tissues, and, after this step is taken, cannot ever produce any other kind of cell. The genes needed to produce those other types of cells are inactivated and cannot be expressed. For example, in nerve tissue they are then called *nerve stem cells.* Others become specialized to produce blood cells, others to produce muscle tissue, and still others to form the other tissues of the body. Each major tissue is formed from its own kind of tissue-specific **adult stem cell.** Because an adult stem cell forms only that one kind of tissue, it is not totipotent.

Using Stem Cells to Repair Damaged Tissues

Stem cells offer the exciting possibility of restoring damaged tissues. For some tissues like blood, it is possible to harvest adult stem cells for this use. For other tissues, like nerve cells, this is unfortunately not yet possible. However, it is in theory possible to use embryonic stem cells instead, because they can develop into any tissue. To understand how embryonic stem cells could be used to repair damaged tissue, follow along in figure 13.18. A few days after fertilization, the blastocyst forms ❶. Embryonic stem cells are harvested from its inner cell mass or from cells of the embryo at a later stage ❷. These embryonic stem cells can be grown in tissue culture (see figure 13.16) and in principle be induced to form any type of tissue in the body ❸. The resulting healthy tissue can then be injected into the patient where it will grow and replace damaged tissue ❹. Alternatively, where possible, adult stem cells can be isolated and when injected back into the body, can form certain types of tissue cells.

Both adult and embryonic stem cell transfer experiments have been carried out successfully in mice. Adult blood stem cells have been used to cure leukemia. Heart muscle cells grown from mouse embryonic stem cells have successfully replaced the damaged heart tissue of a living mouse. In other experiments, damaged spinal neurons have been partially repaired. DOPA-producing neurons of mouse brains, whose progressive loss is responsible for Parkinson's disease, have been successfully replaced with embryonic stem cells, as have the islet cells of the pancreas whose loss leads to juvenile diabetes.

Because the course of development is broadly similar in all mammals, these experiments in mice suggest exciting possibilities, for stem cell therapy in humans. The hope is that individuals with Parkinson's disease like Michael J. Fox (figure 13.17) might be partially or fully cured with stem cell therapy. As you might imagine, work proceeds intensively in this field of research.

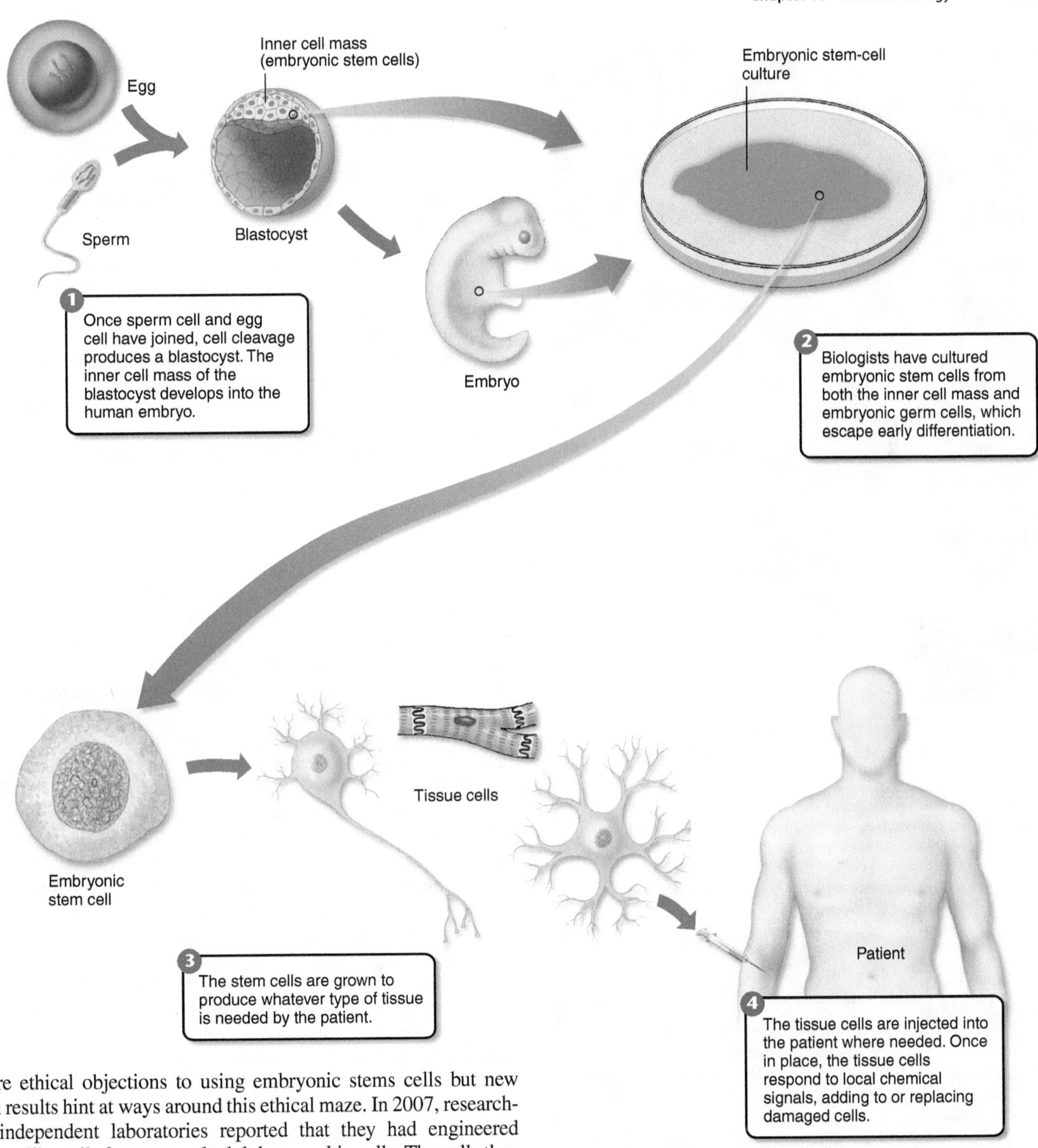

Inner cell mass
(embryonic stem cells)
Egg
Sperm
Blastocyst
Embryonic stem-cell
culture
Embryo
1 Once sperm cell and egg cell have joined, cell cleavage produces a blastocyst. The inner cell mass of the blastocyst develops into the human embryo.
2 Biologists have cultured embryonic stem cells from both the inner cell mass and embryonic germ cells, which escape early differentiation.
Tissue cells
Embryonic
stem cell
Patient
3 The stem cells are grown to produce whatever type of tissue is needed by the patient.
4 The tissue cells are injected into the patient where needed. Once in place, the tissue cells respond to local chemical signals, adding to or replacing damaged cells.

Figure 13.18 Using embryonic stem cells to restore damaged tissue.

Embryonic stem cells can develop into any body tissue. Methods for growing the tissue and using it to repair damaged tissue in adults, such as the brain cells of multiple sclerosis patients, heart muscle, and spinal nerves, are being developed.

There are ethical objections to using embryonic stems cells but new experimental results hint at ways around this ethical maze. In 2007, researchers in two independent laboratories reported that they had engineered embryonic stemlike cells from normal adult human skin cells. The cells they created were pluripotent—they could differentiate into many different cell types. Whether pluripotency extends to totipotency is still being investigated. How were these cells transformed? The essential clue came six years earlier, when fusing adult cells with embryonic stem cells transformed the adult cells into pluripotent cells, as if factors had been transmitted to the adult cells that conferred pluripotency. The 2007 researchers introduced genes for just four transcription factors into adult human skin cells piggyback on viruses, an approach discussed on page 226. Once inside, these four factors induced a series of events that led to pluripotency. From proof of principle in a laboratory culture dish to actual medical application is still a leap, but the possibility is exciting.

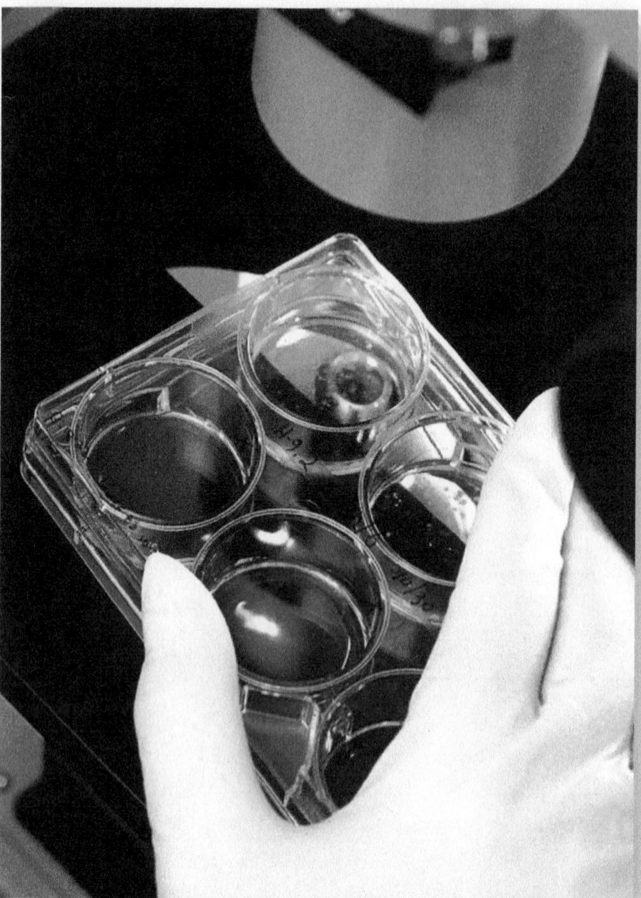

Figure 13.19 Embryonic stem cells growing in cell culture.

These embryonic stem cells, at the University of Wisconsin–Madison, are derived from early human embryos and will grow indefinitely in tissue culture. When transplanted, they can sometimes be induced to form new cells of the adult tissue into which they have been placed. This suggests exciting therapeutic uses.

IN THE NEWS

Turning One Cell Type Into Another. In 2008 doctors at Children's Hospital in Boston set out to cure type I diabetes, in which individuals lack the pancreatic beta cells needed to produce insulin. For two years they sifted through more than 1,000 transcription factors (proteins that tell cells which genes to turn on and off) to find ones that would turn the normal cells of the pancreas into beta cells. In the end they found that just three were needed to do the trick. When the three factors were injected into living mice whose islet cells had been destroyed, normal cells in the pancreas were turned into insulin-producing beta cells. The added insulin led to significant lowering of blood sugar levels, although not enough cells were transformed to cure diabetes. The new beta cells remained stable for many months. Although work needs to be done to improve efficiency, and a mouse is not a human, this result is proof in principle that adult cell transformation can work to cure tissue diseases.

13.8 Therapeutic Cloning

CONCEPT PREVIEW: Therapeutic cloning involves initiating blastocyst development from a patient's tissue using nuclear transplant procedures, then using the blastocyst's embryonic stem cells to replace the patient's damaged or lost tissue. Reprogramming adult tissue cells may allow a less controversial approach.

While exciting, the therapeutic uses of stem cells to cure leukemia, type I diabetes, Parkinson's disease, damaged heart muscle, and injured nerve tissue were all achieved in experiments carried out using strains of mice without functioning immune systems. Why is this important? Because had these mice possessed fully functional immune systems, they almost certainly would have rejected the implanted stem cells as foreign. Humans with normal immune systems might well refuse to accept transplanted stem cells simply because they are from another individual. For such stem cell therapy to work in humans, this problem needs to be addressed and solved.

Cloning to Achieve Immune Acceptance

Early in 2001, a research team at the Rockefeller University reported a way around this potentially serious problem. Their solution? They first isolated skin cells from a mouse, then using the same procedure that created Dolly, they created a 120-cell embryo from them. The embryo was then destroyed, its embryonic stem cells harvested and cultured (figure 13.19) for transfer to replace injured tissue. This procedure is called **therapeutic cloning.** Therapeutic cloning and the procedure that was used to create Dolly, called **reproductive cloning,** are contrasted in figure 13.20. You can see that steps (1) through (5) are essentially the same for both procedures, but the two methods proceed differently after that. In reproductive cloning, the blastocyst from step (5) is implanted in a surrogate mother in step (6a), developing into a baby that is genetically identical to the nucleus donor, step (7a). In therapeutic cloning, by contrast, stem cells from the blastocyst of step (5) are removed and grown in culture, step (6). These stem cells develop into pancreatic islet cells in step (7) and are injected or transplanted into the diabetic patient, where they begin producing insulin.

Therapeutic cloning, or, more technically, *somatic cell nuclear transfer,* successfully addresses the key problem that must be solved before embryonic stem cells can be used to repair damaged human tissues, which is immune acceptance. Because stem cells are cloned from the body's own tissues in therapeutic cloning, they pass the immune system's "self" identity check, and the body readily accepts them.

Reprogramming to Achieve Immune Acceptance

In therapeutic cloning, the cloned embryo is destroyed to obtain embryonic stem cells. What is the moral standing of a six-day human embryo? Considering it a living individual, many people regard therapeutic cloning to be ethically unacceptable. Recent research discussed on the previous page suggests an alternative approach that avoids this problem: reprogramming adult cells into embryonic stemlike cells by introducing just a few genes into the adult cells. The genes are so-called transcription factors, turning on key genes that act to reverse the "shut off" changes that have occurred during development of the adult cells. Human applications, if even possible, are probably far into the future, but the possibility of reprogramming adult cells is exciting.

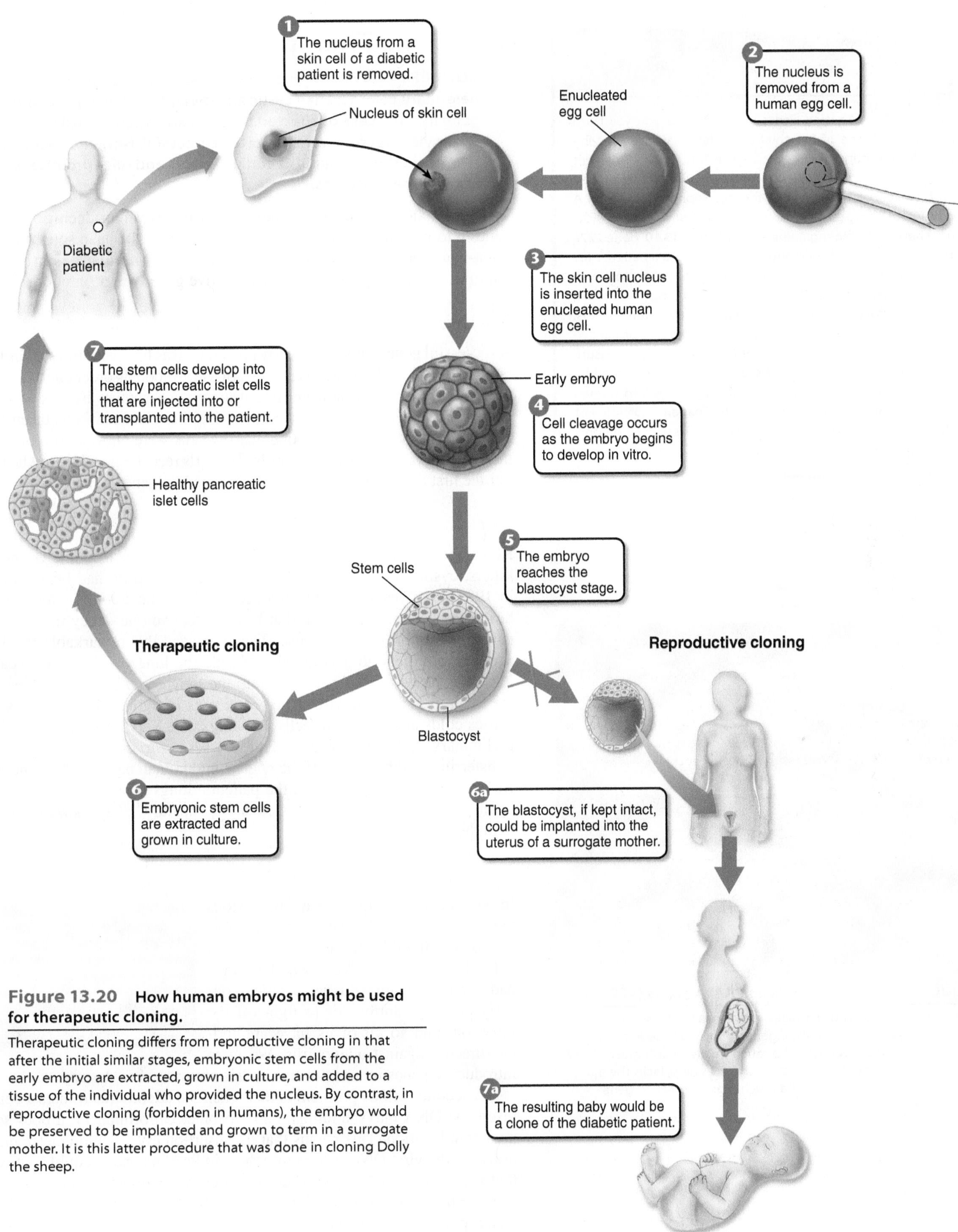

Figure 13.20 How human embryos might be used for therapeutic cloning.

Therapeutic cloning differs from reproductive cloning in that after the initial similar stages, embryonic stem cells from the early embryo are extracted, grown in culture, and added to a tissue of the individual who provided the nucleus. By contrast, in reproductive cloning (forbidden in humans), the embryo would be preserved to be implanted and grown to term in a surrogate mother. It is this latter procedure that was done in cloning Dolly the sheep.

IN THE NEWS

Shooting Genes into Cells. As you will learn on this page, one of the chief obstacles to successful gene therapy is getting the desired gene into a patient's cells without harming the patient. The usual virus vectors proved problematic, often leading to the development of cancer. A novel new approach has been taken in Germany that picks up where plant bioengineers left off (figure 13.10, page 227). These researchers literally shoot the genes into a patient's tissue. While plant bioengineers must use gold pellets to pierce the plant cell wall, the German researchers simply squirt the genes in across the plasma membranes of the patient's cells. Jet injection of "naked" genes (that is, without a protective virus coat) in a fine beam of water delivered at high pressure does not harm the genes and seems to be well tolerated by the tissue cells. Importantly, introducing genes into human tissues in this way is safe. Because the patient's DNA is not altered, there is no danger of cancer as there is with commonly used adenovirus vectors.

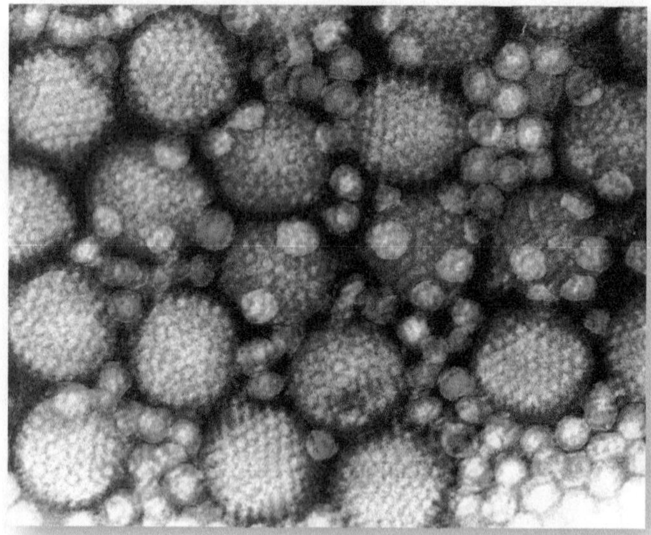

Figure 13.21 Adenovirus and AAV vectors (×200,000).
Adenovirus, the *red* virus particles above, has been used to carry healthy genes in clinical trials of gene therapy. Its use as a vector is problematic, however. AAV, the much smaller *bluish-green* virus particles seen in association with adenovirus here, lacks the many problems of adenovirus and is a much more promising gene transfer vector.

13.9 Gene Therapy

CONCEPT PREVIEW: In principle, it should be possible to cure hereditary disorders like cystic fibrosis by transferring a healthy gene into the cells of affected tissues. Early attempts using adenovirus vectors were not often successful. New virus vectors like AAV avoid the problems of earlier vectors and offer promise of gene transfer therapy cures.

The third major advance in cell technology involves introducing "healthy" genes into cells that lack them. For decades scientists have sought to cure often-fatal genetic disorders like cystic fibrosis, muscular dystrophy, and multiple sclerosis by replacing the defective gene with a functional one.

Early Success

A successful **gene transfer therapy** procedure was first demonstrated in 1990 (see section 13.3). Two girls were cured of a rare blood disorder due to a defective gene for the enzyme adenosine deaminase. Scientists isolated working copies of this gene and introduced them into bone marrow cells taken from the girls. The gene-modified bone marrow cells were allowed to proliferate, then were injected back into the girls. The girls recovered and stayed healthy. For the first time, a genetic disorder was cured by gene therapy.

The Rush to Cure Cystic Fibrosis

Researchers quickly set out to apply the new approach to one of the big killers, cystic fibrosis. The defective gene, labelled *cf,* had been isolated in 1989. Five years later, in 1994, researchers successfully transferred a healthy *cf* gene into a mouse that had a defective one—they in effect had cured cystic fibrosis in a mouse. They achieved this remarkable result by adding the *cf* gene to a virus that infected the lungs of the mouse, carrying the gene with it "piggyback" into the lung cells. The virus chosen as the "vector" was adenovirus (the red viruses in figure 13.21), a virus that causes colds and is very infective of lung cells. Very encouraged by these preliminary trials with mice, several labs set out to cure cystic fibrosis by transferring healthy copies of the *cf* gene into human patients the same way. But the gene-modified cells in the patients' lungs soon came under attack by the patients' own immune systems. The "healthy" *cf* genes were lost and with them any chance of a cure.

Problems with the Vector

In retrospect, although it was not obvious then, the problem with these early attempts seems predictable. Adenovirus causes colds. Do you know anyone who has never had a cold? When you get a cold, your body produces antibodies to fight off the infection, and so all of us have antibodies directed against adenovirus. We were introducing genes in a vector our bodies are primed to destroy.

The human immune response, the subject of chapter 28, primes the body with a first exposure to a virus and so the immune response, called the secondary response, discussed on pages 536 to 541, can quickly fight subsequent infections by the same type of virus.

A second serious problem is that when the adenovirus infects a cell, it inserts its DNA into the human chromosome. Unfortunately, it does so at a random location. This means that the insertion events could cause mutations—if the viral DNA inserts into the middle of a gene, it could inactivate that gene. Because the spot where the adenovirus inserts is random, some of the mutations that result can be expected to cause cancer, certainly an unacceptable consequence.

A More Promising Vector

Researchers are now investigating a much more promising vector, a tiny virus called *adeno-associated virus* (AAV—the smaller bluish-green viruses in figure 13.21) that has only two genes. To create a vector for gene transfer, researchers remove both of the AAV genes. The shell that remains is still quite infective and can carry human genes into patients. AAV does not elicit a strong immune response—cells infected with AAV are not eliminated by a patient's immune system. Importantly, AAV enters human DNA far less frequently than adenovirus, and so is less likely to produce cancer-causing mutations.

A simple experiment using AAV cured dogs of a hereditary disorder leading to retinal degeneration and blindness. These dogs had a defective gene that produced a mutant form of a protein associated with the retina of the eye and were blind. Recombinant viral DNA was made using a healthy version of the gene, shown in steps 1 and 2 in figure 13.22. Injection of AAV bearing the needed gene into the fluid-filled compartment behind the retina in step 3 restored their sight in step 4. This procedure was recently tried on human patients with some success.

Human clinical trials are under way again. Scientists have performed the first gene therapy experiment for muscular dystrophy, injecting genes into a 35-year-old South Dakota man. He is an early traveler on what is likely to become a well-traveled therapeutic highway. Trials are also under way for cystic fibrosis, rheumatoid arthritis, hemophilia, and a wide variety of cancers. The way seems open, the possibility of progress tantalizingly close.

Concept Check

1. Explain why the development of cloned animals often goes wrong.
2. What is the difference between an embryonic and an adult stem cell?
3. What makes AAV safer than adenovirus as a gene therapy vector?

Figure 13.22 Using gene therapy to cure a retinal degenerative disease in dogs.

Researchers were able to use genes from healthy dogs to restore vision in dogs blinded by an inherited retinal degenerative disease. This disease also occurs in human infants and is caused by a defective gene that leads to early vision loss, degeneration of the retinas, and blindness. In the gene therapy experiments, genes from dogs without the disease were inserted into three-month-old dogs that were known to carry the defective gene and that had been blind since birth. Six weeks after the treatment, the dogs' eyes were producing the normal form of the gene's protein product, and by three months, tests showed that the dogs' vision was restored.

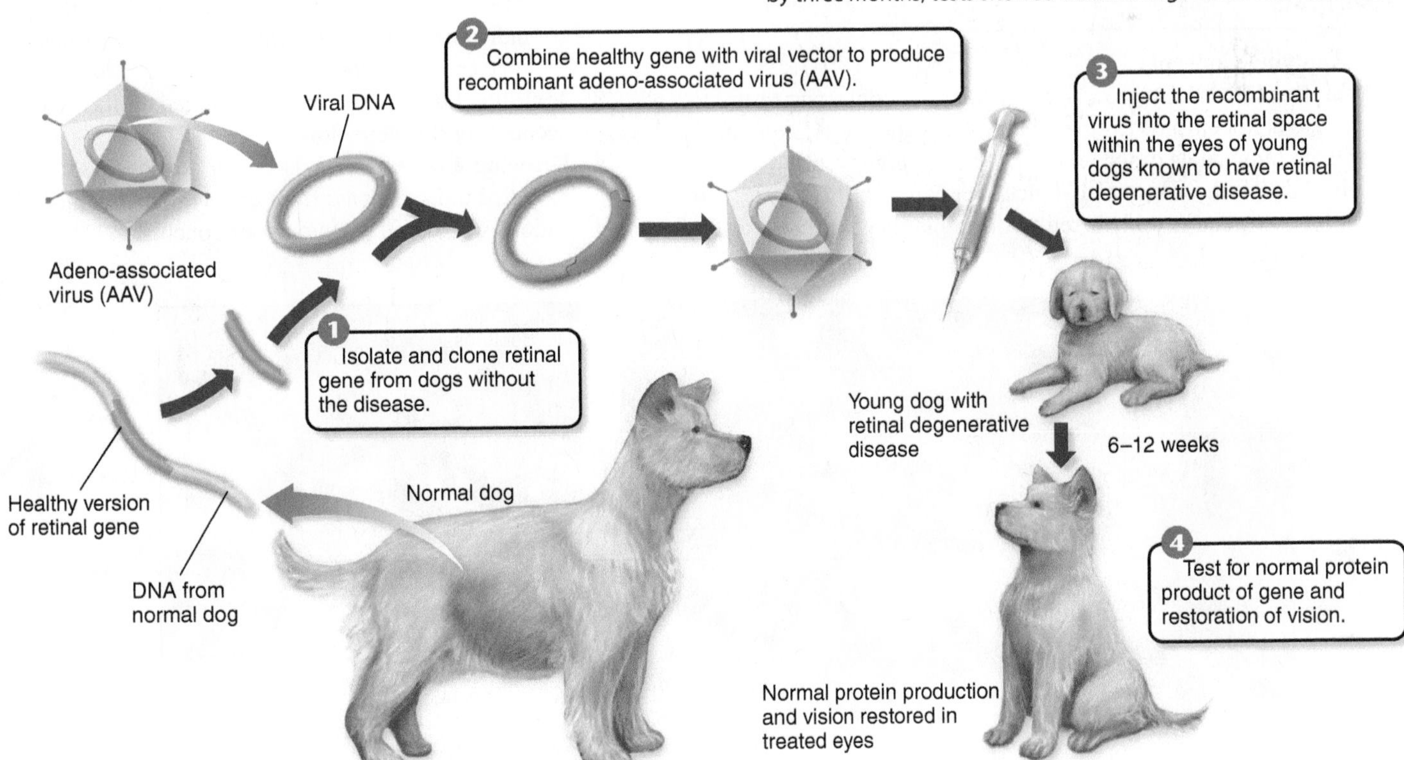
2 Combine healthy gene with viral vector to produce recombinant adeno-associated virus (AAV).
Viral DNA
3 Inject the recombinant virus into the retinal space within the eyes of young dogs known to have retinal degenerative disease.
Adeno-associated virus (AAV)
1 Isolate and clone retinal gene from dogs without the disease.
Young dog with retinal degenerative disease
6–12 weeks
Normal dog
Healthy version of retinal gene
DNA from normal dog
4 Test for normal protein product of gene and restoration of vision.
Normal protein production and vision restored in treated eyes

Inquiry & Analysis

Can Modified Genes Escape from GM Crops?

On page 229, the question of whether gene flow of GM crops posed a problem to the environment was discussed. A field experiment conducted in 2004 by the Environmental Protection Agency assessed the possibility that introduced genes could pass from genetically modified golf course grass to other plants. Investigators introduced a gene conferring herbicide resistance (the EPSP synthetase gene for resistance to glyphosate) into golf course bentgrass, *Agrostis stolonifera,* and then looked to see if the gene passed from the GM grass to other plants of the same species, and also if it passed to other related species.

The map at the bottom displays the setup of this elaborate field study. A total of 178 *A. stolonifera* plants were placed outside the golf course, many of them downwind. An additional 69 bentgrass plants were found to be already growing downwind, most of them the related species *A. gigantea.* Seeds were collected from each of these plants, and the DNA of resulting seedlings tested for the presence of the gene introduced into the GM golf course grass. In the graph, the upper red histogram (a **histogram** is a "bar graph" that sorts data into a series of discontinuous categories, the value of each bar representing the number of individuals in a category, or, as in this case, the average value of entries in that category) presents the relative frequency with which the gene was found in *A. stolonifera* plants located at various distances from the golf course. The lower blue histogram does the same for *A. gigantea* plants.

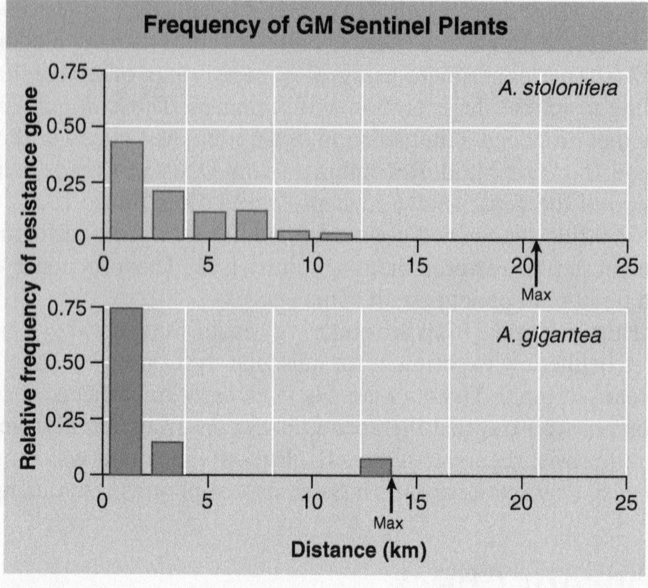

Analysis

1. **Applying Concepts**
   - **a. Reading a Histogram.** Does the gene conferring resistance to herbicide pass to other plants of this species, *A. stolonifera*? to individuals of the related species *A. gigantea*?
   - **b.** What is the maximal distance over which the herbicide resistance gene is transferred to other plants of this species? of the related species? what are these distances, expressed in miles (km × 0.62 = mile)?
2. **Interpreting Data**
   - **a.** What general statement can be made about the effect of distance on the likelihood that the herbicide resistance gene will pass to another plant?
   - **b.** Are there any significant differences in the gene flow to individuals of *A. stolonifera* and to individuals of the related species *A. gigantea*?
3. **Making Inferences** What mechanism do you propose to account for this gene flow?
4. **Drawing Conclusions** Is it fair to conclude that genetically modified traits can pass from crops to other plants? What qualifications would you place on your conclusion?

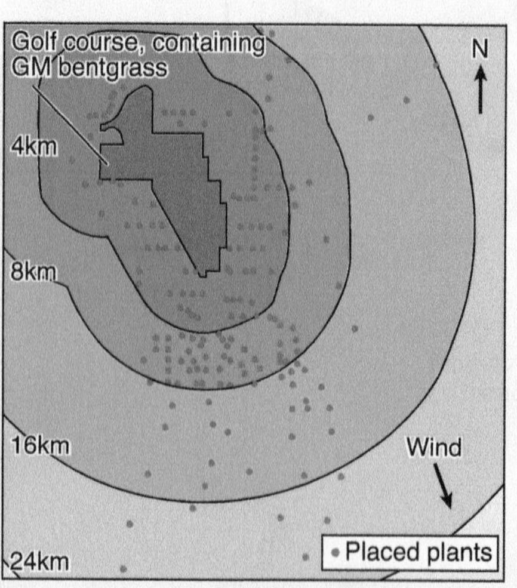

Concept Summary

Sequencing Entire Genomes

13.1 Genomics

- The genetic information of an organism, its genes and other DNA, is called its genome. The sequencing and study of genomes is an area of biology called genomics.
- The sequencing of entire genomes, a once long and tedious process, has been made faster and easier with automated systems (**figure 13.1**).

13.2 The Human Genome

- The human genome contains about 20,000 to 25,000 genes, not much more than other organisms (**table 13.1**) and far less than what was expected based on the number of unique mRNA molecules present in our cells.
- Genes are organized in different ways in the genome, with nearly 99% of the human genome containing noncoding segments of DNA (**figure 13.2** and **table 13.2**).

Genetic Engineering

13.3 A Scientific Revolution

- Genetic engineering is the process of moving genes from one organism to another. It is having a major impact on medicine and agriculture (**figure 13.4**).
- Restriction enzymes are a special kind of enzyme that binds to specific short sequences of DNA and cuts them. The cut made is often a staggered cut producing "sticky ends," which are sections of single-stranded DNA (**figure 13.5 ❷**). The significance of these sticky ends is that any two molecules of DNA cut with the same restriction enzyme will have the same sticky end sequences. This allows the two sources of DNA to combine through base pairing of their sticky ends (**figure 13.5 ❸**).
- Before transferring a eukaryotic gene into a bacterial cell, the intron regions must be removed. This is accomplished with the use of cDNA, a complementary copy of the gene using the processed mRNA to make double-stranded DNA that doesn't contain the introns (**figure 13.6**).
- DNA fingerprinting is a process using probes to compare two samples of DNA. The probes bind to the DNA samples, creating restriction patterns that can be compared. Two DNA samples with the same restriction patterns are likely from the same source (**figure 13.7**).

13.4 Genetic Engineering and Medicine

- Genetic engineering is used in the production of medically important proteins used to treat illnesses. Genes encoding the proteins are inserted into bacteria that produce large quantities of proteins that can then be administered to patients.
- Vaccines are developed using genetic engineering. A gene that encodes a viral protein of a pathogenic virus is inserted into the DNA of a harmless virus that serves as a vector, as shown here from **figure 13.9.** The vector carrying the recombinant DNA is injected into a human. The vector infects the body, replicates, and the recombinant DNA is translated producing the viral proteins. The body elicits an immune response against the proteins, which protects the person from an infection by the pathogenic virus in the future.

13.5 Genetic Engineering and Agriculture

- Genetic engineering has been used in crop plants to make them more cost effective to grow or more nutritious (**figures 13.10–13.12**).
- GM plants are a source of controversy because of potential dangers that may result from the genetic manipulation of crop plants.

The Revolution in Cell Technology

13.6 Reproductive Cloning

- The idea of cloning animals, placing the nucleus from an adult cell into an enucleated egg cell, is not new, but early cloning attempts had mixed results. In 1996, Ian Wilmut and colleagues succeeded in cloning a sheep by synchronizing the donated nucleus and the egg cell to the same stage of the cell cycle (**figure 13.14**).
- Other animals have been successfully cloned (**figure 13.15**), but problems and complications arise, often causing premature death. The problems with cloning appear to be caused by the lack of modifications that need to be made to the DNA, which turns certain genes on or off, a process called genomic imprinting.

13.7 Stem Cell Therapy

- Embryonic stem cells are totipotent cells, which are cells that are able to divide and develop into any type of cell in the body or develop into an entire individual. These cells are present in the early embryo. Because of the totipotent nature of embryonic stem cells, they could be used to replace tissues lost or damaged due to accident or disease (**figure 13.18**).

13.8 Therapeutic Cloning

- The use of embryonic stem cells to replace damaged tissue has one major drawback: tissue rejection. The embryonic stem cells are treated as foreign cells by the patient's body and are rejected. A process called therapeutic cloning could alleviate this problem.
- Therapeutic cloning is the process whereby a cell from an individual who has lost tissue function is cloned, producing an embryo that is genetically identical to the person. Embryonic stem cells are then harvested from the cloned embryo and injected into the same individual. The embryonic stem cells regrow the lost or damaged tissue without eliciting an immune response (**figure 13.20**). However, this procedure, like others using embryonic stem cells, is controversial. Adult cells reprogrammed to behave like embryonic stem cells might prove to be an acceptable treatment.

13.9 Gene Therapy

- Using gene therapy, a patient with a genetic disorder is cured by replacing a defective gene with a "healthy" gene. In theory, this should work—but early attempts to cure cystic fibrosis failed because of immunological reactions to the adenovirus vector used to carry the healthy genes into the patient.
- The recent focus of gene therapy has been to identify a vector that avoids the problems encountered with the adenovirus vector. Promising results in experiments using a virus called adeno-associated virus (AAV) has scientists hopeful that this vector will eliminate the problems seen with adenovirus (**figure 13.22**).

Self-Test

1. The total amount of DNA in an organism, including all of its genes and other DNA, is its
   a. heredity. c. genome.
   b. genetics. d. genomics.
2. A possible reason why humans have such a small number of genes as opposed to what was anticipated by scientists is that
   a. humans don't need more than 25,000 genes to function.
   b. the exons used to make a specific mRNA can be rearranged to form different proteins.
   c. the sample size used to sequence the human genome was not big enough, so the number of genes estimated could be low.
   d. the number of genes will increase as scientists find out what all of the noncoding DNA actually does.
3. A protein that can cut DNA at specific DNA base sequences is called a
   a. DNase. c. restriction enzyme.
   b. DNA ligase. d. DNA polymerase.
4. Complementary DNA or cDNA is produced by
   a. inserting a gene into a bacterial cell.
   b. exposing the mRNA of the desired eukaryotic gene to reverse transcriptase.
   c. exposing the source DNA to restriction enzymes.
   d. exposing the source DNA to a probe.
5. Which of the following statements is correct.
   a. DNA fingerprinting is not admissible in court.
   b. DNA fingerprinting can prove with 100% certainty that two samples of DNA are from the same person.
   c. DNA fingerprinting becomes more and more reliable as more probes are used.
   d. No two people will ever have the same restriction pattern.
6. Using drugs produced by genetically engineered bacteria allows
   a. the drug to be produced in far larger amounts than in the past.
   b. humans to permanently correct the effect of a missing gene from their own systems.
   c. humans to cure cystic fibrosis.
   d. All these answers are correct.
7. Some of the advantages to using genetically modified organisms in agriculture include
   a. increased yield.
   b. maintaining current nutritive value.
   c. mass producing proteins.
   d. curing genetic diseases.
8. Which of the following is *not* a concern about the use of genetically modified crops?
   a. possible danger to humans after consumption
   b. insecticide resistance developing in pest species
   c. gene flow into natural relatives of GM crops
   d. harm to the crop itself from mutations
9. One of the main biological problems with replacing damaged tissue through the use of embryonic stem cells is
   a. immunological rejection of the tissue by the patient.
   b. that stem cells may not target appropriate tissue.
   c. the time needed to grow sufficient amounts of tissue.
   d. that genetic mutation of chosen stem cells may cause future problems.
10. In gene therapy, healthy genes are placed into animal cells that have defective genes by using
    a. DNA particle gun.
    b. micropipettes (needles).
    c. viruses.
    d. Cells are not modified genetically. Instead, healthy tissue is grown and transplanted into the patient.

Visual Understanding

1. **Figure 13.1** Can you sequence the unknown section of DNA with the DNA fragments obtained from the following DNA analysis?

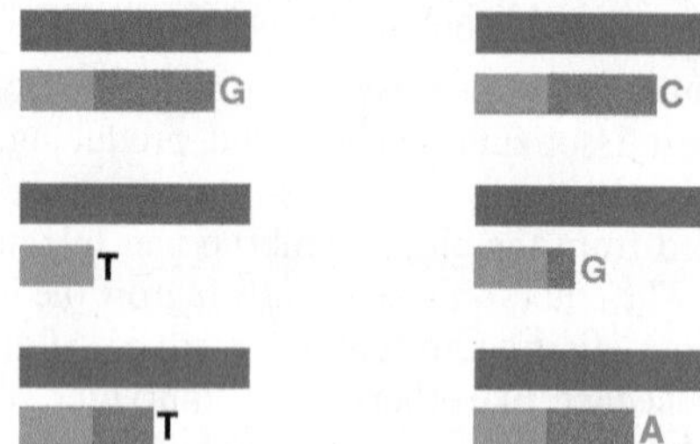

2. **Figure 13.14** Your friend Thomas wants to know why scientists can't just take the egg cell, with its own nucleus intact, and shock it to begin cell division. How do you answer him?

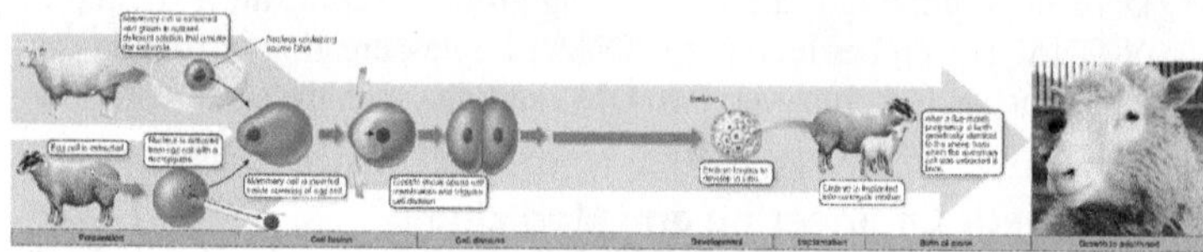

Challenge Questions

1. The goal behind therapeutic cloning is to replace tissue that is damaged due to an accident or nongenetic disease. Why wouldn't therapeutic cloning as shown in figure 13.20 work to replace tissue damage caused by genetic disorders?

2. If a person has a genetic disease such as cystic fibrosis, the hope is that we will be able to use gene therapy to cure him or her. When that happens, will the patient no longer be able to pass the *cf* gene on to his or her children?

3. Much of the technology for producing GM foods is owned by multinational corporations, which seek to maintain intellectual ownership of their creations. As one example, Monsanto Corporation requires farmers to sign contracts for glyphosate-tolerant soybeans that prevent the farmers from saving seed for replanting the next year. The company has aggressively brought suit against violators. On the one hand, companies need to be able to profit from their products, and the development costs of GM foods are enormous. Without potential profit, future GM crops will not be developed. On the other hand, in many highly populated regions of the world, people who face famine when their crops fail simply cannot afford to pay the price of seeds every year. How would you want to see this challenging issue handled?

Chapter 14

Exploring Biological Diversity

CHAPTER AT A GLANCE

The Classification of Organisms

Figure 14.1 Carolus Linnaeus (1707-1778).

This eighteenth-century Swedish professor, physician, and naturalist devised the binomial system for naming species of organisms and established the major categories that are used in the hierarchical system of biological classification. When he was 25, Linnaeus spent five months exploring Lapland for the Swedish Academy of Sciences; he is shown here wearing his Lapland collector's outfit.

14.1 The Invention of the Linnaean System

CONCEPT PREVIEW: Two-part (binomial) Latin names, first used by Linnaeus, are now universally employed by biologists to name organisms.

It is estimated that our world is populated by some 10 to 100 million different kinds of organisms. To talk about them and study them, it is necessary to give them names, just as it is necessary that people have names. Of course, no one can remember the name of every kind of organism, so biologists use a kind of multilevel grouping of individuals called **classification.**

Organisms were first classified more than 2,000 years ago by the Greek philosopher Aristotle, who categorized living things as either plants or animals. He classified animals as either land, water, or air dwellers, and he divided plants into three kinds based on stem differences. This simple classification system was expanded by the Greeks and Romans, who grouped animals and plants into basic units such as cats, horses, and oaks. Eventually, these units began to be called **genera** (singular, **genus**), the Latin word for "group." Starting in the Middle Ages, these names began to be systematically written down, using Latin, the language used by scholars at that time. Thus, cats were assigned to the genus *Felis,* horses to *Equus,* and oaks to *Quercus*—names that the Romans had applied to these groups. For genera that were not known to the Romans, new names were invented.

The classification system of the Middle Ages, called the *polynomial system,* was used virtually unchanged for hundreds of years, until it was replaced about 250 years ago by the **binomial system** introduced by Linnaeus.

The Polynomial System

Until the mid-1700s, biologists usually added a series of descriptive terms to the name of the genus when they wanted to refer to a particular kind of organism, which they called a **species.** These phrases, starting with the name of the genus, came to be known as **polynomials** (*poly,* many, and *nomial,* name), strings of Latin words and phrases consisting of up to 12 or more words. For example, the common wild briar rose was called *Rosa sylvestris inodora seu canina* by some and *Rosa sylvestris alba cum rubore, folio glabro* by others. This would be like the mayor of New York referring to a particular citizen as "Brooklyn resident: Democrat, male, Caucasian, middle income, Protestant, elderly, likely voter, short, bald, heavyset, wears glasses, works in the Bronx selling shoes." As you can imagine, these polynomial names were cumbersome. Even more worrisome, the names were altered at will by later authors, so that a given organism really did not have a single name that was its alone, as was the case with the briar rose.

The Binomial System

A much simpler system of naming animals, plants, and other organisms stems from the work of the Swedish biologist Carolus Linnaeus (1707–78). Linnaeus (figure 14.1) devoted his life to a challenge that had defeated many biologists before him—cataloging all the different kinds of organisms. Linnaeus, a botanist studying the plants of Sweden and from around the world, developed a plant classification system that grouped plants based on their reproductive structures. This system resulted in some seemingly unnatural groupings and therefore was never universally accepted. However, in the 1750s he produced several major works that, like his earlier books, employed the polynomial system. But as a kind of shorthand, Linnaeus also included in these books a two-part name for each species (others had also occasionally done this, but Linnaeus used these shorthand names consistently). These two-part names, or **binomials** (*bi* is the Latin prefix for "two"), have become our standard way of designating species. For example, he designated the willow oak (shown in figure 14.2*a* with its smaller, unlobed leaves) *Quercus phellos* and the red oak (with the larger deeply lobed leaves in figure 14.2*b*) *Quercus rubra,* even though he also included the polynomial name for these species. We also use binomial names for ourselves, our so-called given and family names. So, this naming system is like the mayor of New York calling the Brooklyn resident Sylvester Kingston.

Linnaeus took the naming of organisms a step further, grouping similar organisms into higher-level categories based on similar characteristics (discussed later). Although not intended to show evolutionary connections between different organisms, this hierarchical system acknowledged that there were broad similarities shared by groups of species that distinguished them from other groups.

Figure 14.2 How Linnaeus named two species of oaks.

(a) Willow oak, *Quercus phellos.* (b) Red oak, *Quercus rubra.* Although they are clearly oaks (members of the genus *Quercus*), these two species differ sharply in the shapes and sizes of their leaves and in many other features, including their overall geographical distributions.

14.2 Species Names

CONCEPT PREVIEW: By convention, the first part of a binomial species name identifies the genus to which it belongs, and the second part distinguishes that particular species from other species in the genus.

A group of organisms at a particular level in a classification system is called a **taxon** (plural, **taxa**), and the branch of biology that identifies and names such groups of organisms is called **taxonomy.** Taxonomists are in a real sense detectives, biologists who must use clues of appearance and behavior to identify and assign names to organisms.

By formal agreement among taxonomists throughout the world, no two organisms can have the same name. So that no one country is favored, a language spoken by no country—Latin—is used for the names. Because the scientific name of an organism is the same anywhere in the world, this system provides a standard and precise way of communicating, whether the language of a particular biologist is Chinese, Arabic, Spanish, or English. This is a great improvement over the use of common names, which often vary from one place to the next. As you can see in figure 14.3, in America corn refers to the plant in the upper left photo, but in Europe it refers to the plant Americans call wheat, the lower left photo. A bear is a large placental omnivore in the United States (the upper right photo), but in Australia it is a koala, a vegetarian marsupial (the lower right photo).

By convention, the first word of the binomial name is the genus to which the organism belongs. This word is always capitalized. The second word, called the *specific epithet,* refers to the particular species and is not capitalized. The two words together are called the **scientific name,** or species name, and are written in italics. The system of naming animals, plants, and other organisms established by Linnaeus has served the science of biology well for nearly 250 years.

Throughout this text, you will often see scientific names provided for examples of organisms discussed or shown in photos. You will notice that the same system is used whether identifying a prokaryote, protist, fungus, plant, or animal.

Figure 14.3 Common names make poor labels.

The common names corn (a) and bear (b) bring clear images to our minds (photos on *top*), but the images would be very different to someone living in Europe or Australia (photos on *bottom*). There, the same common names are used to label very different species.

Figure 14.4 The hierarchical system used to classify a gray squirrel.

In this example, the organism is first recognized as a eukaryote (domain: Eukarya). Second, within this domain, it is an animal (kingdom: Animalia). Among the different phyla of animals, it is a vertebrate (phylum: Chordata, subphylum: Vertebrata). The organism's fur characterizes it as a mammal (class: Mammalia). Within this class, it is distinguished by its gnawing teeth (order: Rodentia). Next, because it has four front toes and five back toes, it is a squirrel (family: Sciuridae). Within this family, it is a tree squirrel (genus: *Sciurus*), with gray fur and white-tipped hairs on the tail (species: *Sciurus carolinensis*, the eastern gray squirrel).

14.3 Higher Categories

CONCEPT PREVIEW: A hierarchical system is used to classify organisms, in which higher categories convey more general information about the group.

A biologist needs more than two categories to classify all the world's living things. Taxonomists group the genera with similar properties into a cluster called a **family.** For example, the Eastern gray squirrel at the bottom in figure 14.4 is placed in a family with other squirrel-like animals including prairie dogs, marmots, and chipmunks. Similarly, families that share major characteristics are placed into the same **order** (for example, squirrels placed in with other rodents). Orders with common properties are placed into the same **class** (squirrels in the class Mammalia), and classes with similar characteristics into the same **phylum** (plural, **phyla**) such as the Chordata. Botanists (that is, those who study plants) also call plant phyla "divisions." Finally, the phyla are assigned to one of several gigantic groups, the **kingdoms.** Biologists currently recognize six kingdoms: two kinds of prokaryotes (Archaea and Bacteria), a largely unicellular group of eukaryotes (Protista), and three multicellular groups (Fungi, Plantae, and Animalia). To remember the seven categories in their proper order, it may prove useful to memorize a phrase such as "**k**indly **p**ay **c**ash **o**r **f**urnish **g**ood **s**ecurity" or "**K**ing **P**hilip **c**ame **o**ver **f**or **g**reen **s**paghetti" (**k**ingdom–**p**hylum–**c**lass–**o**rder–**f**amily–**g**enus–**s**pecies).

In addition, an eighth level of classification, called *domains,* is sometimes used. Domains are the broadest and most inclusive taxa, and biologists recognize three of them, Bacteria, Archaea, and Eukarya—which are discussed later in this chapter.

Each of the categories in this Linnaean system of classification is loaded with information. For example, consider a honeybee:

Level 1: Its species name, *Apis mellifera,* identifies the particular species of honey bee.
Level 2: Its genus name, *Apis,* tells you it is a honey bee.
Level 3: Its family, Apidae, are all bees, some solitary, others living in hives as *A. mellifera* does.
Level 4: Its order, Hymenoptera, tells you that it is likely able to sting and may live in colonies.
Level 5: Its class, Insecta, says that *A. mellifera* has three major body segments, with wings and three pairs of legs attached to the middle segment.
Level 6: Its phylum, Arthropoda, tells us that it has a hard cuticle of chitin and jointed appendages.
Level 7: Its kingdom, Animalia, says that it is a multicellular heterotroph whose cells lack cell walls.
Level 8: An addition to the Linnaean system, its domain, Eukarya, says that its cells contain membrane-bounded organelles.

14.4 What Is a Species?

CONCEPT PREVIEW: Among animals, species are generally defined as reproductively isolated groups; among the other kingdoms such a definition is less useful, as their species typically have weaker barriers to hybridization.

The basic biological unit in the Linnaean system of classification is the species. John Ray (1627–1705), an English clergyman and scientist, was one of the first to propose a general definition of species. In about 1700, he suggested a simple way to recognize a species: all the individuals that belong to it can breed with one another and produce fertile offspring. By Ray's definition, the offspring of a single mating were all considered to belong to the same species, even if they contained different-looking individuals, as long as these individuals could interbreed. All domestic cats are one species (they can all interbreed), while carp are not the same species as goldfish (they cannot interbreed). The donkey you see in figure 14.5 is not the same species as the horse, because when they interbreed, the offspring—mules—are sterile.

Horse

Donkey

Mule

Figure 14.5 Ray's definition of a species.

According to Ray, donkeys and horses are not the same species. Even though they produce very hardy offspring (mules) when they mate, the mules are sterile, meaning that two mules that mate cannot produce offspring. The sterility arises because the two species have different numbers of chromosomes: donkeys have 62 chromosomes, whereas horses have 64.

IMPLICATION Horses, donkeys, and zebras are all members of the same genus, *Equus,* and, when interbred, produce hardy but sterile offspring: a "zonky" is the offspring of a zebra and a donkey, while a "zorse" is the offspring of a zebra and a horse. In the film *Racing Stripes,* the son of Stripes (a zebra) and Sandy (a white filly horse) is a zorse. Do you think Stripes has the same number of chromosomes as Sandy? Explain your answer.

The Biological Species Concept

Linnaeus used Ray's species concept, and it is still widely used today. The *biological species concept* defines species as groups that are reproductively isolated. Hybrids (offspring of different species that mate) are rare in nature, while individuals that belong to the same species are able to interbreed freely.

The biological species concept works fairly well for animals, where strong barriers to hybridization between species exist, but very poorly for members of the other kingdoms. The problem is that in prokaryotes and many protists, fungi, and plants, asexual reproduction (reproduction without sex) predominates. These species clearly cannot be characterized in the same way as animals—they do not breed with one another, much less with individuals of other species.

Complicating matters further, the reproductive barriers that are key to the biological species concept, although common among animal species, are not typical of other kinds of organisms. In fact, there are essentially no barriers to hybridization between the species in many groups of trees, such as oaks, and other plants, such as orchids. Even among animals, fish species are able to form fertile hybrids with one another, though they may not do so in nature.

In practice, biologists today recognize species in different groups in much the way they always did, as groups that differ from one another in their visible features. Molecular data are causing a reevaluation of traditional classification systems, and are changing the way scientists classify plants, protists, fungi, prokaryotes, and even animals.

How Many Kinds of Species Are There?

Since the time of Linnaeus, about 1.5 million species have been named. But the actual number of species in the world is undoubtedly much greater, judging from the very large numbers that are still being discovered. Some scientists estimate that at least 10 million species exist on earth, two-thirds in the tropics.

Concept Check

1. List the eight levels of classification in order of inclusiveness.
2. Explain why the biological species concept works so much better for animals than for other kinds of organisms.
3. Distinguish between what Linnaeus and Ray contributed to taxonomy.

Inferring Phylogeny

14.5 How to Build a Family Tree

CONCEPT PREVIEW: A phylogeny may be represented as a cladogram based on the order in which groups evolved or as a traditional taxonomic tree that weights characters according to assumed importance.

By looking at the differences and similarities between organisms, biologists attempt to reconstruct the tree of life, inferring which organisms evolved from which other ones, in what order, and when. The evolutionary history of an organism and its relationship to other species is called **phylogeny.**

Cladistics

A simple and objective way to construct an evolutionary history, or **phylogenetic tree,** is to focus on key characters that some organisms share because they have inherited them from a common ancestor. A **clade** is a group of organisms related by descent, and this approach to constructing a phylogeny is called **cladistics.** Cladistics infers phylogeny (that is, builds family trees) according to similarities derived from a common ancestor, so-called **derived characters.** Derived characters are defined as characters that are present in a group of organisms that arose from a common ancestor that lacked the character. The key to the approach is being able to identify morphological, physiological, or behavioral traits that differ among the organisms being studied and can be attributed to a common ancestor. By examining the distribution of these traits among the organisms, it is possible to construct a **cladogram,** a branching diagram that represents the phylogeny. A cladogram of the vertebrates is shown in figure 14.6.

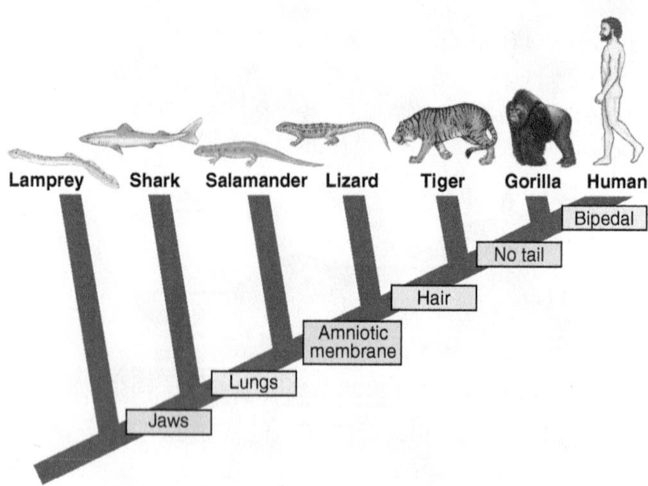

Figure 14.6 A cladogram of vertebrate animals.

The derived characters between the branch points are shared by all the animals to the right of each character and are not present in any organisms to the left of it.

IMPLICATION Do you think you would obtain the same tree of relationships you see here if instead of looking at derived characters you instead simply counted the number of DNA bases different from humans in the genomes of each of the groups in the figure above? Explain your answer.

Cladograms are not true family trees, derived directly from data that document ancestors and descendants like the fossil record does. Instead, cladograms convey comparative information about *relative* relationships. Organisms that are closer together on a cladogram simply share a more recent common ancestor than those that are farther apart. Because the analysis is comparative, it is necessary to have something to anchor the comparison to, some solid ground against which the comparisons can be made. To achieve this, each cladogram must contain an **outgroup,** a rather different organism (but not *too* different) to serve as a baseline for comparisons among the other organisms being evaluated, called the **ingroup.** For example, in figure 14.6, the lamprey is the outgroup to the clade of animals that have jaws. Comparisons are then made up the cladogram, beginning with lampreys and sharks, based on the emergence of derived characters. For example, the shark differs from the lamprey in that it has jaws, the derived character missing in the lamprey. The derived characters are in the colored boxes along the main line of the cladogram. Salamanders differ from sharks in that they have lungs, and so on up the cladogram.

Sometimes cladograms are adjusted to "weight" characters, or take into account the variation in the "strength" (importance) of a character—the size or location of a fin, the effectiveness of a lung. For example, let's say that the following are five unique events that occurred on September 11, 2001: (1) my cat was declawed, (2) I had a wisdom tooth pulled, (3) I sold my first car, (4) terrorists attacked the United States using commercial airplanes, and (5) I passed physics. Without weighting the events, each one is assigned equal importance. In a nonweighted cladistic sense, they are equal (all happened only once, and on that day), but in a practical, real-world sense, they certainly are not. One event, the terrorist attack, had a far

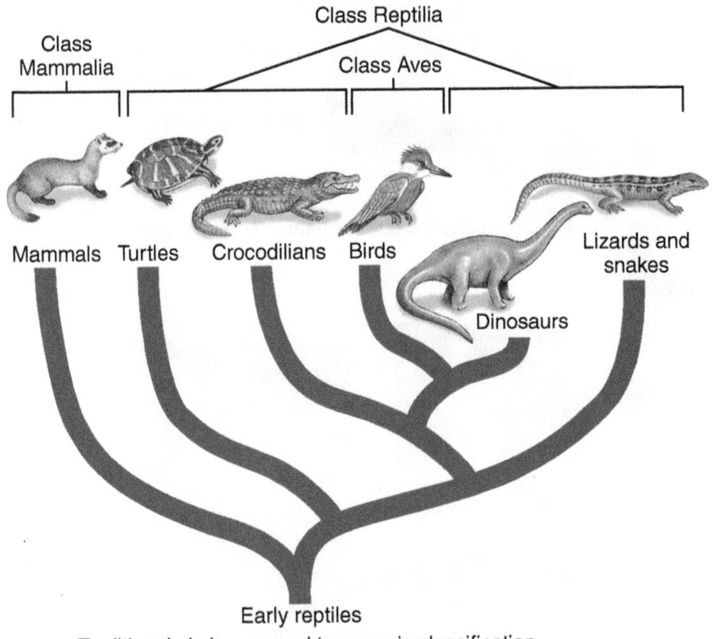

Traditional phylogeny and taxonomic classification

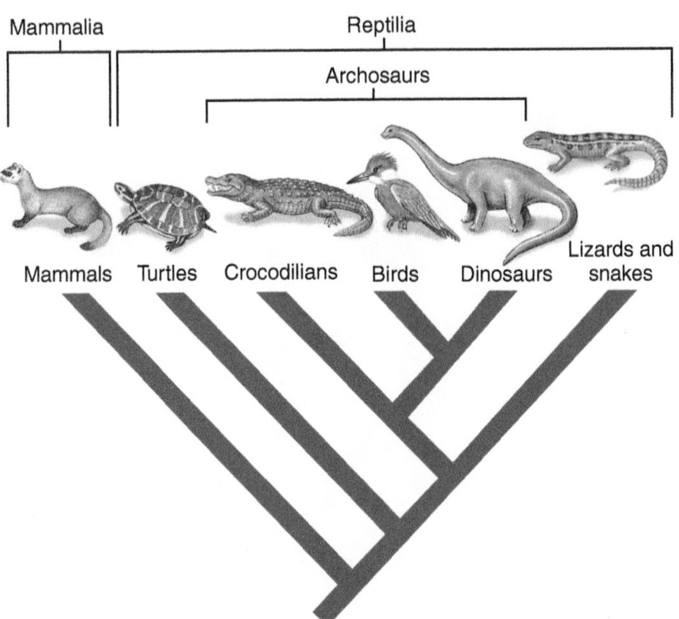

Cladogram and cladistic classification

Figure 14.7 Two ways to classify terrestrial vertebrates.

Traditional taxonomic analyses place birds in their own class (Aves) because birds have evolved several unique adaptations that separate them from the reptiles. Cladistic analyses, however, place crocodiles, dinosaurs, and birds together (as archosaurs) because they share many derived characters, indicating a recent shared ancestry. In practice, most biologists adopt the traditional approach and consider birds as members of the class Aves rather than Reptilia.

greater impact and importance than the others. Because evolutionary success depends so critically on just such high-impact events, these weighted cladograms attempt to assign extra weight to the evolutionary significance of key characters.

Traditional Taxonomy

Weighting characters lies at the core of **traditional taxonomy.** In this approach, phylogenies are constructed based on all available information about the morphology and biology of the organism. The large amount of information permits a knowledgeable weighting of characters according to their biological significance. For example, in classifying the terrestrial vertebrates, traditional taxonomists, shown by the phylogeny on the left in figure 14.7, place birds in their own class (Aves), giving great weight to the characters that made powered flight possible, such as feathers. However, a cladogram of vertebrate evolution, as shown on the right, lumps birds in among the reptiles with crocodiles and dinosaurs. This accurately reflects their ancestry but ignores the immense evolutionary impact of a derived character such as feathers.

Overall, phylogenetic trees based on traditional taxonomy are information-rich, while cladograms often do a better job of deciphering evolutionary histories. Traditional taxonomy is the better approach when a great deal of information is available to guide character weighting. However, cladistics is the preferred approach when less information is available about how the character affects the life of the organism. For example, the cat family tree in figure 14.8 on the next page is based on thousands of DNA differences among the different groups of felines, few of which affect the life of the cats in ways we know and understand.

Concept Check

1. Define cladistics.
2. Can a derived character be present in an outgroup?
3. Is a bird really a reptile? Justify your answer.

IN THE NEWS

The Biodiversity Crisis. Biologists, worried by the rapid rate of extinction of animals and plants, have recently announced completion of a comprehensive survey of threatened species. For plants, invertebrate animals, and the five major categories of vertebrates, they first determined the number of species that had been evaluated in the last decade, and then for each group counted how many of these had proven to be threatened. They concluded that our world now faces a biodiversity crisis, with over a third of all species living on it threatened today with extinction. Birds seemed to be doing better than the others, and plants worse. All mammalian species had been evaluated, and over 20% of them proved to be endangered, most by habitat loss or poaching.

Taxonomic Group	Threatened
Mammals	21%
Birds	12%
Reptiles	31%
Amphibians	30%
Fishes	37%
Invertebrates	41%
Plants	70%

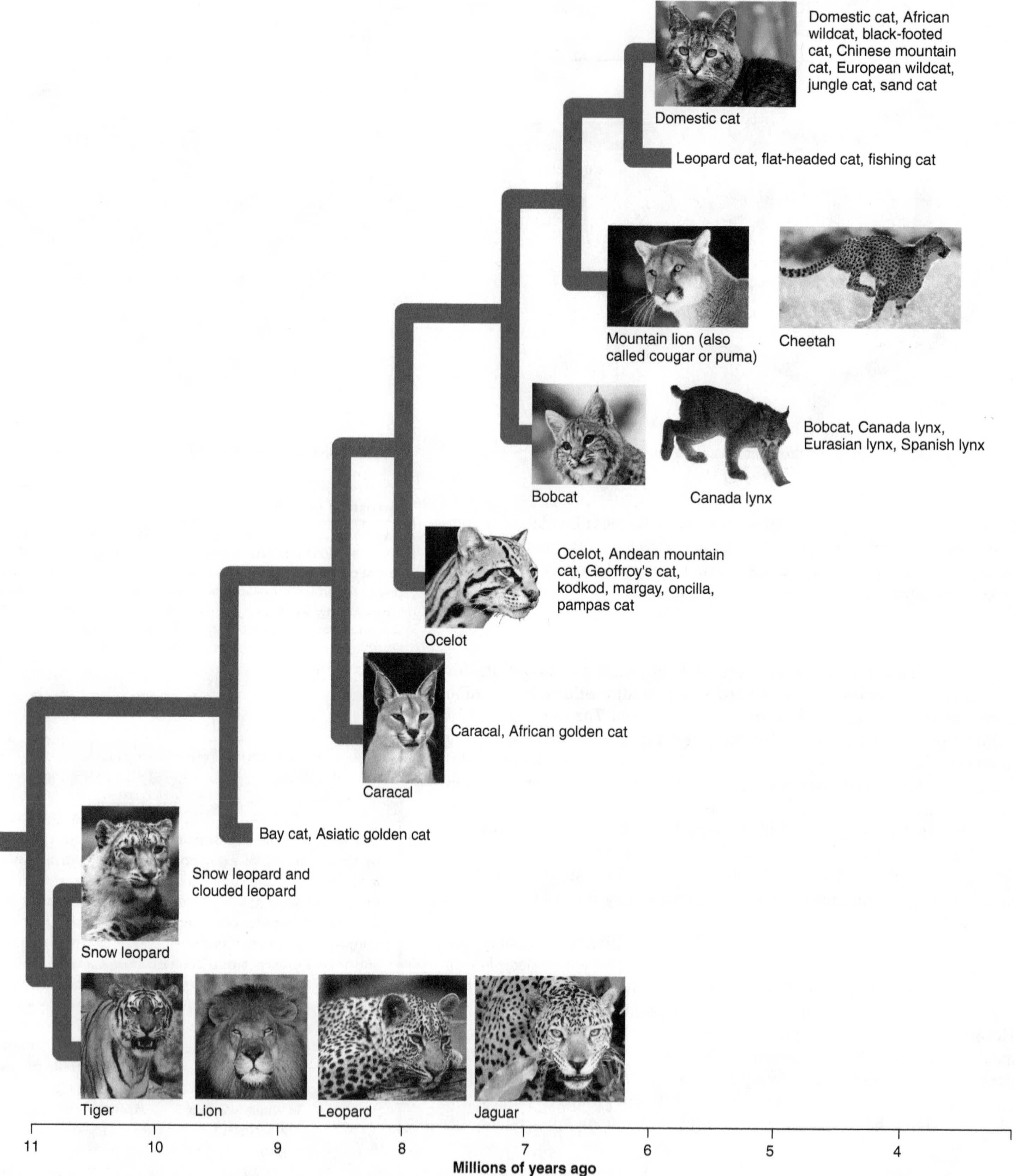

Figure 14.8 The cat family tree.

Recent studies of DNA similarities reported in 2006 have allowed biologists to construct this feline family tree of the eight major cat lineages and their individual species. Among the oldest of all cats are the four big panthers: tiger, lion, leopard, and jaguar. The other big cats, the cheetah and mountain lion, are members of a much younger lineage and are not close relatives of the big four. Domestic cats evolved most recently.

Race and Medicine

Few issues in biology have stirred more social controversy than race. Race has a deceptively simple definition, referring to groups of individuals related by ancestry that differ from other groups, but not enough to constitute separate species. The controversy arises because of the way people have used the concept of race to justify the abuse of humans. The African slave trade is but one obvious example. Perhaps in some measure responding to these sorts of injustice, scientists have largely abandoned the concept of race except as a social construct. However, scientists are again evaluating the biology of race. This reevaluation had its beginnings in 1972, when geneticists pointed out that if one looked at genes rather than faces, the differences between the genes of an African and a European would be hardly greater than the difference between those of any two Europeans. For thirty years, gene data has continually reinforced the validity of this observation, and the concept of genetic races has been largely abandoned.

Recent detailed comparisons of the genomes of people around the world reveal that particular alleles defining human features often occur in clusters on chromosomes. Because they are close together, the genes experience little recombination over the centuries. The descendants of a person who has a particular combination of alleles will almost always have that same combination. The set of alleles, technically called a "haplotype," reflects the common ancestry of these descendants from that ancestor.

Ignoring skin color and eye shape, and instead comparing the DNA sequences of hundreds of regions of the human genome, investigators at the University of Southern California showed in 2002 that when a large sample of people from around the world are compared, the computer sorts them into five large groups containing similar clusters of variation: Europe, East Asia, Africa, America, and Australasia. That these are more or less the major races of traditional anthropology is not the point. The point is that humanity evolved in these five regions in isolation from one another, that today each of these groups is composed of individuals with a shared ancestry, and that by analyzing the DNA of an individual we can deduce that ancestry.

Why bother making that rather arcane and socially controversial point? Because analysis of the human genome is revealing that many diseases are influenced by alleles that have arisen since the five major branches of the human family tree separated from one another, and are much more common in the human ancestral group within which the DNA mutation causing the disease first occurred. For example, a mutation causing hemochromatosis, a disorder of iron metabolism, is rare or absent among Indians or Chinese, but very common among northern Europeans (it occurs in 7.5% of Swedes), who also commonly possess an allele leading to adult lactose intolerance (inability to digest lactose) not common in many other groups. Similarly, the hemoglobin S mutation causing sickle cell disease is common among Africans of Bantu ancestry, but seems to have arisen only there.

This is a pattern we see again and again as we compare genomes of people living in different parts of the world—and it has a very important consequence. Because of common ancestry, genetic diseases (disorders that are inherited) have a lot to do with geography. The risk that an African American man will be afflicted with hypertensive heart disease or prostate cancer is nearly three times greater than that for a European American man, while the European American is far more likely to develop cystic fibrosis or multiple sclerosis.

These differences in medically important DNA variants carry over to genetic differences in how individuals respond to treatment. African Americans, for example, respond poorly to some of the main drugs used to treat heart conditions, such as beta-blockers and angiotensin enzyme inhibitors.

Scientists and doctors that recognize this unfortunate fact are not racists. They fully agree that while using the races of traditional anthropology to pin-point which therapeutic treatment to recommend is an improvement over treating all patients alike, it is still a very poor way of getting at these differences. It would be far better to simply ignore skin color and other single-gene differences and instead perform for each patient a broad "gene variation" analysis. Hopelessly difficult only a few years ago, this now seems an attractive avenue to improve medical treatment for all of us.

It is important to keep clearly in mind the goal of sorting out individual human ancestry, which is to identify common lines of descent that share common response to potential therapies. It is NOT to assign people to over-arching racial categories. This point is being made with great clarity in a course being taught at Pennsylvania State University, where about 90 students had their DNA sampled and compared with four of the five major human groups. Many of these students had thought of themselves as "100% white," but only a few were. One "white" student learned that 14% of his DNA came from Africa, and 6% from East Asia. Similarly, "black" students found that as much as half of their genetic material came from Europe, and a significant amount from Asia as well.

The point is, rigid ideas about the biological basis of identity are wrong. Humanity is much more complex than indicated by a few genes affecting skin color and eye shape. The more clearly we can understand that complexity, the better we can deal with the medical consequences, and the great potential that human diversity provides all of us.

Kingdoms and Domains

BIOLOGY & YOU

How Biodiversity Benefits You—Direct Economic Value. Many threatened species have direct value to you as sources of food, medicine, clothing, energy, and shelter:

1. **Gene variation.** Most of the world's food crops, such as corn, wheat, and rice, are derived from a small number of domesticated plants and so contain relatively little genetic variation; on the other hand, their wild relatives have great diversity. In the future, genetic variation from wild strains will be needed if we are to improve yields or find a way to breed resistance to new pests.
2. **Medicine.** About 70% of the world's population depends directly on wild plants as their source of medicine. In addition, some 40% of the prescription drugs used today have active ingredients extracted from animals or plants. Aspirin was first extracted from the leaves of a tropical willow tree. Vinblastine, the most effective drug for combatting childhood leukemia, is extracted from the rosy periwinkle vine. The cancer-fighting drug taxol is produced from the bark of the Pacific yew tree.
3. **Gene prospecting.** Genetic engineers are using the advances described in chapter 13 to transfer beneficial genes into crops. We have been able to examine only a minute proportion of the world's species to see if they contain genes that have useful properties for humans. When a species is extinct, its entire library of genes is lost to us forever.

14.6 The Kingdoms of Life

CONCEPT PREVIEW: Living organisms are grouped into three categories called domains. One of the domains, Eukarya, is divided into four kingdoms: Protista, Fungi, Plantae, and Animalia.

Classification systems have gone through their own evolution of sorts, as illustrated in figure 14.9. The earliest classification systems recognized only two kingdoms of living things: animals, shown in blue in (*a*), and plants, shown in green. But as biologists discovered microorganisms (the yellow-colored boxes in *b*) and learned more about other organisms like the protists (in teal) and the fungi (in light brown), they added kingdoms in recognition of fundamental differences. Most biologists now use a six-kingdom system (indicated by the six different-colored boxes in *c*) first proposed by Carl Woese of the University of Illinois.

In this system, four kingdoms consist of eukaryotic organisms. The two most familiar kingdoms, **Animalia** and **Plantae,** contain organisms that are multicellular during most of their life cycle. These groups of animals and plants are no doubt familiar to you. The kingdom **Fungi** contains multicellular forms, such as mushrooms and molds, and single-celled yeasts, which are thought to have multicellular ancestors. Fundamental differences divide these three kingdoms. Plants are mainly stationary, but some have motile sperm; fungi have no motile cells; animals are mainly motile. Animals ingest their food, plants manufacture it, and fungi digest it by means of secreted extracellular enzymes. Each of these kingdoms probably evolved from a different single-celled ancestor.

The large number of unicellular eukaryotes are arbitrarily grouped into a single kingdom called **Protista.** They include the algae and many kinds of microscopic aquatic organisms. This kingdom is an artificial group in that many of these organisms are only distantly related, and the classification of the protists is in flux.

Prokaryotic organisms, as described on page 65, are single-celled organisms that lack a nucleus and other internal membrane-bounded structures.

The remaining two kingdoms, **Archaea** and **Bacteria,** consist of prokaryotic organisms, which are vastly different from all other living things. The prokaryotes with which you are most familiar, those that cause disease or

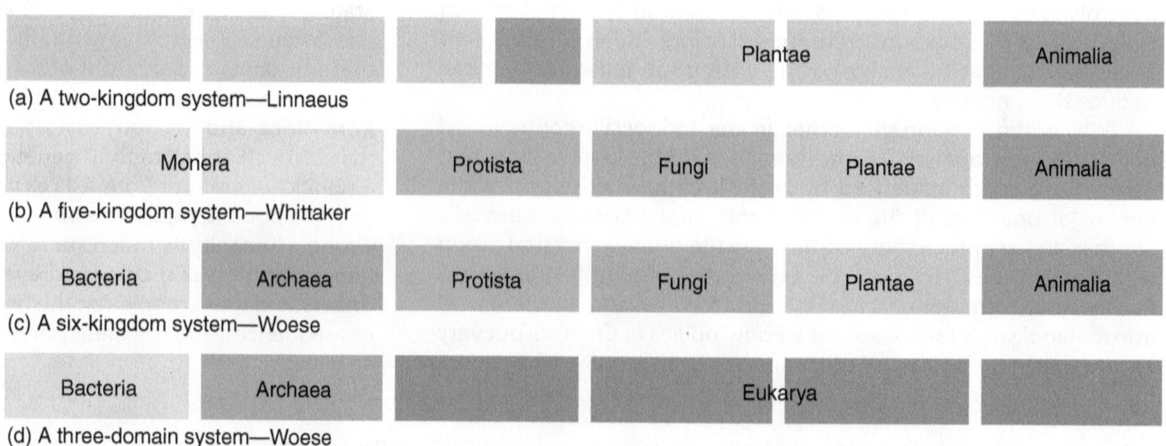

Figure 14.9 Different approaches to classifying living organisms.

(a) Linnaeus popularized a two-kingdom approach, in which the fungi and the photosynthetic protists were classified as plants and the nonphotosynthetic protists as animals; when prokaryotes were described, they too were considered plants. (b) Whittaker in 1969 proposed a five-kingdom system that soon became widely accepted. (c) Woese has championed splitting the prokaryotes into two kingdoms for a total of six kingdoms or even assigning them separate domains, with a third domain containing the four eukaryotic kingdoms (d).

are used in industry, are members of the kingdom Bacteria. Archaea are a diverse group including the methanogens and some that live in physically extreme conditions, such as the extreme thermophiles. They differ greatly from bacteria in many ways. The characteristics of these six kingdoms are presented in table 14.1.

As biologists have learned more about the archaea, it has become increasingly clear that this ancient group is very different from all other organisms. When the full genomic DNA sequences of an archaean and a bacterium were first compared in 1996, the differences proved striking. Based on comparing DNA and cell structures, archaea are as different from bacteria as bacteria are from eukaryotes. Recognizing this, biologists have in recent years adopted a taxonomic level higher than kingdom that recognizes three **domains** (figure 14.9*d*). Archaea (red-colored box) are in one domain, bacteria (yellow-colored box) in a second, and eukaryotes (the four purple boxes representing the four eukaryotic kingdoms) in the third. While the domain Eukarya contains four kingdoms of organisms, the domains Bacteria and Archaea contain only one kingdom in each. Because of this, the kingdom level of classification for Bacteria and Archaea is now often omitted, with biologists using just their domain and phyla names.

BIOLOGY & YOU

How Biodiversity Benefits You—Ecosystem Services. The most important value of biological diversity to you is indirect, as diversity is of vital importance to the health of ecosystems (communities of organisms and the places where they live). Diverse biological communities help maintain the chemical quality of natural water, buffer natural areas against storms and drought, preserve soils and prevent loss of minerals, moderate local and regional climate, absorb pollution, and promote the breakdown of organic wastes and the recycling of minerals. All of these benefits are grouped together by economists as so-called ecosystem services. The stability and productivity of the world's ecosystems depend critically on these services, and they in turn depend critically on the number of different species present in an area, called species richness. By destroying biodiversity we are creating conditions of instability and lessened productivity, and promoting desertification (the natural transformation of lands into deserts), tropical soil loss through mineralization, and many other undesirable outcomes throughout the world.

TABLE 14.1 Characteristics of the Six Kingdoms

Domain	**Bacteria**	**Archaea**	**Eukarya**			
Kingdom	**Bacteria**	**Archaea**	**Protista**	**Plantae**	**Fungi**	**Animalia**
Cell type	Prokaryotic	Prokaryotic	Eukaryotic	Eukaryotic	Eukaryotic	Eukaryotic
Nuclear envelope	Absent	Absent	Present	Present	Present	Present
Mitochondria	Absent	Absent	Present or absent	Present	Present or absent	Present
Chloroplasts	None (photosynthetic membranes in some types)	None (bacteriorhodopsin in one species)	Present in some forms	Present	Absent	Absent
Cell wall	Present in most; peptidoglycan	Present in most; polysaccharide, glycoprotein, or protein	Present in some forms; various types	Cellulose and other polysaccharides	Chitin and other noncellulose polysaccharides	Absent
Means of genetic recombination, if present	Conjugation, transduction, transformation	Conjugation, transduction, transformation	Fertilization and meiosis	Fertilization and meiosis	Fertilization and meiosis	Fertilization and meiosis
Mode of nutrition	Autotrophic (chemosynthetic, photosynthetic) or heterotrophic	Autotrophic (photosynthesis in one species) or heterotrophic	Photosynthetic or heterotrophic or combination of both	Photosynthetic, chlorophylls *a* and *b*	Absorption	Digestion
Motility	Bacterial flagella, gliding, or nonmotile	Unique flagella in some	9 + 2 cilia and flagella; amoeboid, contractile fibrils	None in most forms, 9 + 2 cilia and flagella in gametes of some forms	Nonmotile	9 + 2 cilia and flagella, contractile fibrils
Multicellularity	Absent	Absent	Absent in most forms	Present in all forms	Present in most forms	Present in all forms

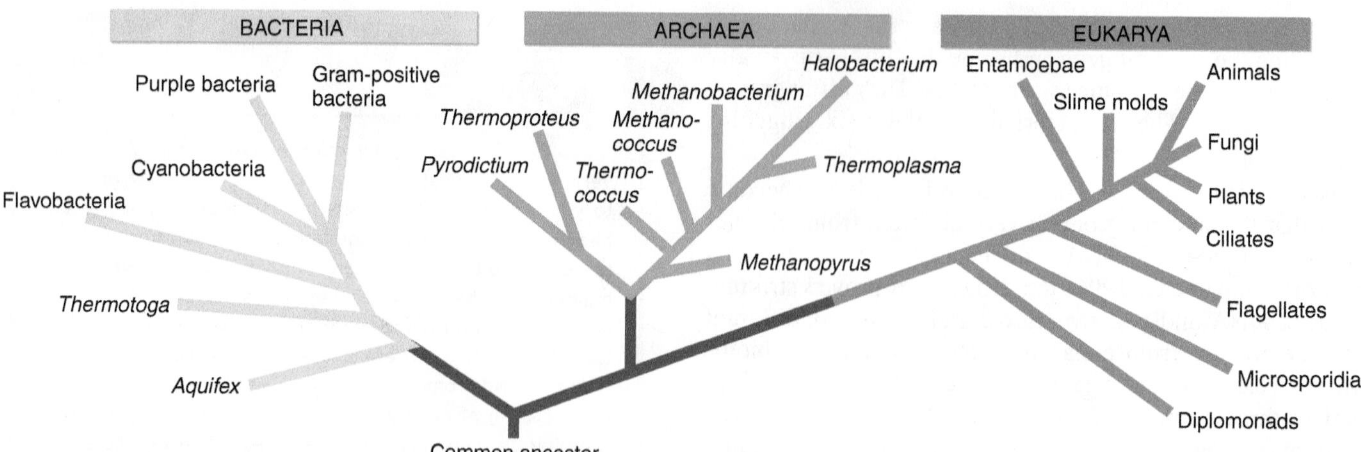

Figure 14.10 A tree of life.

This phylogeny, prepared from rRNA analyses, shows the evolutionary relationships among the three domains. The base of the tree was determined by examining genes that are duplicated in all three domains, the duplication presumably having occurred in the common ancestor. When one of the duplicates is used to construct the tree, the other can be used to root it. This approach clearly indicates that the root of the tree is within the bacterial domain. Archaea and eukaryotes diverged later and are more closely related to each other than either is to bacteria.

14.7 Domain: A Higher Level of Classification

CONCEPT PREVIEW: Organisms in the three domains differ in basic cellular structure. Bacteria and Archaea are prokaryotes but vary in several aspects. Eukarya contains single-celled and multicellular eukaryotic organisms.

Domain Bacteria

The domain Bacteria contains one kingdom of the same name, Bacteria. The bacteria are the most abundant organisms on earth. There are more living bacteria in your mouth than there are mammals living on earth. Although too tiny to see with the unaided eye, bacteria play critical roles throughout the biosphere. For example, they extract from the air all the nitrogen used by organisms, and they play key roles in cycling carbon and sulfur.

All organisms need nitrogen, but only a few kinds of bacteria can transform the nitrogen in the air into a form that can be used by other organisms. This process, called nitrogen fixation, is discussed on page 266.

There are many different kinds of bacteria, and the evolutionary links between them are not well understood. The archaea and eukaryotes are more closely related to each other than to bacteria and are on a separate evolutionary branch of the phylogenetic tree in figure 14.10.

Domain Archaea

The domain Archaea contains one kingdom by the same name, the Archaea. The term *archaea* (Greek, *archaio,* ancient) refers to the ancient origin of this group of prokaryotes, which most likely diverged very early from the bacteria. Notice in figure 14.10 that the Archaea, in red, branched off from a line of prokaryotic ancestors that led to the evolution of eukaryotes. Though a diverse group, all archaea share certain key characteristics: They possess very unusual cell walls, lipids, and ribosomal RNA (rRNA) sequences. Some of their genes possess introns, unlike those of bacteria.

As the genomes of archaea have become better known, microbiologists have been able to identify signature sequences of DNA present in all archaea and in no other organisms. When samples from soil or seawater are tested for genes matching these signature sequences, many of the prokaryotes living there prove to be archaea. Clearly, archaea are not restricted to extreme habitats, as microbiologists used to think.

How Biodiversity Benefits You—Ethical and Aesthetic Value.

Ethics. Many people believe that extinction is an ethical issue, that every species is of value in its own right and has its own right to exist, even if humans are not able to exploit or benefit from it. As the only organism capable of eliminating large numbers of species and entire ecosystems, and as the only organism capable of reflecting on what we are doing, humans have an ethical responsibility to act as stewards and guardians for the diversity of life with which we share the planet.

Aesthetics. Almost no one would deny the aesthetic value of biodiversity—a wild mountain range, a beautiful flower, or a noble elephant—all make our hearts sing. But how do we place a value on beauty, or on the renewal many of us feel when we are in natural surroundings? Perhaps the best we can do is to consider the deep sense of loss we would feel if it no longer existed.

Domain Eukarya

For at least 1 billion years, prokaryotes ruled the earth. No other organisms existed to eat them or compete with them, and their tiny cells formed the world's oldest fossils. The third great domain of life, the eukaryotes, appear in the fossil record much later, only about 1.5 billion years ago.

Three Largely Multicellular Kingdoms. Fungi, plants, and animals are well-defined evolutionary groups. They are largely multicellular, each group clearly stemming from a different single-celled eukaryotic ancestor. The ancestor of each distinct evolutionary line would be classified in the kingdom Protista.

The amount of diversity among the protists, however, is much greater than that within or between the three largely multicellular kingdoms derived from the protists. Because of the size and ecological dominance of plants, animals, and fungi, and because they are predominantly multicellular, we recognize them as kingdoms distinct from Protista.

A Fourth Very Diverse Kingdom. When multicellularity evolved, the diverse kinds of single-celled organisms that existed at that time did not simply become extinct. A wide variety of unicellular eukaryotes and their relatives exist today. They are grouped together in the kingdom Protista solely because they are not fungi, plants, or animals. Protists are a fascinating group containing many organisms of intense interest and great biological significance.

Symbiosis and the Origin of Eukaryotes. The hallmark of eukaryotes is complex cellular organization, highlighted by an extensive endomembrane system that subdivides the eukaryotic cell into functional compartments called organelles (see chapter 4). Not all of these organelles, however, are derived from the endomembrane system. Mitochondria and chloroplasts are both believed to have entered early eukaryotic cells by a process called endosymbiosis (*endo,* inside) where an organism such as a bacterium is taken into the cell and remains functional inside the cell.

With few exceptions, all modern eukaryotic cells possess energy-producing organelles, the mitochondria. Mitochondria are about the size of bacteria and contain DNA. Comparison of the nucleotide sequence of this mitochondrial DNA with that of a variety of organisms indicates clearly that mitochondria are the descendants of purple bacteria that were incorporated into eukaryotic cells early in the history of the group. Some protist phyla have also acquired chloroplasts during the course of their evolution and thus are photosynthetic. These chloroplasts are derived from cyanobacteria that became symbiotic in several groups of protists early in their history. Figure 14.11*a* shows how this could have happened, with the green cyanobacterium being engulfed by an early protist. Some of these photosynthetic protists gave rise to land plants. Endosymbiosis still happens today (the green structures inside the coral in figure 14.11*b* are endosymbiotic protists). We discussed the endosymbiotic origin of mitochondria and chloroplasts in chapter 4.

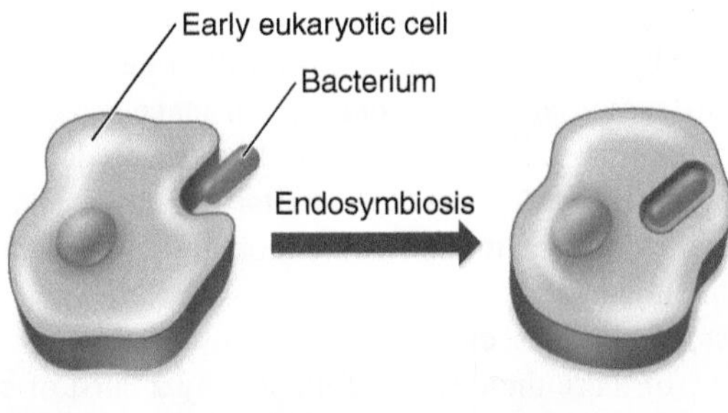

(a)

(b)

Figure 14.11 Endosymbiosis.

(a) This figure shows how an organelle could have arisen in early eukaryotic cells through a process called endosymbiosis. An organism, such as a bacterium, is taken into the cell through a process similar to endocytosis but remains functional inside the host cell. (b) Many corals contain endosymbionts, algae called zooxanthellae that carry out photosynthesis and provide the coral with nutrients. In this photograph, the zooxanthellae are the golden-brown spheres packed into the tentacles of a coral animal.

Concept Check

1. Which domain contains humans?
2. What is the difference between archaea and bacteria?
3. Which kingdom is the most diverse?

Inquiry & Analysis

What Causes New Forms to Arise?

Biologists once presumed that new forms—genera, families, and orders—arose most often during times of massive geological disturbance, stimulated by the resulting environmental changes. But no such relationship exists. An alternative hypothesis was proposed by evolutionist George Simpson in 1953. He proposed that diversification followed new evolutionary innovations, "inventions" that permitted an organism to occupy a new "adaptive zone." After a burst of new orders that define the major groups, subsequent specialization would lead to new genera.

The early bony fishes, typified by the sturgeon below, had feeble jaws and long shark-like tails. They dominated the Devonian (the Age of Fishes), but were succeeded in the Triassic (the period when dinosaurs appeared) by fishes like the gar pike with a more powerful jaw that improved feeding and a shortened more maneuverable tail that improved locomotion. Gar pikes were in turn succeeded by teleost fishes like the perch, with an even better tail for fast, maneuverable swimming, and a complex mouth with a mobile upper jaw that slides forward as the mouth opens.

This history allows a clear test of Simpson's hypothesis. Was the appearance of these three orders followed by a burst of evolution as Simpson predicts, the new innovations in feeding and locomotion opening wide the door of opportunity? If so, many new genera should be seen in the fossil record soon after the appearance of each new order. If not, the pattern of when new genera appear should not track the appearance of new orders.

The graph shows the evolutionary history of the class Osteichthyes, the bony fishes, since they first appeared in the Silurian some 420 million years ago.

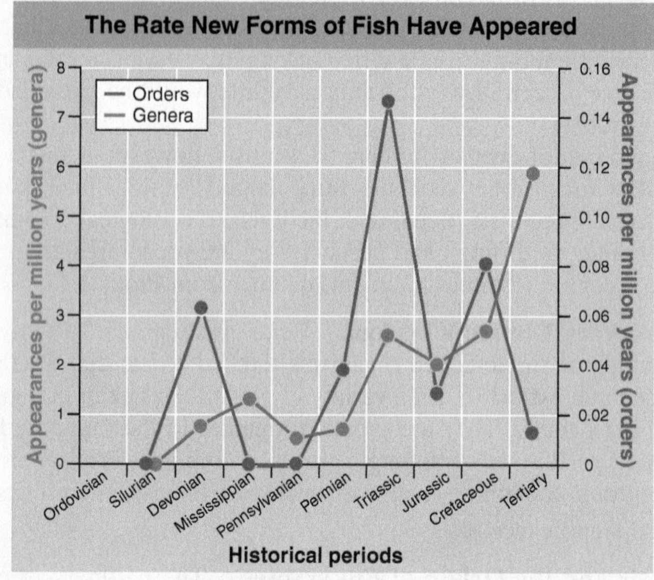

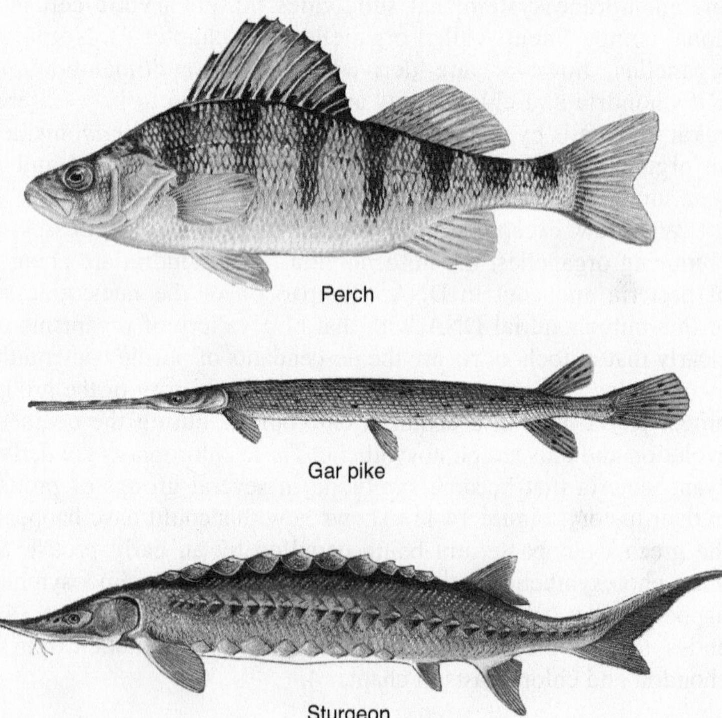

Analysis

1. **Interpreting Data** Three great innovations in jaw and tail occur during the history of the bony fishes, producing the superorders represented by sturgeons, then gars, and then teleost fishes. In what period did each innovation occur?
2. **Making Inferences** Do bursts of new genera appear at these same three times, or later?
3. **Drawing Conclusions** Does the data presented in the graph support Simpson's hypothesis? Explain.

Concept Summary

The Classification of Organisms

14.1 The Invention of the Linnaean System

- Scientists use a system of grouping similar organisms together, called classification. Latin is used because it was the language used by earlier philosophers and scientists.
- The polynomial system of classification named an organism by using a list of adjectives that described the organism. The binomial system, using a two-part name, was originally developed as a "shorthand" reference to the polynomial name. Linnaeus used this two-part naming system consistently and its use became widespread (**figure 14.2**).

14.2 Species Names

- Taxonomy is the area of biology involved in identifying, naming, and grouping organisms. Scientific names consist of two parts, the genus and species. The genus name is capitalized but the species name is not. The two parts of the name are italicized. Scientific names are standardized, universal names that are less confusing than common names (**figure 14.3**).

14.3 Higher Categories

- In addition to the genus and species names, an organism is also assigned to higher levels of classification. The higher categories convey more general information about the organisms in a particular group. The most general category, domain, is the largest grouping followed by ever-increasingly specific information that is used to group organisms into a kingdom, phylum, class, order, family, genus, and species (**figure 14.4**).

14.4 What Is a Species?

- The biological species concept states that a species is a group of organisms that is reproductively isolated, meaning that the individuals mate and produce fertile offspring with each other but not with those of other species.
- This concept works well to define animal species because animals regularly outcross (mate with other individuals—**figure 14.5**) as do many kinds of plants. However, the concept does not apply to other organisms (fungi, protists, prokaryotes, and some plants) that regularly reproduce without mating through asexual reproduction. The classification of these organisms relies more on physical, behavioral, and molecular characteristics.

Inferring Phylogeny

14.5 How to Build a Family Tree

- In addition to organizing a great number of organisms, the study of taxonomy also gives us a glimpse of the evolutionary history of life on earth. Organisms with similar characteristics are more likely to be related to each other. The evolutionary history of an organism and its relationship to other species is called phylogeny, and relationships are often mapped out using phylogenetic trees.
- Phylogenetic trees can be created using key characteristics that are shared by some organisms, presumably having been inherited from a common ancestor. A group of organisms that are related by descent is called a clade, and a phylogenetic tree organized in this manner is called a cladogram (**figure 14.6**). A cladogram suggests the order in which evolutionary changes occurred.
- Cladograms can sometimes be misleading when the characteristics are weighted, placing more importance on a characteristic that seems to have a more significant impact on evolution. The problem with this system is that some characteristics may turn out to be less important than first thought. For this reason, cladograms work best when all characteristics are weighted equally.
- Traditional taxonomy focuses more on the significance or evolutionary impact of a characteristic and not just on the commonality of the characteristic. For example, in traditional taxonomy, birds are placed in their own class, as shown here from **figure 14.7**, even though, evolutionarily, birds fall within the reptile group. Traditional taxonomy is used when more information is available to weight characteristics that seem more significant (**figure 14.8**), while cladistics places more emphasis on the order or timing in which unique, or derived, characteristics appear.

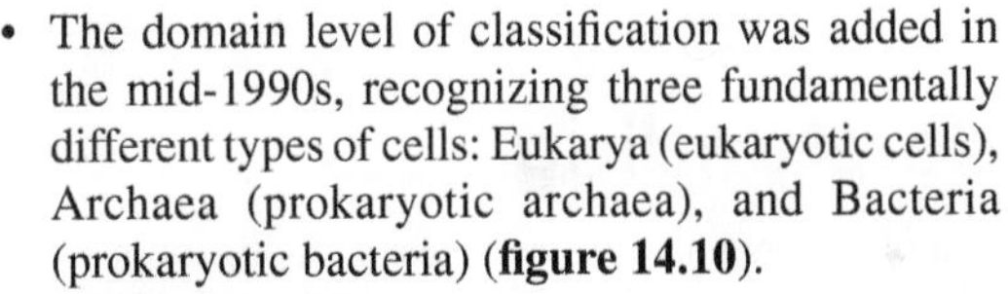

Kingdoms and Domains

14.6 The Kingdoms of Life

- The designation of kingdoms, the second-highest category used in classification, has changed over the years as more and more information about organisms has been uncovered. Currently six kingdoms have been identified: Bacteria, Archaea, Protista, Fungi, Plantae, and Animalia, (**figure 14.9** and **table 14.1**).
- The domain level of classification was added in the mid-1990s, recognizing three fundamentally different types of cells: Eukarya (eukaryotic cells), Archaea (prokaryotic archaea), and Bacteria (prokaryotic bacteria) (**figure 14.10**).

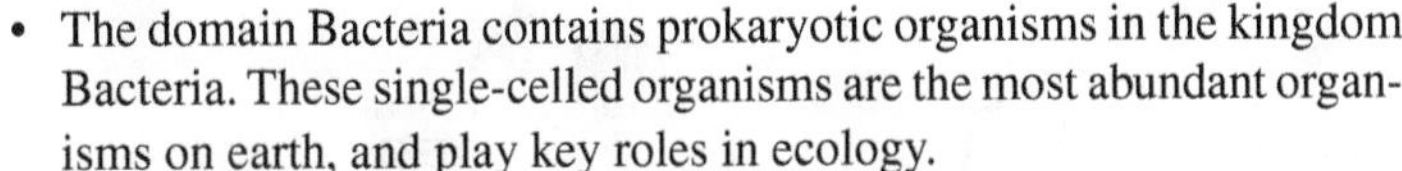

14.7 Domain: A Higher Level of Classification

- The domain Bacteria contains prokaryotic organisms in the kingdom Bacteria. These single-celled organisms are the most abundant organisms on earth, and play key roles in ecology.
- The domain Archaea contains prokaryotic organisms in the kingdom Archaea. Although they are prokaryotes, archaea are as different from bacteria as they are from eukaryotes. These single-celled organisms are found in diverse environments including very extreme environments.
- The domain Eukarya contains very diverse organisms from four kingdoms but are similar in that they are all eukaryotes. Fungi, plants, and animals are multicellular organisms, and the protists are primarily single-celled but very diverse. Eukaryotes contain cellular organelles, some that were most likely acquired through endosymbiosis, the process shown here from **figure 14.11.**

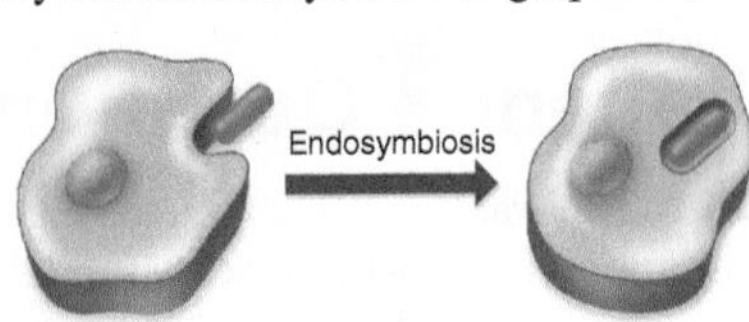

Self-Test

1. The wolf, domestic dog, and red fox are all in the same family, Canidae. The scientific name for the wolf is *Canis lupus,* the domestic dog is *Canis familiaris,* and the red fox is *Vulpes vulpes.* This means that
   a. the red fox is in the same family, but different genus than dogs and wolves.
   b. the dog is in the same family, but different genus than red fox and wolves.
   c. the wolf is in the same family, but different genus than dogs and red foxes.
   d. all three organisms are in different genera.
2. The evolutionary relationship of organisms, and their relationships to other species, is called
   a. taxonomy. **c.** ontogeny.
   b. phylogeny. **d.** systematics.
3. Organisms are classified based on
   a. physical, behavioral, and molecular characteristics.
   b where the organism lives.
   c. what the organism eats.
   d. the size of the organism.
4. Organisms that are closer together on a cladogram
   a. are in the same family.
   b. comprise an outgroup.
   c. share a more recent common ancestor than those organisms that are farther apart.
   d. share fewer derived characters than organisms that are farther apart.
5. The six kingdoms of organisms can be organized into three domains based on
   a. where the organism lives.
   b. what the organism eats.
   c. how the organism moves.
   d. cell structure and DNA sequence.
6. All of the extremophiles belong to the domain of
   a. Bacteria. **c.** Prokarya.
   b. Archaea. **d.** Eukarya.
7. Bacteria are similar to Archaea in that they
   a. arose through endosymbiosis.
   b. are multicellular.
   c. live in extreme environments.
   d. are prokaryotes.
8. It is theorized that the ancestral organisms that gave rise to the plants, animals, and fungi originated in the kingdom
   a. Bacteria.
   b. Archaea.
   c. Protista.
   d. All of the above, each giving rise to one of the three kingdoms listed.
9. One difference between the kingdom Protista and the other three kingdoms in the domain Eukarya is that the other kingdoms are mostly
   a. prokaryotic. **c.** eukaryotic.
   b. multicellular. **d.** unicellular.
10. It is thought that mitochondrion and chloroplast organelles found in eukaryotic cells came from
    a. development of the internal membrane system.
    b. protists.
    c. mutation.
    d. endosymbiosis of bacteria.

Visual Understanding

1. **Figure 14.6** Which of the organisms shown have amniotic membranes that surround the fetus? (If necessary, go back to the figure in the chapter to clearly see it.)

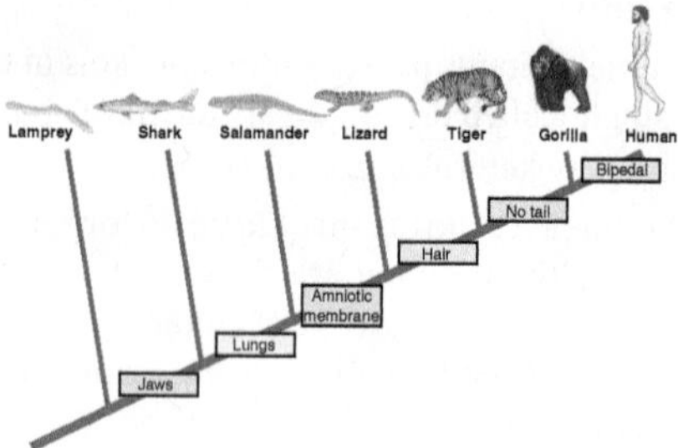

2. **Figure 14.10** Compared to the bacteria and archaea, how similar are animals and plants?

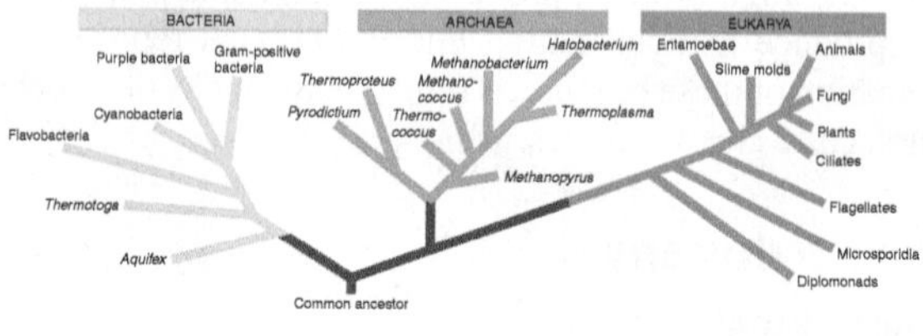

Challenge Questions

1. A friend wants to know what the big deal is—everyone knows that a rose is a rose, why bother with all the fancy Latin stuff, like *Rosa odorata?* What do you tell him?
2. Why are birds classified so differently in traditional phylogeny and in cladistics?
3. If we already have organisms divided into kingdoms, why do we also need domains?

Chapter 15

Ecosystems

CHAPTER AT A GLANCE

The Energy in Ecosystems

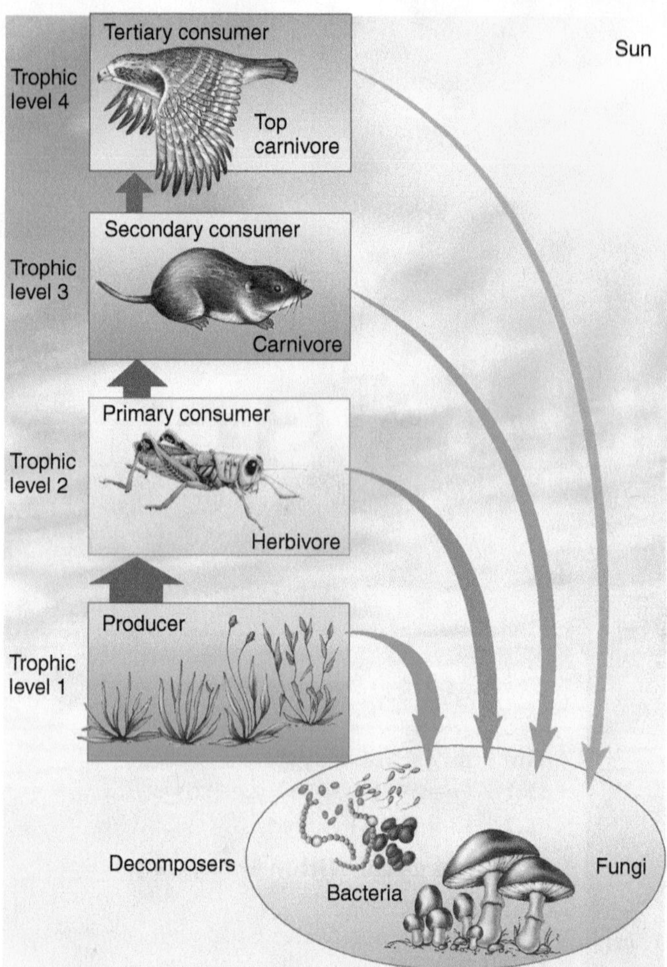

Figure 15.1 Trophic levels within an ecosystem.

Ecologists assign all the members of a community to various trophic levels based on feeding relationships.

BIOLOGY & YOU

Your Own Personal Ecosystem. You may not realize it, but you are a walking ecosystem. Tiny, eight-legged mites nestle head down inside the follicles of your eye lashes, feasting unnoticed on skin cells. Microscopic bacteria live on your tongue, teeth, and skin. There are about 3.3 pounds of bacteria living in your gut. Most of the time we share our bodies harmoniously with these other inhabitants, a balanced ecological community. A few examples of the neighbors with whom you share your body: **1.** Over 500 species of bacteria live inside your gut, breaking down carbohydrates for you, making essential vitamins like K and B_{12}, and crowding out harmful bacteria. **2.** Bacteria that inhabit the vagina secrete lactic acid, which fends off hostile invaders like pathogenic *Candida* yeast. **3.** A flat, wingless insect called a head louse has been found attached to a strand of human hair 10,000 years old. Less than a tenth of an inch long, head lice suck on your blood, cementing their eggs, or nits, to your hair.

15.1 Energy Flows Through Ecosystems

CONCEPT PREVIEW: Energy moves through ecosystems from producers, to herbivores, to carnivores, and finally to detritivores and decomposers, which consume the dead bodies of all the others. Much energy is lost at each stage of a food chain.

What Is an Ecosystem?

The ecosystem is the most complex level of biological organization. The biosphere includes all the ecosystems on earth. The earth is a closed system with respect to chemicals but an open system in terms of energy. The organisms in ecosystems regulate the capture and expenditure of energy and the cycling of chemicals. All organisms depend on the ability of photosynthetic organisms to recycle the basic components of life.

Ecologists, the scientists who study ecology, view the world as a patchwork quilt of different environments, all bordering on and interacting with one another. Consider for a moment a patch of forest, the sort of place a deer might live. Ecologists call the collection of creatures that live in a particular place a **community**—all the animals, plants, fungi, and microorganisms that live together in a forest, for example, are the forest community. Ecologists call the place where a community lives its **habitat**—the soil, and the water flowing through it, are key components of the forest habitat. The sum of these two, community and habitat, is an ecological system, or **ecosystem.** An ecosystem is a largely self-sustaining collection of organisms and their physical environment. An ecosystem can be as large as a forest or as small as a tidepool.

The Path of Energy: Who Eats Whom in Ecosystems

Energy flows into the biological world from the sun, which shines a constant beam of light on our earth. Life exists on earth because some of that light energy can be captured and transformed into chemical energy through the process of photosynthesis and used to make organic molecules such as carbohydrates, nucleic acids, proteins, and fats. These organic molecules are what we call food. Living organisms use the energy in food to make new materials for growth, to repair damaged tissues, to reproduce, and to do a myriad of other things requiring energy.

You can think of all the organisms in an ecosystem as chemical machines fueled by energy captured in photosynthesis. The organisms that first capture the energy, the **producers,** are plants, algae and some bacteria, which produce their own energy-storing molecules by carrying out photosynthesis. They are also referred to as *autotrophs.* All other organisms in an ecosystem are **consumers,** obtaining energy-storing molecules by consuming plants or other animals, and are referred to as *heterotrophs.* Ecologists assign every organism in an ecosystem to a trophic (or feeding) level, depending on the source of its energy. A **trophic level** is composed of those organisms within an ecosystem whose source of energy is the same number of consumption "steps" away from the sun. Thus, as shown in figure 15.1, a plant's trophic level is 1, while *herbivores* (animals that graze on plants) are in trophic level 2, and *carnivores* (animals that eat these grazers) are in trophic level 3.

Heterotrophs consume food to acquire energy stored in the chemical bonds of the food's molecules. As described on page 121, this energy is converted to ATP, which the cell uses to fuel metabolism. If ATP isn't needed, the energy is converted into fat for long term storage.

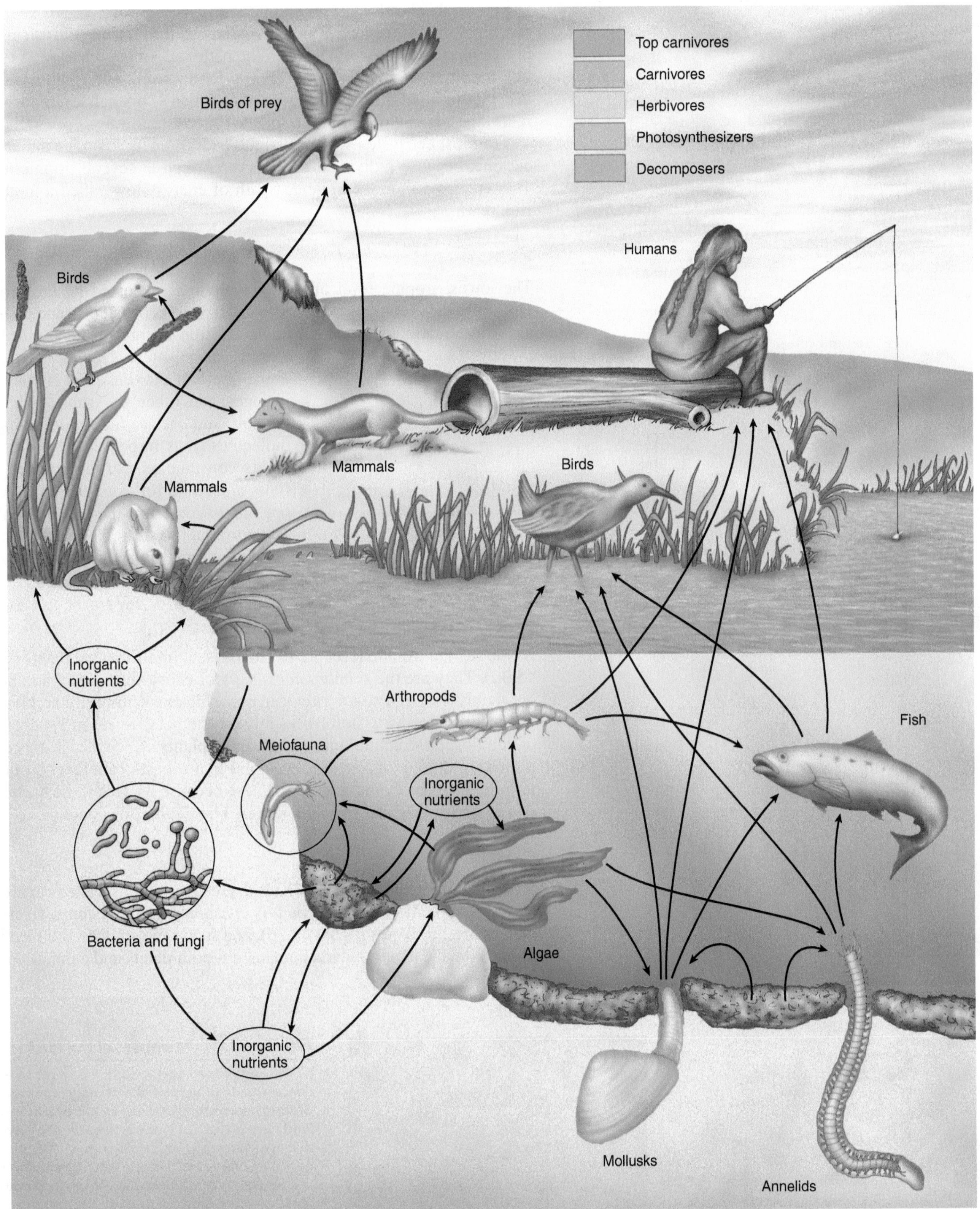

Figure 15.2 A food web.

A food web is much more complicated than a linear food chain. The path of energy passes from one trophic level to another and back again in complex ways.

(a) Producers and herbivores

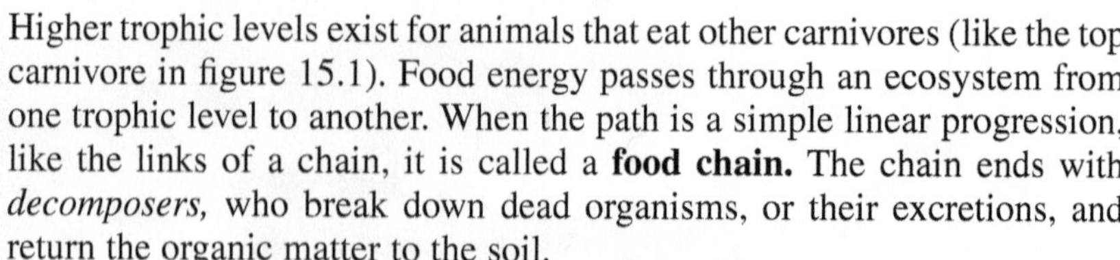

Higher trophic levels exist for animals that eat other carnivores (like the top carnivore in figure 15.1). Food energy passes through an ecosystem from one trophic level to another. When the path is a simple linear progression, like the links of a chain, it is called a **food chain.** The chain ends with *decomposers,* who break down dead organisms, or their excretions, and return the organic matter to the soil.

In most ecosystems, however, the path of energy is not a simple linear one, because individual animals often feed at several trophic levels. This creates a more complicated path of energy flow called a **food web** (figure 15.2).

Producers

The lowest trophic level of any ecosystem is occupied by the producers (figure 15.3*a*)—green plants in most land ecosystems (and, usually, algae in aquatic ecosystems). Plants use the energy of the sun to build energy-rich sugar molecules. They also absorb carbon dioxide from the air, and nitrogen and other key substances from the soil, and use them to build biological molecules. It is important to realize that plants consume as well as produce. The roots of a plant, for example, do not carry out photosynthesis—there is no sunlight underground. Roots obtain their energy the same way you do, by using energy-storing molecules produced elsewhere (in this case, in the leaves of the plant).

The Calvin cycle of photosynthesis uses the energy from the sun to build carbohydrate molecules, as discussed on pages 100 to 103. Plants use energy from the sun, carbon dioxide from the atmosphere, and water and nutrients from the soil to make organic molecules.

(b) Carnivores

Herbivores

At the second trophic level are **herbivores,** animals that eat plants (figure 15.3*a*). They are the *primary consumers* of ecosystems. Deer and horses are herbivores, and so are rhinoceroses, chickens (primarily herbivores), and caterpillars. Most herbivores rely on "helpers" to aid in the digestion of cellulose, a structural material found in plants. A cow, for instance, has a thriving colony of bacteria in its gut that digests cellulose. So does a termite. Humans cannot digest cellulose because we lack these bacteria—that is why a cow can live on a diet of grass and you cannot.

(c) Omnivore

Carnivores

At the third trophic level are animals that eat herbivores, called **carnivores** (meat-eaters). They are the *secondary consumers* of ecosystems. Tigers and wolves are carnivores (figure 15.3*b*), and so are mosquitoes and blue jays. Some animals, like bears and humans, eat both plants and animals and are

(d) Detritivore

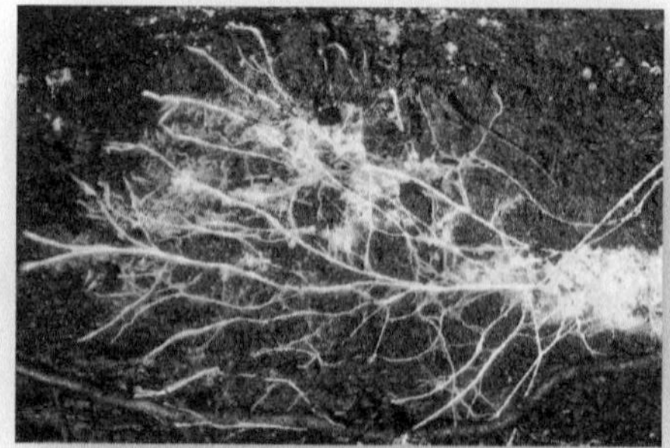
(e) Decomposer

Figure 15.3 Members of the food chain.

(a) The East African grasslands are covered by a dense growth of grasses, the primary producers. Grazing herbivores like these zebras obtain their food from plants. (b) These wolves are carnivores that live in North American forests. (c) This grizzly bear is an omnivore, this one fishing for salmon. (d) This crab is a detritivore. (e) Fungi, such as this basidiomycete growing through the soil, and bacteria are the primary decomposers of terrestrial ecosystems.

called **omnivores** (figure 15.3*c*). They use the simple sugars and starches stored in plants as food but not the cellulose. Many complex ecosystems contain a fourth trophic level, composed of animals that consume other carnivores. They are called *tertiary consumers,* or *top carnivores.* A weasel that eats a blue jay is a tertiary consumer. Only rarely do ecosystems contain more than four trophic levels, for reasons we will discuss later.

Detritivores and Decomposers

In every ecosystem there is a special class of consumers that include **detritivores** (figure 15.3*d*), organisms that eat dead organisms (also referred to as scavengers) and **decomposers,** organisms that break down organic substances making the nutrients available to other organisms (figure 15.3*e*). Worms, arthropods, and vultures are examples of detritivores. Bacteria and fungi are the principal decomposers in land ecosystems.

Energy Flows Through Trophic Levels

How much energy passes through an ecosystem? **Primary productivity** is the total amount of light energy converted by photosynthetic organisms into organic compounds in a given area per unit of time. An ecosystem's **net primary productivity** is the total amount of energy fixed by photosynthesis per unit of time, minus that which is expended by photosynthetic organisms to fuel metabolic activities. In short, it is the energy stored in organic compounds that is available to heterotrophs. The total weight of all an ecosystem's organisms, called its **biomass,** increases as a result of the ecosystem's net productivity.

When a plant uses the energy from sunlight to make structural molecules such as cellulose, it loses a lot of the energy as heat. In fact, only about half of the energy captured by the plant ends up stored in its molecules. The other half of the energy is lost. This is the first of many such losses as the energy passes through the ecosystem. When the energy flow through an ecosystem is measured at each trophic level, we find that 80% to 95% of the energy available at one trophic level is not transferred to the next. In other words, only 5% to 20% of the available energy passes from one trophic level to the next. For example, the amount of energy that ends up in the beetle's body in figure 15.4 is approximately only 17% of the energy present in the plant molecules it eats. Similarly, when a carnivore eats the herbivore, a comparable amount of energy is lost from the amount of energy present in the herbivore's molecules. This is why food chains generally consist of only three or four steps. So much energy is lost at each step that little usable energy remains after it has been incorporated into the bodies of organisms at four successive trophic levels.

Lamont Cole of Cornell University studied the flow of energy in a freshwater ecosystem in Cayuga Lake in upstate New York. Figure 15.5 shows how much energy flowed through the ecosystem, indicated by the red arrows. Each block represents the energy obtained by a different trophic level, with the producers, the algae and cyanobacteria, being the largest block. He calculated that about 150 of each 1,000 calories of potential energy fixed by algae and cyanobacteria are transferred into the bodies of animal plankton (small heterotrophs). Of these, about 30 calories are incorporated into the bodies of a type of small fish called a smelt, the principal secondary consumers of the system. If humans eat the smelt, they gain about 6 of the 1,000 calories that originally entered the system. If trout eat the smelt and humans eat the trout, humans gain only about 1.2 of the 1,000 calories.

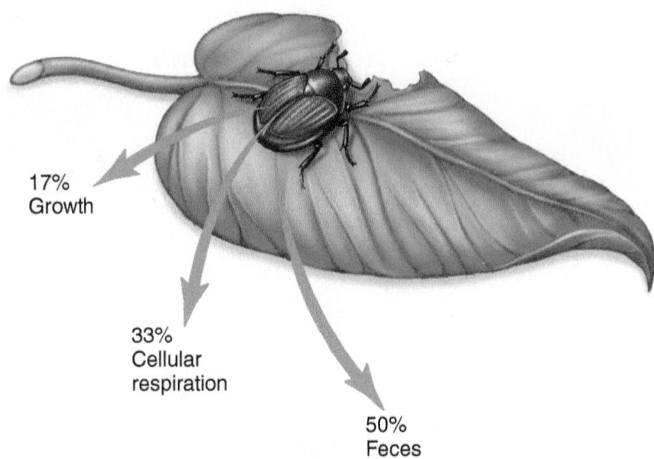

Figure 15.4 How heterotrophs use food energy.

A heterotroph assimilates only a fraction of the energy it consumes. For example, if a "bite" is composed of 500 Joules of energy (1 Joule = 0.239 calories), about 50%, 250 J, is lost in feces, about 33%, 165 J, is used to fuel cellular respiration, and about 17%, 85 J, is converted into consumer biomass. Only this 85 J (or roughly 20 calories) is available to the next trophic level.

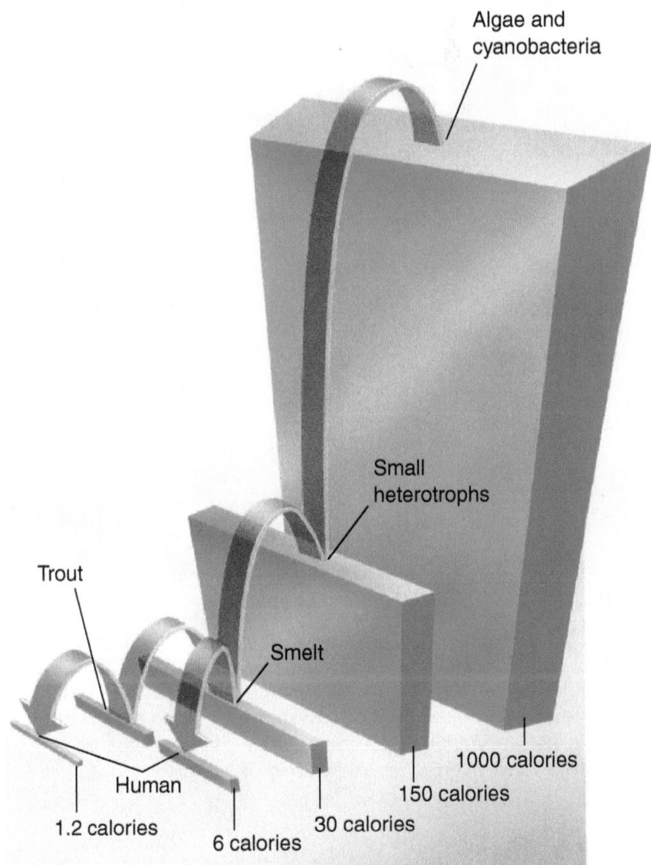

Figure 15.5 Energy loss in an ecosystem.

In a classic study of Cayuga Lake in New York, the path of energy was measured precisely at all points in the food web.

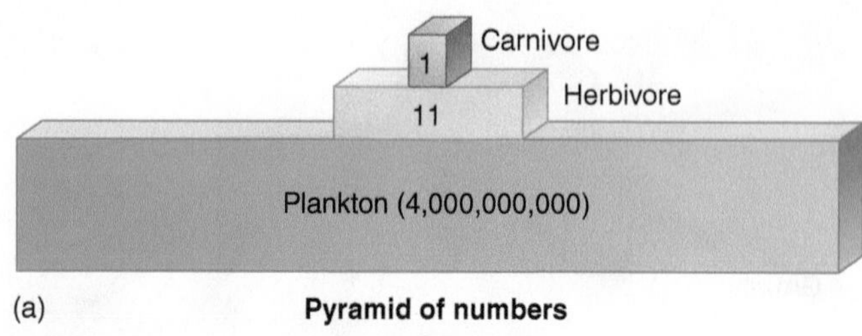

(a) **Pyramid of numbers**

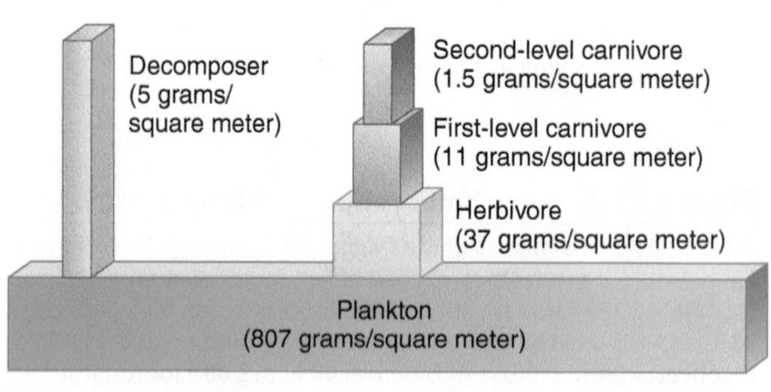

(b)

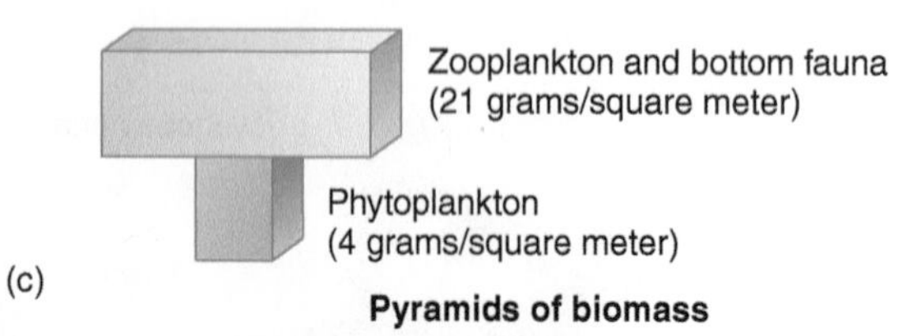

(c) **Pyramids of biomass**

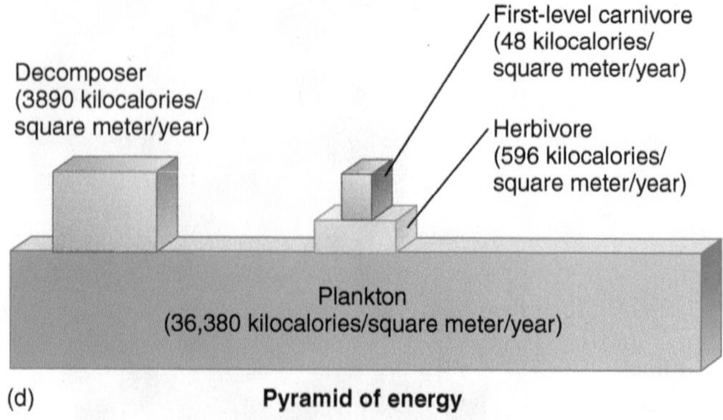

(d) **Pyramid of energy**

Figure 15.6 Ecological pyramids.

Ecological pyramids measure different characteristics of each trophic level. In these aquatic ecosystems, plankton are the primary producers. (a) Pyramid of numbers. Pyramids of biomass, both normal (b) and inverted (c). (d) Pyramid of energy.

15.2 Ecological Pyramids

CONCEPT PREVIEW: Because energy is lost at every step of a food chain, the biomass of primary producers (photosynthesizers) tends to be greater than that of the herbivores that consume them, and herbivore biomass tends to be greater than that of the carnivores that consume them.

A plant fixes about 1% of the sun's energy that falls on its green parts. The successive members of a food chain, in turn, process into their own bodies on average about 10% of the energy available in the organisms on which they feed. For this reason, there are generally far more individuals at the lower trophic levels of any ecosystem than at the higher levels. Similarly, the biomass of the primary producers present in a given ecosystem is greater than the biomass of the primary consumers, with successive trophic levels having a lower and lower biomass and so less and less potential energy.

These key ecological relationships appear as pyramids when expressed as diagrams. Ecologists speak of "pyramids of numbers," where the sizes of the blocks reflect the number of individuals at each trophic level. The producers in the green box of figure 15.6*a* represent the largest number of individuals. Similarly, the producers (plankton) represent the largest group in "pyramids of biomass," shown in figure 15.6*b*. The inverted pyramid in figure 15.6*c* is an exception and is discussed below. The "pyramid of energy" in figure 15.6*d* shows the producers as the largest block.

Inverted Pyramids

Some aquatic ecosystems have inverted biomass pyramids, like in figure 15.6*c*. In a planktonic ecosystem—dominated by small organisms floating in water—the turnover of photosynthetic phytoplankton at the lowest level is very rapid, with zooplankton consuming phytoplankton so quickly that the phytoplankton (the producers at the base of the food chain) can never develop a large population size. Because the phytoplankton reproduce very rapidly, the community can support a population of heterotrophs that is larger in biomass and more numerous than the phytoplankton. However, don't confuse the sizes of these bars with the energy present at each level. The zooplankton that eat the phytoplankton are present in greater numbers but contain about only 10% of the energy.

Top Carnivores

The loss of energy that occurs at each trophic level places a limit on how many top-level carnivores a community can support. As we have seen, only about one-thousandth of the energy captured by photosynthesis passes all the way through a three-stage food chain to a tertiary consumer such as a snake or hawk. This explains why there are no predators that subsist on lions—the biomass of these animals is simply insufficient to support another trophic level.

In the pyramid of numbers, top-level predators tend to be fairly large animals. Thus, the small residual biomass available at the top of the pyramid is concentrated in a relatively small number of individuals.

Concept Check

1. What does an ecosystem include that a habitat does not?
2. What trophic level do you occupy in a food chain? Explain.
3. Explain how the pyramid of biomass can be inverted in oceans when the pyramid of energy is not.

Materials Cycle Within Ecosystems

15.3 The Water Cycle

CONCEPT PREVIEW: Water cycles through ecosystems in the atmosphere via precipitation and evaporation, some of it passing through plants on the way.

Unlike energy, which flows through the earth's ecosystems in one direction (from the sun to producers to consumers), the physical components of ecosystems are passed around and reused within ecosystems. Ecologists speak of such constant reuse as recycling or, more commonly, cycling. Materials that are constantly recycled include all the chemicals that make up the soil, water, and air. While many are important, the proper cycling of four materials is particularly critical to the health of any ecosystem: water, carbon, and the soil nutrients nitrogen and phosphorus.

The paths of water, carbon, and soil nutrients as they pass from the environment to living organisms and back form closed circles, or cycles. In each cycle, the chemical resides for a time in an organism and then returns to the nonliving environment, often referred to as a *biogeochemical cycle.*

Of all the nonliving components of an ecosystem, water has the greatest influence on the living portion. The availability of water and the way in which it cycles in an ecosystem in large measure determines the biological richness of that ecosystem—the kinds of creatures that live there and how many of each.

Water cycles within an ecosystem in two ways: the environmental water cycle and the organismic water cycle. Both cycles are shown in figure 15.7.

BIOLOGY & YOU

You and the Water Cycle. How many gallons of water do you personally consume in a day? Take a guess. Here are some numbers to help you make an estimate: *bath*: 40 gallons; *shower*: 2 gallons per minute; *teeth brushing*: 1 gallon; *hands/face washing*: 1 gallon; *dishwasher*: 15 gallons/load; *clothes machine load*: 25 gallons/load; *toilet flush*: 3 gallons; *glasses of water drunk*: 1/16 gallon/glass. Your per-capita water use (*per* is Latin for "by" and *capita* is Latin for "head") can rapidly become quite alarming—and the number you get from a calculation like this is quite likely an underestimation. It does not take into account everything you use water for, such as cooking, washing your dog, or cleaning muddy shoes. You might water your lawn, wash your car, or leave the water running while you brush your teeth. It all adds up. Even using water conservation measures such as low-flow shower heads and toilets, few of us have a per-capita water use less than 100 gallons a day.

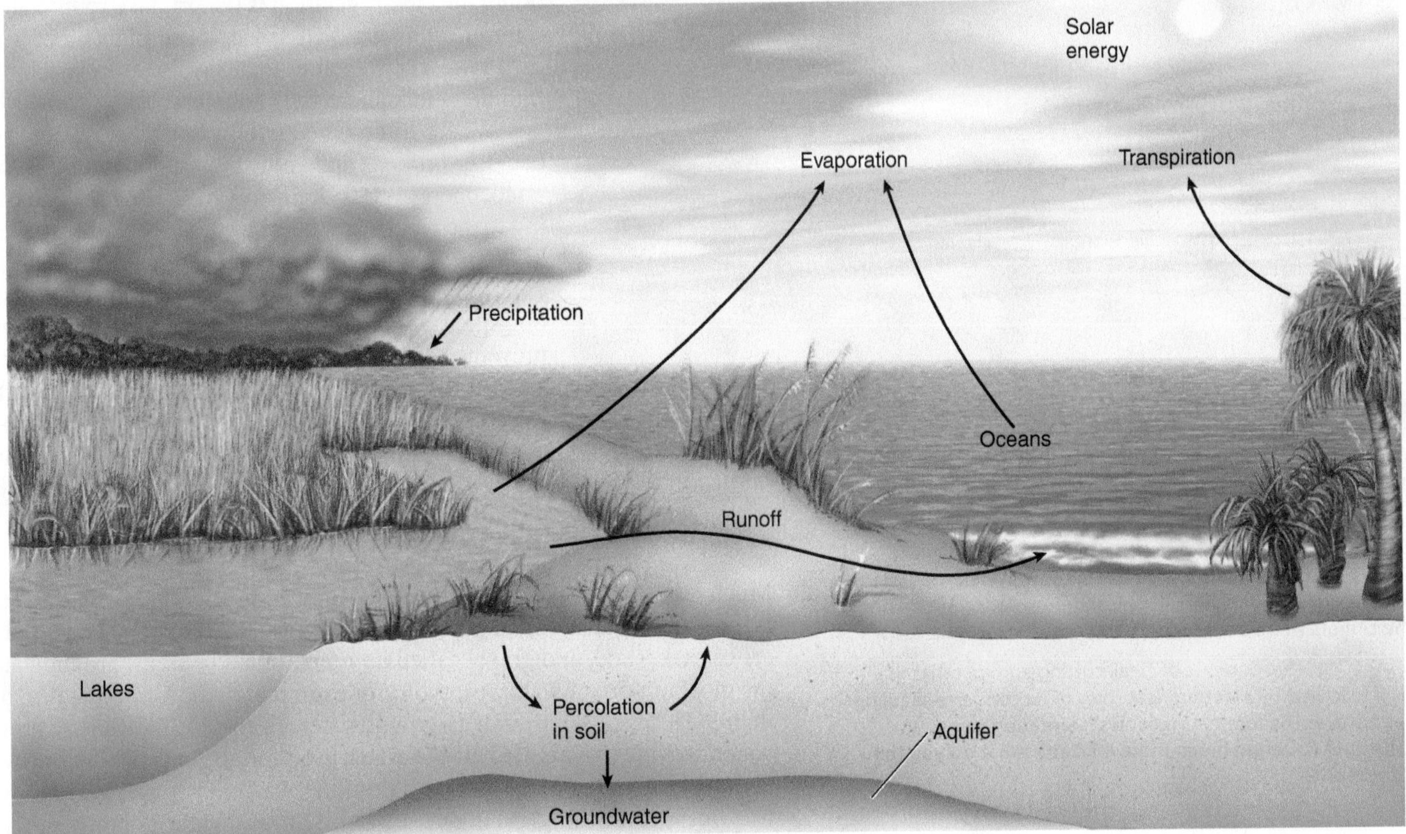

Figure 15.7 The water cycle.

Precipitation on land eventually makes its way to the ocean via groundwater, lakes, and rivers. Solar energy causes evaporation, adding water to the atmosphere. Plants give off excess water through transpiration, also adding water to the atmosphere. Atmospheric water falls as rain or snow over land and oceans, completing the water cycle.

The Environmental Water Cycle

In the environmental water cycle, water vapor in the atmosphere condenses and falls to the earth's surface as rain or snow (called precipitation in figure 15.7). Heated there by the sun, it reenters the atmosphere by **evaporation** from lakes, rivers, and oceans, where it condenses and falls to the earth again.

The Organismic Water Cycle

In the organismic water cycle, surface water does not return directly to the atmosphere. Instead, it is taken up by the roots of plants. After passing through the plant, the water reenters the atmosphere through tiny openings (stomata) in the leaves, evaporating from their surface. This evaporation from leaf surfaces is called **transpiration.** Transpiration is also driven by the sun: The sun's heat creates wind currents that draw moisture from the plant by passing air over the leaves.

Air moving across the stomata in the leaves causes water to evaporate from the leaf tissue. The water in the leaves is replaced by water passing into the roots.

Breaking the Cycle

In very dense forest ecosystems, such as tropical rain forests, more than 90% of the moisture in the ecosystem is taken up by plants and then transpired back into the air. Because so many plants in a rain forest are doing this, the vegetation is the primary source of local rainfall. In a very real sense, these plants create their own rain: The moisture that travels up from the plants into the atmosphere falls back to earth as rain.

Where forests are cut down, the organismic water cycle is broken, and moisture is not returned to the atmosphere. Water drains off to the sea instead of rising to the clouds and falling again on the forest. During his expeditions from 1799–1805, the great German explorer Alexander von Humboldt reported that stripping the trees from a tropical rain forest in Colombia prevented water from returning to the atmosphere and created a semiarid desert. It is a tragedy of our time that just such a transformation is occurring in many tropical areas, as rain forests are being clear-cut or burned in the name of "development" (figure 15.8).

Figure 15.8 Burning or clear-cutting forests breaks the water cycle.

The high density and large size of plants in a forest translate into great quantities of water being transpired to the atmosphere, creating rain over the forests. In this way rain forests perpetuate the wet climate that supports them. Tropical deforestation permanently alters the climate in these areas, creating arid zones.

IMPLICATION Proponents of clear-cutting suggest that this practice, if followed by planting neat rows of lumber tree seedlings, actually improves the forest, as it allows "plantation forestry," making future lumbering much more efficient. What do you think of this argument?

Groundwater

Much less obvious than the surface waters seen in streams, lakes, and ponds is the groundwater, which occurs in permeable, saturated, underground layers of rock, sand, and gravel called *aquifers.* In many areas, groundwater is the most important water reservoir; for example, in the United States, more than 96% of all freshwater is groundwater. In the United States, groundwater provides about 25% of the water used for all purposes and provides about 50% of the population with drinking water.

Because of the greater rate at which groundwater is being used, the increasing chemical pollution of groundwater is a very serious problem. Pesticides, herbicides, and fertilizers are key sources of groundwater pollution. Because of the large volume of water, its slow rate of turnover, and its inaccessibility, removing pollutants from aquifers is virtually impossible.

15.4 The Carbon Cycle

CONCEPT PREVIEW: Carbon captured from the atmosphere by photosynthesis is returned to it through respiration, combustion, and erosion.

The earth's atmosphere contains plentiful carbon, present as carbon dioxide (CO_2) gas. This carbon cycles between the atmosphere and living organisms, often being locked up for long periods of time in organisms or deep underground. The cycle is begun by plants that use CO_2 in photosynthesis to build organic molecules—in effect, they trap the carbon atoms of CO_2 within the living world. The carbon atoms are returned to the atmosphere's pool of CO_2 through respiration, combustion, and erosion, as shown in figure 15.9.

Respiration

All organisms in ecosystems respire—that is, they extract energy from organic food molecules, which involves stripping away the carbon atoms and combining them with oxygen to form CO_2. This end product of respiration is released into the atmosphere.

Carbon dioxide is generated at two points during cellular respiration. First, two molecules of CO_2 are produced in the oxidation of pyruvate to acetyl-CoA, discussed on page 117. Another four molecules of CO_2 are produced in the Krebs cycle, discussed on page 118.

Combustion

Plants that become buried in sediment may be transformed by pressure into coal or oil. The carbon originally trapped by these plants is only released back into the atmosphere when the coal or oil (called **fossil fuels**) is burned.

Human activity is causing the carbon cycle to become unbalanced. The influx of large amounts of carbon dioxide into the atmosphere by the burning of fossil fuels is causing atmospheric temperatures to rise, a process called global warming.

Erosion

Very large amounts of carbon are present in limestone, formed from calcium carbonate shells of marine organisms. When the limestone becomes exposed to weather and erodes, the carbon washes back and is dissolved again in oceans.

BIOLOGY & YOU

You and the Carbon Cycle. You and every American make a contribution to global warming, because the way we live each day adds a lot of carbon dioxide to the earth's atmosphere. Your "carbon footprint" is a measure of the amount of carbon dioxide produced to fuel your daily life. In the diagram below, your carbon footprint is the sum of two parts: the *primary footprint* over which you have direct control, and the *secondary footprint* which measures the CO_2 emissions associated with the manufacture and breakdown of products we use. The average worldwide carbon footprint is about 4 tons per year. The average footprint of people in the United States is five times that, over 20 tons per year! The worldwide target to combat global warming is 2 tons per year. Imagine what your life would be like with your carbon footprint reduced 90%. The world's future depends upon it.

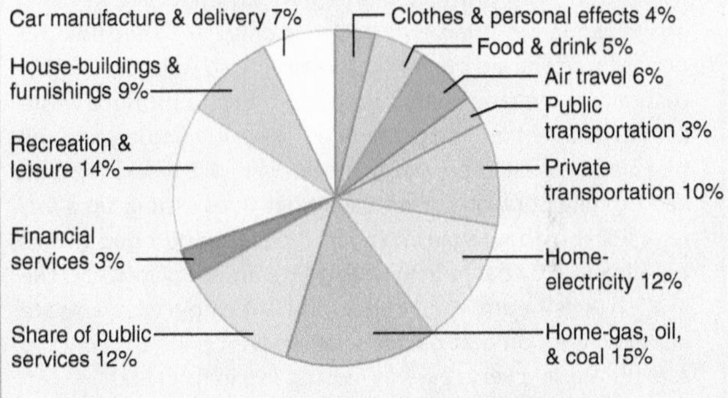

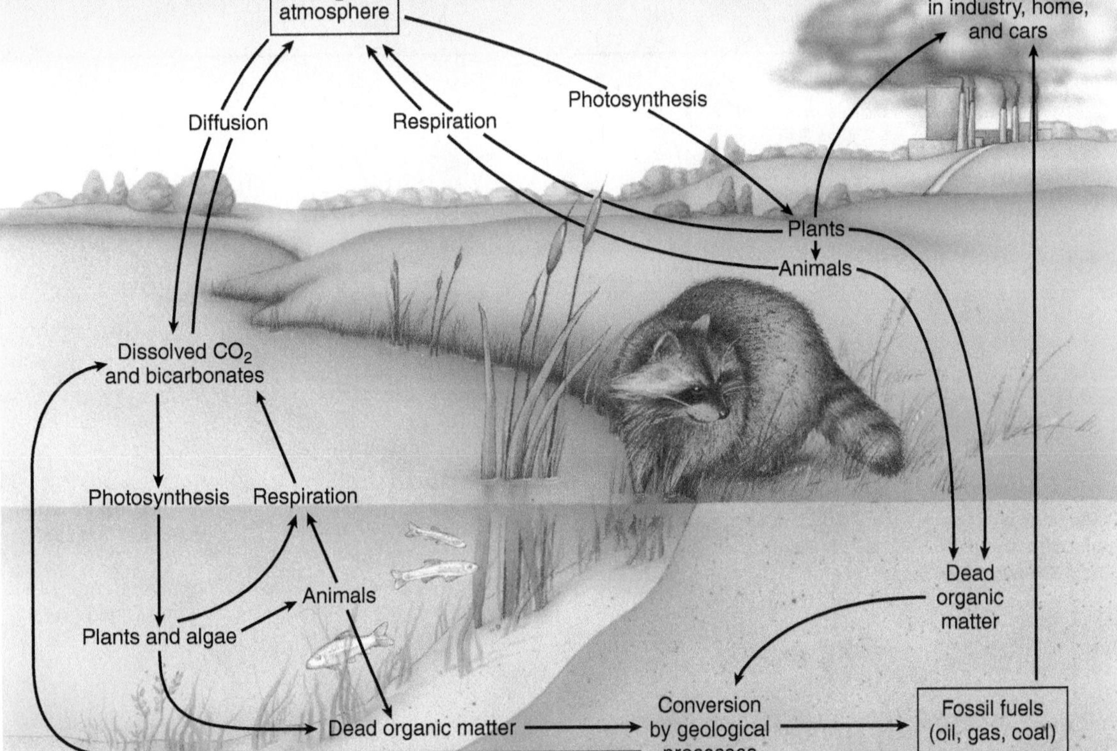

Figure 15.9
The carbon cycle.
Carbon from the atmosphere and from water is fixed by photosynthetic organisms and returned through respiration, combustion, and erosion.

BIOLOGY & YOU

You and the Nitrogen Cycle. As a way to step back and see the larger picture of how the nitrogen cycle affects your life, imagine setting up an aquarium tank with many fish. To care for the fish, plants, and other aquatic life you add to the tank, you have to provide light (for the plants) and fish food (for the critters). If that is all you do, however, the fish will soon die. Why? While fish get along fine in rivers and lakes, a fish tank is a confined body of water, and that turns out to make a critical difference. Fish food contains a lot of protein. A combination of uneaten fish food, decaying plant life, and urine and feces excreted by the fish will soon cause a toxic buildup of ammonia in the tank. *Nitrosomonas* bacteria in the water convert the ammonia into the chemical compound nitrite, and other *Nitrobacter* bacteria oxidize the nitrite, adding an oxygen to produce nitrate, much less harmful to the fish and the end product of the nitrogen cycle. The key to a healthy aquarium, then, is to start with only one or two fish. The desired bacteria are present in the air, and so will start to grow naturally in the tank water as the fish begin to produce waste products. Over time the bacteria will grow in numbers and will be able to handle more waste products. In 6–8 weeks the tank can be fully populated with fish. What does setting up a fish tank tell you about your nitrogen cycle? Our nitrogen wastes are "cleaned" by bacteria in sewage treatment plants, and like in a fish tank the ammonia concentrations within the plants are kept low enough that bacteria can convert toxic ammonia to safe nitrate. In a very real way, we too live in fish tanks.

15.5 The Nitrogen and Phosphorus Cycles

CONCEPT PREVIEW: Certain bacteria are able to convert atmospheric nitrogen gas into usable ammonia. Phosphorus, also critical to organisms, is available in soil and dissolved in water. These two chemicals are often the limiting factors determining what lives in an ecosystem.

The Nitrogen Cycle

Earth's atmosphere is 78.08% nitrogen gas (N_2), but most living organisms are unable to use the N_2 so plentifully available in the air surrounding them. The two nitrogen atoms of N_2 are bound together by a particularly strong "triple" covalent bond that is very difficult to break. Luckily, a few kinds of bacteria can break this triple bond and bind nitrogen atoms to hydrogen, forming "fixed" nitrogen, ammonia (NH_3), in a process called **nitrogen fixation.**

Recall from the discussion of covalent bonds on page 36, that a triple covalent bond involves the sharing of three pairs of electrons. This is a lot of energy holding together two atoms, which is why the bond holding the nitrogen atoms together in nitrogen gas is so difficult to break.

Bacteria evolved the ability to fix nitrogen early in the history of life, before photosynthesis had introduced oxygen gas into the earth's atmosphere, and that is still the only way the bacteria are able to do it—even a trace of oxygen poisons the process. In today's world, awash with oxygen, these bacteria live encased within bubbles called cysts that admit no oxygen or within special airtight cells in nodules of tissue on the roots of beans, aspen trees, and a few other plants. Figure 15.10 shows the workings of the nitrogen cycle.

The growth of plants in ecosystems is often severely limited by the availability of "fixed" nitrogen in the soil, which is why farmers fertilize fields. Today most fixed nitrogen added to soils by farmers is produced in factories by industrial rather than bacterial nitrogen fixation—this industrial process today accounts for a prodigious 30% of the entire nitrogen cycle.

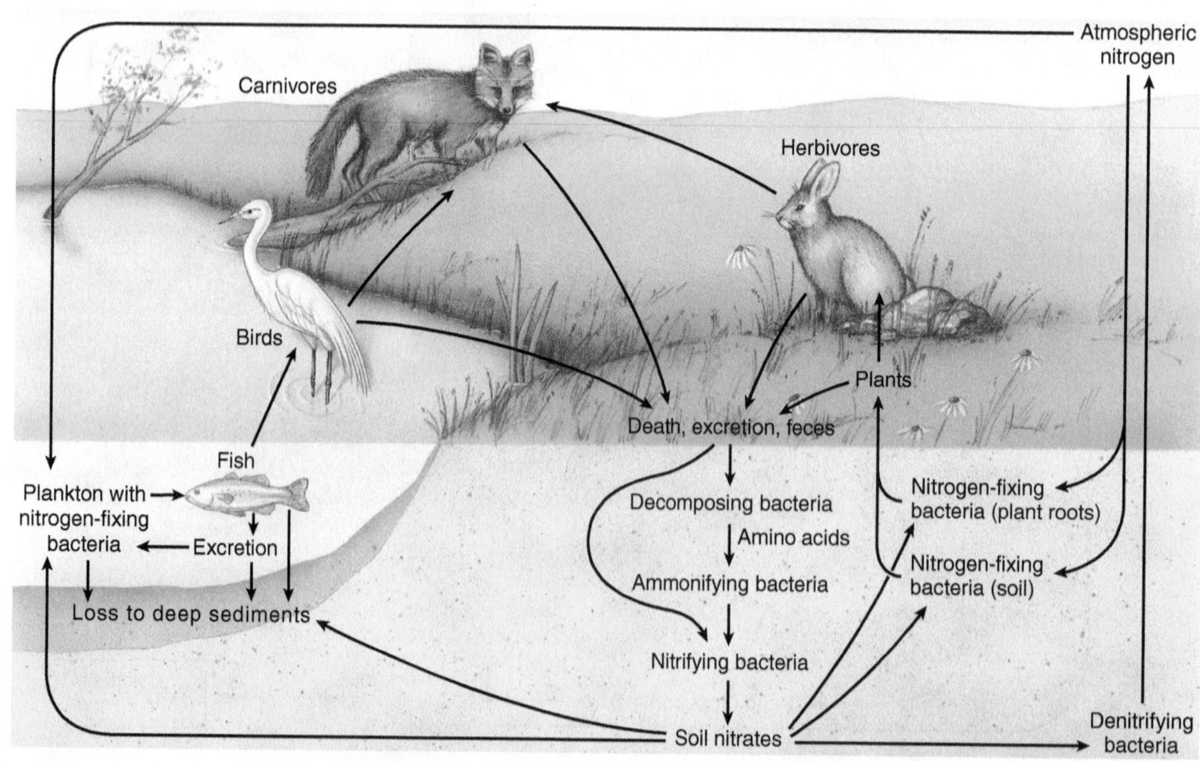

Figure 15.10
The nitrogen cycle.
Relatively few kinds of organisms—all of them bacteria—can convert atmospheric nitrogen into forms that can be used for biological processes.

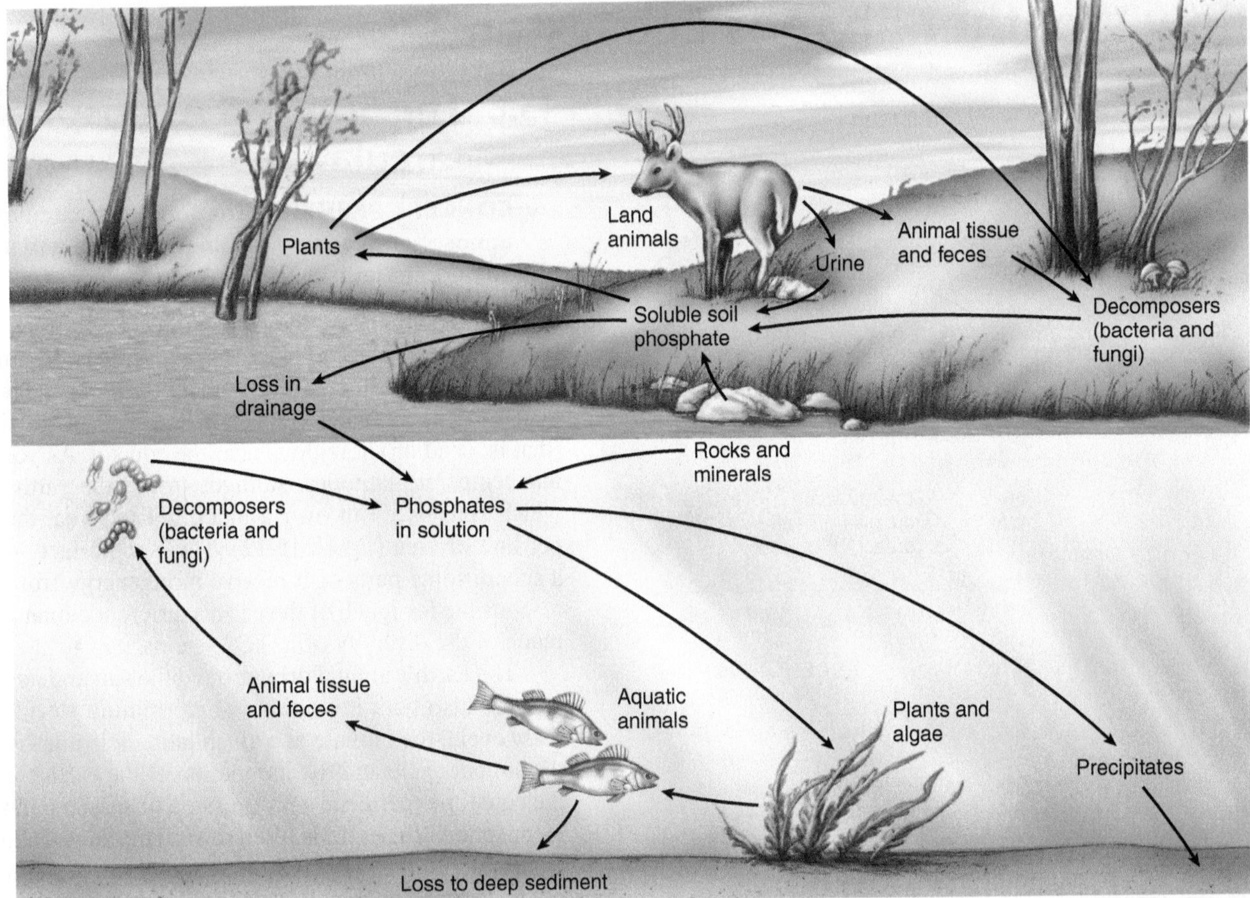

Figure 15.11 The phosphorus cycle.

Phosphorus plays a critical role in plant nutrition; next to nitrogen, phosphorus is the element most likely to be so scarce that it limits plant growth.

The Phosphorus Cycle

Phosphorus is an essential element in all living organisms, a key part of both ATP and DNA. Phosphorus is often in very limited supply in the soil of particular ecosystems, and because phosphorus does not form a gas, none is available in the atmosphere. Most phosphorus exists in soil and rock as the mineral calcium phosphate, which dissolves in water to form phosphate ions, as shown in figure 15.11. These phosphate ions are absorbed by the roots of plants and used by them to build organic molecules like ATP and DNA. When the plants and animals die and decay, bacteria in the soil convert the organic phosphorus back into phosphorus ions, completing the cycle.

The phosphorus level in freshwater lake ecosystems is often quite low, preventing much growth of photosynthetic algae in these systems. Pollution of a lake by the inadvertent addition of phosphorus to its waters (agricultural fertilizers and many commercial detergents are rich in phosphorus) first produces a green scum of algal growth on the surface of the lake, and then proceeds to "kill" the lake: As aging algae die, bacteria feeding on the dead algae cells use up so much of the lake's dissolved oxygen that fish and invertebrate animals suffocate. Such rapid, uncontrolled growth caused by excessive nutrients in an aquatic ecosystem is called **eutrophication.**

Concept Check

1. Explain how clear-cutting breaks the environmental water cycle.
2. How is carbon released into the atmosphere from plants?
3. If air is 78% nitrogen gas, why is plant growth often severely limited by available nitrogen?

BIOLOGY & YOU

You and the Phosphorus Cycle. Most of us have little direct impact on the phosphorus cycle, with one glaring exception: fertilizing lawns and gardens. Soils in most states already have an adequate amount of phosphorus to grow healthy lawns and gardens. Adding more phosphorus in fertilizers does not benefit the plants. Instead, the extra phosphorus runs off in rainwater and is washed down the nearest street or storm drain, ending up in your local lake or river. Soon the phosphorus produces algal blooms, a green scum over what was once clear water. States like Minnesota have passed laws that meet this problem head on. Starting in 2005, it became illegal to use fertilizers containing phosphorus on lawns anywhere in Minnesota. If you want to help keep phosphorus levels down in your community, look at the bag or box of fertilizer before you buy it. On its label there is a string of three numbers that list its percent nitrogen, phosphorus, and potassium content, in that order. A "0" in the middle means a phosphorus-free fertilizer.

How Weather Shapes Ecosystems

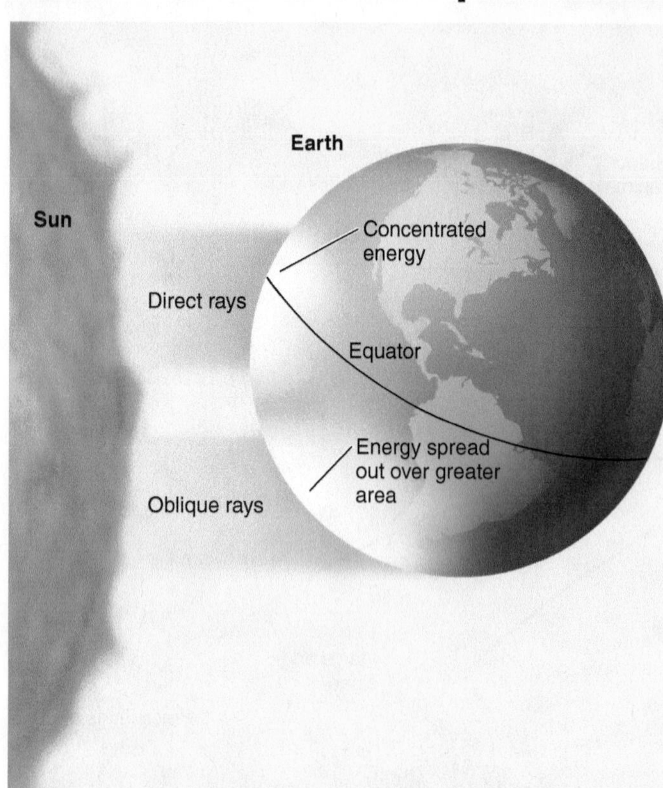

Figure 15.12 Latitude affects climate.

The relationship between the earth and sun is critical in determining the nature and distribution of life on earth. The tropics are warmer than the temperate regions because the sun's rays strike at a direct angle, providing more energy per unit of area.

15.6 The Sun and Atmospheric Circulation

CONCEPT PREVIEW: The sun drives circulation of the atmosphere, causing rain in the tropics and a band of deserts at 30 degrees latitude.

The world contains a wide variety of ecosystems because its climate varies a great deal from place to place. On a given day, Miami and Boston often have very different weather. There is no mystery about this. The tropics are warmer than the temperate regions because the sun's rays arrive almost perpendicular (that is, dead on) at regions near the equator. As you move from the equator into temperate latitudes, sunlight strikes the earth at more oblique angles, which spreads it out over a much greater area, thus providing less energy per unit of area (figure 15.12). This simple fact—that because the earth is a sphere some parts of it receive more energy from the sun than others—is responsible for much of the earth's different climates and thus, indirectly, for much of the diversity of its ecosystems.

The earth's annual orbit around the sun and its daily rotation on its own axis are also both important in determining world climate. Because of the daily cycle, the climate at a given latitude is relatively constant. Because of the annual cycle and the inclination of the earth's axis, all parts away from the equator experience a progression of seasons. In summer in the Southern Hemisphere, the earth is tilted toward the sun as shown in figure 15.12, and rays hit more directly leading to higher temperatures; in the winter, the tilt of the earth is opposite, with the Northern Hemisphere nearer to the sun, experiencing summer.

The major atmospheric circulation patterns result from the interactions between six large air masses. These great air masses (shown as circulating arrows in figure 15.13) occur in pairs, with one air mass of the pair occurring in the northern latitudes and the other occurring in the southern latitudes. These air masses affect climate because the rising and falling of an air mass influence its temperature, which, in turn, influences its moisture-holding capacity.

Near the equator, warm air rises and flows toward the poles (indicated by arrows at the equator that rise and circle toward the poles). As it rises and cools, this air loses most of its moisture because cool air holds less water vapor than warm air. (This explains why it rains so much in the tropics where the air is warm.) When this air has traveled to about 30 degrees north and south latitudes, the cool, dry air sinks and becomes reheated, soaking up water like a sponge as it warms, producing a broad zone of low rainfall. It is no accident that all of the great deserts of the world lie near 30 degrees north or 30 degrees south latitude. Air at these latitudes is still warmer than it is in the polar regions, and thus it continues to flow toward the poles. At about 60 degrees north and south latitudes, air rises and cools and sheds its moisture, and such are the locations of the great temperate forests of the world. Finally, this rising air descends near the poles, producing zones of very low precipitation.

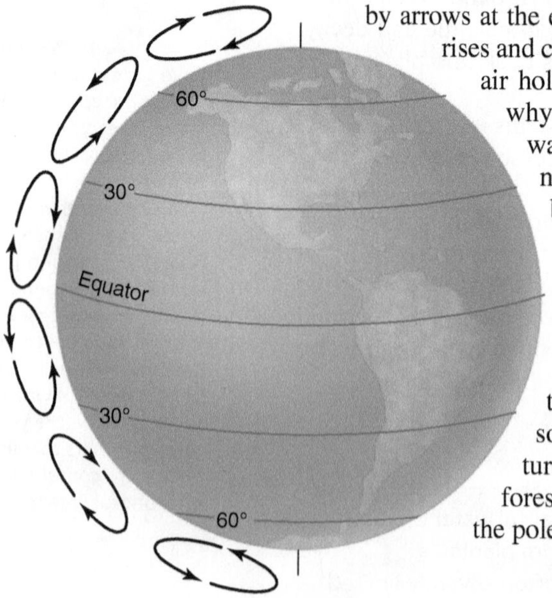

Figure 15.13 Air rises at the equator and then falls.

The pattern of air movement out from and back to the earth's surface forms three pairs of great cycles.

15.7 Latitude and Elevation

CONCEPT PREVIEW: Temperatures fall with increasing latitude and also with increasing elevation. Rainfall is higher on the windward side of mountains, with air losing its moisture as it rises up the mountain; descending on the far side, the dry air warms and sucks up moisture, creating deserts.

Temperatures are higher in tropical ecosystems for a simple reason: more sunlight per unit area falls on tropical latitudes (see figure 15.12). Solar radiation is most intense when the sun is directly overhead, and this occurs only in the tropics, where sunlight strikes the equator perpendicularly. Temperature also varies with elevation, with higher altitudes becoming progressively colder. At any given latitude, air temperature falls about 6°C for every 1,000-meter increase in elevation. The ecological consequences of temperature varying with elevation are the same as temperature varying with latitude. Figure 15.14 illustrates this principle comparing changes in ecosystems that occur with increasing latitudes in North America with the ecosystem changes that occur with increasing elevation at the tropics. A 1,000-meter increase in elevation on a mountain in southern Mexico (figure 15.14*b*) results in a temperature drop equal to that of an 880-kilometer increase in latitude on the North American continent (figure 15.14*a*). This is why "timberline" (the elevation above which trees do not grow) occurs at progressively lower elevations as one moves farther from the equator.

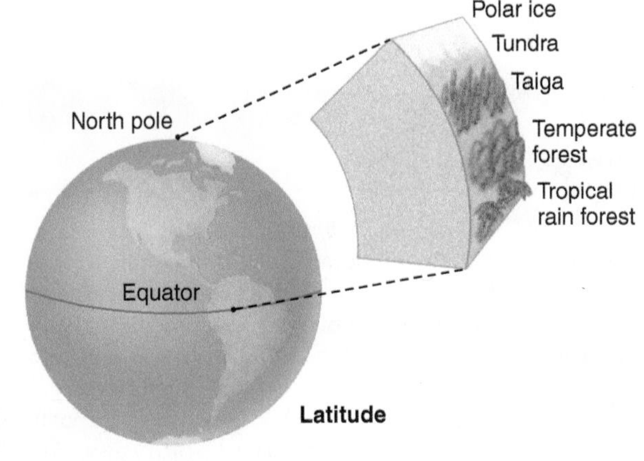

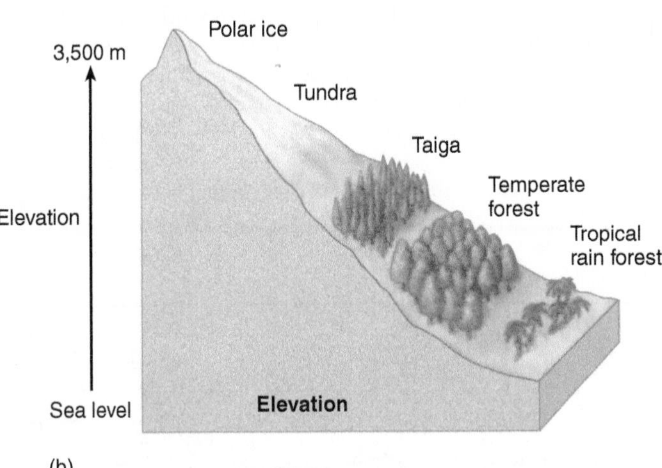

Figure 15.14 How elevation affects ecosystems.

The same land ecosystems that normally occur as latitude increases north and south of the equator at sea level (a) can occur in the tropics as elevation increases (b).

Rain Shadows

When a moving body of air encounters a mountain (figure 15.15), it is forced upward, and as it is cooled at higher elevations the air's moisture-holding capacity decreases, producing the rain you see on the windward side of the mountains—the side from which the wind is blowing. The effect on the other side of the mountain—the leeward side—is quite different. As the air passes the peak and descends on the far side of the mountains, it is warmed, so its moisture-holding capacity increases. Sucking up all available moisture, the air dries the surrounding landscape, often producing a desert. This effect, called a **rain shadow,** is responsible for deserts such as Death Valley, which is in the rain shadow of Mount Whitney, the tallest mountain in the Sierra Nevada.

Similar effects can occur on a larger scale. Regional climates are areas that are located on different parts of the globe but share similar climates because of similar geography. A so-called Mediterranean climate results when winds blow from a cool ocean onto warm land during the summer. As a result, the air's moisture-holding capacity is increased and precipitation is blocked, similar to what occurs on the leeward side of mountains. This effect accounts for dry, hot summers and cool, moist winters in areas with a Mediterranean climate such as portions of southern California or Oregon, central Chile, southwestern Australia, and the Cape region of South Africa. Such a climate is unusual on a world scale. In the regions where it occurs, many unusual kinds of endemic (local in distribution) plants and animals have evolved.

Rain shadow
Arid
Wind direction
Moist
Sierra Nevada
Pacific Ocean

Figure 15.15 The rain shadow effect.

Moisture-laden winds from the Pacific Ocean rise and are cooled when they encounter the Sierra Nevada. As they cool, their moisture-holding capacity decreases and precipitation occurs. As the air descends on the east side of the range, it warms, its moisture-holding capacity increases, and the air picks up moisture from its surroundings. As a result, arid conditions prevail on the east side of these mountains.

15.8 Patterns of Circulation in the Ocean

CONCEPT PREVIEW: The world's oceans circulate in huge gyres deflected by continental landmasses. Disturbances in ocean currents like an El Niño can have profound influences on world climate.

Patterns of ocean circulation are determined by the patterns of atmospheric circulation, which means that indirectly, the currents are driven by solar energy. The radiant input of heat from the sun sets the atmosphere in motion as already described, and then the winds set the ocean in motion. Oceanic circulation is dominated by the movement of surface waters in huge spiral patterns called gyres, which move around the subtropical zones of high pressure between approximately 30 degrees north and south latitudes. These gyres, indicated by the red and blue arrows in figure 15.16, move clockwise in the Northern Hemisphere and counterclockwise in the Southern Hemisphere. The ways they redistribute heat profoundly affects life not only in the oceans but also on coastal lands. For example, the Gulf Stream, in the North Atlantic (the red-colored arrow, meaning it carries warm waters), swings away from North America near Cape Hatteras, North Carolina, and reaches Europe near the southern British Isles. Because of the Gulf Stream, western Europe is much warmer and more temperate than eastern North America at similar latitudes.

IN THE NEWS

Message in a Bottle. Scientists learned of the huge gyres that form ocean currents long before satellites allowed them to measure mid-ocean currents. Instead, researchers tossed thousands of plastic cards and bottles with messages inside into the sea, hoping they would drift with the current and wash up on a beach somewhere. Messages in these "drift bottles" would ask the discoverer to notify scientists, allowing ocean scientists to track which way surface currents were moving. Using a similar approach, researcher Curtis Ebbesmeyer maps ocean currents in a semiwacky but wildly interesting way: by studying movements of random junk. With help from a worldwide army of beachcombers he organized in the 1990s, Ebbesmeyer has documented spills of everything from onions to hockey gloves. Plastic is found everywhere, even in the midocean far from any land. Our oceans are becoming a huge refuse dump. The message in a bottle, it seems, is that we should clean up our act.

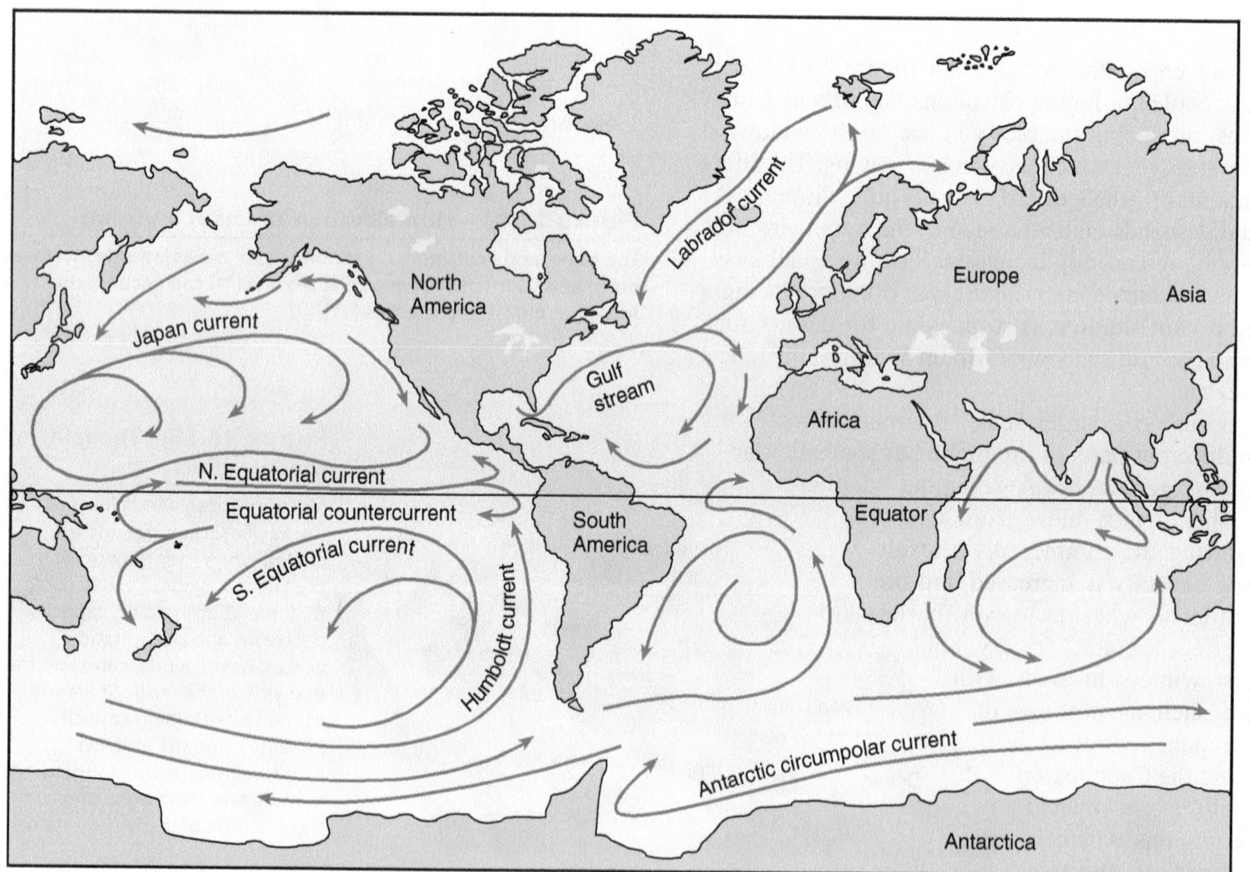

Figure 15.16 Oceanic circulation. The circulation in the oceans moves in great surface spiral patterns called gyres; oceanic circulation affects the climate on adjacent lands.

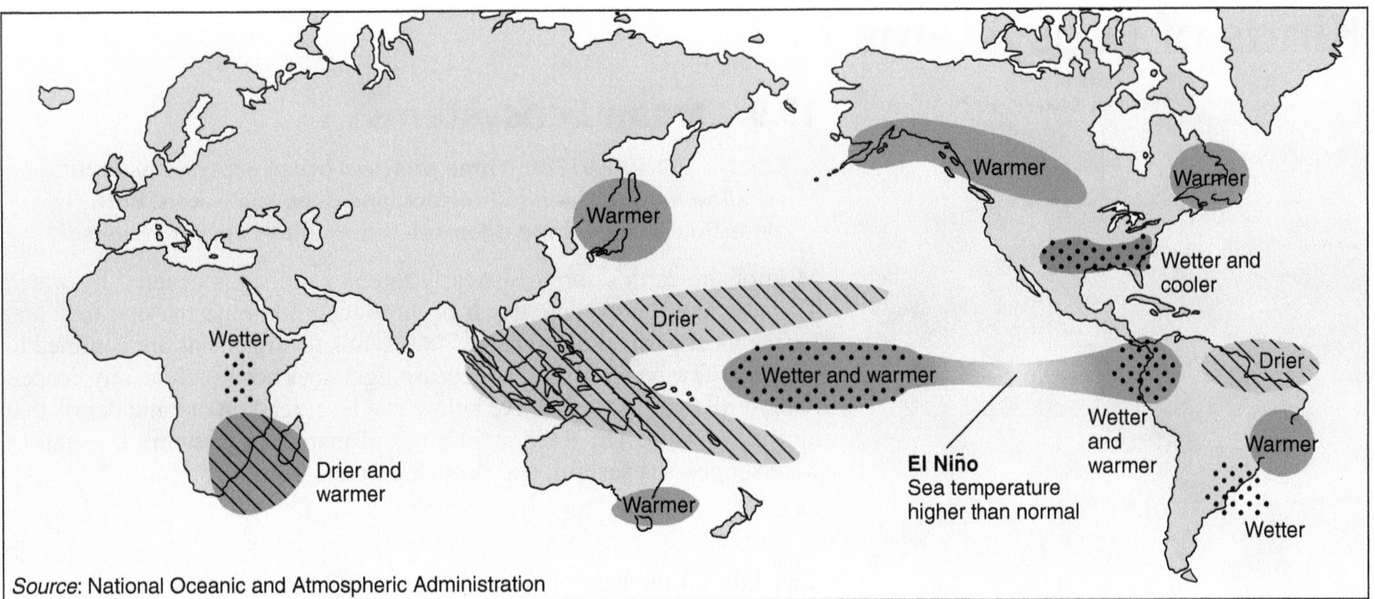

Figure 15.17 An El Niño winter.

El Niño currents produce unusual weather patterns all over the world as warm waters from the western Pacific move eastward.

El Niño Southern Oscillations and Ocean Ecology

Every Christmas a warm current sweeps down the coast of Peru and Ecuador from the tropics, reducing the fish population slightly and giving local fishers some time off. The local fishers named this Christmas current *El Niño* (literally, "the child," after the Christ Child). A dramatic version of the same phenomenon occurs every two to seven years, felt on a global scale.

Scientists now have a pretty good idea of what goes on in an El Niño. Normally the Pacific Ocean is fanned by constantly blowing east-to-west trade winds. These winds push warm surface water away from the ocean's eastern side (Peru, Ecuador, and Chile) and allow cold water to well up from the depths in its place, carrying nutrients that feed plankton and hence fish. This warm surface water piles up in the west, around Australia and the Philippines, making it several degrees warmer and a meter or so higher than the eastern side of the ocean. But if the winds slacken briefly, warm water begins to slosh back across the ocean (indicated by the darker red band stretching between Australia and the northern coast of South America in figure 15.17), causing an El Niño.

The end result is to shift the weather systems of the western Pacific Ocean 6,000 kilometers eastward. The tropical rainstorms that usually drench Indonesia and the Philippines soak the western edge of South America, leaving the previously rainy areas in drought (indicated by the light pink, hatched areas in figure 15.17).

IN THE NEWS

El Niño and Global Warming. El Niño, the unusual rise in sea-surface temperatures in the equatorial Pacific Ocean, visited three times from 1990 to 1995, an unwanted guest that wouldn't go away. In between, temperatures never went quite back to normal, as if it were all one long El Niño. This has led some scientists like Kevin Trenberth at the National Center for Atmospheric Research in Boulder, Colorado, to speculate that the apparent increase in El Niño events may be linked to warmer ocean temperatures resulting from global warming. He believes that as global warming drives temperatures higher, ocean currents and weather systems are not able to release all the extra heat getting pumped into tropical seas. El Niño, in his view, acts as a kind of pressure release valve, expelling the excess heat. As global warming becomes more pronounced, El Niño events become more intense and frequent. Other scientists suspect that the recent upturn in El Niño events are a statistical blip—we would have expected to see one to two events between 1990 and 1995 anyway. Without better computer models or decades of data, we are not going to know with any certainty who is right.

Concept Check

1. Explain why the earth's great deserts all lie near 30° latitude.
2. Death Valley, within 160 miles of the Pacific Ocean, is one of the driest places on earth. How could it be so dry, if it is so close to so much water?
3. What sets the water in the earth's oceans into motion?

Major Kinds of Ecosystems

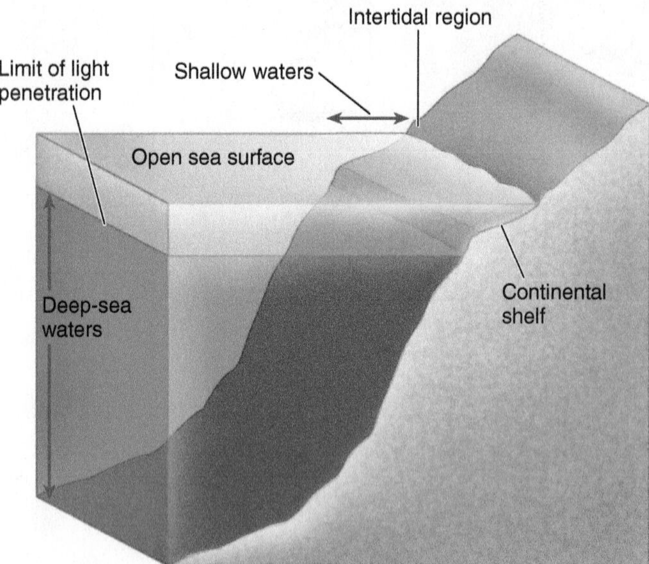

Figure 15.18 Ocean ecosystems.

There are three primary ecosystems found in the earth's oceans. Shallow water ecosystems occur along the shoreline and at areas of coral reefs. Open sea surface ecosystems occur in the upper 100 meters where light can penetrate. Finally, deep-sea water ecosystems are bottom areas below 300 meters.

15.9 Ocean Ecosystems

CONCEPT PREVIEW: Three principal ocean ecosystems occur: shallow waters, open-sea surface, and deep-sea waters. Both intertidal shallows and deep-sea communities are very diverse.

Most of the earth's surface—nearly three-quarters—is covered by water. The seas have an average depth of more than 3 kilometers, and they are, for the most part, cold and dark. Photosynthetic organisms are confined to the upper few hundred meters because light does not penetrate any deeper. Almost all organisms that live below this level feed on organic debris that rains downward. The three main kinds of marine ecosystems are shallow waters, open-sea surface, and deep-sea waters (figure 15.18).

Shallow Waters

Very little of the earth's ocean surface is shallow—mostly that along the shoreline—but this small area contains many more species than other parts of the ocean (figure 15.19*a*). The world's great commercial fisheries occur on banks in the coastal zones, where nutrients derived from the land are more abundant than in the open ocean. Part of this zone consists of the **intertidal region,** which is exposed to the air whenever the tides recede. Partly enclosed bodies of water, such as those that often form at river mouths and in coastal bays, where the salinity is intermediate between that of seawater and freshwater, are called **estuaries.** Estuaries are among the most naturally fertile areas in the world, often containing rich stands of submerged and emergent plants, algae, and microscopic organisms. They provide the breeding grounds for most of the coastal fish and shellfish that are harvested both in the estuaries and in open water.

Open-Sea Surface

Drifting freely in the upper, better-illuminated waters of the ocean is a diverse biological community of microscopic organisms. Most of the plankton occurs in the top 100 meters of the sea. Many fish swim in these waters as well, feeding on the plankton and one another (figure 15.19*b*). Some members of the plankton, including algae and some bacteria, are

(a)

(b)

Figure 15.19 Shallow waters and open sea surface.

(a) Fish and many other kinds of animals find food and shelter among the coral in the coastal waters of some regions. (b) The upper layers of the open ocean contain plankton and large schools of fish, like these bigeye snappers.

photosynthetic and are called phytoplankton. Collectively, these organisms are responsible for about 40% of all photosynthesis that takes place on earth. Over half of this is carried out by organisms less than 10 micrometers in diameter—at the lower limits of size for organisms—and almost all of it near the surface of the sea, in the zone into which light from the surface penetrates freely.

Deep-Sea Waters

In the deep waters of the sea, below 300 meters, little light penetrates. Very few organisms live there, compared to the rest of the ocean, but those that do include some of the most bizarre organisms found anywhere on earth. Many deep-sea inhabitants have bioluminescent (light-producing) body parts that they use to communicate or to attract prey (figure 15.20*a*).

The supply of oxygen can often be critical in the deep ocean, and as water temperatures become warmer, the water holds less oxygen. For this reason, the amount of available oxygen becomes an important limiting factor for deep-sea organisms in warmer marine regions of the globe. Carbon dioxide, in contrast, is almost never limited in the deep ocean. The distribution of minerals is much more uniform in the ocean than it is on land, where individual soils reflect the composition of the parent rocks from which they have weathered.

Frigid and bare, the floors of the deep sea have long been considered a biological desert. Recent close-up looks taken by marine biologists, however, paint a different picture (figure 15.20*b*). The ocean floor is teeming with life. Often kilometers deep, thriving in pitch darkness under enormous pressure, crowds of marine invertebrates have been found in hundreds of deep samples from the Atlantic and Pacific. Rough estimates of deep-sea diversity have soared to hundreds of thousands of species. Many appear endemic (local). The diversity of species is so high it may rival that of tropical rain forests! This profusion is unexpected. The formation of new species usually require some kind of barrier to diverge, and the ocean floor seems boringly uniform. However, little migration occurs among deep populations, and this lack of movement may encourage local specialization and species formation. A patchy environment may also contribute to species formation there; deep-sea ecologists find evidence that fine but nonetheless formidable resource barriers arise in the deep sea.

No light falls in the deep ocean. From where do deep-sea organisms obtain their energy? While some utilize energy falling to the ocean floor as debris from above, other deep-sea organisms are autotrophic, gaining their energy from **hydrothermal vent systems,** areas in which seawater circulates through porous rock surrounding fissures where molten material from beneath the earth's crust comes close to the surface. Hydrothermal vent systems, also called deep-sea vents, support a broad array of heterotrophic life (figure 15.20*c*). Water in the area of these hydrothermal vents is heated to temperatures in excess of 350°C, and contains high concentrations of hydrogen sulfide. Prokaryotes that live by these deep-sea vents obtain energy and produce carbohydrates through chemosynthesis instead of photosynthesis. Like plants, they are autotrophs; they extract energy from hydrogen sulfide to manufacture food, much as a plant extracts energy from the sun to manufacture its food. These prokaryotes live symbiotically within the tissues of heterotrophs that live around the deep-sea vents. The animals provide a place for the prokaryotes to live and obtain nutrients, and in turn the prokaryotes supply the animal with organic compounds to use as food.

Figure 15.20 Deep-sea waters.

(a) The luminous spot below the eye of this deep-sea fish results from the presence of a symbiotic colony of luminous bacteria. (b) Looking for all the world like some undersea sunflower, these two sea anemones (actually animals) use a glass-sponge stalk to catch "marine snow," food particles raining down on the ocean floor from the ocean surface several kilometers above. (c) These giant beardworms live along vents where water jets from fissures at 350°C and then cools to the 2°C of the surrounding water.

IMPLICATION No sunlight penetrates to the bottom of the deep sea. Why do you think that fish in this subphotic region have eyes, often extremely large, rather than evolution having selected for no eyes, as it has done for freshwater fish that inhabit deep dark caves?

Figure 15.21 **Freshwater organism.**

Some organisms, such as this giant waterbug with eggs on its back, can only live in freshwater habitats.

15.10 Freshwater Ecosystems

CONCEPT PREVIEW: Freshwater ecosystems cover only about 2% of the earth's surface, and all are strongly tied to adjacent terrestrial ecosystems. In some, organic materials are common, and in others, scarce. The temperature zones in lakes overturn twice a year, in spring and fall.

Freshwater ecosystems (lakes, ponds, rivers, and wetlands) are distinct from both ocean and land ecosystems, and they are very limited in area. Inland lakes cover about 1.8% of the earth's surface and rivers, streams, and wetlands about 0.4%. All freshwater habitats are strongly connected to land habitats, with marshes and swamps (wetlands) constituting intermediate habitats. In addition, a large amount of organic and inorganic material continually enters bodies of freshwater from communities growing on the land nearby. Many kinds of organisms are restricted to freshwater habitats (figure 15.21). When they occur in rivers and streams, they must be able to attach themselves in such a way as to resist or avoid the effects of current or risk being swept away.

Like the ocean, ponds and lakes have three zones in which organisms live (figure 15.22*a*): a shallow "edge" zone (the littoral zone), an open-water surface zone (the limnetic zone), and a deep-water zone where light does not penetrate (the profundal zone). Also, lakes can be divided into two categories, based on their production of organic material. In **oligotrophic lakes** (figure 15.22*b*), organic matter and nutrients are relatively scarce. Such lakes are often deep, and their deep waters are always rich in

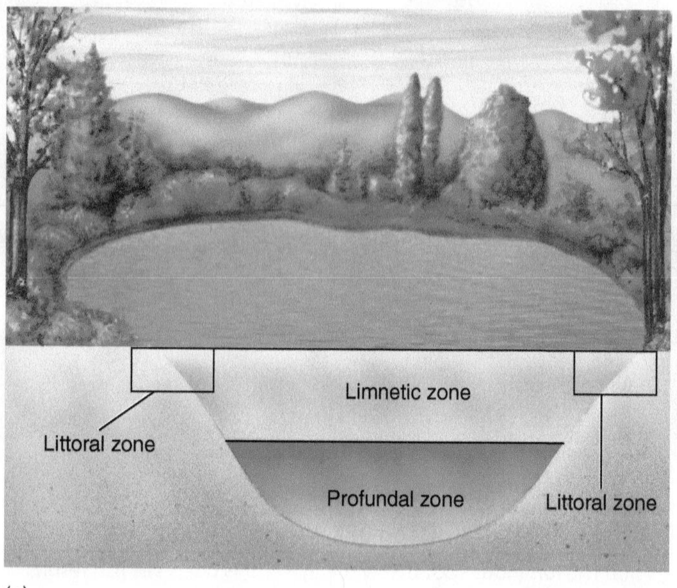

(a)

(b) Oligotrophic lake

(c) Eutrophic lake

Figure 15.22 **Characteristics of ponds and lakes.**

(a) Ponds and lakes can be divided into three zones based on the types of organisms that live in each. A shallow "edge" (littoral) zone lines the periphery of the lake where attached algae and their insect herbivores live. An open-water surface (limnetic) zone lies across the entire lake and is inhabited by floating algae, zooplankton, and fish. A dark, deep-water (profundal) zone overlies the sediments at the bottom of the lake. The profundal zone contains numerous bacteria and wormlike organisms that consume dead debris settling at the bottom of the lake. Lakes can be oligotrophic (b), containing scarce amounts of organic material, or eutrophic (c), containing abundant amounts of organic material.

oxygen. Oligotrophic lakes are highly susceptible to pollution from excess phosphorus from such sources as fertilizer runoff, sewage, and detergents. **Eutrophic lakes,** on the other hand, have an abundant supply of minerals and organic matter (figure 15.22*c*). Oxygen is depleted at the lower depths in the summer because of the abundant organic material and high rate at which aerobic decomposers in the lower layer use oxygen. These stagnant waters circulate to the surface in the fall (during the fall overturn, as discussed below) and are then infused with more oxygen.

Aerobic decomposers consume dead organisms as a means of acquiring energy. Because they carry out aerobic respiration, they need oxygen as the final electron acceptor in the electron transport chain, as discussed on page 121. Their active metabolism uses up a lot of oxygen.

Thermal stratification, characteristic of the larger lakes in temperate regions, is the process whereby water at a temperature of 4°C (which is when water is most dense) sinks beneath water that is either warmer or cooler. Follow through the changes in a large lake in figure 15.23 beginning in winter (1), where water at 4°C sinks beneath cooler water that freezes at the surface at 0°C. Below the ice, the water remains between 0° and 4°C, and plants and animals survive there. In spring (2), as the ice melts, the surface water is warmed to 4°C and sinks below the cooler water, bringing the cooler water to the top with nutrients from the lake's lower regions. This process is known as the *spring overturn.*

In summer (3), warmer water forms a layer over the cooler water that lies below. In the area between these two layers, called the thermocline, temperature changes abruptly. You may have experienced the existence of these layers if you have dived into a pond in temperate regions in the summer. Depending on the climate of the particular area, the warm upper layer may become as much as 20 meters thick during the summer. In autumn (4), its surface temperature drops until it reaches that of the cooler layer underneath—4°C. When this occurs, the upper and lower layers mix—a process called the fall overturn. Therefore, colder waters reach the surfaces of lakes in the spring and fall, bringing up fresh supplies of dissolved nutrients.

Putting Thermal Stratification to Work: Ice Fishing. When a large lake freezes in winter, it doesn't freeze solid like a huge ice cube. Only the surface freezes. Beneath its hard skin lies cold, dense water where game fish like pickerel, walleye, and pike thrive all winter long. Ice fishing is the activity of catching these fish with lines and fish hooks through a small opening augured through the ice. Some hardy ice anglers sit on a stool in the open on a frozen lake; other less adventurous souls await a catch in a heated cabin on the ice, some with bunks, kitchens, and portable bathrooms! Ice fishing has long been a popular solitary pastime in Finland, Norway, and Sweden, with fish houses a rare occurrence. In the United States, by contrast, ice fishing is often a social activity, with fish houses rented out by the day in states like Minnesota or Wisconsin—indeed, any state with lakes and long cold winters. Winter fishing makes up nearly 1/4 the annual catch in Wisconsin. Some confident but reckless ice fishers will walk out on 2.5 inches of ice, but because ice thickness can vary across an area, a full 4 inches of good ice is recommended—"thick and blue, tried and true." If you are on a snowmobile (it can be a long way from a lake's edge out to its center) you need 6 inches of ice; in a pickup or car, you must have 12–14 inches if you don't want your vehicle to join the fishes you seek to catch.

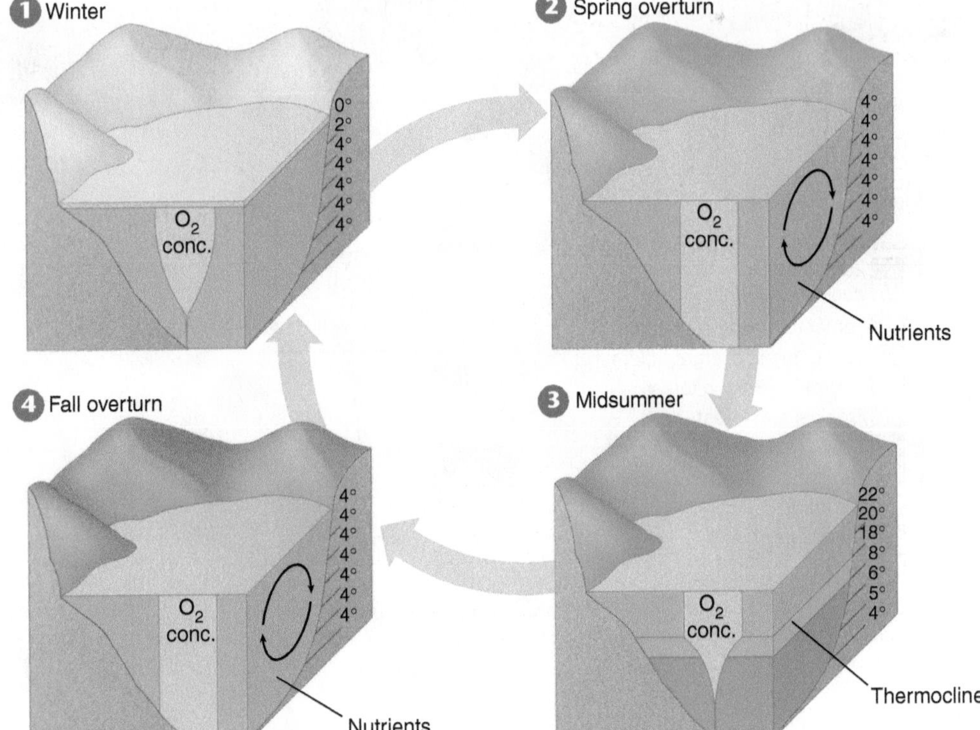

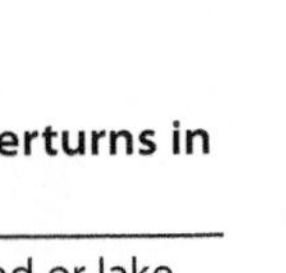

Figure 15.23 Spring and fall overturns in freshwater ponds or lakes.

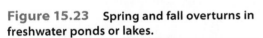

The pattern of stratification in a large pond or lake in temperate regions is upset in the spring and fall overturns. Of the three layers of water shown in midsummer (*lower right*), the densest water occurs at 4°C. The warmer water at the surface is less dense. The thermocline is the zone of abrupt change in temperature that lies between them. In summer and winter, oxygen concentrations are lower at greater depths, whereas in the spring and fall, they are more similar at all depths.

IN THE NEWS

California Wildfires. Each autumn the Los Angeles region is plagued by wildfires. During a two-week period in October 2003, 721,791 acres burned and in 2007, some 426,000 acres. In 2008 a single fire in the Los Padres National Forest burned 134,000 acres, nearly 210 square miles. Every year there are fires—fall is the "fire season" in Southern California. Ever wonder why? Turns out it is no mystery. Every fall strong, extremely dry winds called Santa Ana winds sweep down across Southern California from the Mohave Desert, bringing with them hot dry air, often very hot and very dry—the perfect incubator for a forest fire. What sort of biome would you expect to find in the path of annual Santa Ana winds? One that has evolved to tolerate fire—chaparral. Indeed, many chaparral plants can germinate only when exposed to the extreme heat of a forest fire. Fall forest fires are a normal and necessary part of the chaparral biome. It is only because we humans insist on building so many homes within this chaparral biome that damage is done and life lost. Unlike chaparral plants, human homes are not a natural part of this biome.

15.11 Land Ecosystems

CONCEPT PREVIEW: Biomes are major terrestrial communities defined largely by temperature and rainfall patterns.

Biomes are major types of ecosystems that occur on land. Each biome occurs over a broad area and is characterized by a particular climate and a defined group of organisms. While biomes can be classified in a number of ways, the seven most widely occurring biomes are (1) tropical rain forest, (2) savanna, (3) desert, (4) temperate grassland, (5) temperate deciduous forest, (6) taiga, and (7) tundra (figure 15.24). The reason that there are seven primary biomes, and not one or 80, is that they have evolved to suit the climate of the region, and the earth has seven principal climates. The seven biomes differ remarkably from one another but show many consistencies within; a particular biome often looks similar, with many of the same types of creatures living there, wherever it occurs on earth.

There are seven other less widespread biomes also shown in figure 15.24: chaparral; polar ice; mountain zone; temperate evergreen forest; warm, moist evergreen forest; tropical monsoon forest; and semidesert.

If there were no mountains and no climatic effects caused by the irregular outlines of the continents and by different sea temperatures, each biome would form an even belt around the globe. In fact, their distribution is greatly affected by these factors, especially by elevation. Thus, the summits of the Rocky Mountains are covered with a vegetation type that resembles tundra, whereas other forest types that resemble taiga occur farther down. It is for reasons such as these that the distributions of the biomes are so irregular. One trend that is apparent is that those

Figure 15.24 Distribution of the earth's biomes.

The seven primary types of biomes are tropical rain forest, savanna, desert, temperate grassland, temperate deciduous forest, taiga, and tundra. In addition, seven less widespread biomes are shown.

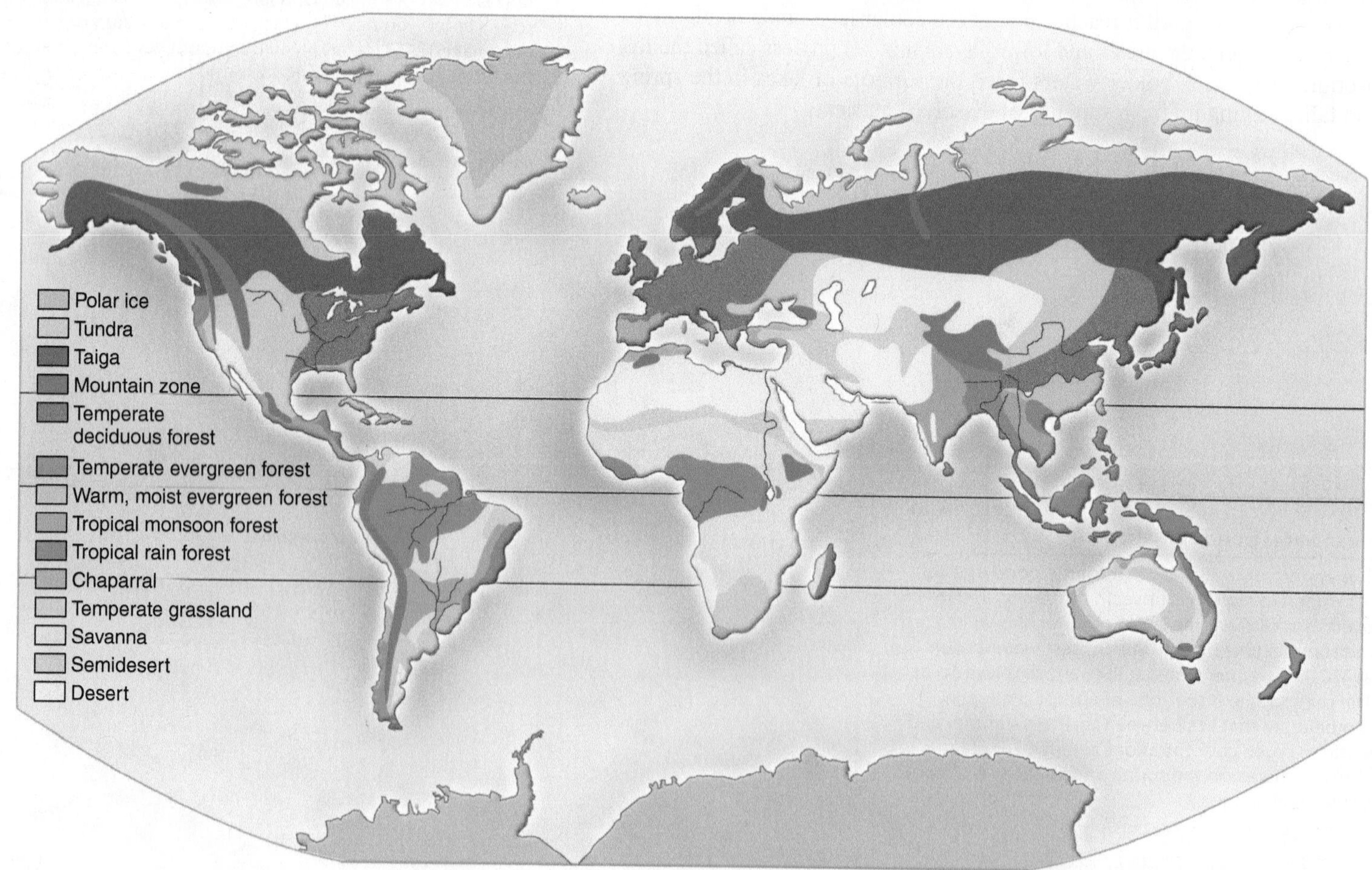

biomes that normally occur at high latitudes also follow an altitudinal gradient along mountains. That is, biomes found far north and far south of the equator at sea level also occur in the tropics but at high mountain elevations (see figure 15.14).

Lush Tropical Rain Forests

Rain forests, which experience over 250 centimeters of rain a year, are the richest ecosystems on earth (figure 15.25). They contain at least half of the earth's species of terrestrial plants and animals—more than 2 million species! In a single square mile of tropical forest in Rondonia, Brazil, there are 1,200 species of butterflies—twice the total number found in the United States and Canada combined. The communities that make up tropical rain forests are diverse in that each kind of animal, plant, or microorganism is often represented in a given area by very few individuals. There are extensive tropical rain forests in South America, Africa, and Southeast Asia. But the world's tropical rain forests are being destroyed, and with them, countless species, many of them never seen by humans. Perhaps a quarter of the world's species will disappear with the rain forests during the lifetime of many of us.

Figure 15.25 Tropical rain forest.

Savannas: Dry Tropical Grasslands

In the dry climates that border the tropics are found the world's great grasslands, called **savannas.** Landscapes are open, often with widely spaced trees, and rainfall (75 to 125 cm annually) is seasonal. Many of the animals and plants are active only during the rainy season. The huge herds of grazing animals that inhabit the African savanna are familiar to all of us (figure 15.26). Such animal communities occurred in the temperate grasslands of North America during the Pleistocene epoch but have persisted mainly in Africa. On a global scale, the savanna biome is transitional between tropical rain forest and desert. As these savannas are increasingly converted to agricultural use to feed rapidly expanding human populations in subtropical areas, their inhabitants are finding it difficult to survive. The elephant and rhino are now endangered species; the lion, giraffe, and cheetah will soon follow them.

Figure 15.26 Savanna.

Deserts: Burning Hot Sands

In the interior of continents are found the world's great deserts, especially in Africa (the Sahara), Asia (the Gobi), and Australia (the Great Sandy Desert). **Deserts** are dry places where less than 25 centimeters of rain falls in a year—an amount so low that vegetation is sparse and survival depends on water conservation (figure 15.27). One quarter of the world's land surface is desert. The plants and animals that live in deserts may restrict their activity to favorable times of the year, when water is present. To avoid high temperatures, most desert vertebrates live in deep, cool, and sometimes even somewhat moist burrows. Those that are active over a greater portion of the year emerge only at night, when temperatures are relatively cool. Some, such as camels, can drink large quantities of water when it is available and then survive long, dry periods. Many animals simply migrate to or through the desert, where they exploit food that may be abundant seasonally.

Figure 15.27 Desert.

Figure 15.28 Temperate grassland.

Grasslands: Seas of Grass

Halfway between the equator and the poles are temperate regions where rich **grasslands** grow. These grasslands once covered much of the interior of North America, and they were widespread in Eurasia and South America as well. Such grasslands are often highly productive when converted to agriculture. Many of the rich agricultural lands in the United States and southern Canada were originally occupied by **prairies,** another name for temperate grasslands. These natural temperate grasslands are one of the biomes adapted to periodic fire.

The roots of perennial grasses characteristically penetrate far into the soil, and grassland soils tend to be deep and fertile. Temperate grasslands are often populated by herds of grazing mammals. In North America, the prairies were once inhabited by huge herds of bison and pronghorns (figure 15.28). The herds are almost all gone now, with most of the prairies having been converted to the richest agricultural region on earth.

Figure 15.29 Temperate deciduous forest.

Deciduous Forests: Rich Hardwood Forests

Mild climates (warm summers and cool winters) and plentiful rains promote the growth of **deciduous** ("hardwood") **forests** in Eurasia, the northeastern United States, and eastern Canada (figure 15.29). A deciduous tree is one that drops its leaves in the winter. Deer, bears, beavers, and raccoons are the familiar animals of the temperate regions. Because the temperate deciduous forests represent the remnants of more extensive forests that stretched across North America and Eurasia several million years ago, these remaining areas—especially those in eastern Asia and eastern North America—share animals and plants that were once more widespread. Alligators, for example, are found only in China and in the southeastern United States. The deciduous forest in eastern Asia is rich in species because climatic conditions have remained constant.

Figure 15.30 Taiga.

Taiga: Trackless Conifer Forests

A great ring of northern forests of coniferous trees (spruce, hemlock, larch, and fir) extends across vast areas of Asia and North America. Coniferous trees are ones with leaves like needles that are kept all year long. This ecosystem, called **taiga,** is one of the largest on earth (figure 15.30). Here, the winters are long and cold. Rain, often as little as in hot deserts, falls in the summer. Because it has too short a growing season for farming, few people live there. Many large mammals, including elk, moose, deer, and such carnivores as wolves, bears, lynx, and wolverines, live in the taiga. Traditionally, fur trapping has been extensive in this region. Lumber production is also important. Marshes, lakes, and ponds are common and are often fringed by willows or birches. Most of the trees occur in dense stands of one or a few species.

Tundra: Cold Boggy Plains

In the far north, above the great coniferous forests and below the polar ice, there are few trees. There the grassland, called **tundra,** is open, windswept, and often boggy (figure 15.31). Enormous in extent, this ecosystem covers one-fifth of the earth's land surface. Very little rain or snow falls. When rain does fall during the brief arctic summer, it sits on frozen ground, creating a sea of boggy ground. **Permafrost,** or permanent ice, usually exists within a meter of the surface. Trees are small and are mostly confined to the margins of streams and lakes. Large grazing mammals, including musk-oxen, caribou, reindeer, and carnivores such as wolves, foxes, and lynx, live in the tundra. Lemming populations rise and fall on a long-term cycle, with important effects on the animals that prey on them.

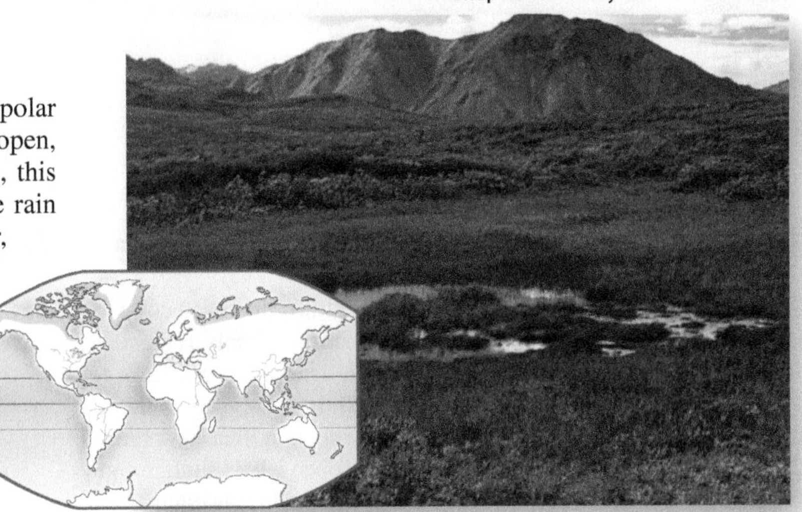

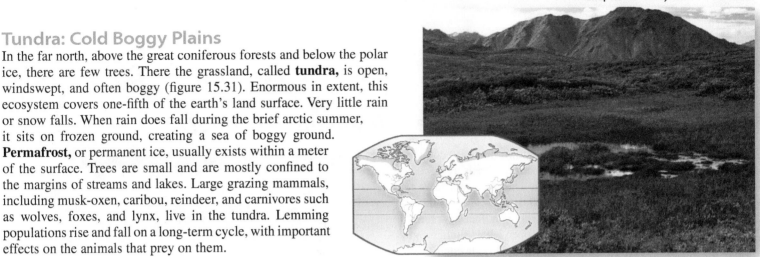

Figure 15.31 Tundra.

Chaparral

Chaparral consists of evergreen, often spiny shrubs and low trees that form communities in regions with what is called a "Mediterranean," dry summer climate. These regions include California, central Chile, the Cape region of South Africa, southwestern Australia, and the Mediterranean area itself (figure 15.32). Many plant species found in chaparral can germinate only when they have been exposed to the hot temperatures generated during a fire. The chaparral of California and adjacent regions is historically derived from deciduous forests.

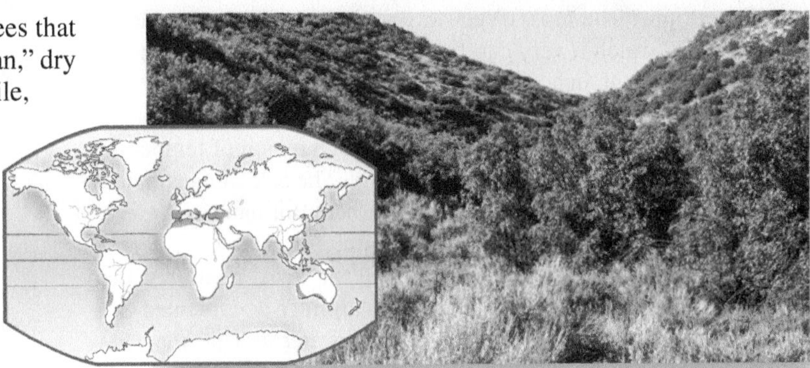

Figure 15.32 Chaparral.

Polar Ice Caps

Polar ice caps lie over the Arctic Ocean in the north and Antarctica in the south (figure 15.33). The poles receive almost no precipitation, so although ice is abundant, freshwater is scarce. The sun barely rises in the winter months. Life in Antarctica is largely limited to the coasts. Because the Antarctic ice cap lies over a landmass, it is not warmed by the latent heat of circulating ocean water and becomes very cold, so only prokaryotes, algae, and some small insects inhabit the vast Antarctic interior.

Figure 15.33 Polar ice.

Tropical Monsoon Forest

Tropical upland forests (figure 15.34) occur in the tropics and semitropics at slightly higher latitudes than rain forests or where local climates are drier. Most trees in these forests are deciduous, losing many of their leaves during the dry season. This loss of leaves allows sunlight to penetrate to the understory and ground levels of the forest, where a dense layer of shrubs and small trees grow rapidly. Rainfall is typically very seasonal, measuring several inches daily in the monsoon season and approaching drought conditions in the dry season, particularly in locations far from oceans, such as in central India.

Figure 15.34 Tropical monsoon forest.

Concept Check

1. How can bacteria living near deep sea vents be autotrophs, when no light penetrates so deep?
2. Why are there 7 primary biomes, and not 12?
3. In what biome do you live?

Does Clear-Cutting Forests Cause Permanent Damage?

The lumber industry practice called "clear-cutting" has been common in many states. Loggers find it more efficient to simply remove all trees from a watershed, and sort the logs out later, than to selectively cut only the most desirable mature trees. While the open cuts seem a desolation to the casual observer, the loggers claim that new forests can become established more readily in the open cut as sunlight now more easily reaches seedlings at ground level. Ecologists counter that clear-cutting fundamentally changes the forest in ways which cannot be easily reversed.

Who is right? The most direct way to find out is to try it, clear-cut an area and watch it very carefully. Just this sort of massive field test was carried out in a now-classic experiment at the Hubbard Brook Experimental Forest in New Hampshire. Hubbard Brook is the central stream of a large watershed that drains a region of temperate deciduous forest in northern New Hampshire. The research team, led by then-Dartmouth College professors Herbert Bormann and Gene Likens, first gathered a great deal of information about the forest watershed. Starting in 1963, they censused the trees, measured the flow of water through the watershed, and carefully documented the levels of minerals and other nutrients in the water leaving the ecosystem via Hubbard Brook. To keep track, they constructed concrete dams across each of the six streams that drain the forest and monitored the runoff, chemically analyzing samples. The undisturbed forest proved very efficient at retaining nitrogen and other nutrients. The small amounts of nutrients that entered the ecosystem in rain and snow were approximately equal to the amounts of nutrients that ran out of the valleys into Hubbard Brook.

Now came the test. In the winter of 1965 the investigators felled all the trees and shrubs in 48 acres drained by one stream (as shown in the photo), and examined the water running off. The immediate effect was dramatic: the amount of water running out of the valley increased by 40%. Water that otherwise would have been taken up by vegetation and released into the atmosphere through evaporation was now simply running off. It was clear that the forest was not retaining water as well, but what about the soil nutrients, the key to future forest fertility?

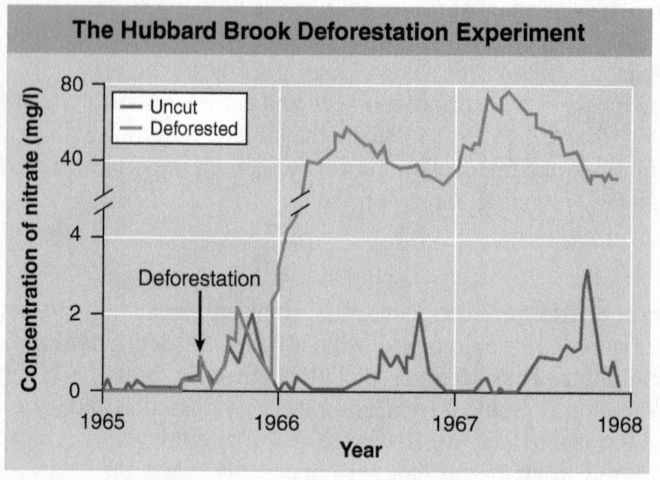

The red line in the graph above shows nitrogen minerals leaving the ecosystem in the runoff water of the stream draining the clear-cut area; the blue line shows the nitrogen runoff in a neighboring stream draining an adjacent uncut portion of the forest.

Analysis

1. **Applying Concepts**
   Scale. What is the significance of the break in the vertical axis between 4 and 40?
2. **Interpreting Data**
   a. What is the approximate concentration of nitrogen in the runoff of the uncut valley before cutting? of the cut valley before cutting?
   b. What is the approximate concentration of nitrogen in the runoff of the uncut valley one year after cutting? of the clear-cut valley one year after cutting?
3. **Making Inferences**
   a. Is there any yearly pattern to the nitrogen runoff in the uncut forest? Can you explain it?
   b. How does the loss of nitrogen from the ecosystem in the clear-cut forest compare with nitrogen loss from the uncut forest?
4. **Drawing Conclusions**
   a. What is the impact of this forest's trees upon its ability to retain nitrogen?
   b. Has clear-cutting harmed this ecosystem? Explain.

Concept Summary

The Energy in Ecosystems

15.1 Energy Flows Through Ecosystems

- An ecosystem includes the community and the habitat present in a particular area. Energy constantly flows into an ecosystem from the sun, and is passed among organisms in a food chain. Energy from the sun is captured by photosynthetic producers, which are eaten by herbivores, which are in turn eaten by carnivores, as shown here from **figure 15.1.** Organisms at all trophic levels die and are consumed by detritivores and decomposers. A food chain is organized linearly, but in nature the flow of energy is often more complex, and is called a food web (**figure 15.2**).

- An ecosystem's net primary productivity is the total amount of energy that is captured by producers. Energy is lost at every level in a food chain, such that only about 5% to 20% of available energy is passed on to the next trophic level (**figures 15.4** and **15.5**).

15.2 Ecological Pyramids

- Because energy is lost as it passes up through the trophic levels of the food chain, there tends to be more individuals at the lower trophic levels. Similarly, the amount of biomass is also less at the higher trophic levels, as is the amount of energy. Ecological pyramids illustrate this distribution of number of individuals, biomass, and energy (**figure 15.6**).

Materials Cycle Within Ecosystems

15.3 The Water Cycle

- Physical components of the ecosystem cycle through the ecosystem, being used then recycled and reused. This cycling of materials often involves living organisms and is referred to as a biogeochemical cycle.
- Water availability can limit the number of organisms in an ecosystem. There are two water cycles: the environmental cycle and the organismic cycle. In the environmental cycle, shown here from **figure 15.7,** water cycles from the atmosphere as precipitation, where it falls to the earth and reenters the atmosphere through evaporation. In the organismic cycle, water cycles through plants, entering through the roots and leaving as water vapor by transpiration. Groundwater held in underground aquifers cycles more slowly through the water cycle.

15.4 The Carbon Cycle

- Carbon cycles from the atmosphere through plants, via carbon fixation of CO_2 in photosynthesis. Carbon then returns to the atmosphere as CO_2 via cellular respiration, but some carbon is also stored in the tissues of the organisms. Eventually, this carbon reenters the atmosphere by the burning of fossil fuels and by diffusion after erosion (**figure 15.9**).

15.5 The Nitrogen and Phosphorus Cycles

- Nitrogen gas in the atmosphere cannot be readily used by organisms and needs to be fixed by certain types of bacteria into ammonia and nitrate that is then used by plants. Animals eat plants that have taken up the fixed nitrogen. Nitrogen reenters the ecosystem through decomposition and animal excretions (**figure 15.10**).
- Phosphorus also cycles through the ecosystem and may limit growth when not available (**figure 15.11**) or it can cause problems in aquatic ecosystems when found in excess amounts. Phosphorus is not a gas and so does not cycle through the atmosphere. Instead it cycles from soil and rock through plants and back to the soil through decomposition.

How Weather Shapes Ecosystems

15.6 The Sun and Atmospheric Circulation

- The heating power of the sun and air currents affect evaporation, causing certain parts of the globe, such as the tropics, to have larger amounts of precipitation (**figures 15.12** and **15.13**).

15.7 Latitude and Elevation

- Temperature and precipitation are similarly affected by elevation and latitude. Changes in ecosystems from the equator to the poles are similarly reflected in the changes in ecosystems from sea level to mountaintops, as shown here from **figure 15.14.** Changes in temperature cause the rain shadow effect, where precipitation is deposited on the windward side of mountains, and deserts form on the leeward side (**figure 15.15**).

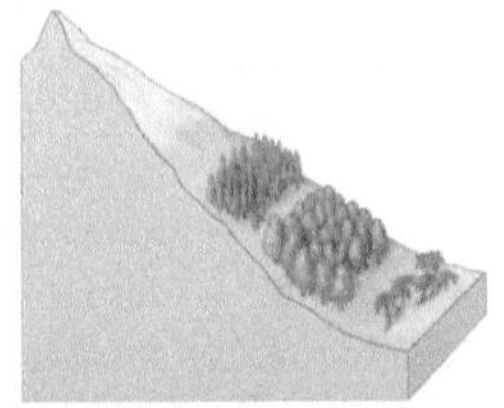

15.8 Patterns of Circulation in the Ocean

- The earth's oceans circulate in patterns that distribute warmer and cooler waters to different areas of the world. These ocean patterns affect climates across the globe (**figures 15.16** and **15.17**).

Major Kinds of Ecosystems

15.9 Ocean Ecosystems

- There are three primary ocean ecosystems: shallow waters, open-sea surfaces, and deep-sea bottoms (**figure 15.18**). Each is affected by light and temperature.

15.10 Freshwater Ecosystems

- Freshwater ecosystems are closely tied to the terrestrial environments that surround them. Freshwater ecosystems are affected by light, temperature, and nutrients. The penetration of light divides a lake into three zones with varying amounts of light (**figure 15.22**). Temperature variations in a lake, called thermal stratification, also bring about an overturning of the lake that distributes nutrients (**figure 15.23**).

15.11 Land Ecosystems

- Biomes are terrestrial communities found throughout the world. Each biome contains its own characteristic group of organisms based on temperature and rainfall patterns (**figure 15.24**).

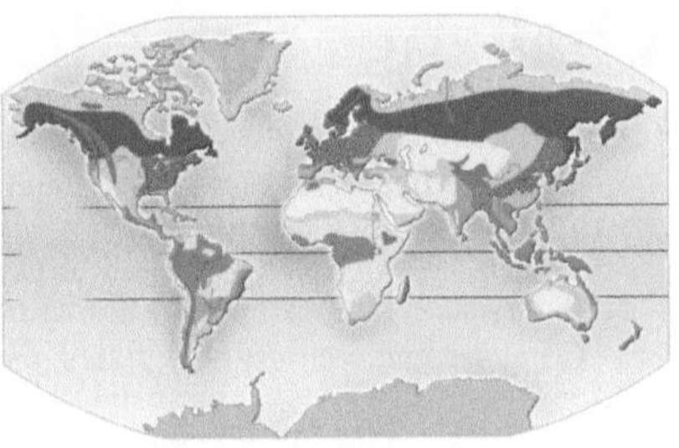

Self-Test

1. Energy from the sun is captured and converted into chemical energy by
   a. herbivores. c. producers.
   b. carnivores. d. detritivores.
2. As energy is transferred from one trophic level to the next, substantial amounts of energy are lost to/as
   a. undigestible biomass. c. metabolism.
   b. heat. d. All answers are correct.
3. The number of carnivores found at the top of an ecological pyramid is limited by the
   a. number of organisms below the top carnivores.
   b. number of trophic levels below the top carnivores.
   c. amount of biomass below the top carnivores.
   d. amount of energy transferred to the top carnivores.
4. Hydrologists, scientists who study the movements and cycles of water, refer to the return of water from the ground to the air as evapotranspiration. The first part of the word refers to evaporation. The second part of the word refers to transpiration, which is evaporation of water
   a. from plants.
   b. through animal perspiration.
   c. off the ground shaded by plants.
   d. from the surface of rivers.
5. The carbon cycle includes a store of carbon as fossil fuels that is released through
   a. respiration. c. erosion.
   b. combustion. d. all of the above.
6. The element phosphorus is needed in organisms to build
   a. proteins. c. ATP.
   b. carbohydrates. d. steroids.
7. A rain shadow results in
   a. extremely wet conditions due to the lack of wind over a mountain range.
   b. dry air moving toward the poles that cools and sinks in regions 15 to 30 degrees north/south latitude.
   c. global polar regions that rarely receive moisture from the warmer, tropical regions, and are therefore dryer.
   d. desert conditions on the downwind side of a mountain due to increased moisture-holding capacity of the winds as the air heats up.
8. As one travels from northern Canada south to the United States, the timberline increases in elevation. This is because as latitude
   a. increases, temperature increases.
   b. decreases, temperature increases.
   c. increases, humidity decreases.
   d. decreases, humidity increases.
9. In freshwater lakes during the summer, layers of sudden temperature change called _____ form.
   a. eutrophy c. oligotrophy
   b. thermal restratification d. thermocline
10. Which of the following biomes is *not* found south of the equator?
   a. polar ice cap c. tundra
   b. savanna d. tropical monsoon forest

Visual Understanding

1. **Figure 15.5** A. One thousand calories of energy is harvested by a certain amount of algae. Explain the probable efficiency of having humans eat, respectively, (1) the algae itself, (2) the small heterotrophs, (3) the smelt, or (4) the trout. B. How many more people could be fed if we all ate algae? C. Why can't we survive just by eating algae?

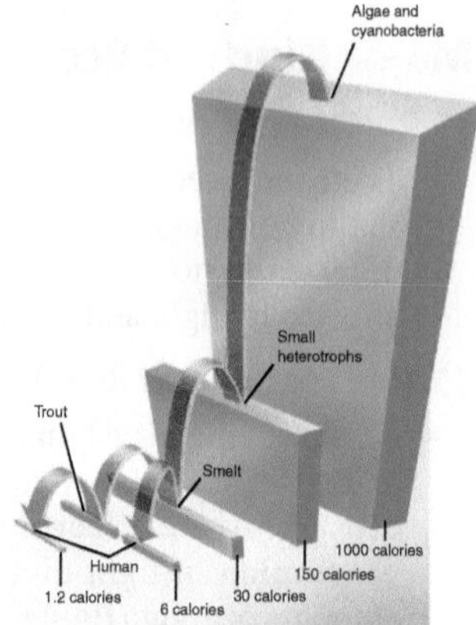

2. **Figure 15.7** Imagine that you are a molecule of water. Create a journey for yourself, starting with falling as part of a drop of rain onto the earth, and ending in a cloud ready to fall once again. Take a trip through a plant along the way.

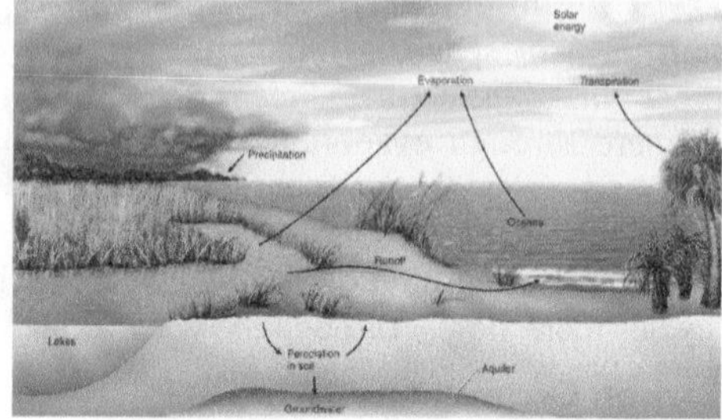

Challenge Questions

1. Given the amount of sunlight that hits the plants on our planet, and the ability of plants for rapid growth and reproduction, how come we aren't all hip deep in dead plants?
2. Plants need both carbon (C) and nitrogen (N) in large amounts. Compare and contrast how plants obtain these two important elements.
3. Why do increasing latitude and increasing elevation affect, in the same way, which plant species grow?
4. Pick two very different biomes and research them. Compare and contrast the sunshine, rainfall, major temperature features, and something about the plants and animals.

Appendix A

Answers to Self-Test Questions

Chapter 1 *The Science of Biology*

1. a. kingdoms 2. c. cellular organization 3. b. atom, molecule, organelle, cell, tissue, organ, organ system, organism, population, species, community, ecosystem 4. d. emergent properties 5. b. evolution, energy flow, cooperation, structure determines function, and homeostasis 6. b. test each hypothesis, using appropriate controls, to rule out as many as possible 7. c. After sufficient testing, you can accept it as probable, being aware that it may be revised or rejected in the future 8. d. all living organisms consist of cells, and all cells come from other cells 9. c. is contained in a long molecule called DNA 10. c. Darwin

Chapter 2 *The Chemistry of Life*

1. b. an atom 2. c. an ion 3. d. ionic, covalent, and hydrogen 4. b. it can form four single covalent bonds 5. d. All of these are correct 6. a. hydrogen bonds between the individual water molecules 7. c. heat storage and heat of vaporization 8. a. cohesion 9. a. (1) acids and (2) bases 10. c. A buffer stops water from ionizing.

Chapter 3 *Molecules of Life*

1. b. proteins, carbohydrates, lipids, and nucleic acids 2. c. polypeptides 3. c. structure, function 4. d. All of the above 5. d. are information storage devices found in body cells 6. a. Adenine forms hydrogen bonds with thymine 7. a. structure and energy 8. a. glycogen 9. d. All of these are characteristics of fat molecules. 10. c. energy storage and for some hormones

Chapter 4 *Cells*

1. a. cells are the smallest living things. Nothing smaller than a cell is considered alive 2. d. prokaryotes, eukaryotes 3. b. a double lipid layer with proteins inserted in it, which surrounds every cell individually 4. a. a nucleolus 5. c. endoplasmic reticulum and the Golgi complex 6. d. mitochondria and the chloroplasts 7. b. cristae 8. d. slowly disperse throughout the water; this is because of diffusion 9. b. endocytosis and phagocytosis 10. c. energy and specialized pumps or channels

Chapter 5 *Energy and Life*

1. c. energy 2. d. says that energy can change forms, but cannot be made or destroyed 3. b. says that entropy, or disorder, continually increases in a closed system 4. a. exergonic and release energy 5. b. enzymes 6. c. temperature and pH 7. d. All of the above 8. c. an inhibitor molecule competes with the substrate for the same binding site on the enzyme 9. a. active site 10. a. the breaking of phosphate bonds in ATP

Chapter 6 *Photosynthesis: How Cells Acquire Energy*

1. c. photosynthesis 2. b. with molecules called pigments that absorb photons and use their energy 3. c. a small portion in the middle of the spectrum 4. a. red and blue 5. d. All of these are true 6. c. only go through the system once; they are obtained by splitting a water molecule 7. b. chemiosmosis 8. a. electron transport system of photosystem I, Calvin cycle 9. c. build sugar molecules 10. b. use C_4 photosynthesis or CAM

Chapter 7 *How Cells Harvest Energy from Food*

1. a. breaking down the organic molecules that were consumed 2. c. substrate-level phosphorylation 3. b. glycolysis 4. b. makes ATP by splitting a molecule of glucose in half and capturing the energy 5. b. NAD^+, electron transport chain 6. c. mitochondria of the cell and are broken down in the presence of O_2 to make more ATP 7. d. during the electron transport chain 8. b. fermentation 9. a. pyruvate 10. c. each type of macromolecule is broken down into its subunits, which enter the oxidative respiration pathway

Chapter 8 *Mitosis*

1. a. copying DNA then undergoing binary fission 2. c. in the production of genetically identical daughter cells 3. c. and most eukaryotes have between 10 and 50 pairs of chromosomes 4. c. carry information about the same traits located in the same places on the chromosome 5. d. All of the above 6. b. metaphase 7. c. cytokinesis 8. a. Interphase/DNA replication 9. d. All of the above 10. b. cancer

Chapter 9 *Meiosis*

1. d. the egg and sperm have only half the number of chromosomes found in the parents because of meiosis 2. d. 23 3. a. $1n$ gametes (haploid), followed by $2n$ zygotes (diploid) 4. a. homologous chromosomes exchange sections of chromosomes 5. b. Homologous chromosomes randomly orient themselves on the metaphase plate, called independent assortment. 6. c. The duplicated sister chromatids separate. 7. a. prophase I 8. c. homologous chromosomes become closely associated 9. a. cells that are genetically identical to the parent cell/haploid cells 10. d. All of the above

Chapter 10 *Foundations of Genetics*

1. d. All of these 2. a. all purple flowers 3. c. $^3/_4$ purple and $^1/_4$ white flowers 4. b. some factor, or information, about traits to their offspring and it may or may not be expressed 5. a. dihybrid cross 6. d. multiple genes 7. c. codominant traits 8. b. sex-linked eye color in fruit flies 9. d. All of the above. 10. b. chromosome karyotype

Chapter 11 *DNA: The Genetic Material*

1. b. hereditary information can be added to cells from other cells 2. d. DNA 3. a. structure of DNA 4. c. the type of nitrogen base 5. d. adenine and guanine 6. b. TAACGTA 7. b. splits down the middle into two single strands, and each one then acts as a template to build its complement 8. a. a primer 9. c. by mutation or by transformation 10. a. germ-line tissues and are passed on to future generations

Chapter 12 *How Genes Work*

1. a. nRNA (nuclear RNA) 2. d. a codon 3.c. a codon consists of three nucleotides 4. c. transcription 5. a. promoter 6. d. translation 7. c. AUG 8. d. Some genes remain off as long as a repressor is bound. 9. d. All of these statements are correct. 10. c. translating a gene as it is being transcribed

Chapter 13 *The New Biology*

1. c. genome 2. b. the exons used to make a specific mRNA can be rearranged to form different proteins. 3. c. restriction enzyme 4. b. exposing the mRNA of the desired eukaryotic gene to reverse transcriptase 5. c. DNA fingerprinting becomes more and more reliable as more probes are used 6. a. the drug to be produced in far larger amounts than in the past 7. a. increased yield 8. d. harm to the crop itself from mutations 9. a. immunological rejection of the tissue by the patient 10. c. viruses

Chapter 14 *Exploring Biological Diversity*

1. a. the red fox is in the same family, but different genus than dogs and wolves 2. b. phylogeny 3. a. physical, behavioral, and molecular characteristics 4. c. share a more recent common ancestor than those organisms that are farther apart 5. d. cell structure and DNA sequence 6. b. Archaea 7. d. are prokaryotes 8. c. Protista 9. b. multicellular 10. d. endosymbiosis of bacteria

Chapter 15 *Ecosystems*

1. c. producers 2. d. All answers are correct 3. d. amount of energy transferred to the top carnivores 4. a. from plants 5. b. combustion 6. c. ATP 7. d. desert conditions on the downwind side of a mountain due to increased moisture-holding capacity of the winds as the air heats up 8. a. decreases, temperature increases 9. d. thermocline 10. c. tundra

Glossary

Terms and Concepts

A

absorption (L. *absorbere,* to swallow down) The movement of water and substances dissolved in water into a cell, tissue, or organism.

acid Any substance that dissociates to form H^+ ions when dissolved in water. Having a pH value less than 7.

acoelomate (Gr. *a,* not + *koiloma,* cavity) A bilaterally symmetrical animal not possessing a body cavity, such as a flatworm.

actin (Gr. *actis,* ray) One of the two major proteins that make up myofilaments (the other is myosin). It provides the cell with mechanical support and plays major roles in determining cell shape and cell movement.

action potential A single nerve impulse. A transient all-or-none reversal of the electrical potential across a neuron membrane. Because it can activate nearby voltage-sensitive channels, an action potential propagates along a nerve cell.

activation energy The energy a molecule must acquire to undergo a specific chemical reaction.

activator A regulatory protein that binds to the DNA and makes it more accessible for transcription.

active transport The transport of a solute across a membrane by protein carrier molecules to a region of higher concentration by the expenditure of chemical energy. One of the most important functions of any cell.

adaptation (L. *adaptare,* to fit) Any peculiarity of structure, physiology, or behavior that promotes the likelihood of an organism's survival and reproduction in a particular environment.

adenosine triphosphate (ATP) A molecule composed of ribose, adenine, and a triphosphate group. ATP is the chief energy currency of all cells. Cells focus all of their energy resources on the manufacture of ATP from ADP and phosphate, which requires the cell to supply 7 kilocalories of energy obtained from photosynthesis or from electrons stripped from foodstuffs to form 1 mole of ATP. Cells then use this ATP to drive endergonic reactions.

adhesion (L. *adhaerere,* to stick to) The molecular attraction exerted between the surfaces of unlike bodies in contact, as water molecules to the walls of the narrow tubes that occur in plants.

aerobic (Gr. *aer,* air + *bios,* life) Oxygen-requiring.

allele (Gr. *allelon,* of one another) One of two or more alternative forms of a gene.

allele frequency The relative proportion of a particular allele among individuals of a population. Not equivalent to gene frequency, although the two terms are sometimes confused.

allosteric interaction (Gr. *allos,* other + *stereos,* shape) The change in shape that occurs when an activator or repressor binds to an enzyme. These changes result when specific, small molecules bind to the enzyme, molecules that are not substrates of that enzyme.

alternation of generations A reproductive life cycle in which the multicellular diploid phase produces spores that give rise to the multicellular haploid phase and the multicellular haploid phase produces gametes that fuse to give rise to the zygote. The zygote is the first cell of the multicellular diploid phase.

alveolus, *pl.* alveoli (L. *alveus,* a small cavity) One of the many small, thin-walled air sacs within the lungs in which the bronchioles terminate.

amniotic egg An egg that is isolated and protected from the environment by a more or less impervious shell. The shell protects the embryo from drying out, nourishes it, and enables it to develop outside of water.

anaerobic (Gr. *an,* without + *aer,* air + *bios,* life) Any process that can occur without oxygen. Includes glycolysis and fermentation. Anaerobic organisms can live without free oxygen.

anaphase In mitosis and meiosis II, the stage initiated by the separation of sister chromatids, during which the daughter chromosomes move to opposite poles of the cell; in meiosis I, marked by separation of replicated homologous chromosomes.

angiosperms The flowering plants, one of five phyla of seed plants. In angiosperms, the ovules at the time of pollination are completely enclosed by tissues.

anterior (L. *ante,* before) Located before or toward the front. In animals, the head end of an organism.

anther (Gr. *anthos,* flower) The part of the stamen of a flower that bears the pollen.

antibody (Gr. *anti,* against) A protein substance produced by a B cell lymphocyte in response to a foreign substance (antigen) and released into the bloodstream. Binding to the antigen, antibodies mark them for destruction by other elements of the immune system.

anticodon The three-nucleotide sequence of a tRNA molecule that is complementary to, and base pairs with, an amino acid-specifying codon in mRNA.

antigen (Gr. *anti,* against + *genos,* origin) A foreign substance, usually a protein, that stimulates lymphocytes to proliferate and secrete specific antibodies that bind to the foreign substance, labeling it as foreign and destined for destruction.

apical meristem (L. *apex,* top + Gr. *meristos,* divided) In vascular plants, the growing point at the tip of the root or stem.

aposematic coloration An ecological strategy of some organisms that "advertise" their poisonous nature by the use of bright colors.

appendicular skeleton (L. *appendicula,* a small appendage) The skeleton of the limbs of the human body containing 126 bones.

archaea A group of prokaryotes that are among the most primitive still in existence, characterized by the absence of peptidoglycan in their cell walls, a feature that distinguishes them from bacteria.

asexual Reproducing without forming gametes. Asexual reproduction does not involve sex. Its outstanding characteristic is that an individual offspring is genetically identical to its parent.

association neuron A nerve cell found only in the CNS that acts as a functional link between sensory neurons and motor neurons. Also called interneuron.

atom (Gr. *atomos,* indivisible) A core (nucleus) of protons and neutrons surrounded by an orbiting cloud of electrons. The chemical behavior of an atom is largely determined by the distribution of its electrons, particularly the number of electrons in its outermost level.

atomic number The number of protons in the nucleus of an atom. In an atom that does not bear an electric charge (that is, one that is not an ion), the atomic number is also equal to the number of electrons.

autonomic nervous system (Gr. *autos,* self + *nomos,* law) The motor pathways that carry commands from the central nervous system to regulate the glands and nonskeletal muscles of the body. Also called the involuntary nervous system.

autosome (Gr. *autos,* self + *soma,* body) Any of the 22 pairs of human chromosomes that are similar in size and morphology in both males and females.

autotroph (Gr. *autos,* self + *trophos,* feeder) An organism that can harvest light energy from the sun or from the oxidation of inorganic compounds to make organic molecules.

axial skeleton The skeleton of the head and trunk of the human body containing 80 bones.

axon (Gr., axle) A process extending out from a neuron that conducts impulses away from the cell body.

B

bacterium, ***pl.*** **bacteria (Gr.** ***bakterion,*** **dim. of** ***baktron,*** **a staff)** The simplest cellular organism. Its cell is smaller and prokaryotic in structure, and it lacks internal organization.

basal body In eukaryotic cells that contain flagella or cilia, a form of centriole that anchors each flagellum.

base Any substance that combines with H^+ ions thereby reducing the H^+ ion concentration of a solution. Having a pH value above 7.

Batesian mimicry After Henry W. Bates, English naturalist. A situation in which a palatable or nontoxic organism resembles another kind of organism that is distasteful or toxic. Both species exhibit warning coloration.

B cell A lymphocyte that recognizes invading pathogens much as T cells do, but instead of attacking the pathogens directly, it marks them with antibodies for destruction by the nonspecific body defenses.

bilateral symmetry (L. ***bi,*** **two +** ***lateris,*** **side; Gr.** ***symmetria,*** **symmetry)** A body form in which the right and left halves of an organism are approximate mirror images of each other.

binary fission (L. ***binarius,*** **consisting of two things or parts +** ***fissus,*** **split)** Asexual reproduction of a cell by division into two equal, or nearly equal, parts. Bacteria divide by binary fission.

binomial system (L. ***bi,*** **twice, two + Gr.** ***nomos,*** **usage, law)** A system of nomenclature that uses two words. The first names the genus, and the second designates the species.

biomass (Gr. ***bios,*** **life +** ***maza,*** **lump or mass)** The total weight of all of the organisms living in an ecosystem.

biome (Gr. ***bios,*** **life +** ***-oma,*** **mass, group)** A major terrestrial assemblage of plants, animals, and microorganisms that occur over wide geographical areas and have distinct characteristics. The largest ecological unit.

buffer A substance that takes up or releases hydrogen ions (H^+) to maintain the pH within a certain range.

C

calorie (L. ***calor,*** **heat)** The amount of energy in the form of heat required to raise the temperature of 1 gram of water 1 degree Celsius.

calyx (Gr. ***kalyx,*** **a husk, cup)** The sepals collectively. The outermost flower whorl.

cancer Unrestrained invasive cell growth. A tumor or cell mass resulting from uncontrollable cell division.

capillary (L. ***capillaris,*** **hairlike)** A blood vessel with a very small diameter. Blood exchanges gases and metabolites across capillary walls. Capillaries join the end of an arteriole to the beginning of a venule.

carbohydrate (L. ***carbo,*** **charcoal +** ***hydro,*** **water)** An organic compound consisting of a chain or ring of carbon atoms to which hydrogen and oxygen atoms are attached in a ratio of approximately 1:2:1. A compound of carbon, hydrogen, and oxygen having the generalized formula $(CH_2O)_n$, where *n* is the number of carbon atoms.

carcinogen (Gr. ***karkinos,*** **cancer + -gen)** Any cancer-causing agent.

cardiovascular system (Gr. ***kardia,*** **heart + L.** ***vasculum,*** **vessel)** The blood circulatory system and the heart that pumps it. Collectively, the blood, heart, and blood vessels.

carpel (Gr. ***karpos,*** **fruit)** A leaflike organ in angiosperms that encloses one or more ovules.

carrying capacity The maximum population size that a habitat can support.

catabolism (Gr. ***katabole,*** **throwing down)** A process in which complex molecules are broken down into simpler ones.

catalysis (Gr. ***katalysis,*** **dissolution +** ***lyein,*** **to loosen)** The enzyme-mediated process in which the subunits of polymers are positioned so that their bonds undergo chemical reactions.

catalyst (Gr. ***kata,*** **down +** ***lysis,*** **a loosening)** A general term for a substance that speeds up a specific chemical reaction by lowering the energy required to activate or start the reaction. An enzyme is a biological catalyst.

cell (L. ***cella,*** **a chamber or small room)** The smallest unit of life. The basic organizational unit of all organisms. Composed of a nuclear region containing the hereditary apparatus within a larger volume called the cytoplasm bounded by a lipid membrane.

cell cycle The repeating sequence of growth and division through which cells pass each generation.

cellular respiration The process in which the energy stored in a glucose molecule is released by oxidation. Hydrogen atoms are lost by glucose and gained by oxygen.

central nervous system The brain and spinal cord, the site of information processing and control within the nervous system.

centromere (Gr. ***kentron,*** **center +** ***meros,*** **a part)** A constricted region of the chromosome joining two sister chromatids, to which the kinetochore is attached.

chemical bond The force holding two atoms together. The force can result from the attraction of opposite charges (ionic bond) or from the sharing of one or more pairs of electrons (a covalent bond).

chemiosmosis The cellular process responsible for almost all of the adenosine triphosphate (ATP) harvested from food and for all the ATP produced by photosynthesis.

chemoautotroph An autotrophic bacterium that uses chemical energy released by specific inorganic reactions to power its life processes, including the synthesis of organic molecules.

chiasma, ***pl.*** **chiasmata (Gr. a cross)** In meiosis, the points of crossing over where portions of chromosomes have been exchanged during synapsis. A chiasma appears as an X-shaped structure under a light microscope.

chloroplast (Gr. ***chloros,*** **green +** ***plastos,*** **molded)** A cell-like organelle present in algae and plants that contains chlorophyll (and usually other pigments) and is the site of photosynthesis.

chromatid (Gr. ***chroma,*** **color + L.** ***-id,*** **daughters of)** One of two daughter strands of a duplicated chromosome that is joined by a single centromere.

chromatin (Gr. ***chroma,*** **color)** The complex of DNA and proteins of which eukaryotic chromosomes are composed.

chromosome (Gr. ***chroma,*** **color +** ***soma,*** **body)** The vehicle by which hereditary information is physically transmitted from one generation to the next. In a eukaryotic cell, long threads of DNA that are associated with protein and that contain hereditary information.

cilium, ***pl.*** **cilia (L. eyelash)** Refers to flagella, which are numerous and organized in dense rows. Cilia propel cells through water. In human tissue, they move water or mucus over the tissue surface.

cladistics A taxonomic technique used for creating hierarchies of organisms based on derived characters that represent true phylogenetic relationship and descent.

class A taxonomic category ranking below a phylum (division) and above an order.

clone (Gr. ***klon,*** **twig)** A line of cells, all of which have arisen from the same single cell by mitotic division. One of a population of individuals derived by asexual reproduction from a single ancestor. One of a population of genetically identical individuals.

codominance In genetics, a situation in which the effects of both alleles at a particular locus are apparent in the phenotype of the heterozygote.

codon (L. code) The basic unit of the genetic code. A sequence of three adjacent nucleotides in DNA or mRNA that codes for one amino acid or for polypeptide termination.

coelom (Gr. ***koilos,*** **a hollow)** A body cavity formed between layers of mesoderm and in which the digestive tract and other internal organs are suspended.

coenzyme A cofactor of an enzyme that is a nonprotein organic molecule.

coevolution (L. ***co-,*** **together +** ***e-,*** **out +** ***volvere,*** **to fill)** A term that describes the long-term evolutionary adjustment of one group of organisms to another.

commensalism (L. ***cum,*** **together with +** ***mensa,*** **table)** A symbiotic relationship in which one species benefits while the other neither benefits nor is harmed.

community (L. ***communitas,*** **community, fellowship)** The populations of different species that live together and interact in a particular place.

competition Interaction between individuals for the same scarce resources. Intraspecific competition is competition between individuals of a single species. Interspecific competition is competition between individuals of different species.

competitive exclusion The hypothesis that if two species are competing with one another for the same limited resource in the same place, one will be able to use that resource more efficiently than the other and eventually will drive that second species to extinction locally.

complement system The chemical defense of a vertebrate body that consists of a battery of proteins that insert in bacterial and fungal cells, causing holes that destroy the cells.

concentration gradient The concentration difference of a substance as a function of distance. In a cell, a greater concentration of its molecules in one region than in another.

condensation The coiling of the chromosomes into more and more tightly compacted bodies begun during the G_2 phase of the cell cycle.

conjugation (L. *conjugare,* to yoke together) An unusual mode of reproduction in unicellular organisms in which genetic material is exchanged between individuals through tubes connecting them during conjugation.

consumer In ecology, a heterotroph that derives its energy from living or freshly killed organisms or parts thereof. Primary consumers are herbivores; secondary consumers are carnivores or parasites.

cortex (L. bark) In vascular plants, the primary ground tissue of a stem or root, bounded externally by the epidermis and internally by the central cylinder of vascular tissue. In animals, the outer, as opposed to the inner, part of an organ, as in the adrenal, kidney, and cerebral cortexes.

cotyledon (Gr. *kotyledon,* a cup-shaped hollow) Seed leaf. Monocot embryos have one cotyledon, and dicots have two.

countercurrent flow In organisms, the passage of heat or of molecules (such as oxygen, water, or sodium ions) from one circulation path to another moving in the opposite direction. Because the flow of the two paths is in opposite directions, a concentration difference always exists between the two channels, facilitating transfer.

covalent bond (L. *co-,* together + *valare,* to be strong) A chemical bond formed by the sharing of one or more pairs of electrons.

crossing over An essential element of meiosis occurring during prophase when nonsister chromatids exchange portions of DNA strands.

cuticle (L. *cutis,* skin) A very thin film covering the outer skin of many plants.

cytokinesis (Gr. *kytos,* hollow vessel + *kinesis,* movement) The C phase of cell division in which the cell itself divides, creating two daughter cells.

cytoplasm (Gr. *kytos,* hollow vessel + *plasma,* anything molded) A semifluid matrix that occupies the volume between the nuclear region and the cell membrane. It contains the sugars, amino acids, proteins, and organelles (in eukaryotes) with which the cell carries out its everyday activities of growth and reproduction.

cytoskeleton (Gr. *kytos,* hollow vessel + *skeleton,* a dried body) In the cytoplasm of all eukaryotic cells, a network of protein fibers that supports the shape of the cell and anchors organelles, such as the nucleus, to fixed locations.

D

deciduous (L. *decidere,* to fall off) In vascular plants, shedding all the leaves at a certain season.

dehydration reaction Water-losing. The process in which a hydroxyl (OH) group is removed from one subunit of a polymer and a hydrogen (H) group is removed from the other subunit, linking the subunits together and forming a water molecule as a by-product.

demography (Gr. *demos,* people + *graphein,* to draw) The statistical study of population. The measurement of people or, by extension, of the characteristics of people.

density The number of individuals in a population in a given area.

deoxyribonucleic acid (DNA) The basic storage vehicle or central plan of heredity information. It is stored as a sequence of nucleotides in a linear nucleotide polymer. Two of the polymers wind around each other like the outside and inside rails of a circular staircase.

depolarization The movement of ions across a cell membrane that wipes out locally an electrical potential difference.

deuterostome (Gr. *deuteros,* second + *stoma,* mouth) An animal in whose embryonic development the anus forms from or near the blastopore, and the mouth forms later on another part of the blastula. Also characterized by radial cleavage.

dicot Short for dicotyledon; a class of flowering plants generally characterized by having two cotyledons, netlike veins, and flower parts in fours or fives.

diffusion (L. *diffundere,* to pour out) The net movement of molecules to regions of lower concentration as a result of random, spontaneous molecular motions. The process tends to distribute molecules uniformly.

dihybrid (Gr. *dis,* twice + L. *hibrida,* mixed offspring) An individual heterozygous for two genes.

dioecious (Gr. *di,* two + *eikos,* house) Having male and female flowers on separate plants of the same species.

diploid (Gr. *diploos,* double + *eidos,* form) A cell, tissue, or individual with a double set of chromosomes.

directional selection A form of selection in which selection acts to eliminate one extreme from an array of phenotypes. Thus, the genes promoting this extreme become less frequent in the population.

disaccharide (Gr. *dis,* twice + *sakcharon,* sugar) A sugar formed by linking two monosaccharide molecules together. Sucrose (table sugar) is a disaccharide formed by linking a molecule of glucose to a molecule of fructose.

disruptive selection A form of selection in which selection acts to eliminate rather than favor the intermediate type.

diurnal (L. *diurnalis,* day) Active during the day.

division Traditionally, a major taxonomic group of the plant kingdom comparable to a phylum of the animal kingdom. Today divisions are called phyla.

dominant allele An allele that dictates the appearance of heterozygotes. One allele is said to be dominant over another if an individual heterozygous for that allele has the same appearance as an individual homozygous for it.

dorsal (L. *dorsum,* the back) Toward the back, or upper surface. Opposite of ventral.

double fertilization A process unique to the angiosperms, in which one sperm nucleus fertilizes the egg and the second one fuses with the polar nuclei. These two events result in the formation of the zygote and the primary endosperm nucleus, respectively.

E

ecdysis (Gr. *ekdysis,* stripping off) The shedding of the outer covering or skin of certain animals. Especially the shedding of the exoskeleton by arthropods.

ecology (Gr. *oikos,* house + *logos,* word) The study of the relationships of organisms with one another and with their environment.

ecosystem (Gr. *oikos,* house + *systema,* that which is put together) A community, together with the nonliving factors with which it interacts.

ectoderm (Gr. *ecto,* outside + *derma,* skin) One of three embryonic germ layers that forms in the gastrula; giving rise to the outer epithelium and to nerve tissue.

ectothermic Referring to animals whose body temperature is regulated by their behavior or their surroundings.

electron A subatomic particle with a negative electrical charge. The negative charge of one electron exactly balances the positive charge of one proton. Electrons orbit the atom's positively charged nucleus and determine its chemical properties.

electron transport chain A collective term describing the series of membrane-associated electron carriers embedded in the inner mitochondrial membrane. It puts the electrons harvested from the oxidation of glucose to work driving proton-pumping channels.

electron transport system A collective term describing the series of membrane-associated electron carriers embedded in the thylakoid membrane of the chloroplast. It puts the electrons harvested from water molecules and energized by photons of light to work driving proton-pumping channels.

element A substance that cannot be separated into different substances by ordinary chemical methods.

emergent properties Novel properties in the hierarchy of life that were not present at the simpler levels of organization.

endergonic (Gr. *endon,* within + *ergon,* work) Reactions in which the products contain more energy than the reactants and require an input of usable energy from an outside source before they can proceed. These reactions are not spontaneous.

endocrine gland (Gr. *endon,* within + *krinein,* to separate) A ductless gland producing hormonal secretions that pass directly into the bloodstream or lymph.

endocrine system The dozen or so major endocrine glands of a vertebrate.

endocytosis (Gr. *endon,* within + *kytos,* cell) The process by which the edges of plasma membranes fuse together and form an enclosed chamber called a vesicle. It involves the incorporation of a portion of an exterior medium into the cytoplasm of the cell by capturing it within the vesicle.

endoderm (Gr. *endon,* outside + *derma,* skin) One of three embryonic germ layers that forms in the gastrula; giving rise to the epithelium that lines internal organs and most of the digestive and respiratory tracts.

endoplasmic reticulum (ER) (L. *endoplasmic,* within the cytoplasm + *reticulum,* little net) An extensive network of membrane compartments within a eukaryotic cell; attached ribosomes synthesize proteins to be exported.

endoskeleton (Gr. *endon,* within + *skeletos,* hard) In vertebrates, an internal scaffold of bone or cartilage to which muscles are attached.

endosperm (Gr. *endon,* within + *sperma,* seed) A nutritive tissue characteristic of the seeds of angiosperms that develops from the union of a male nucleus and the polar nuclei of the embryo sac. The endosperm is either digested by the growing embryo or retained in the mature seed to nourish the germinating seedling.

endosymbiotic (Gr. *endon,* within + *bios,* life) theory A theory that proposes how eukaryotic cells arose from large prokaryotic cells that engulfed smaller ones of a different species. The smaller cells were not consumed but continued to live and function within the larger host cell. Organelles that are believed to have entered larger cells in this way are mitochondria and chloroplasts.

endothermic The ability of animals to maintain a constant body temperature.

energy The capacity to bring about change, to do work.

enhancer A site of regulatory protein binding on the DNA molecule distant from the promoter and start site for a gene's transcription.

entropy (Gr. *en,* in + *tropos,* change in manner) A measure of the disorder of a system. A measure of energy that has become so randomized and uniform in a system that the energy is no longer available to do work.

enzyme (Gr. *enzymos,* leavened; from *en,* in + *zyme,* leaven) A protein capable of speeding up specific chemical reactions by lowering the energy required to activate or start the reaction but that remains unaltered in the process.

epidermis (Gr. *epi,* on or over + *derma,* skin) The outermost layer of cells. In vertebrates, the non-vascular external layer of skin of ectodermal origin; in invertebrates, a single layer of ectodermal epithelium; in plants, the flattened, skinlike outer layer of cells.

epistasis (Gr. *epistasis,* a standing still) An interaction between the products of two genes in which one modifies the phenotypic expression produced by the other.

epithelium (Gr. *epi,* on + *thele,* nipple) A thin layer of cells forming a tissue that covers the internal and external surfaces of the body. Simple epithelium consists of the membranes that line the lungs and major body cavities and that are a single cell layer thick. Stratified epithelium (the skin or epidermis) is composed of more complex epithelial cells that are several cell layers thick.

erythrocyte (Gr. *erythros,* red + *kytos,* hollow vessel) A red blood cell, the carrier of hemoglobin. Erythrocytes act as the transporters of oxygen in the vertebrate body. During the process of their maturation in mammals, they lose their nuclei and mitochondria, and their endoplasmic reticulum is reabsorbed.

estrus (L. *oestrus,* frenzy) The period of maximum female sexual receptivity. Associated with ovulation of the egg. Being "in heat."

estuary (L. *aestus,* tide) A partly enclosed body of water, such as those that often form at river mouths and in coastal bays, where the salinity is intermediate between that of saltwater and freshwater.

ethology (Gr. *ethos,* habit or custom + *logos,* discourse) The study of patterns of animal behavior in nature.

euchromatin (Gr. *eu,* true + *chroma,* color) Chromatin that is extended except during cell division, from which RNA is transcribed.

eukaryote (Gr. *eu,* true + *karyon,* kernel) A cell that possesses membrane-bounded organelles, most notably a cell nucleus, and chromosomes whose DNA is associated with proteins; an organism composed of such cells. The appearance of eukaryotes marks a major event in the evolution of life, as all organisms on earth other than bacteria and archaea are eukaryotes.

eumetazoan (Gr. *eu,* true + *meta,* with + *zoion,* animal) A "true animal." An animal with a definite shape and symmetry and nearly always distinct tissues.

eutrophic (Gr. *eutrophos,* thriving) Refers to a lake in which an abundant supply of minerals and organic matter exists.

evaporation The escape of water molecules from the liquid to the gas phase at the surface of a body of water.

evolution (L. *evolvere,* to unfold) Genetic change in a population of organisms over time (generations). Darwin proposed that natural selection was the mechanism of evolution.

exergonic (L. *ex,* out + Gr. *ergon,* work) Any reaction that produces products that contain less free energy than that possessed by the original reactants and that tends to proceed spontaneously.

exocytosis (Gr. *ex,* out of + *kytos,* cell) The extrusion of material from a cell by discharging it from vesicles at the cell surface. The reverse of endocytosis.

exoskeleton (Gr. *exo,* outside + *skeletos,* hard) An external hard shell that encases a body. In arthropods, comprised mainly of chitin.

experiment The test of a hypothesis. An experiment that tests one or more alternative hypotheses and those that are demonstrated to be inconsistent with experimental observation and are rejected.

F

facilitated diffusion The transport of molecules across a membrane by a carrier protein in the direction of lowest concentration.

family A taxonomic group ranking below an order and above a genus.

feedback inhibition A regulatory mechanism in which a biochemical pathway is regulated by the amount of the product that the pathway produces.

fermentation (L. *fermentum,* ferment) A catabolic process in which the final electron acceptor is an organic molecule.

fertilization (L. *ferre,* to bear) The union of male and female gametes to form a zygote.

fitness The genetic contribution of an individual to succeeding generations, relative to the contributions of other individuals in the population.

flagellum, *pl.* flagella (L. *flagellum,* whip) A fine, long, threadlike organelle protruding from the surface of a cell. In bacteria, a single protein fiber capable of rotary motion that propels the cell through the water. In eukaryotes, an array of microtubules with a characteristic internal 9 + 2 microtubule structure that is capable of vibratory but not rotary motion. Used in locomotion and feeding. Common in protists and motile gametes. A cilium is a short flagellum.

food web The food relationships within a community. A diagram of who eats whom.

founder effect The effect by which rare alleles and combinations of alleles may be enhanced in new populations.

frequency In statistics, defined as the proportion of individuals in a certain category, relative to the total number of individuals being considered.

fruit In angiosperms, a mature, ripened ovary (or group of ovaries) containing the seeds.

G

gamete (Gr. wife) A haploid reproductive cell. Upon fertilization, its nucleus fuses with that of another gamete of the opposite sex. The resulting diploid cell (zygote) may develop into a new diploid individual, or in some protists and fungi, may undergo meiosis to form haploid somatic cells.

gametophyte (Gr. *gamete,* wife + *phyton,* plant) In plants, the haploid (n), gamete-producing generation, which alternates with the diploid ($2n$) sporophyte.

ganglion, *pl.* ganglia (Gr. a swelling) A group of nerve cells forming a nerve center in the peripheral nervous system.

gastrulation The inward movement of certain cell groups from the surface of the blastula.

gene (Gr. *genos,* birth, race) The basic unit of heredity. A sequence of DNA nucleotides on a chromosome that encodes a polypeptide or RNA molecule and so determines the nature of an individual's inherited traits.

gene expression The process in which an RNA copy of each active gene is made, and the RNA copy directs the sequential assembly of a chain of amino acids at a ribosome.

gene frequency The frequency with which individuals in a population possess a particular gene. Often confused with allele frequency.

genetic code The "language" of the genes. The mRNA codons specific for the 20 common amino acids constitute the genetic code.

genetic drift Random fluctuations in allele frequencies in a small population over time.

genetic map A diagram showing the relative positions of genes.

genetics (Gr. *genos,* birth, race) The study of the way in which an individual's traits are transmitted from one generation to the next.

genome (Gr. *genos,* offspring + L. *oma,* abstract group) The genetic information of an organism.

genomics The study of genomes as opposed to individual genes.

genotype (Gr. *genos,* offspring + *typos,* form) The total set of genes present in the cells of an organism. Also used to refer to the set of alleles at a single gene locus.

genus, *pl.* genera (L. race) A taxonomic group that ranks below a family and above a species.

germination (L. *germinare,* to sprout) The resumption of growth and development by a spore or seed.

gland (L. *glandis,* acorn) Any of several organs in the body, such as exocrine or endocrine, that secrete substances for use in the body. Glands are composed of epithelial tissue.

glomerulus (L. a little ball) A network of capillaries in a vertebrate kidney, whose walls act as a filtration device.

glycolysis (Gr. *glykys,* sweet + *lyein,* to loosen) The anaerobic breakdown of glucose; this enzyme-catalyzed process yields two molecules of pyruvate with a net of two molecules of ATP.

golgi complex Flattened stacks of membrane compartments that collect, package, and distribute molecules made in the endoplasmic reticulum.

gravitropism (L. *gravis*, heavy + *tropes*, turning) The response of a plant to gravity, which generally causes shoots to grow up and roots to grow down.

greenhouse effect The process in which carbon dioxide and certain other gases, such as methane, that occur in the earth's atmosphere transmit radiant energy from the sun but trap the longer wavelengths of infrared light, or heat, and prevent them from radiating into space.

guard cells Pairs of specialized epidermal cells that surround a stoma. When the guard cells are turgid, the stoma is open; when they are flaccid, it is closed.

gymnosperm (Gr. *gymnos*, naked + *sperma*, seed) A seed plant with seeds not enclosed in an ovary. The conifers are the most familiar group.

H

habitat (L. *habitare*, to inhabit) The place where individuals of a species live.

half-life The length of time it takes for half of a radioactive substance to decay.

haploid (Gr. *haploos*, single + *eidos*, form) The gametes of a cell or an individual with only one set of chromosomes.

Hardy-Weinberg equilibrium After G. H. Hardy, English mathematician, and G. Weinberg, German physician. A mathematical description of the fact that the relative frequencies of two or more alleles in a population do not change because of Mendelian segregation. Allele and genotype frequencies remain constant in a random-mating population in the absence of inbreeding, selection, or other evolutionary forces. Usually stated as: If the frequency of allele A is p and the frequency of allele a is q, then the genotype frequencies after one generation of random mating will always be $(p + q)^2 = p^2 + 2pq + q^2$.

Haversian canal After Clopton Havers, English anatomist. Narrow channels that run parallel to the length of a bone and contain blood vessels and nerve cells.

helper T cell A class of white blood cells that initiates both the cell-mediated immune response and the humoral immune response; helper T cells are the targets of the AIDS virus (HIV).

hemoglobin (Gr. *haima*, blood + L. *globus*, a ball) A globular protein in vertebrate red blood cells and in the plasma of many invertebrates that carries oxygen and carbon dioxide.

herbivore (L. *herba*, grass + *vorare*, to devour) Any organism that eats only plants.

heredity (L. *heredis*, heir) The transmission of characteristics from parent to offspring.

heterochromatin (Gr. *heteros*, different + *chroma*, color) That portion of a eukaryotic chromosome that remains permanently condensed and therefore is not transcribed into RNA. Most centromere regions are heterochromatic.

heterokaryon (Gr. *heteros*, other + *karyon*, kernel) A fungal hypha that has two or more genetically distinct types of nuclei.

heterotroph (Gr. *heteros*, other + *trophos*, feeder) An organism that does not have the ability to produce its own food. *See also* autotroph.

heterozygote (Gr. *heteros*, other + *zygotos*, a pair) A diploid individual carrying two different alleles of a gene on its two homologous chromosomes.

hierarchical (Gr. *hieros*, sacred + *archos*, leader) Refers to a system of classification in which successively smaller units of classification are included within one another.

histone (Gr. *histos*, tissue) A complex of small, very basic polypeptides rich in the amino acids arginine and lysine. A basic part of chromosomes, histones form the core around which DNA is wrapped.

homeostasis (Gr. *homeos*, similar + *stasis*, standing) The maintaining of a relatively stable internal physiological environment in an organism or steady-state equilibrium in a population or ecosystem.

homeotherm (Gr. *homeo*, similar + *therme*, heat) An organism, such as a bird or mammal, capable of maintaining a stable body temperature independent of the environmental temperature. "Warm-blooded."

hominid (L. *homo*, man) Human beings and their direct ancestors. A member of the family Hominidae. *Homo sapiens* is the only living member.

homologous chromosome (Gr. *homologia*, agreement) One of the two nearly identical versions of each chromosome. Chromosomes that associate in pairs in the first stage of meiosis. In diploid cells, one chromosome of a pair that carries equivalent genes.

homology (Gr. *homologia*, agreement) A condition in which the similarity between two structures or functions is indicative of a common evolutionary origin.

homozygote (Gr. *homos*, same or similar + *zygotos*, a pair) A diploid individual whose two copies of a gene are the same. An individual carrying identical alleles on both homologous chromosomes is said to be homozygous for that gene.

hormone (Gr. *hormaein*, to excite) A chemical messenger, often a steroid or peptide, produced in a small quantity in one part of an organism and then transported to another part of the organism, where it brings about a physiological response.

hybrid (L. *hybrida*, the offspring of a tame sow and a wild boar) A plant or animal that results from the crossing of dissimilar parents.

hybridization The mating of unlike parents of different taxa.

hydrogen bond A molecular force formed by the attraction of the partial positive charge of one hydrogen atom of a water molecule with the partial negative charge of the oxygen atom of another.

hydrolysis reaction (Gr. *hydro*, water + *lyse*, break) The process of tearing down a polymer by adding a molecule of water. A hydrogen is attached to one subunit and a hydroxyl to the other, which breaks the covalent bond. Essentially the reverse of a dehydration reaction.

hydrophilic (Gr. *hydro*, water + *philic*, loving) Describes polar molecules, which form hydrogen bonds with water and therefore are soluble in water.

hydrophobic (Gr. *hydro*, water + *phobos*, hating) Describes nonpolar molecules, which do not form hydrogen bonds with water and therefore are not soluble in water.

hydroskeleton (Gr. *hydro*, water + *skeletos*, hard) The skeleton of most soft-bodied invertebrates that have neither an internal nor an external skeleton. They use the relative incompressibility of the water within their bodies as a kind of skeleton.

hypertonic (Gr. *hyper*, above + *tonos*, tension) A cell that contains a higher concentration of solutes than its surrounding solution.

hypha, *pl.* hyphae (Gr. *hyphe*, web) A filament of a fungus. A mass of hyphae comprises a mycelium.

hypothalamus (Gr. *hypo*, under + *thalamos*, inner room) The region of the brain under the thalamus that controls temperature, hunger, and thirst and that produces hormones that influence the pituitary gland.

hypothesis (Gr. *hypo*, under + *tithenai*, to put) A proposal that might be true. No hypothesis is ever proven correct. All hypotheses are provisional—proposals that are retained for the time being as useful but that may be rejected in the future if found to be inconsistent with new information. A hypothesis that stands the test of time—often tested and never rejected—is called a theory.

hypotonic (Gr. *hypo*, under + *tonos*, tension) A solution surrounding a cell that has a lower concentration of solutes than does the cell.

I

inbreeding The breeding of genetically related plants or animals. In plants, inbreeding results from self-pollination. In animals, inbreeding results from matings between relatives. Inbreeding tends to increase homozygosity.

incomplete dominance The ability of two alleles to produce a heterozygous phenotype that is different from either homozygous phenotype.

independent assortment Mendel's second law: The principle that segregation of alternative alleles at one locus into gametes is independent of the segregation of alleles at other loci. Only true for gene loci located on different chromosomes or those so far apart on one chromosome that crossing over is very frequent between the loci.

industrial melanism (Gr. *melas*, black) The evolutionary process in which a population of initially light-colored organisms becomes a population of dark organisms as a result of natural selection.

inflammatory response (L. *inflammare*, to flame) A generalized nonspecific response to infection that acts to clear an infected area of infecting microbes and dead tissue cells so that tissue repair can begin.

integument (L. *integumentum*, covering) The natural outer covering layers of an animal. Develops from the ectoderm.

interneuron A nerve cell found only in the CNS that acts as a functional link between sensory neurons and motor neurons. Also called association neuron.

internode The region of a plant stem between nodes where stems and leaves attach.

interoception (L. *interus*, inner + Eng. *[re]ceptive*) The sensing of information that relates to the body itself, its internal condition, and its position.

interphase That portion of the cell cycle preceding mitosis. It includes the G_1 phase, when cells grow, the S phase, when a replica of the genome is synthesized, and a G_2 phase, when preparations are made for genomic separation.

intron (L. *intra,* within) A segment of DNA transcribed into mRNA but removed before translation. These untranslated regions make up the bulk of most eukaryotic genes.

ion An atom in which the number of electrons does not equal the number of protons. An ion carries an electrical charge.

ionic bond A chemical bond formed between ions as a result of the attraction of opposite electrical charges.

ionizing radiation High-energy radiation, such as X rays and gamma rays.

isolating mechanisms Mechanisms that prevent genetic exchange between individuals of different populations or species.

isotonic (Gr. *isos,* equal + *tonos,* tension) A cell with the same concentration of solutes as its environment.

isotope (Gr. *isos,* equal + *topos,* place) An atom that has the same number of protons but different numbers of neutrons.

J

joint The part of a vertebrate where one bone meets and moves on another.

K

karyotype (Gr. *karyon,* kernel + *typos,* stamp or print) The particular array of chromosomes that an individual possesses.

kinetic energy The energy of motion.

kinetochore (Gr. *kinetikos,* putting in motion + *choros,* chorus) A disk of protein bound to the centromere to which microtubules attach during cell division, linking chromatids to the spindle.

kingdom The chief taxonomic category. This book recognizes six kingdoms: Archaea, Bacteria, Protista, Fungi, Animalia, and Plantae.

L

lamella, *pl.* lamellae (L. a little plate) A thin, platelike structure. In chloroplasts, a layer of chlorophyll-containing membranes. In bivalve mollusks, one of the two plates forming a gill. In vertebrates, one of the thin layers of bone laid concentrically around the Haversian canals.

ligament (L. *ligare,* to bind) A band or sheet of connective tissue that links bone to bone.

linkage The patterns of assortment of genes that are located on the same chromosome. Important because if the genes are located relatively far apart, crossing over is more likely to occur between them than if they are close together.

lipid (Gr. *lipos,* fat) A loosely defined group of molecules that are insoluble in water but soluble in oil. Oils such as olive, corn, and coconut are lipids, as well as waxes, such as beeswax and earwax.

lipid bilayer The basic foundation of all biological membranes. In such a layer, the nonpolar tails of phospholipid molecules point inward, forming a nonpolar zone in the interior of the bilayers. Lipid bilayers are selectively permeable and do not permit the diffusion of water-soluble molecules into the cell.

littoral (L. *litus,* shore) Referring to the shoreline zone of a lake or pond or the ocean that is exposed to the air whenever water recedes.

locus, *pl.* loci (L. place) The position on a chromosome where a gene is located.

loop of Henle After F. G. J. Henle, German anatomist. A hairpin loop formed by a urine-conveying tubule when it enters the inner layer of the kidney and then turns around to pass up again into the outer layer of the kidney.

lymph (L. *lympha,* clear water) In animals, a colorless fluid derived from blood by filtration through capillary walls in the tissues.

lymphatic system An open circulatory system composed of a network of vessels that function to collect the water within blood plasma forced out during passage through the capillaries and to return it to the bloodstream. The lymphatic system also returns proteins to the circulation, transports fats absorbed from the intestine, and carries bacteria and dead blood cells to the lymph nodes and spleen for destruction.

lymphocyte (Gr. *lympha,* water + Gr. *kytos,* hollow vessel) A white blood cell. A cell of the immune system that either synthesizes antibodies (B cells) or attacks virus-infected cells (T cells).

lyse (Gr. *lysis,* loosening) To disintegrate a cell by rupturing its plasma membrane.

M

macromolecule (Gr. *makros,* large + L. *moliculus,* a little mass) An extremely large molecule. Refers specifically to carbohydrates, lipids, proteins, and nucleic acids.

macrophage (Gr. *makros,* large + *-phage,* eat) A phagocytic cell of the immune system able to engulf and digest invading bacteria, fungi, and other microorganisms, as well as cellular debris.

marrow The soft tissue that fills the cavities of most bones and is the source of red blood cells.

mass flow The overall process by which materials move in the phloem of plants.

mass number The mass number of an atom consists of the combined mass of all of its protons and neutrons.

meiosis (Gr. *meioun,* to make smaller) A special form of nuclear division that precedes gamete formation in sexually reproducing eukaryotes. It results in four haploid daughter cells.

Mendelian ratio After Gregor Mendel, Austrian monk. Refers to the characteristic 3:1 segregation ratio that Mendel observed, in which pairs of alternative traits are expressed in the F_2 generation in the ratio of three-fourths dominant to one-fourth recessive.

menstruation (L. *mens,* month) Periodic sloughing off of the blood-enriched lining of the uterus when pregnancy does not occur.

meristem (Gr. *merizein,* to divide) In plants, a zone of unspecialized cells whose only function is to divide.

mesoderm (Gr. *mesos,* middle + *derma,* skin) One of the three embryonic germ layers that form in the gastrula. Gives rise to muscle, bone, and other connective tissue; the peritoneum; the circulatory system; and most of the excretory and reproductive systems.

mesophyll (Gr. *mesos,* middle + *phyllon,* leaf) The photosynthetic parenchyma of a leaf, located within the epidermis. The vascular strands (veins) run through the mesophyll.

metabolism (Gr. *metabole,* change) The process by which all living things assimilate energy and use it to grow.

metamorphosis (Gr. *meta,* after + *morphe,* form + *osis,* state of) Process in which form changes markedly during postembryonic development—for example, tadpole to frog or larval insect to adult.

metaphase (Gr. *meta,* middle + *phasis,* form) The stage of mitosis characterized by the alignment of the chromosomes on a plane in the center of the cell.

metastasis, *pl.* metastases (Gr. to place in another way) The spread of cancerous cells to other parts of the body, forming new tumors at distant sites.

microevolution (Gr. *mikros,* small + L. *evolvere,* to unfold) Refers to the evolutionary process itself. Evolution within a species. Also called adaptation.

microtubule (Gr. *mikros,* small + L. *tubulus,* little pipe) In eukaryotic cells, a long, hollow cylinder about 25 nanometers in diameter and composed of the protein tubulin. Microtubules influence cell shape, move the chromosomes in cell division, and provide the functional internal structure of cilia and flagella.

mimicry (Gr. *mimos,* mime) The resemblance in form, color, or behavior of certain organisms (mimics) to other more powerful or more protected ones (models), which results in the mimics being protected in some way.

mitochondrion, *pl.* mitochondria (Gr. *mitos,* thread + *chondrion,* small grain) A tubular or sausage-shaped organelle 1 to 3 micrometers long. Bounded by two membranes, mitochondria closely resemble the aerobic bacteria from which they were originally derived. As chemical furnaces of the cell, they carry out its oxidative metabolism.

mitosis (Gr. *mitos,* thread) The M phase of cell division in which the microtubular apparatus is assembled, binds to the chromosomes, and moves them apart. This phase is the essential step in the separation of the two daughter cell genomes.

mole (L. *moles,* mass) The atomic weight of a substance, expressed in grams. One mole is defined as the mass of 6.0222×10^{23} atoms.

molecule (L. *moliculus,* a small mass) The smallest unit of a compound that displays the properties of that compound.

monocot Short for monocotyledon; flowering plant in which the embryos have only one cotyledon, the flower parts are often in threes, and the leaves typically are parallel-veined.

monomers (Gr. *mono,* single + *meris,* part) Simple molecules that can join together to form polymers.

monosaccharide (Gr. *monos,* one + *sakcharon,* sugar) A simple sugar.

morphogenesis (Gr. *morphe,* form + *genesis,* origin) The formation of shape. The growth and differentiation of cells and tissues during development.

motor endplate The point where a neuron attaches to a muscle. A neuromuscular synapse.

multicellularity A condition in which the activities of the individual cells are coordinated and the cells themselves are in contact. A property of eukaryotes alone and one of their major characteristics.

muscle (L. *musculus,* mouse) The tissue in the body of humans and animals that can be contracted and relaxed to make the body move.

muscle cell A long, cylindrical, multinucleated cell that contains numerous myofibrils and is capable of contraction when stimulated.

muscle spindle A sensory organ that is attached to a muscle and sensitive to stretching.

mutagen (L. *mutare,* to change) A chemical capable of damaging DNA.

mutation (L. *mutare,* to change) A change in a cell's genetic message.

mutualism (L. *mutuus,* lent, borrowed) A symbiotic relationship in which both participating species benefit.

mycelium, *pl.* mycelia (Gr. *mykes,* fungus) In fungi, a mass of hyphae.

mycology (Gr. *mykes,* fungus) The study of fungi. A person who studies fungi is called a mycologist.

mycorrhiza, *pl.* mycorrhizae (Gr. *mykes,* fungus + *rhiza,* root) A symbiotic association between fungi and plant roots.

myofibril (Gr. *myos,* muscle + L. *fibrilla,* little fiber) An elongated structure in a muscle fiber, composed of myosin and actin.

myosin (Gr. *myos,* muscle + *in,* belonging to) One of two protein components of myofilaments. (The other is actin.)

N

natural selection The differential reproduction of genotypes caused by factors in the environment. Leads to evolutionary change.

nematocyst (Gr. *nema,* thread + *kystos,* bladder) A coiled, threadlike stinging structure of cnidarians that is discharged to capture prey and for defense.

nephron (Gr. *nephros,* kidney) The functional unit of the vertebrate kidney. A human kidney has more than 1 million nephrons that filter waste matter from the blood. Each nephron consists of a Bowman's capsule, glomerulus, and tubule.

nerve A bundle of axons with accompanying supportive cells, held together by connective tissue.

nerve impulse A rapid, transient, self-propagating reversal in electrical potential that travels along the membrane of a neuron.

neuromodulator A chemical transmitter that mediates effects that are slow and longer lasting and that typically involve second messengers within the cell.

neuromuscular junction The structure formed when the tips of axons contact (innervate) a muscle fiber.

neuron (Gr. nerve) A nerve cell specialized for signal transmission.

neurotransmitter (Gr. *neuron,* nerve + L. *trans,* across + *mitere,* to send) A chemical released at an axon tip that travels across the synapse and binds a specific receptor protein in the membrane on the far side.

neurulation (Gr. *neuron,* nerve) The elaboration of a notochord and a dorsal nerve cord that marks the evolution of the chordates.

neutron (L. *neuter,* neither) A subatomic particle located within the nucleus of an atom. Similar to a proton in mass, but as its name implies, a neutron is neutral and possesses no charge.

neutrophil An abundant type of white blood cell capable of engulfing microorganisms and other foreign particles.

niche (L. *nidus,* nest) The role an organism plays in the environment; realized niche is the niche that an organism occupies under natural circumstances; fundamental niche is the niche an organism would occupy if competitors were not present.

nitrogen fixation The incorporation of atmospheric nitrogen into nitrogen compounds, a process that can be carried out only by certain microorganisms.

nocturnal (L. *nocturnus,* night) Active primarily at night.

node (L. *nodus,* knot) The place on the stem where a leaf is formed.

node of Ranvier After L. A. Ranvier, French histologist. A gap formed at the point where two Schwann cells meet and where the axon is in direct contact with the surrounding intercellular fluid.

nondisjunction The failure of homologous chromosomes to separate in meiosis I. The cause of Down syndrome.

nonrandom mating A phenomenon in which individuals with certain genotypes sometimes mate with one another more commonly than would be expected on a random basis.

notochord (Gr. *noto,* back + L. *chorda,* cord) In chordates, a dorsal rod of cartilage that forms between the nerve cord and the developing gut in the early embryo.

nucleic acid A nucleotide polymer. A long chain of nucleotides. Chief types are deoxyribonucleic acid (DNA), which is double-stranded, and ribonucleic acid (RNA), which is typically single-stranded.

nucleosome (L. *nucleus,* kernel + *soma,* body) The basic packaging unit of eukaryotic chromosomes, in which the DNA molecule is wound around a ball of histone proteins. Chromatin is composed of long strings of nucleosomes, like beads on a string.

nucleotide A single unit of nucleic acid, composed of a phosphate, a five-carbon sugar (either ribose or deoxyribose), and a purine or a pyrimidine.

nucleolus A region inside the nucleus where rRNA and ribosomes are produced.

nucleus (L. *a kernel,* dim. Fr. *nux,* nut) A spherical organelle (structure) characteristic of eukaryotic cells. The repository of the genetic information that directs all activities of a living cell. In atoms, the central core, containing positively charged protons and (in all but hydrogen) electrically neutral neutrons.

O

oocyte (Gr. *oion,* egg + *kytos,* vessel) A cell in the outer layer of the ovary that gives rise to an ovum. A primary oocyte is any of the 2 million oocytes a female is born with, all of which have begun the first meiotic division.

operon (L. *operis,* work) A cluster of functionally related genes transcribed onto a single mRNA molecule. A common mode of gene regulation in prokaryotes; it is rare in eukaryotes other than fungi.

order A taxonomic category ranking below a class and above a family.

organ (L. *organon,* tool) A complex body structure composed of several different kinds of tissue grouped together in a structural and functional unit.

organelle (Gr. *organella,* little tool) A specialized compartment of a cell. Mitochondria are organelles.

organism Any individual living creature, either unicellular or multicellular.

organ system A group of organs that function together to carry out the principal activities of the body.

osmoconformer An animal that maintains the osmotic concentration of its body fluids at about the same level as that of the medium in which it is living.

osmoregulation The maintenance of a constant internal solute concentration by an organism, regardless of the environment in which it lives.

osmosis (Gr. *osmos,* act of pushing, thrust) The diffusion of water across a membrane that permits the free passage of water but not that of one or more solutes. Water moves from an area of low solute concentration to an area with higher solute concentration.

osmotic pressure The increase of hydrostatic water pressure within a cell as a result of water molecules that continue to diffuse inward toward the area of lower water concentration (the water concentration is lower inside than outside the cell because of the dissolved solutes in the cell).

osteoblast (Gr. *osteon,* bone + *blastos,* bud) A bone-forming cell.

osteocyte (Gr. *osteon,* bone + *kytos,* hollow vessel) A mature osteoblast.

outcross A term used to describe species that interbreed with individuals other than those like themselves.

oviparous (L. *ovum,* egg + *parere,* to bring forth) Refers to reproduction in which the eggs are developed after leaving the body of the mother, as in reptiles.

ovulation The successful development and release of an egg by the ovary.

ovule (L. *ovulum,* a little egg) A structure in a seed plant that becomes a seed when mature.

ovum, *pl.* ova (L. egg) A mature egg cell. A female gamete.

oxidation (Fr. *oxider,* to oxidize) The loss of an electron during a chemical reaction from one atom to another. Occurs simultaneously with reduction. Is the second stage of the 10 reactions of glycolysis.

oxidative metabolism A collective term for metabolic reactions requiring oxygen.

oxidative respiration Respiration in which the final electron acceptor is molecular oxygen.

P

parasitism (Gr. *para,* beside + *sitos,* food) A symbiotic relationship in which one organism benefits and the other is harmed.

parthenogenesis (Gr. *parthenos,* virgin + Eng. *genesis,* beginning) The development of an adult from an unfertilized egg. A common form of reproduction in insects.

partial pressures (P) The components of each individual gas—such as nitrogen, oxygen, and carbon dioxide—that together constitute the total air pressure.

pathogen (Gr. *pathos,* suffering + Eng. *genesis,* beginning) A disease-causing organism.

pedigree (L. *pes,* foot + *grus,* crane) A family tree. The patterns of inheritance observed in family histories. Used to determine the mode of inheritance of a particular trait.

peptide (Gr. *peptein,* to soften, digest) Two or more amino acids linked by peptide bonds.

peptide bond A covalent bond linking two amino acids. Formed when the positive (amino, or NH_2) group at one end and a negative (carboxyl, or COOH) group at the other end undergo a chemical reaction and lose a molecule of water.

peristalsis (Gr. *peri,* around + *stellein,* to wrap) The rhythmic sequences of waves of muscular contraction in the walls of a tube.

pH Refers to the concentration of H^+ ions in a solution. The numerical value of the pH is the negative of the exponent of the molar concentration. Low pH values indicate high concentrations of H^+ ions (acids), and high pH values indicate low concentrations (bases).

phagocyte (Gr. *phagein,* to eat + *kytos,* hollow vessel) A cell that kills invading cells by engulfing them. Includes neutrophils and macrophages.

phagocytosis (Gr. *phagein,* to eat + *kytos,* hollow vessel) A form of endocytosis in which cells engulf organisms or fragments of organisms.

phenotype (Gr. *phainein,* to show + *typos,* stamp or print) The realized expression of the genotype. The observable expression of a trait (affecting an individual's structure, physiology, or behavior) that results from the biological activity of proteins or RNA molecules transcribed from the DNA.

pheromone (Gr. *pherein,* to carry + [hor]mone) A chemical signal emitted by certain animals as a means of communication.

phloem (Gr. *phloos,* bark) In vascular plants, a food-conducting tissue basically composed of sieve elements, various kinds of parenchyma cells, fibers, and sclereids.

phosphodiester bond The bond that results from the formation of a nucleic acid chain in which individual sugars are linked together in a line by the phosphate groups. The phosphate group of one sugar binds to the hydroxyl group of another, forming an—O—P—O bond.

photon (Gr. *photos,* light) The unit of light energy.

photoperiodism (Gr. *photos,* light + *periodos,* a period) A mechanism that organisms use to measure seasonal changes in relative day and night length.

photorespiration A process in which carbon dioxide is released without the production of ATP or NADPH. Because it produces neither ATP nor NADPH, photorespiration acts to undo the work of photosynthesis.

photosynthesis (Gr. *photos,* light + *-syn,* together + *tithenai,* to place) The process by which plants, algae, and some bacteria use the energy of sunlight to create from carbon dioxide (CO_2) and water (H_2O) the more complicated molecules that make up living organisms.

phototropism (Gr. *photos,* light + *trope,* turning to light) A plant's growth response to a unidirectional light source.

phylogeny (Gr. *phylon,* race, tribe) The evolutionary relationships among any group of organisms.

phylum, *pl.* phyla (Gr. *phylon,* race, tribe) A major taxonomic category, ranking above a class.

physiology (Gr. *physis,* nature + *logos,* a discourse) The study of the function of cells, tissues, and organs.

pigment (L. *pigmentum,* paint) A molecule that absorbs light.

pili (pilus) Short flagella that occur on the cell surface of some prokaryotes.

pinocytosis (Gr. *pinein,* to drink + *kytos,* cell) A form of endocytosis in which the material brought into the cell is a liquid containing dissolved molecules.

pistil (L. *pistillum,* pestle) Central organ of flowers, typically consisting of ovary, style, and stigma; a pistil may consist of one or more fused carpels and is more technically and better known as the gynoecium.

plankton (Gr. *planktos,* wandering) The small organisms that float or drift in water, especially at or near the surface.

plasma (Gr. form) The fluid of vertebrate blood. Contains dissolved salts, metabolic wastes, hormones, and a variety of proteins, including antibodies and albumin. Blood minus the blood cells.

plasma membrane A lipid bilayer with embedded proteins that control the cell's permeability to water and dissolved substances.

plasmid (Gr. *plasma,* a form or something molded) A small fragment of DNA that replicates independently of the bacterial chromosome.

platelet (Gr. dim of *plattus,* flat) In mammals, a fragment of a white blood cell that circulates in the blood and functions in the formation of blood clots at sites of injury.

pleiotropy (Gr. *pleros,* more + *trope,* a turning) A gene that produces more than one phenotypic effect.

polarization The charge difference of a neuron so that the interior of the cell is negative with respect to the exterior.

polar molecule A molecule with positively and negatively charged ends. One portion of a polar molecule attracts electrons more strongly than another portion, with the result that the molecule has electron-rich (–) and electron-poor (+) regions, giving it magnetlike positive and negative poles. Water is one of the most polar molecules known.

pollen (L. fine dust) A fine, yellowish powder consisting of grains or microspores, each of which contains a mature or immature male gametophyte. In flowering plants, pollen is released from the anthers of flowers and fertilizes the pistils.

pollen tube A tube that grows from a pollen grain. Male reproductive cells move through the pollen tube into the ovule.

pollination The transfer of pollen from the anthers to the stigmas of flowers for fertilization, as by insects or the wind.

polygyny (Gr. *poly,* many + *gyne,* woman, wife) A mating choice in which a male mates with more than one female.

polymer (Gr. *polus,* many + *meris,* part) A large molecule formed of long chains of similar molecules called subunits.

polymerase chain reaction (PCR) A process by which DNA polymerase is used to copy a sequence of DNA repeatedly, making millions of copies of the same DNA.

polymorphism (Gr. *polys,* many + *morphe,* form) The presence in a population of more than one allele of a gene at a frequency greater than that of newly arising mutations.

polynomial system (Gr. *polys,* many + [bi]nomial) Before Linnaeus, naming a genus by use of a cumbersome string of Latin words and phrases.

polyp A cylindrical, pipe-shaped cnidarian usually attached to a rock with the mouth facing away from the rock on which it is growing. Coral is made up of polyps.

polypeptide (Gr. *polys,* many + *peptein,* to digest) A general term for a long chain of amino acids linked end to end by peptide bonds. A protein is a long, complex polypeptide.

polysaccharide (Gr. *polys,* many + *sakcharon,* sugar) A sugar polymer. A carbohydrate composed of many monosaccharide sugar subunits linked together in a long chain.

population (L. *populus,* the people) Any group of individuals of a single species, occupying a given area at the same time.

posterior (L. *post,* after) Situated behind or farther back.

potential difference A difference in electrical charge on two sides of a membrane caused by an unequal distribution of ions.

potential energy Energy with the potential to do work. Stored energy.

predation (L. *praeda,* prey) The eating of other organisms. The one doing the eating is called a predator, and the one being consumed is called the prey.

primary growth In vascular plants, growth originating in the apical meristems of shoots and roots, as contrasted with secondary growth; results in an increase in length.

primary plant body The part of a plant that arises from the apical meristems.

primary producers Photosynthetic organisms, including plants, algae, and photosynthetic bacteria.

primary structure of a protein The sequence of amino acids that makes up a particular polypeptide chain.

primordium, *pl.* primordia (L. *primus,* first + *ordiri,* begin) The first cells in the earliest stages of the development of an organ or structure.

productivity The total amount of energy of an ecosystem fixed by photosynthesis per unit of time. Net productivity is productivity minus that which is expended by the metabolic activity of the organisms in the community.

prokaryote (Gr. *pro,* before + *karyon,* kernel) A simple organism that is small, single-celled, and has little evidence of internal structure.

promoter An RNA polymerase binding site. The nucleotide sequence at the end of a gene to which RNA polymerase attaches to initiate transcription of mRNA.

prophase (Gr. *pro,* before + *phasis,* form) The first stage of mitosis during which the chromosomes become more condensed, the nuclear envelope is reabsorbed, and a network of microtubules (called the spindle) forms between opposite poles of the cell.

protein (Gr. *proteios,* primary) A long chain of amino acids linked end to end by peptide bonds. Because the 20 amino acids that occur in proteins have side groups with very different chemical properties, the function and shape of a protein is critically affected by its particular sequence of amino acids.

protist (Gr. *protos,* first) A member of the kingdom Protista, which includes unicellular eukaryotic organisms and some multicellular lines derived from them.

proton A subatomic particle in the nucleus of an atom that carries a positive charge. The number of protons determines the chemical character of the atom because it dictates the number of electrons orbiting the nucleus and available for chemical activity.

protostome (Gr. *protos,* first + *stoma,* mouth) An animal in whose embryonic development the mouth forms at or near the blastopore. Also characterized by spiral cleavage.

protozoa (Gr. *protos,* first + *zoion,* animal) The traditional name given to heterotrophic protists.

pseudocoel (Gr. *pseudos,* false + *koiloma,* cavity) A body cavity similar to the coelom except that it forms between the mesoderm and endoderm.

punctuated equilibrium A hypothesis of the mechanism of evolutionary change that proposes that long periods of little or no change are punctuated by periods of rapid evolution.

Q

quaternary structure of a protein A term to describe the way multiple protein subunits are assembled into a whole.

R

radial symmetry (L. *radius,* a spoke of a wheel + Gr. *summetros,* symmetry) The regular arrangement of parts around a central axis so that any plane passing through the central axis divides the organism into halves that are approximate mirror images.

radioactivity The emission of nuclear particles and rays by unstable atoms as they decay into more stable forms. Measured in curies, with 1 curie equal to 37 billion disintegrations a second.

radula (L. scraper) A rasping, tonguelike organ characteristic of most mollusks.

recessive allele An allele whose phenotype effects are masked in heterozygotes by the presence of a dominant allele.

recombination The formation of new gene combinations. In bacteria, it is accomplished by the transfer of genes into cells, often in association with viruses. In eukaryotes, it is accomplished by reassortment of chromosomes during meiosis and by crossing over.

reducing power The use of light energy to extract hydrogen atoms from water.

reduction (L. *reductio,* a bringing back; originally, "bringing back" a metal from its oxide) The gain of an electron during a chemical reaction from one atom to another. Occurs simultaneously with oxidation.

reflex (L. *reflectere,* to bend back) An automatic consequence of a nerve stimulation. The motion that results from a nerve impulse passing through the system of neurons, eventually reaching the body muscles and causing them to contract.

refractory period The recovery period after membrane depolarization during which the membrane is unable to respond to additional stimulation.

renal (L. *renes,* kidneys) Pertaining to the kidney.

repression (L. *reprimere,* to press back, keep back) The process of blocking transcription by the placement of the regulatory protein between the polymerase and the gene, thus blocking movement of the polymerase to the gene.

repressor (L. *reprimere,* to press back, keep back) A protein that regulates transcription of mRNA from DNA by binding to the operator and so preventing RNA polymerase from attaching to the promoter.

resolving power The ability of a microscope to distinguish two points as separate.

respiration (L. *respirare,* to breathe) The utilization of oxygen. In terrestrial vertebrates, the inhalation of oxygen and the exhalation of carbon dioxide.

resting membrane potential The charge difference that exists across a neuron's membrane at rest (about 70 millivolts).

restriction endonuclease A special kind of enzyme that can recognize and cleave DNA molecules into fragments. One of the basic tools of genetic engineering.

restriction fragment-length polymorphism (RFLP) An associated genetic mutation marker detected because the mutation alters the length of DNA segments.

retrovirus (L. *retro,* turning back) A virus whose genetic material is RNA rather than DNA. When a retrovirus infects a cell, it makes a DNA copy of itself, which it can then insert into the cellular DNA as if it were a cellular gene.

ribose A five-carbon sugar.

ribosome A cell structure composed of protein and RNA that translates RNA copies of genes into protein.

RNA polymerase The enzyme that transcribes RNA from DNA.

S

saltatory conduction A very fast form of nerve impulse conduction in which the impulses leap from node to node over insulated portions.

sarcoma (Gr. *sarx,* flesh) A cancerous tumor that involves connective or hard tissue, such as muscle.

sarcomere (Gr. *sarx,* flesh + *meris,* part of) The fundamental unit of contraction in skeletal muscle. The repeating bands of actin and myosin that appear between two Z lines.

sarcoplasmic reticulum (Gr. *sarx,* flesh + *plassein,* to form, mold; L. *reticulum,* network) The endoplasmic reticulum of a muscle cell. A sleeve of membrane that wraps around each myofilament.

scientific creationism A view that the biblical account of the origin of the earth is literally true, that the earth is much younger than most scientists believe, and that all species of organisms were individually created just as they are today.

secondary growth In vascular plants, growth that results from the division of a cylinder of cells around the plant's periphery. Secondary growth causes a plant to grow in diameter.

secondary structure of a protein The folding and bending of a polypeptide chain, which is held in place by hydrogen bonds.

second messenger An intermediary compound that couples extracellular signals to intracellular processes and also amplifies a hormonal signal.

seed A structure that develops from the mature ovule of a seed plant. Contains an embryo and a food source surrounded by a protective coat.

selection The process by which some organisms leave more offspring than competing ones and their genetic traits tend to appear in greater proportions among members of succeeding generations than the traits of those individuals that leave fewer offspring.

self-fertilization The transfer of pollen from an anther to a stigma in the same flower or to another flower of the same plant.

sepal (L. *sepalum,* a covering) A member of the outermost whorl of a flowering plant. Collectively, the sepals constitute the calyx.

septum, *pl.* septa (L. *saeptum,* a fence) A partition or cross-wall, such as those that divide fungal hyphae into cells.

sex chromosomes In humans, the X and Y chromosomes, which are different in the two sexes and are involved in sex determination.

sex-linked characteristic A genetic characteristic that is determined by genes located on the sex chromosomes.

sexual reproduction Reproduction that involves the regular alternation between syngamy and meiosis. Its outstanding characteristic is that an individual offspring inherits genes from two parent individuals.

shoot In vascular plants, the aboveground parts, such as the stem and leaves.

sieve cell In the phloem (food-conducting tissue) of vascular plants, a long, slender sieve element with relatively unspecialized sieve areas and with tapering end walls that lack sieve plates. Found in all vascular plants except angiosperms, which have sieve-tube members.

soluble Refers to polar molecules that dissolve in water and are surrounded by a hydration shell.

solute The molecules dissolved in a solution. *See also* solution, solvent.

solution A mixture of molecules, such as sugars, amino acids, and ions, dissolved in water.

solvent The most common of the molecules in a solution. Usually a liquid, commonly water.

somatic cells (Gr. *soma,* body) All the diploid body cells of an animal that are not involved in gamete formation.

somite A segmented block of tissue on either side of a developing notochord.

species, ***pl.*** **species (L. kind, sort)** A level of taxonomic hierarchy; a species ranks next below a genus.

sperm (Gr. ***sperma,*** **sperm, seed)** A sperm cell. The male gamete.

spindle The mitotic assembly that carries out the separation of chromosomes during cell division. Composed of microtubules and assembled during prophase at the centrioles of the dividing cell.

spore (Gr. ***spora,*** **seed)** A haploid reproductive cell, usually unicellular, that is capable of developing into an adult without fusion with another cell. Spores result from meiosis, as do gametes, but gametes fuse immediately to produce a new diploid cell.

sporophyte (Gr. ***spora,*** **seed +** ***phyton,*** **plant)** The spore-producing, diploid ($2n$) phase in the life cycle of a plant having alternation of generations.

stabilizing selection A form of selection in which selection acts to eliminate both extremes from a range of phenotypes.

stamen (L. thread) The part of the flower that contains the pollen. Consists of a slender filament that supports the anther. A flower that produces only pollen is called staminate and is functionally male.

steroid (Gr. ***stereos,*** **solid + L.** ***ol,*** **from oleum, oil)** A kind of lipid. Many of the molecules that function as messengers and pass across cell membranes are steroids, such as the male and female sex hormones and cholesterol.

steroid hormone A hormone derived from cholesterol. Those that promote the development of the secondary sexual characteristics are steroids.

stigma (Gr. mark) A specialized area of the carpel of a flowering plant that receives the pollen.

stoma, ***pl.*** **stomata (Gr. mouth)** A specialized opening in the leaves of some plants that allows carbon dioxide to pass into the plant body and allows water vapor and oxygen to pass out of them.

stratum corneum The outer layer of the epidermis of the skin of the vertebrate body.

substrate (L. ***substratus,*** **strewn under)** A molecule on which an enzyme acts.

substrate-level phosphorylation The generation of ATP by coupling its synthesis to a strongly exergonic (energy-yielding) reaction.

succession In ecology, the slow, orderly progression of changes in community composition that takes place through time. Primary succession occurs in nature on bare substrates, over long periods of time. Secondary succession occurs when a climax community has been disturbed.

sugar Any monosaccharide or disaccharide.

surface tension A tautness of the surface of a liquid, caused by the cohesion of the liquid molecules. Water has an extremely high surface tension.

surface-to-volume ratio Describes cell size increases. Cell volume grows much more rapidly than surface area.

symbiosis (Gr. ***syn,*** **together with +** ***bios,*** **life)** The condition in which two or more dissimilar organisms live together in close association; includes parasitism, commensalism, and mutualism.

synapse (Gr. ***synapsis,*** **a union)** A junction between a neuron and another neuron or muscle cell. The two cells do not touch. Instead, neurotransmitters cross the narrow space between them.

synapsis (Gr. ***synapsis,*** **contact, union)** The close pairing of homologous chromosomes that occurs early in prophase I of meiosis. With the genes of the chromosomes thus aligned, a DNA strand of one homologue can pair with the complementary DNA strand of the other.

syngamy (Gr. ***syn,*** **together with +** ***gamos,*** **marriage)** Fertilization. The union of male and female gametes.

T

taxonomy (Gr. ***taxis,*** **arrangement +** ***nomos,*** **law)** The science of the classification of organisms.

T cell A type of lymphocyte involved in cell-mediated immune responses and interactions with B cells. Also called a T lymphocyte.

tendon (Gr. ***tenon,*** **stretch)** A strap of connective tissue that attaches muscle to bone.

tertiary structure of a protein The three-dimensional shape of a protein. Primarily the result of hydrophobic interactions of amino acid side groups and, to a lesser extent, of hydrogen bonds between them. Forms spontaneously.

test cross A cross between a heterozygote and a recessive homozygote. A procedure Mendel used to further test his hypotheses.

theory (Gr. ***theorein,*** **to look at)** A well-tested hypothesis supported by a great deal of evidence.

thigmotropism (Gr. ***thigma,*** **touch +** ***trope,*** **a turning)** The growth response of a plant to touch.

thorax (Gr. a breastplate) The part of the body between the head and the abdomen.

thylakoid (Gr. ***thylakos,*** **sac +** ***-oides,*** **like)** A flattened, saclike membrane in the chloroplast of a eukaryote. Thylakoids are stacked on top of one another in arrangements called grana and are the sites of photosystem reactions.

tissue (L. ***texere,*** **to weave)** A group of similar cells organized into a structural and functional unit.

trachea, ***pl.*** **tracheae (L. windpipe)** In vertebrates, the windpipe.

tracheid (Gr. ***tracheia,*** **rough)** An elongated cell with thick, perforated walls that carries water and dissolved minerals through a plant and provides support. Tracheids form an essential element of the xylem of vascular plants.

transcription (L. ***trans,*** **across +** ***scribere,*** **to write)** The first stage of gene expression in which the RNA polymerase enzyme synthesizes an mRNA molecule whose sequence is complementary to the DNA.

translation (L. ***trans,*** **across +** ***latus,*** **that which is carried)** The second stage of gene expression in which a ribosome assembles a polypeptide, using the mRNA to specify the amino acids.

translocation (L. ***trans,*** **across +** ***locare,*** **to put or place)** In plants, the process in which most of the carbohydrates manufactured in the leaves and other green parts of the plant are moved through the phloem to other parts of the plant.

transpiration (L. ***trans,*** **across +** ***spirare,*** **to breathe)** The loss of water vapor by plant parts, primarily through the stomata.

transposon (L. ***transponere,*** **to change the position of)** A DNA sequence carrying one or more genes and flanked by insertion sequences that confer the ability to move from one DNA molecule to another. An element capable of transposition (the changing of chromosomal location).

trophic level (Gr. ***trophos,*** **feeder)** A step in the movement of energy through an ecosystem.

tropism (Gr. ***trop,*** **turning)** A plant's response to external stimuli. A positive tropism is one in which the movement or reaction is in the direction of the source of the stimulus. A negative tropism is one in which the movement or growth is in the opposite direction.

turgor pressure (L. ***turgor,*** **a swelling)** The pressure within a cell that results from the movement of water into the cell. A cell with high turgor pressure is said to be turgid.

U

unicellular Composed of a single cell.

urea (Gr. ***ouron,*** **urine)** An organic molecule formed in the vertebrate liver. The principal form of disposal of nitrogenous wastes by mammals.

urine (Gr. ***ouron,*** **urine)** The liquid waste filtered from the blood by the kidneys.

V

vaccination The injection of a harmless microbe into a person or animal to confer resistance to a dangerous microbe.

vacuole (L. ***vacuus,*** **empty)** A cavity in the cytoplasm of a cell that is bound by a single membrane and contains water and waste products of cell metabolism. Typically found in plant cells.

van der Waals forces Weak chemical attractions between atoms that can occur when atoms are very close to each other.

variable Any factor that influences a process. In evaluating alternative hypotheses about one variable, all other variables are held constant so that the investigator is not misled or confused by other influences.

vascular bundle In vascular plants, a strand of tissue containing primary xylem and primary phloem. These bundles of elongated cells conduct water with dissolved minerals and carbohydrates throughout the plant body.

vascular cambium In vascular plants, the meristematic layer of cells that gives rise to secondary phloem and secondary xylem. The activity of the vascular cambium increases stem or root diameter.

ventral (L. ***venter,*** **belly)** Refers to the bottom portion of an animal. Opposite of dorsal.

vertebrate An animal having a backbone made of bony segments called vertebrae.

vesicle (L. ***vesicula,*** **a little (ladder)** Membrane-enclosed sacs within eukaryotic cells.

vessel element In vascular plants, a typically elongated cell, dead at maturity, that conducts water and solutes in the xylem.

villus, ***pl.*** **villi (L. a tuft of hair)** In vertebrates, fine, microscopic, fingerlike projections on epithelial cells lining the small intestine that serve to increase the absorptive surface area of the intestine.

vitamin (L. ***vita,*** **life +** ***amine,*** **of chemical origin)** An organic substance that the organism cannot synthesize, but is required in minute quantities by an organism for growth and activity.

viviparous (L. *vivus,* alive + *parere,* to bring forth) Refers to reproduction in which eggs develop within the mother's body and young are born free-living.

voltage-gated channel A transmembrane pathway for an ion that is opened or closed by a change in the voltage, or charge difference, across the cell membrane.

water vascular system The system of water-filled canals connecting the tube feet of echinoderms.

whorl A circle of leaves or of flower parts present at a single level along an axis.

wood Accumulated secondary xylem. Heartwood is the central, nonliving wood in the trunk of a tree. Hardwood is the wood of dicots, regardless of how hard or soft it actually is. Softwood is the wood of conifers.

xylem (Gr. *xylon,* wood) In vascular plants, a specialized tissue, composed primarily of elongate, thick-walled conducting cells, that transports water and solutes through the plant body.

yolk (O.E. *geolu,* yellow) The stored substance in egg cells that provides the embryo's primary food supply.

zygote (Gr. *zygotos,* paired together) The diploid (2*n*) cell resulting from the fusion of male and female gametes (fertilization).

Index

Applications Index